Dr. Dr. h. c. Carl W. Correns, Prof. em., University of Göttingen

Dr. Josef Zemann, Prof., University of Wien

Dr. Sigmund Koritnig, Prof., University of Göttingen

Dr. William D. Johns, Prof., Washington University, St. Louis

Carl W. Correns

Introduction to Min

Crystallography and Petro

Second Edition, in Cooperatio
Josef Zemann (Part One)
Sigmund Koritnig (Mineral T

Translated by William D. J

With 391 Figures and 1 Plate

Springer-Verlag New York Inc.

Preface to the Second Edition

The first edition of this book has been out of print for seven years. The question as to whether a new edition should be produced was answered affirmatively on many counts. I think that the considerations which led me to write this book in 1949 are still valid (see Preface to the First Edition). Moreover, a description of those areas of interest which together comprise the field of Mineralogy seems to be more necessary than ever, because of the rapid advances which have been made.

Due to the rapid extension of our knowledge, I did not dare again to treat the whole field by myself. Accordingly, Professor ZEMANN kindly agreed to revise the first part of the book dealing with Crystallography. He made many important corrections.

In Part II the basic question arose as to whether the physical-chemical approach to rock forming processes, becoming more and more important, required inclusive treatment of the fundamentals of physical chemistry in the book. I see certain dangers in trying to produce a petrology text which is physical chemically self-sufficient. Thus, I retain the same opinion which prevailed when I wrote the previous edition; namely that the necessary basic knowledge should be acquired in lectures and laboratory classes in physics, chemistry, and physical chemistry, and with the help of standard literature dealing with these subjects. This background is, therefore, presumed and fundamentals are only referred to occasionally.

In considering which of the new data and areas of interest to include, I attempted to keep in mind the introductory nature of the text and to select that which seemed of fundamental importance for a student in his scientific work. Thus, I deleted old material as well as adding new, in bringing the subject matter up-to-date. Important additions were made particularly in sections dealing with volatile constituents, metamorphic facies, and isotope geochemistry. These changes resulted in no significantnet change in the size of the volume.

The appended tables have been rearranged, particularly in the case of sedimentary and metamorphic rocks. Here the reader may locate detailed data which could not be mentioned in the text. In particular this gives the reader the opportunity to familiarize himself with the variability of natural rocks, in contrast to the simplified diagrams presented for comprehensive survey. I am indebted to Professor KORITNIG for compiling again and revising the mineral tables. Along with the tabulated rock data, they are an important supplement to the text.

Professor WEDEPOHL kindly read the proof for Part II. Dr. SMYKATZ-KLOSS compiled the indices. I am grateful to both of them for this valuable assistance. My wife did most of the writing for me and assisted in reading proof.

Göttingen, July 1967   CARL W. CORRENS

Preface to the First Edition

To write an introductory text covering the entire field of mineralogy, including crystallography, petrology, and ore deposits, may seem presumptuous to many today. The fact that the author has taught this subject regularly through lectures and laboratories for 22 years is not in itself sufficient reason in his view. The motivation to do so arose out of the necessity to provide for students of this science and sister sciences a single useful and comprehensive book. Previous texts have been designed with subjects selected to conform to the courses taught at German Universities. It is questionable whether this limitation is still or ever was fortunate. Boundaries between the natural sciences have developed historically and should be maintained, in my opinion, only as practicality dictates, such as in teaching. Each science is so intimately linked with its sister science that boundaries tend to disappear. It is known that interdisciplinary approaches frequently promote particularly successful research. Thus, also in the field of mineralogy, the influence of the allied sciences has been of great importance. This is particularly true of the influence of mathematics and physics on crystallography and of geology on petrology. The changing emphasis on the one or the other branches of our science, however, has not always been beneficial. For example, it has resulted in judgments such as the following, attributed to the renowned mineralogist A. G. WERNER, relative to HAÜY, one of the founders of crystallography. The far-sighted geologist L. VON BUCH says in a letter of May 17, 1804 to D. G. L. KARSTEN: "No, I do not agree with WERNER's judgment of HAÜY. He says he is no mineralogist." This book, on the other hand, attempts to prove that crystallography, especially in its recent developments, is an indispensable prerequisite to petrology, and conversely, the problems of petrology offer many stimuli to crystallography. Important supporting sciences, in addition to the examples already given, are chemistry and physical chemistry. Biology is an important allied science to sedimentary petrology. Similarly, mineralogy plays a role among allied sciences, supporting them as well. I do not deny that it is not always easy for students of sister sciences or beginners to enter the field of mineralogy. Practical teaching experience suggests several reasons why this is so. Overstressing formal principles in crystallography, along with the great number of technical terms, are probably the greatest obstacles. A certain amount of knowledge of crystal forms is, in my opinion, indispensible and should be acquired like the formula-language of the chemists. I have tried to keep within bounds in this respect. The number of really necessary mineral and rock names is small, certainly when compared to the profusion of specific names in the biological sciences.

On the other hand, former as well as living authors have continued to formulate new technical terms, mostly derived from the Greek, and these have been continuously introduced into later publications. I did not see it to be my task to increase the quantity of technical terms or to replace existing ones by new ones. I have tried to explain the most frequently used terms and, moreover, to use as often as possible the terminology of the allied sciences.

In this way the book attempts to lead to an understanding of mineralogy, but is not intended to replace a systematic textbook. My first aim was to provide the fundamentals for a genetic consideration of crystals and rocks. In order to provide space to deal with these questions, much information is presented as tables in the appendix. I believe that the 300 minerals (522 mineral names) will be sufficient for the ordinary student and that the 93 rock types give him a sufficient survey of variety.

The book results from the general lectures I have given since 1927 in Rostock and Göttingen. In the literature index I have specified the sources of illustrations and some statements, but many suggestions by others may have been forgotten in the course of years. Results of my own investigation and reflection, which would have been published separately in normal times, have also been incorporated. The diagrams of the 32 crystal classes are drawn according to NIGGLI. The crystal structures, unless otherwise specified, have been taken from the Strukturbericht. I owe thanks for much assistance to the former and present members of the Institutes in Rostock and Göttingen. In particular, the crystal drawings were, for the most part, drawn anew by Mr. WALTER SCHERF, and some by Dr. I. MEGGENDORFER, who also made the microscopic illustrations using the Edinger drawing apparatus. She also drew the diagrams of close-packed spheres as well as some others. Dr. K. JASMUND provided the Figs. 230, 233—235, 277, and 350. Professor KORITNIG compiled the mineral tables and Dr. P. SCHNEIDERHÖHN the subject index. Both assisted in reading proof.

Foreign literature, as far as it was attainable at the end of 1947, was taken into consideration. Some references were added even during the correction of proofs.

April 1949   CARL W. CORRENS

Contents

III. Crystal Physics

IV. Crystal Growth and Dissolution

PART II. PETROLOGY

V. Some Physical-Chemical Fundamentals

VI. Formation of Magmatic (Igneous) Rocks

VII. Weathering and Soil Mineral Formation

VIII. Sedimentary Rocks

IX. Metamorphic Petrogenesis

X. Geochemical Considerations

PART III. APPENDIX

A. Crystallographic Tables

B. Summary of the Common Minerals and Their Properties

C. Petrologic Tables

PART ONE

Crystallography

I. Crystal Mathematics

1. Introduction

We are all familiar with the subdivision of the natural world into the plant, animal, and mineral kingdoms. Of these the realm of minerals is the study and research area of mineralogy. A mineralogist uses the word mineral, however, in a much more restricted sense than prevails with common usage. If we examine a rock rather closely, we notice, for example, that a sandstone is composed of individual quartz grains. When we examine a specimen of granite, we can recoginze feldspar, dark mica, and perhaps also hornblende, in addition to quartz. From a specimen of certain ores, galena, chalcopyrite, and sphalerite all shine forth brilliantly. Any such individual rock constituent is a mineral. Mineralogy encompasses the study of these minerals and the manner in which they occur, and includes the properties of all rock materials, which, in the sense used here, embrace ore and salt deposits, as well as other useful mineral deposits.

Minerals occur as constituents of rocks not only in assemblage, but are found also as separate individuals. Frequently these have the opportunity to develop without restriction in cavities or in surrounding media which could yield to their growth. Under these conditions they often develop into polyhedral forms called crystals. These have from time immemorial attracted the attention of thoughtful natural scientists as well as laymen.

Earlier all natural bodies with planar external boundaries were called crystals. For example, A. G. WERNER, the patriarch of mineralogy, considered that basalt columns were crystals, because of their somewhat polyhedral shape. Today the concept of a crystal and a mineral is restricted to a *homogeneous* body, that is, one composed of only one substance. Basalt columns, which are composed of feldspar, augite, and other minerals, are not crystals in the modern sense. In addition we know now that the regular outer form or morphology of a crystal is neither the unique nor truly diagnostic characteristic of the crystalline state. It is the regularity of the internal structure which determines the unique characteristics of crystalline matter. As this knowledge developed during the last century, it was further recognized that almost all solid bodies are crystalline. Since the earlier studies of crystals involved almost exclusively natural products, minerals, the study of crystals developed as a branch of mineralogy.

The regular internal structure of crystals determines their external geometric form and is also manifest by other phenomena. If, for example, we strike a piece of galena or rock salt, it always breaks along planes parallel to the surfaces of a cube. The mineral hornblende on the other hand breaks or cleaves into four-sided prismatic forms with prism angles of 124 and 56°. A property common to many minerals is exemplified by kyanite, which also occurs as prismatic crystals. Kyanite can be scratched with a steel needle in the direction of elongation of the prism, but not perpendicular to it. Another interesting mineral is cordierite, a magnesium aluminium silicate named after the French mineralogist CORDIER. If a cube is cut from a cordierite crystal in the proper orientation and viewed in each of the three perpendicular directions corresponding to the cube edges, it will be noticed that the color is different in each direction, namely blue, lilac, and yellow. Directional dependence of color has been established for many other minerals also. If in addition we investigate the heat conductivity of quartz, we can ascertain that it is about 40% greater in the direction parallel to a prism edge, than perpendicular to it. This difference can be demonstrated very nicely also in the case of gypsum. If a cleavage fragment is coated with wax or paraffin and then probed with a hot needle, the wax melts around the source of the heat clearly in the form of an ellipse, not a circle.

All of these observations lead to the conclusion that crystals are bodies for which many properties, such as external shape, cleavage, color, hardness, and heat conductivity, are dependent upon direction. This directional dependency of geometrical and physical properties is called *anisotropism* (Greek. *iso*, equal; *tropos*, direction; *an*, neg.). It is characteristic of every kind of crystal. Crystals of very high symmetry show no directional dependence for certain physical properties, such as the transmission of light, and are said to be isotropic. With respect to other properties, such as tensile strength, the same crystal may be anisotropic. Crystals are, therefore, first of all homogeneous substances, and secondly they are anisotropic.

Very long ago the recognition of the directional dependence of properties led to attempts at an explanation. The idea finally evolved that crystals were constructed of tiny building blocks. Thus the Hollander, Chr. Huygens in 1678 explained the cleavability, the directional variation in hardness, and the double refraction of calcite, in terms of an arrangement and orderly grouping together of very small and invisible flattened ellipsoidal units. In Sweden Torbern Bergmann (1773) and in France Renée Just Haüy (1782) introduced the concept of "integrating molecules", of building blocks, whose shapes should correspond to the shapes of cleavage fragments of crystals. As early as 1824, Seeber, in Freiburg i. Br., formulated a concept of the arrangement of points in space quite similar to that which prevails today. So we see that the fundamental property of a crystal, its directional nonequivalence, has led from the very beginning directly to a concept of orderly arranged building units.

For some time mathematicians, mineralogists, and physicists have been concerned with theoretical investigation of such regular repetitive arrangements. As early as 1891 the mineralogist Fedorov in Petersburg and independently the mathematician Schönfliess in Koenigsberg proved that there are only 230 symmetrically different ways of arranging points in space. These regular spatial arrangements are called *space groups*. Since 1912 it has been possible to investigate these space groups experimentally, thanks to the discovery by Max von Laue of X-ray interference by crystals. This discovery has been of the greatest significance to crystal science. It has been learned since that the "centers of gravity" of atoms, or ions and molecules, actually confrom to regular point group arrangements. Their spatial relationships can be measured. The interatomic distances are of the order of magnitude of 1 Angstrom (10^{-8} cm $= 1/100,000,000$ cm). Discussion of the methods of measurement will be reserved for a later chapter. We shall next familiarize ourselves with space lattice relationships.

A disordered array of points also shows different relationships in different directions, but only as long as we consider a region of few points within the total array. If we integrate some property over long distances in the disordered point system, we will encounter like conditions in all directions. The situation is quite different in ordered point systems. It can be rather easily demonstrated that there is no arrangement of points in space whose regular and periodic spacings do not vary with direction. This would appear to be inconsistent with the concept of isotropism. Isotropism arises only statistically as the result of integration of some property over long distances in a point array. The separation of lattice particles from one another is so small, that over large distances we obtain only average values with the usual methods of measuring properties. For example, a gas in which particles are constantly in motion is isotropic, as is a fluid or a glass, which is a fluid solidified as a result of supercooling. Such incompletely ordered matter in the solid state is said to be amorphous because it possesses no tendency toward development of a characteristic form. The most important characteristic of a crystal, on the other hand, is its regular atomic arrangement in space. Thus the directional dependence of crystalline properties can be understood.

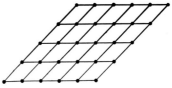

Fig. 1. Planar lattice

A planar net or lattice is shown in Fig. 1. Along any particular set of parallel lattice lines, points are distributed periodically. In different directions the spacing of points differs. The arrangement is anisotropic.

What can we say about the homogeneity of such lattices ? As far as the small portion in Fig. 1 is concerned, the structure is discontinuous, not homogeneous.

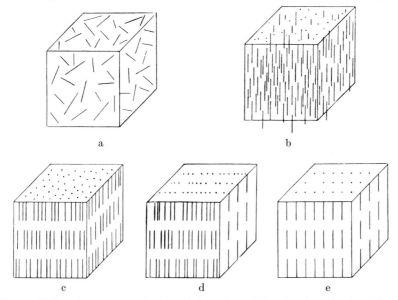

Fig. 2a—e. Different arrangements of rod-shaped particles showing the transition from amorphous (a) to nematic (b) (nema, Gr., thread) and smectitic (c, d) (smektein, Gr., salve) mesophases and to a crystal (e)

A point array becomes homogeneous if we consider larger expanses of an unlimited, extended array: that is to say, when each point possesses an infinitely large number of corresponding or equivalent points in the extended arrangement (BARLOW,1888). We can mark off a repetition of points in a straight line giving rows. We can project these linear patterns within a plane creating planar point nets, and finally we can stack and build these together in space producing a space lattice. The only pre-requisite for real homogeneity is that the structure be regular. The structural units are repeated periodically. Space lattices conform, therefore, not only to the property of anisotropism, but also to that of genuine homogeneity. Crystals possess a corresponding atomic arrangement.

An amorphous body also possesses a sort of homogeneity. Like isotropism, it is in this case statistically related. In a disordered array the constituent particles are on the average similarly surrounded. In contrast to this statistical homogeneity, crystals have a three-dimensional periodic homogeneity to their space lattices. Only that matter which possesses such a space lattice is denoted as crystalline in this restricted sense. The deviations of real crystals from this ideally ordered state will be dealt with later in the section on crystal chemistry. Here let us refer only to the so-called "fluid crystals", which are constructed from one- and two-dimensional molecular arrangements. They form a sort of transition to crystals and for that reason are also considered as *mesophases* (Greek; *mesos*, medium). Fig. 2a—e illustrates the arrangement possibilities of rod-shaped particles, ranging from the completely disordered to the crystalline state. Here it is assumed that the rods are perfect cylinders. Departure from this ideal shape would lead to different arrangement possibilities.

2. Descriptive Crystallography

Law of Constancy of Interfacial Angles. We shall be concerned above all in the following sections with ideal crystals. Before we discuss the existing arrangement possibilities, we must familiarize ourselves with the terminology and the most elementary aids to crystal description. These have been developed for macroscopic crystals with face development. The faces of a crystal correspond to some planar net in the space lattice. From this fundamental fact we can deduce directly the first and oldest law of crystal science: the angles between the existing faces of like kinds of crystals are under like external conditions (temperature, pressure) always the same. Today it is self-evident to us that the angle between two planar nets of identical space lattices will always be the same, and that for a particular structure it does not matter if we displace a lattice plane parallel to itself. However, when the Danish scientist NIELS STENSEN (latinized to NICOLAUS STENO) in 1669 found that identical faces on quartz crystals always included the identical angle, it was no foregone conclusion but an important achievement, providing a clue to further understanding. This law signifies that only the angles between faces are important, not the relative sizes of the faces. If we observe a collection of quartz crystals from different localities, it is easy to surmise the difficulty in discovering that they have in common equal angles between corresponding faces (Fig. 3). In 1783 ROMÉ DE L'ISLE first established the law of constancy of interfacial angles as a generally valid law, applying to all crystals.

Angular Measurement. By measuring the interfacial angles on crystals it was possible to reconstruct the ideal form of a crystal from the often very distorted natural crystal, and then to reveal the conformity of crystal development to fundamental principles. This led to further development of crystal science and finally to recognition of the concept of space lattices. STENSEN's discovery initiated a long series of angular measurements of crystals. These have been continued up to the present time, even though today they are considered by some to be of less importance than X-ray methods. At first, simple devices held in contact with a crystal were used for angular measurement (contact goniometer). Since the beginning of the 19th century (WOLLASTON, 1809), optical apparatus, the *reflection goniometer*, has come into use. With this the crystal

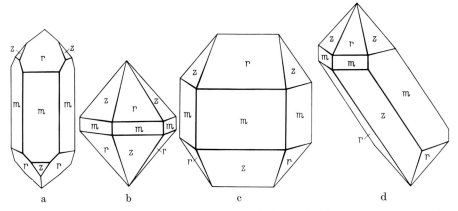

Fig. 3a—d. Development of quartz crystals. (a) ideal crystal; (b) symmetry appears too high as result of equal development of the r and z faces; (c, d) irregularly distorted crystals

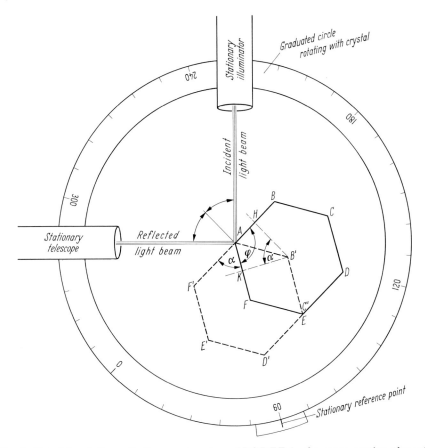

Fig. 4. Principle of the reflection goniometer. $ABCDEF$ is the cross section through a regular hexagonal prism. A light beam shining on the face AB is again reflected into the telescope after rotation about the angle $\alpha = 60°$ to the position $AB'C'D'E'F'$; α is the external facial angle, equivalent to the angle between the face normals KB' and HB'. φ is the interfacial angle

is mounted so that an edge or several parallel edges stand vertical. The crystal
is illuminated with a collimated light beam. When the crystal is rotated about
the external facial angle α (Fig. 4), a light reflection (signal) is observed each
time in the viewing telescope.

The "external" face angle which is measured is equal to the angle which the
face normals make with each other. These relations are readily apparent in Fig. 4.
AB and AF (AB' and AF' after rotation) each represent the outline of one
crystal face of a hexagonal prism. HB' and KB' are the face normals. With a
contact goniometer the "internal" angle φ is measured ($\alpha + \varphi = 180°$). With
the original one-circle goniometer, it was necessary to remount and adjust the

Fig. 5. Two-circle reflection goniometer after V. Goldschmidt by Stoe, Heidelberg. One
graduated circle stands vertical, the other horizontal; both are read by magnifiers

crystal each time in order to measure angles between faces whose edges were
not parallel. The modern two-circle goniometer avoids this inconvenience. All
face normal angles can be ascertained with a single setting, since the two
graduated circles are mounted perpendicular to each other and can be moved
independently (Fig. 5).

Axial Intercepts and Indices. We come now to the description or naming of
crystallographic faces and edges (planes and directions). In crystallography, as
in geometry, a plane can be referred to a system of coordinate axes. When
dealing with space lattices, three lattice lines are chosen as coordinate axes. For
the general case, the plane cuts the three axes at different distances from the
origin.

The axial intercepts of a plane ABC shown in Fig. 6 are indicated by the
distances OA, OB, and OC. A different plane will cut off other segments of the
axes; for example, OA', OB', OC'. Let us choose one plane as the fundamental
or unit plane, and assign values of unity to each of its three intercepts; for
example, plane ABC. Since the intercepts of our unit plane are now 1, 1, 1, a

second plane $A'B'C'$ will have the intercepts 4, 2, 2. In this notation (4, 2, 2) the first numeral represents the intercept of the forward projecting axis, the a-axis; the second numeral, the b-axis, projecting from left to right; the third numeral, the c-axis, projecting vertically. To describe the position of the intercept, ratios

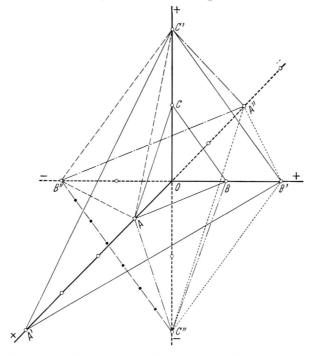

Fig. 6. Coordinate axes with the intercepts of different planes

Plane			Intercepts			Indices		
A	B	C	1	1	1	1	1	1
A'	B'	C'	4	2	2	1	2	2
A	B''	C'	1	-2	2	2	$\bar{1}$	1
A	B	C''	1	1	-2	2	2	$\bar{1}$
A	B''	C''	1	-2	-2	2	$\bar{1}$	$\bar{1}$
A''	B'	C'	-2	2	2	$\bar{1}$	1	1
A''	B''	C'	-2	-2	2	$\bar{1}$	$\bar{1}$	1
A''	B'	C''	-2	2	-2	$\bar{1}$	1	$\bar{1}$
A''	B''	C''	-2	-2	-2	$\bar{1}$	$\bar{1}$	$\bar{1}$

are used. We may therefore translate planes, as long as we do not change the intercept ratios. That is, we can make the intercepts indivisible by a common denominator, writing them in the case of plane $A'B'C'$ as (2, 1, 1) instead of (4, 2, 2)

   The equation for a plane in space can be used instead of intercepts to define a plane:

$$A x + B y + C z = K.$$

Dividing by K and setting:

$$\frac{A}{K} = h; \qquad \frac{B}{K} = k; \qquad \frac{C}{K} = l$$

then

$$h \cdot x + k \cdot y + l \cdot z = 1.$$

The point of intersection of the plane $A\,B\,C$ with the a axis, with intercept $\overline{OA}$, has the coordinates $x = \overline{OA}$, $y = 0$, $z = 0$. Therefore, $\overline{OA} \cdot h = 1$; $\overline{OA} = 1/h$.

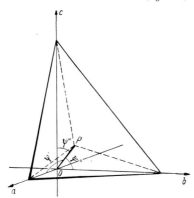

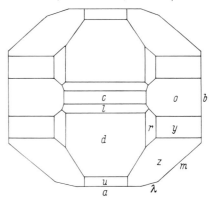

Fig. 7. Relations between face normals, coordinate axes, and direction cosines

Fig. 8. Top view of a barite crystal. [Projected parallel (001)]

Similarly it follows: $\overline{OB} = 1/k$, $\overline{OC} = 1/l$. That is, the intercepts are the reciprocals of the factors of the equation.

A third possibility for describing the position of a plane in space is by stating its *angular relationships*, in terms of the angle between each of the coordinate axes and the perpendicular from the origin to the plane. The perpendicular is the plane normal. Angular measurements with the reflection goniometer give the angles between these plane normals directly. The angles, ψ', ψ'', ψ''' between the normals and the coordinate axes, as Fig. 7 shows, are related to the axial intercepts and the normal $\overline{OP} = d$ as follows:

$$\cos \psi' = \frac{d}{\overline{OA}}; \qquad \cos \psi'' = \frac{d}{\overline{OB}}; \qquad \cos \psi''' = \frac{d}{\overline{OC}}$$

therefore

$$\cos \psi' : \cos \psi'' : \cos \psi''' = \frac{1}{\overline{OA}} : \frac{1}{\overline{OB}} : \frac{1}{\overline{OC}} = h : k : l.$$

These relationships are used to calculate the axial intercepts of the fundamental or unit plane. In the case of mutually perpendicular (orthogonal) coordinate axes, $\cos^2 \psi' + \cos^2 \psi'' + \cos^2 \psi''' = 1$.

In this manner, as in the case of the equation for a plane, we end up again with reciprocal values of the intercepts. Following the suggestion of MILLER (1839), we generally use today these reciprocal values of the intercepts for plane and crystal description. As units of measure on the three axes, the axial intercepts of the unit plane are always used. By multiplication by a suitable number h, k, l can be made integers. These h, k, l values are called *Miller indices*. The indices for plane $A\,B\,C$ (Fig. 6) are $\frac{1}{1} : \frac{1}{1} : \frac{1}{1}$, 111; for $A'\,B'\,C'$ $\frac{1}{4} : \frac{1}{2} : \frac{1}{2}$, 122. The indices in the octant discussed so far have positive values. In the other seven octants, some indices can be negative according to which axes are appropriately intersected (see Fig. 6). The minus signs are placed above the index numerals. Thus the indices of a plane can be represented, for example, as $(1\bar{2}\bar{2})$ read: one, minus two, minus two. Planes parallel to an axis have the intercept ∞ and the index 0. If the plane's position is only partially or not at all known, the letters h, k, l are used. The indices of a single plane are enclosed in parentheses (111); those for an entire set of planes, a *form*, in curved brackets, { }, for example {122}. That plane which is to serve as the unit plane is determined by trial. A plane is chosen, so that the indices of the entire collection of faces are as simple as possible. In spite of many attempts, rigid rules for the choice of the unit plane have not been satisfactorily formulated. If the space lattice is known, the plane consistent with lattice measurements should be chosen.

Crystal Calculations. We shall now calculate the indices of a crystal with the help of angular cosine relationships. For this purpose we shall choose the barite $(BaSO_4)$ crystal shown in top view in Fig. 8, keeping in mind the relationships described above. An oblique view of the same crystal is illustrated in Fig. 48, p. 28. As our later discussion of symmetry will show, we can base the barite lattice on an orthogonal coordinate system. We shall choose the direction of the edge between planes o and c as the a axis, between l and c as the b axis, and between b and m as the c axis. Therefore, the c axis is perpendicular to the plane of the drawing and the plane c is indexed (001). The angle between planes c and o is $52°43'$. Therefore, for o:

$$\psi_0' = 90°, \qquad \psi_0'' = 90° - 52°43' = 37°17', \qquad \psi_0''' = 52°43'.$$

From the angle between face a, standing perpendicular to the plane of the drawing, and $m = 39°11'$, it follows that for m:

$$\psi_m' = 39°11', \qquad \psi_m'' = 50°49', \qquad \psi_m''' = 90°;$$

similarly for λ from $a \wedge \lambda = 22°10'$:

$$\psi_\lambda' = 22°10', \qquad \psi_\lambda'' = 67°50', \qquad \psi_\lambda''' = 90°,$$

for l, from $a \wedge l = 68°4'$:

$$\psi_l' = 68°4', \qquad \psi_l'' = 90°, \qquad \psi_l''' = 21°56',$$

for d, from $c \wedge d = 38°52'$:

$$\psi_d' = 51°8', \qquad \psi_d'' = 90°, \qquad \psi_d''' = 38°52'.$$

for u, from $c \wedge u = 58°11'$:

$$\psi_u' = 31°49', \qquad \psi_u'' = 90°, \qquad \psi_u''' = 58°11'.$$

For face z, we calculate, from $a \wedge z = 45°42'$; $\quad \psi_z' = 45°42'$

from $c \wedge z = 64°19'$; $\quad \psi_z'' = 64°19'$

From $\cos^2 \psi' + \cos^2 \psi'' + \cos^2 \psi''' = 1$, it follows: $\psi_z''' = 55°17'$.

Similarly, for face r we find, from $c \wedge r = 46°6'$ and $b \wedge r = 62°55'$:

$$\psi_r' = 56°3', \qquad \psi_r'' = 62°55', \qquad \psi_r''' = 46°6'.$$

From $a \wedge y = 63°59'$ and $b \wedge y = 44°21'$, it follows:

$$\psi_y' = 63°59', \qquad \psi_y'' = 44°21', \qquad \psi_y''' = 57°1'.$$

From the relation

$$\frac{1}{\cos \psi'} : \frac{1}{\cos \psi''} : \frac{1}{\cos \psi'''} = a:b:c \text{ (for the unit plane),}$$

we first calculate the axial intercepts, and, so that we can make $b = 1$, the ratios are multiplied by cos ψ''. In this manner the values tabulated in Table 1 were derived.

Table 1

Face	$\dfrac{\cos \psi''}{\cos \psi'} :1: \dfrac{\cos \psi''}{\cos \psi'''}$	With z as unit plane		With r as unit plane		With y as unit plane	
		$a:b:c$	hkl	$a:b:c$	hkl	$a:b:c$	hkl
o	∞ :1 :1,3135	∞:1 :1	011	∞:1 :2	021	∞:1 :1	011
m	0.8151:1 :∞	1 :1 :∞	110	1 :1 :∞	110	1 :2 :∞	210
λ	0.4077:1 :∞	1 :2 :∞	210	1 :2 :∞	210	1 :4 :∞	410
l^a	2.6772:∞:1.0780	4 :∞:1	104	2 :∞:1	102	2 :∞:1	102
d^a	1.5936:∞:1.2844	2 :∞:1	102	1 :∞:1	101	1 :∞:1	101
u^a	1.1754:∞:1.8972	1 :∞:1	101	1 :∞:2	201	1 :∞:2	201
z	0.8153:1 :1.3138	1 :1 :1	111	1 :1 :2	221	1 :2 :2	211
r	0.8152:1 :0.6566	2 :2 :1	112	1 :1 :1	111	1 :2 :1	212
y	1.6303:1 :1.3138	2 :1 :1	122	2 :1 :2	121	1 :1 :1	111

$\quad$ [a] Since cos $\psi'' = 0$ instead of $\dfrac{\cos \psi''}{\cos \psi'} :1: \dfrac{\cos \psi''}{\cos \psi'''}$ we use $\dfrac{1}{\cos \psi'} : \dfrac{1}{\cos \psi''} : \dfrac{1}{\cos \psi'''}$.

The indices of the individual faces are different, depending on whether the face z, r, or y was chosen as the unit face. Since in all three cases the complexity of the indices is approximately equal, it is possible to be in doubt as to which of the three faces actually represents the unit face. For characterization of barite, it suffices to select the axial ratio $0.8153:1:1.3138$, based on the choice of z as the unit face. However, the axial ratios based on lattice constants determined by X-rays is doubled in the a axis direction: $a_0:b_0:c_0 = 1.627:1:1.311$. Thus the y face is consistent with the structurally determined unit plane.

Law of Rational Indices. As can be seen from Table 1, the derived intercepts and indices can be expressed as whole numbers, including ∞ and 0. As early as the time of HAÜY it was recognized that the faces developed on crystals could always be so simply indexed. A look at the space lattice shows us today that this must be so, even though a century ago this was not self-evident. On the other hand, HAÜY's empirical studies did lead first to the postulation of such point systems and finally to their discovery. As a general rule the intercept ratios and Miller indices can be represented as small whole numbers. This does not follow directly from space lattice structure. In order to explain the frequency of faces with low indices on crystals, it is necessary to postulate that there must be quite simple structurally important relationships, which are favored in the development of growth and cleavage faces. BRAVAIS proposed that the common simple faces which develop on crystals contain particularly densely populated lattice planes.

Zones. We have already utilized the edge boundaries of crystals in determining axial directions. We speak of several faces whose edges are mutually parallel as lying in a "zone". The common direction to which these edges are parallel is the zone axis. The symbols representing edges or zones are placed in brackets $[uvw]$. Their derivation is illustrated in Fig. 9, where we have the edge d passing through the origin of the coordinate system. The relation of the coordinates of some point P to the axes is established, $u:v:w = [uvw]$. The intercepts of the unit plane again serve as the units of measure on the a, b, and c axes. If the location of two faces is known, their intersecting edge, a zone, is also fixed. It is possible to calculate the zone symbols from the indices of two faces from the following considerations:

The equation of a plane with the intercepts $1/h$, $1/k$, $1/l$ is $hx+ky+lz=1$ (compare with p. 20). If a plane is translated parallel to itself so that it is made to pass through the origin, the equation becomes $hx+ky+lx=0$. Let us consider two planes with the indices $h_1k_1l_1$ and $h_2k_2l_2$; both are translated so that each passes through the origin. The ratio of the coordinates of some arbitrary point on the line of intersection, the zone axis, gives the zone symbols sought:

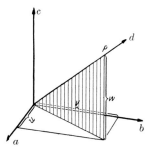

Fig. 9. Coordinates of a zone

$$h_1 \cdot u + k_1 \cdot v + l_1 \cdot w = 0$$
$$h_2 \cdot u + k_2 \cdot v + l_2 \cdot w = 0.$$

From this it follows:

$$u:v:w = (k_1 \cdot l_2 - k_2 \cdot l_1):(l_1 \cdot h_2 - l_2 \cdot h_1):(h_1 \cdot k_2 - h_2 \cdot k_1).$$

Conversely, two edges or zone axes determine the plane that lies between them. The indices of the plane follow from the two equations of planes (hkl) with different zone symbols, $u_1v_1w_1$ and $u_2v_2w_2$:

$$h:k:l = (v_1 \cdot w_2 - v_2 \cdot w_1):(w_1 \cdot u_2 - w_2 \cdot u_1):(u_1 \cdot v_2 - u_2 \cdot v_1).$$

The determinant form is convenient for the calculation:

In this case particular attention must be paid to the signs. One can obtain all possible faces on a crystal by proceeding from four faces which do not, to three which do lie in a zone and determining first from these the zone directions or zone symbols of the edges lying between these faces; from the zone directions so obtained, possible new faces are denoted and from these new zones, etc. It is a general rule that only those faces occur on a crystal which occur together in zonal assemblages (zone law).

Axial Systems. The study of crystal edges allows us to choose coordinate axes whose relations are quite simple. Study of many such crystals leads to the conclusion that there are six unique axial systems. This was recognized in 1804 by CHR. S. WEISS in an introduction to the German translation of the works of HAÜY. In the case of three of these axial systems, the intercepts of the unit plane are of different lengths along all three axes. In the case of the *triclinic* system, none of the three axes intersect at right angles; in the *monoclinic*, two form right angles; and in the *orthorhombic*, all three are mutually perpendicular or orthogonal. In all three systems, in order to uniquely characterize a crystal, the ratios of the axial intercepts of their unit faces $a:b:c$ must be ascertained. In order to define the triclinic coordinate axes, the angles between axes must be defined also. The angle between the a and b axis is designated as γ, that between the b and c axes as α, and between the a and c axes as β. The monoclinic coordinate axes are oriented so that the general angle lies between the c- and a-axes, and is thus β^1, in the monoclinic. For the so-called tetragonal system, two of the three axial intercepts are equal and the axes are orthogonal. Only the $c:a$ ratio must be determined to characterize a tetragonal crystal.

The hexagonal coordinate system consists of one vertical axis (c axis) and three additional axes, a_1, a_2, and a_3, perpendicular to it and intersecting each other at $120°$. As shown in Fig. 10, the a_3 axis (running forward and to the right) is considered to be negative. For this axis the general index i is assigned, while the other axes, a_1 and a_2, are given the indices h and k. The order of the assigned indices, varying from alphabetical, is $hkil$, corresponding to the a_1, a_2, a_3 and c axes respectively. These four combined indices are called the Bravais indices. The ratio $c:a$, therefore, suffices to characterize hexagonal crystals.

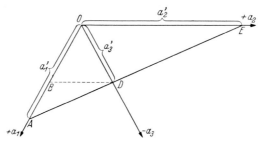

Fig. 10. Calculation of indices with hexagonal coordinates

Since only three axes are required to define a plane in space, i is related to h and k and can be calculated from them. In Fig. 10 let ADE be the outline of a plane and construct BD parallel to OE. Then $\overline{AO}/\overline{AB}=\overline{OE}/\overline{BD}$. Since $\overline{BD}=\overline{OD}=-1/i$, it follows, if we substitute the indices:

$$\frac{1/h}{1/h+1/i} = \frac{1/k}{-1/i} \;; \quad i=-(h+k).$$

The symbol i is assumed here to have a negative value, although the minus sign is not indicated. Although many authors use the indices $hkil(i=h+1)$ for hexagonal crystals, the symbol i is often replaced by an asterisk ($hk*l$).

Finally, in the case of the *isometric* system, the axial intercepts of the unit face are equal and the three axes are orthogonal.

Occasionally another coordinate system is made use of, the rhombohedral. As in the isometric system, the three axes here are equal as are the interaxial angles. However, they are not orthogonal as in the isometric system, but inclined at some general angle ϱ (see Appendix p. 350 and Fig. 391).

The Stereographic Projection. It is important to become familiar with an additional descriptive aid, which permits us to reconstruct the crystal geometrically from the measurement of crystal angles, and to illustrate clearly its angles, faces, and edges as well as its symmetry. Thus we must introduce the stereographic projection.

Let us imagine a large sphere circumscribing a small crystal. Face normals are extended from each face to the surface of the sphere (Fig. 11). We obtain a

---

[1] This selection of orientation is arbitrary. In another possible orientation which has found wide acceptance in recent years, the general angle is placed between the a- and b-axes, and is therefore γ.

system of points on the surface of the sphere. The angular distances between two points, measured along great circles of the sphere, are related to the interfacial angles. If an edge common to two faces is extended to intersect the sphere, its

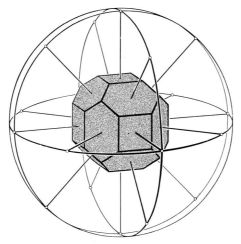

Fig. 11. Projection of a crystal through its face normals onto the surface of a sphere. The face poles are connected by means of great circles

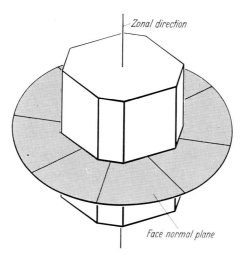

Fig. 12. All face poles lie on a great circle; the zonal axis (parallel to the edge direction) stands perpendicular to this circle

point of intersection must lie 90° from the intersections (poles) of all faces which are parallel to the edge[1]. Therefore it follows that the poles of all faces with parallel edges, that is those faces belonging to a zone, must lie on great circles. They lie on the periphery of sectional planes through the center of the sphere; the zone pole lies then 90° distant (Fig. 12). In this way a system of points and great circles is obtained which permits the reading of angular, zonal, and symmetry

[1] Of course the edges between two faces are situated so as to be displaced with respect to the center of the sphere.

relationships. In order to project this spatial array onto a plane, the stereographic projection is used. For purposes of clarity, we shall adopt the terminology
customarily applied to the earth, and focus our attention on the northern hemisphere. Locations on the northern hemisphere are projected onto the equatorial

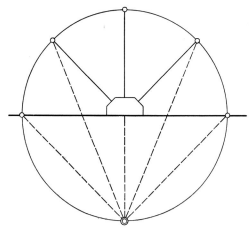

Fig. 13. Stereographic projection of face poles onto the equator (projection plane) by
connecting them to the south pole. Section through the projection sphere in the plane
containing three face normals

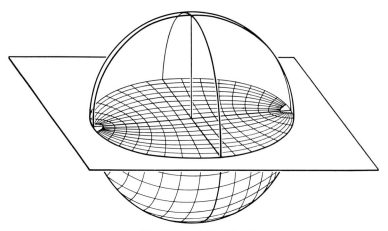

Fig. 14. Origin of the Wulff net

plane by connecting them with straight lines to the south pole. The intersection
of each line with the equatorial plane is the projection point. Angular and symmetry relationships are preserved in the projection. Of practical importance is
the property of the stereographic projection that circles on the sphere appear
as circles in projection. In particular the zone circles of the sphere form circles,
or more correctly, arcs in projection. Points in the southern hemisphere are
projected in like manner by linking with the north pole, and are differentiated
from northern points by utilizing different projection symbols. In Fig. 26ff. the
points in the northern hemisphere are represented by crosses, in the southern by
circles.

Handling of the stereographic projection is simplified by utilizing the stereo-projection of a grid system. A sphere scribed with longitude and latitude lines is oriented so that the north and south poles lie in the projection plane. The latitude and longitude grid is then stereographically projected (Fig. 14). In this way the stereographic or Wulff net is derived. One is reproduced at the end of this book. It should be torn out and pasted onto a piece of plywood or cardboard. The meridians of longitude correspond to great circles, on which zonal assemblages can be plotted. The parallels of latitude are not great circles, with the exception of the equator, and serve only for reckoning angular values. The plotting of a stereographic projection is carried out on a piece of tracing paper placed over the Wulff net.

We will show the first steps in using the stereographic projection, using the barite crystal (Fig. 8 and Table 1) for which we earlier calculated the Miller

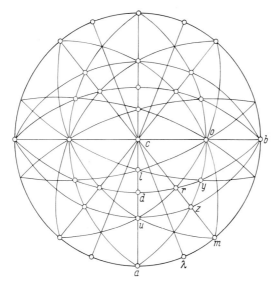

Fig. 15. Stereographic projection of the barite crystal in Fig. 8

indices (Fig. 15). Let us assume that by means of goniometric measurement, we have ascertained that the angle $a:m = 39°11'$ and $c:o = 52°43'$. The faces a and m belong to a zone whose great circle projection is the primitive circle (the circumference of the projection plane). The pole of face a is plotted. Then the pole of face m is plotted $39°11'$ from a on the primitive circle. The pole of face c coincides with the zone pole of the faces whose poles lie on the primitive circle. It lies in the center of the net. Pole o lies $52°43'$ from c, in the zone cob which turns out to be perpendicular to ac. We project o onto the normal to ac. Then b is plotted on the periphery. If we sketch the zones ao and mc as great circles, we find the pole of face z at their intersection; z thus lies in both zones. It is only possible from Fig. 8 to see that z lies in zone ayo. That z also lies in zone mc can be observed, however, by further goniometric study. We could also find z by calculation of the angles cz and az, noted on p. 11, in that we plot the angular distances as circles around c and a. At their intersection lies z. We can now determine the angle ψ_2'', between b and z (see p. 11) without further projection, since we can measure it on the great circle bz. This zone bz furnishes the pole of face u at the intersection with zone ac.

If we find by means of further goniometric study that r lies in the zone from u to o, we find the face pole r at the intersection of this zone with the zone mz. From the zonal array we can further easily find d and y. The pole of face l is obtained at the intersection of zone $audc$ and the zone from y to the left o-face. The existence of the last zonal assemblage is not apparent in Fig. 8, but requires further goniometric investigation[1]. The position of face λ on this crystal must be determined by additional measurement.

The stereographic projection of the crystal gives us the angular relations and represents the crystal in ideal form, undisturbed by growth influences. It enables us immediately to recognize its symmetry relations. This is not always easily discernible by cursory examination of natural distorted crystals.

With the help of the stereoprojection we can also construct an exact drawing of the crystal. For drawing we need to know the edge directions. These are given by the normals to the zone circles. In Fig. 8 the edge between d and r is parallel to ac, from top to bottom, and that between u and a, parallel to cb, from left to right. In this way we can construct a top view like that in Fig. 8 from the stereoprojection. If we rotate the original pole sphere, it is possible to sketch other views of the crystal. For example, when a stands at the center of the net, we get a front view. Finally the axial intercepts and the indices can be graphically ascertained. In addition to its use in pure crystallography the stereographic projection is of use in crystal optics (p. 136), and in rock fabric studies. In the latter case, however, another kind of spherical projection is generally used (p. 312).

3. Crystal Symmetry

Simple Symmetry Operations. We have become familiar thus far with the most important rudiments of crystallographic terminology. For this purpose it

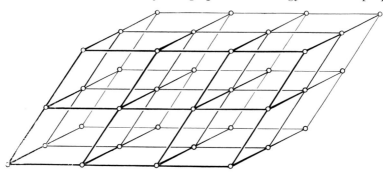

Fig. 16. Simple space lattice

was necessary to accept the fact that the constituents of a crystal are distributed regularly within a space lattice. In order to probe deeper into the understanding of crystals, we must formulate an idea of the various kinds of space lattices. It has already been mentioned on p. 4 that there are 230 symmetrically different kinds of spatial point arrangements (space groups). In order to understand this we must make ourselves familiar with the manner in which such regular arrangements occur. We have already established (p. 5) that a point array is considered to be genuinely homogeneous if each point possesses an infinitely large number of correspondingly different points, whose positions in the array are equivalent.

---

[1] Note that the edges zr and rl in Fig. 8 are not parallel; otherwise they would form a zone zrl.

What do we mean by "equivalent positions in the array"? How can we demonstrate this?

In Fig. 1 we observed a simple planar net. Here it is immediately clear that the above stipulation for each point is valid, if we consider the lattice to be infinitely continuous. We need merely to move from point to point. The arrangement around each point is identical. Such parallel movements can be carried out just as well in three dimensions in a space lattice (Fig. 16). Such movements from point to point are called *translations*.

In the planar lattice illustrated in Fig. 17, we see another possibility for bringing lattice points into coincidence. Here each point can be made to coincide with another by rotation of $120° = 360°/3$. We speak in this case of a three-fold axis of rotation. As shown in the same figure, we can also imagine the points to be brought into coincidence by means of reflection across a *mirror* or *symmetry plane*. Planes of symmetry are familiar to us in the organic world also. Every individual possesses an imperfect plane of symmetry, although the two sides of one's body are always somewhat differently developed. In the case of crystals also, because of external influences during growth, the symmetry is not always easy to recognize. It can be easily ascertained, however, if the angular relations

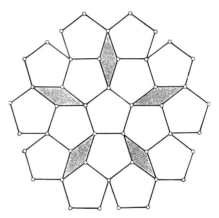

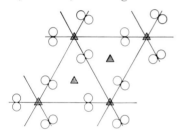

Fig. 17. Periodic pattern containing 3-fold symmetry axes and symmetry planes

Fig. 18. By joining regular pentagons it is not possible to completely fill planar space

rather than face development are considered. The stereographic projection plays an important role in this respect, as we have seen.

Movements, by means of which points can be made to coincide, are called symmetry operations. Examples are the translation, reflection across a symmetry plane, and the 3-fold rotation, with which we have just become familiar. In crystals we find other additional rotation axes. We shall neglect for the moment the 1-fold rotation axis, which transforms a system into itself by rotation through 360°. This is obviously an operation which can be performed with any arbitrary asymmetrical body. Only 2-, 3-, 4-, and 6-fold rotation axes occur in space lattices. 5-, 7-, and other multi-fold axes are excluded. With the latter it is not possible to regularly divide up a planar area into equal units, as a trial with 5- (Fig. 18) or 7-fold point arrays easily shows. Regular polygons bounded by 5, 7, etc. sides cannot be joined together uninterruptedly, completely filling planar space. Because they contain 5-fold axes, two of the five regular shapes which have been known since antiquity do not occur as crystal forms. They are the pentagonal dodecahedron, a twelve-faced form bounded by regular pentagons, and the icosahedron, a twenty faced-form bounded by equilateral triangles. In the organic world we are familiar with examples of five-fold symmetry; for example, rose blossoms and star fish.

Inversion is an additional symmetry operation. In this case every point in a pattern has an equivalent opposing point, as if repeated by inversion through a simple lens. In crystals the inversion center is also called a center of symmetry.

Combined Symmetry Operations. If a point not lying on a symmetry axis is rotated 180°, and immediately inverted through a point lying on the rotation axis, again rotated 180°, etc. the same repetition of points results as with a

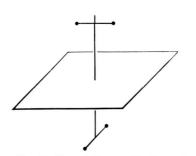

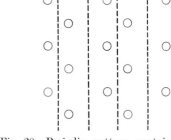

Fig. 19. Four-fold rotoreflection axis   Fig. 20. Periodic pattern containing glide planes

symmetry plane perpendicular to the rotation direction. If a 3-fold axis is combined in a similar way with inversion, the same distribution results as with simultaneous presence of a 3-fold axis and a center of symmetry. By combining a 6-fold axis with inversion as described above, symmetry results which can be

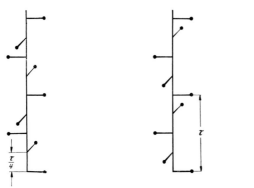

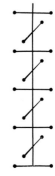

Fig. 21. 4_1-screw axis   Fig. 22. 4_3-screw axis   Fig. 23. 4_2-screw axis together with a two-fold rotation axis

Figs. 21—23. The three four-fold screw axes

described in terms of a 3-fold axis with a plane of symmetry perpendicular to it. It is important that the combination of 90° rotation and inversion gives a point distribution which cannot be described in terms of other rotational symmetry combinations (Fig. 19). We meet the latter combination of symmetry elements, the *4-fold rotoinversion axis* in numerous crystals. One can derive the 4-fold rotoinversion axis by means of another combined symmetry element—by combination of 90° rotation, followed by reflection across a plane perpendicular to the rotation axis *(4-fold rotoreflection axis)*. We shall follow the common usage and refer to these as inversion axes rather than reflection axes. For consistency the one-fold inversion axis is introduced also. It is obviously identical to the symmetry center.

If a symmetry plane is combined with the translation operation, a *glide plane* is produced (Fig. 20). Combination of rotation axes and translation leads to *screw axes*. The three varieties of 4-fold screw axes are illustrated in Figs. 21—23. It can be easily shown that there are only one 2-fold, two 3-fold, in short (*n*-1) *n*-fold screw axes.

Altogether crystals exhibit the following kinds of symmetry:

Table 2. *Forms of symmetry*

1. Mirror plane			9. Translation		
2. Two-fold	⎫		10. Glide plane		
3. Three-fold	⎬ Rotation axes		11. Two-fold	⎫	
4. Four-fold	⎪		12. Two different 3-fold	⎪	
5. Six-fold	⎭		13. Three different 4-fold	⎬ Screw axes	
6. Center of symmetry			14. Five different 6-fold	⎭	
7. Four-fold	⎫ Inversion axes				
8. Six-fold	⎭				

We have now enumerated all of the kinds of symmetry compatible with a space lattice. If we make use of all of these, either alone or in combination, we can arrive at 230 possibilities in which they can be arranged together, the space groups.

Usually the following symbols are utilized to designate the symmetry elements. For the 1-, 2-, 3-, 4-, and 6-fold axes the numbers 1, 2, 3, 4, and 6 are used; for the corresponding inversion axes the numbers $\bar{1}$, $\bar{2}$, $\bar{3}$, $\bar{4}$, and $\bar{6}$ are used (these symbols are read "bar 1, bar 2, etc."). We shall later meet again all the symbols of the usual symmetry axes; of the inversion axes we use only the symbols $\bar{1}$, $\bar{3}$, $\bar{4}$, and $\bar{6}$. Screw axes are each designated according to the rotational repetition of the axis and the amount of translation coupled with the rotation, using the symbols 2_1, 3_1, 3_2, 4_1, 4_2, 4_3, 6_1, 6_2, 6_3, 6_4, and 6_5 (the symbol 6_2, for example, is read "six ... two"). Screw axes are not encountered or revealed by the macro-symmetry of a crystal, since the translation is on the atomic scale. A symmetry or mirror plane is designated by the symbol *m*; a glide plane—as in the case of the screw axis, revealed only by the fine structure—each according to its direction of translation with respect to *a*, *b*, *c*, *n*, or *d*; *a*, *b*, *c*, represent glide planes with $\frac{a}{2}$, $\frac{b}{2}$, or $\frac{c}{2}$ translation; *n* represents a glide plane translation equal to one-half a diagonal; and *d* with a magnitude of one-fourth of the diagonal. The symbol $\bar{1}$ for a one-fold inversion axis is also used to designate a center of symmetry.

4. The 32 Crystal Classes

If from all of the possible symmetry operations we consider only those which apply to macroscopic crystals, that is, if we exclude translation and the symmetry operations resulting from combination with translation, and, therefore, those which are concerned with displacements of sub-microscopic magnitude (10^{-8} cm) (examples 9—14 in Table 2), the number of symmetry groups is reduced to 32. These are the 32 crystal classes which HESSEL deduced for the first time in 1830 from symmetry studies.

The Triclinic Classes. In the following discussion we shall acquaint ourselves with the various classes, deriving them by combining symmetry elements, beginning with the lowest symmetry. The lowest symmetry class is obviously that one which possesses no symmetry at all. The edges and planes of a crystal without symmetry can be related to a triclinic (Greek tris, triple; clinein, angle) coordinate system. In this class the crystal faces are called pedions (Greek, plain) (Fig. 24a). In all classes, any face or plane not related to another face through symmetry is called a pedion. Following the example of P. GROTH, each

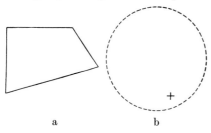

class is named after its most general form, that is, after that combination of faces $\{hkl\}$ which are characteristic of the class. This means that, in stereographic projection, their projection points have arbitrary positions and do no lie on symmetry elements. We shall call the first class the *pedial*. It is given the symbol 1, indicating that it has only a one-fold rotation axis (which is of course always present) (Fig. 24b). In nature such asymmetric crystals of the rare mineral

Fig. 24. (a) Pedion; (b) Stereographic projection of the pedial class 1

strontian hilgardite $(Sr,Ca)_2B_5O_8(OH)_2Cl$ occur. In the laboratory one can prepare crystals of calcium thiosulfate, $CaS_2O_3 \cdot 6H_2O$, which crystallize in this class.

As members of the next class, we consider those crystals which possess only a center of symmetry. Here each face is accompanied by an equivalent and opposite parallel face. This is always the case no matter what its position on the crystal. Such opposing and parallel pairs of faces are called pinacoids (Greek, board) (Fig. 25). The class

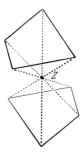

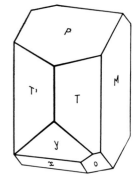

Fig. 25. Pinacoid with center of symmetry noted

Fig. 26.
Stereographic projection of the pinacoidal class Ī

Fig. 27. Anorthite. $P(001)$, M (010), $T'(1\bar{1}0)$, $T(110)$, $x(10\bar{1})$, $y(20\bar{1})$, $o(11\bar{1})$

is called the *pinacoidal*, and is designated by the symbol Ī (Fig. 26). In addition to many other minerals, the important plagioclase group of calcium-sodium feldspars crystallize in this class. These are mixed crystals of $Na[AlSi_3O_8]$ (albite) and $Ca[Al_2Sl_2O_8]$ (anorthite). Their importance is indicated by the fact that they constitute approximately 40% of the composition of the earth's crust. Fig. 27 shows an anorthite crystal with the conventional face symbols. The characteristics of this class are shown also by one of the potassium feldspars $K[AlSi_3O_8]$, called microcline. Bright-green colored specimens are called amazonite and are cut as semi-precious stones. In addition the important mineral kyanite $Al_2O[SiO_4]$ belongs to this class.

The two classes 1 and Ī constitute the triclinic system.

The Monoclinic Classes. The next class that we meet possesses one plane of symmetry. In this class a plane or face occurring perpendicular to the plane of symmetry is a pedion as before. A plane parallel to the symmetry plane becomes a pinacoid, whereas all other planar positions lead to "roof"-shaped pairs of planes called domes (Greek, doma, roof). The planes in this class are related to a monoclinic coordinate system, with the non-orthogonal axes lying in the plane

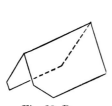

Fig. 28. Dome

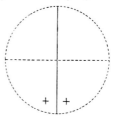

Fig. 29. Stereographic projection of the domatic class m

of symmetry. The symmetry of this and the two following classes is consistent with the symmetry of such a coordinate system. Accordingly these three classes will be grouped together into the monoclinic system. The crystal is usually oriented so that the symmetry plane runs perpendicular to the observer, with

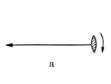

a

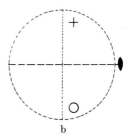

b

Fig. 30a and b. Two-fold symmetry axis (a) and stereographic projection (b) of the sphenoidal class 2

the a axis inclined from back to front (Fig. 29). The class containing one symmetry plane has the symbol m and is called the *domatic* class. Natural examples are rare, but the mineral *clinohedrite*, $Ca_2Zn_2(OH)_2Si_2O_7 \cdot H_2O$, belongs in this class.

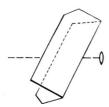

Fig. 31. Sphenoid with two-fold axis noted

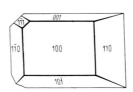

Fig. 32. Sucrose

Crystals containing one two-fold axis constitute the next class 2 (Fig. 30). Planes perpendicular to the rotation axis are again pedions; those parallel form pinacoids. Other pairs of faces are called sphenoids (Greek, sphen, wedge) (Fig. 31). We call this class the *sphenoidal* class. In this class the sugars, sucrose $(C_{12}H_{22}O_{11})$, and lactose $(C_{12}H_{22}O_{11} \cdot H_2O)$ crystallize, as does tartaric acid $(H_2C_4H_4O_6)$ and many other organic substances.

Now we shall combine together in pairs the three symmetry elements used above. This has been done in Fig. 33a—c. In (a) we see a symmetry plane with a two-fold axis perpendicular to it; in (b) a symmetry plane with a center of symmetry; and in (c) a center of symmetry combined with a two-fold axis.

As can be seen the same face arrangement and symmetry appears regardless of how the three elements are combined. If all three are combined, the same symmetry results. This example serves to illustrate that the same symmetry arrangement can be derived in different ways.

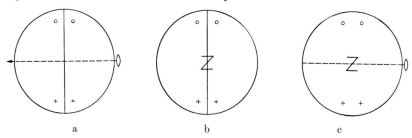

a   b   c

Fig. 33a—c. All combinations using two of the different symmetry elements already used always give the symmetry of the prismatic class 2/m. (a) Symmetry plane with two-fold axis. (b) Symmetry plane with center of symmetry. (c) Two-fold axis with center of symmetry

In the new class just created, the general form consists of four faces symmetrically related, a form designated as the prism (Fig. 34a—c). A pair of parallel faces lying perpendicular to the symmetry plane with face poles lying in the symmetry plane and related to each other through the 2-fold axis as well as the symmetry center, constitutes a pinacoid. Likewise, a pair of faces parallel to the symmetry plane is a pinacoid.

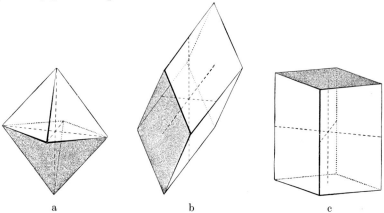

a   b   c

Fig. 34a—c. Prisms of the class 2/m. (a) $\{hkl\}$; (b) $\{0kl\}$; (c) $\{hk0\}$

This class is called the *prismatic* and is given the symbol 2/m (Fig. 35). Many important minerals crystallize in this class. Examples are gypsum, $CaSO_4 \cdot 2H_2O$ (Fig. 36), muscovite mica, $KAl_2(OH)_2[AlSi_3O_{10}]$, and the pyroxene, diopside $CaMg[Si_2O_6]$. Especially important is potassium feldspar $K[AlSi_3O_8]$ which occurs as the "high temperature modification" called *sanidine*, and usually also contains some sodium. Sanidine occurs in eruptive rocks, for example, trachites, and is commonly tabular, parallel to (010). According to its morphology, the common K feldspar, orthoclase, is also monoclinic prismatic (see p. 75). It is found in intrusive rocks or in conjunction with them. The forms $P\{001\}$ and $M\{010\}$ are well-developed on its crystals, as are $T\{110\}$ and $y\{20\bar{1}\}$ (Fig. 37). The potassium feldspar *adularia* occurs in fissures and veins and as

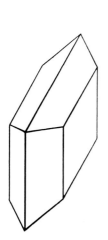
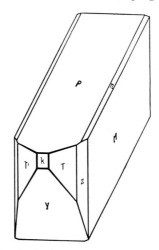

a

b

Fig. 35a and b. Symmetry elements (a) and stereographic projection (b) of the class $2/m$

a semi-precious stone called moonstone. Here the forms T and $x\{10\bar{1}\}$ frequently predominate. Its crystals, therefore, sometimes look similar to rhombohedra (see p. 26) (Fig. 38).

Orthorhombic Classes. We shall continue to utilize the same symmetry elements as before, combining them with each other. If two planes of symmetry are crossed perpendicular to each other, 2-fold axis is created, lying along

Fig. 36. Gypsum. $\{010\}$, $\{110\}$, $\{111\}$

Fig. 37. Orthoclase. $P\,(001)$, $M\,(010)$, $k\,(100)$, $T\,(110)$, $T'\,(1\bar{1}0)$, $y\,(20\bar{1})$, $z\,(130)$, $n\,(021)$

their line of intersection. In this case four faces or planes in general positions combine to form a pyramid (Fig. 39). The cross section of the pyramid is a rhombus, which gives the system, in which this and the next two classes fall, the designation orthorhombic. Therefore, the name of this first class is the *(ortho)rhombic pyramidal*, with the symbol $mm2$ (or mm) (Fig. 40). The three orthorhombic classes are related to an orthogonal coordinate axial system, which is compatible exclusively with their symmetry. In the class $mm2$, two of the coordinate axes, the a- and b-axes, lie in the symmetry planes, whereas the

c-axes coincides with the two-fold axis. The latter is *polar*, that is, different in each direction. Faces intersecting the upper end of the c-axis have no corresponding equivalent faces intersecting the lower end. In addition to pyramids two

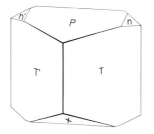

Fig. 38. Adularia. $P(001)$, $x(10\bar{1})$, $T(110)$,
$T'(1\bar{1}0)$, $n(021)$, $n'(0\bar{2}1)$

Fig. 39. Orthorhombic pyramid

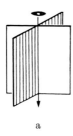

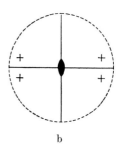

a   b

Fig. 40a and b. Symmetry elements (a) and stereographic projection (b) of the orthorhombic
pyramidal class $mm2$

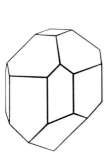

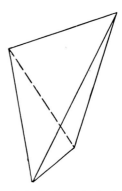

Fig. 41. Hemimorphite. {100}, {010}, {001},
{110}, {301}, {031}, {12$\bar{1}$}

Fig. 42. Orthorhombic disphenoid

pinacoids, pedions (001) and (00$\bar{1}$), domes, and prisms occur. The zinc silicate, hemimorphite (hemi, half; morphe, form), $Zn_4(OH)_2[Si_2O_7] \cdot H_2O$, crystallizes in this class and usually shows clearly the development characteristic of this class.

If we consider two perpendicular 2-fold axes we see that a third axis must appear, standing perpendicular to both of them. Each of these three 2-fold axes is non-polar. All directions and their opposite directions are equivalent. In this

new class we meet for the first time a closed form. It is bounded by four $\{hkl\}$
planes and consists of two wedges or sphenoids symmetrically intergrown (Fig. 42).
This form is the *disphenoid* and the class is called the *orthorhombic disphenoidal*,
with the symbol 222 (Fig. 43). The 2-fold axes are the coordinate axes. The

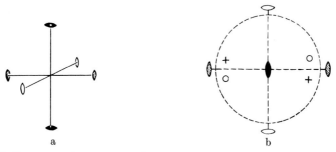

a   b

Fig. 43a and b. Symmetry elements (a) and stereographic projection (b) of the orthorhombic
disphenoidal class 222

disphenoid can be considered as a distorted tetrahedron. With higher 4-fold symmetry it occurs again later as a tetragonal disphenoid (see p. 42). The regular
tetrahedron itself has even higher symmetry. In addition to disphenoids, prisms
and three pinacoids occur in this class. Epsomite, $MgSO_4 \cdot 7H_2O$ (Fig. 44) crystallizes
in the class 222 as do many organic compounds.

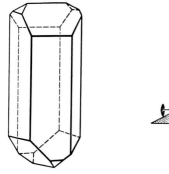

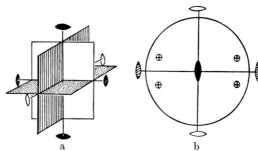

a   b

Fig. 44. Epsomite. {110},   Fig. 45a and b. Symmetry elements (a) and stereographic
{111}, {010}, {1̄11}   projection (b) of the orthorhombic dipyramidal class mmm

We have met for the first time in this crystal class a *closed form*. With it,
it is possible for a crystal in this class (and in many which we have yet to encounter) to consist of only one *simple form*. In the preceeding classes, all simple
forms were *open forms*. That is, no individual form completely enclosed the
crystal and accordingly the crystal had to consist of a combination of different
forms. Such *combinations* of different simple forms are very common, irrespective
of the crystal class. They are indeed the rule as the diagrams in this chapter show.

If we now combine two perpendicular 2-fold axes with a symmetry center,
or two perpendicular symmetry planes with a two-fold axis perpendicular to
one of them, or another symmetry plane perpendicular to both of the original
ones, we encounter the symmetry illustrated in Fig. 45. A horizontal symmetry
plane is illustrated in the figure by means of the solid circle. The general form
which we obtain, if the projection points do not lie on any special position such

as a symmetry plane or axis, is, as Fig. 46 shows, a closed form with eight faces—a double—or dipyramid. The class is called the *orthorhombic dipyramidal*. The appropriate class symbol is $2/m\ 2/m\ 2/m$, or abbreviated, mmm. In addition

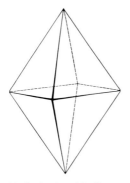

Fig. 46. Orthorhombic dipyramid

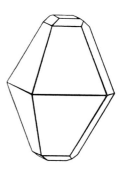

Fig. 47. Sulfur. {111}, {001}, {011}, {113}

to the dipyramid other forms occur. Those parallel to two axes are the pinacoids {100}, {010}, and {001}. If parallel to only one axis, (with projection points on the trace of the plane of symmetry) they are the prisms {0kl}, {h0l}, {hk0}. Many common minerals crystallize in this class. Examples are sulfur (Fig. 47); the anhydrous alkaline earth sulfates, anhydrite ($CaSO_4$), celestite ($SrSO_4$),

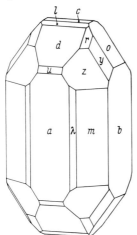

barite ($BaSO_4$) (Figs. 8 and 48), and anglesite ($PbSO_4$); the carbonates aragonite ($CaCO_3$), strontianite ($SrCO_3$), witherite($BaCO_3$), and cerussite($PbCO_3$).

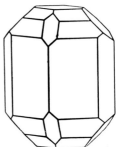

Fig. 48. Barite (oblique view); for indices compare with Table 1 (p. 12)

Fig. 49. Topaz. {110}, {120}, {111}, {112}, {001}, {101}, {011}

In addition the rock forming mineral olivine $(Mg, Fe)_2[SiO_4]$, the precious stones topaz $Al_2[F_2SiO_4]$ (Fig. 49), and chrysoberyl $Al_2[BeO_4]$, and many other chemical compounds produced in the laboratory belong here.

Significance of Class Symbols. The eight crystal classes to which we have already referred are grouped together into three crystal systems according to their coordinate axes: in the triclinic system we have met two classes 1 and $\bar{1}$; in the monoclinic, m, 2, and $2/m$; and in the orthorhombic, the classes $mm2$, 222, and mmm.

The symbols 1, Ī, 2, and m need no further explanation; they indicate the individual symmetry elements for the corresponding class (see p. 21). The symbol of the monoclinic prismatic class, $2/m$ (read "two over m") indicates that a 2-fold axis stands perpendicular to a symmetry plane. The symbols $4/m$ or $6/m$ have fully analogous meanings. We shall refer to these classes later. In listing the symbols in the orthorhombic classes, the symmetry axis in the direction of the a-axis is first given, then in the direction of the b-axis, and finally in the direction of the c-axis[1].

A symmetry plane is always referred to with respect to that axis to which it is perpendicular. Thus we can interpret the symbols 222, $mm2$, and $2/m\ 2/m\ 2/m$.

The 19 classes which now follow contain one unique 3-, 4-, or 6-fold axis. These are referred to in German as "wirtelig" (whorling) crystals. In designating their class symbols, that symmetry axis parallel to the Wirtel or primary axis is indicated first. In orienting the crystal this axis is placed vertical. Then those symmetry axes follow which parallel the horizontal crystallographic axes (secondary axes) and are symmetrically equivalent. The symbol for those symmetry axes which bisect the angles between the secondary axes finally follows (intermediate axes). As in the case of the orthorhombic system, the symbol for a symmetry plane is written, giving its location with respect to that axis to which it is perpendicular.

The crystal class symbols which we have been using were first formulated by C. HERMANN and CH. MAUGUIN and are now called the *Hermann-Mauguin-Symbols*.

The 19 crystal classes which now follow are grouped into the trigonal, the tetragonal, the hexagonal systems, depending on whether their primary axis is three-, four-, or six-fold. We shall not treat these with the same thoroughness as we have the preceding eight, but shall only refer in some detail to those classes in which important minerals crystallize. We shall refer to the remaining classes primarily by means of figures and in the summary in the Appendix, p. 342—349.

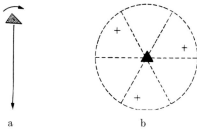
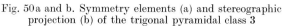
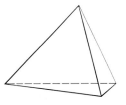

a	b	

Fig. 50a and b. Symmetry elements (a) and stereographic projection (b) of the trigonal pyramidal class 3

Fig. 51. Trigonal pyramid

The Trigonal Classes. We begin with that class which contains a 3-fold axis as its only symmetry element (Fig. 50). In it the general form is a trigonal pyramid (Fig. 51). This class is called the *trigonal-pyramidal*, and has the symbol 3. Nickel sulfite, $NiSO_3 \cdot 6H_2O$, is an important member.

If we then add a center of symmetry, six faces occur in general positions, with three projection points lying in the upper hemisphere and three others rotated 60° with respect to them in the lower hemisphere (Fig. 52). The symbol of this class is $\bar{3}$; face distribution is in accordance with a three-fold inversion axis (see

---

[1] This indicates that in the class $mm2$, the 2-fold axis is the c-axis. Another alternative crystal setting commonly used places the 2-fold axis parallel to b.

p. 20). The general form is a rhombohedron, giving the class its name, *rhombo-hedral*. When orienting a crystal, if a rhombohedral face faces upward and toward the observer, so that its projection point lies in the forward sixth of the stereo-graphic projection, the rhombohedron is designated as positive (Fig. 53). If the face faces forward, but downward, it is then called a negative rhombohedron.

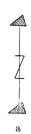
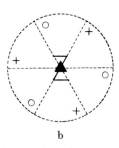
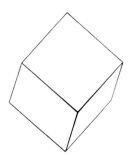

Fig. 52a and b. Symmetry elements (a) and stereoprojection (b) of the rhombohedral class 3

Fig. 53.
Positive rhombohedron

When we consider the rhombohedron merely as a geometrical figure, it has higher apparent symmetry, containing three symmetry planes. However, in the crystal class $\bar{3}$ the rhombohedron as a physical body does not possess these symmetry planes. This can be recognized by means of etch figures (Fig. 54), which reveal that the faces have higher indices and, therefore, are in a more general position. We shall deal with these later (page 177) when discussing the dissolution of crystals. Etch methods are very important in assigning a crystal to its proper class. For example, one can differentiate calcite with its higher symmetry from the mineral dolomite, $CaMg(CO_3)_2$. The latter crystallizes in the class $\bar{3}$. It was named after the French mineralogist DEODAT DE DOLOMIEU (1750—1801), not after the Italian Alpine mountains of the same name. Phenacite, $Be_2[SiO_4]$, willemite, $Zn_2[SiO_4]$, and ilmenite, $FeTiO_3$, belong to this class.

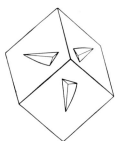

Fig. 54. Rhombohedron of dolomite with etch figures. (It is to be noted that the 3-fold axis does not run from top to bottom, but emerges approximately from the center of the diagram)

A 2-fold axis perpendicular to the 3-fold axis must evoke two additional equivalent 2-fold axes (Fig. 55), giving rise to the *trigonal-trapezohedral* class, with the symbol 32. The general form is called the trapezahedron, of which there are both left- (Fig. 56) and right-handed (Fig. 57) forms. Three faces occur on the upper and three on the lower ends of the crystal, but in this case they are not displaced 60° with respect to each other, as in the case of the rhombo-hedron, but at any general angle. The mineral quartz (SiO_2) crystallizes in this class. This is a very important and common mineral which makes up about 12% of the earth's crust. We shall note next the possible forms in this class. Faces whose projection points lie at the intersection of a twofold axis and the primitive circle, form a three-faced open form, a trigonal prism. If one of the faces faces to the right and toward the observer ($11\bar{2}0$), the form is called a right-handed trigonal prism; the other, for which the face has the indices ($2\bar{1}\bar{1}0$), is a left-handed prism. If the projection point of this prism is moved from the primitive circle, along a line connecting with the center of the projection, a new projection point results, representing a trigonal dipyramid. This form also has left- and right-handed orientations. If we place the projection point on the primitive cricle, near to, but not coinciding with, the intersection with the 2-fold axis, we obtain a ditrigonal prism, also with left- and right-handed orientations. If we make the angular distance between two points on the primitive circle equal to 60°, we create a

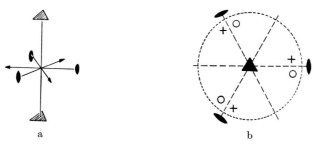

Fig. 55a and b. Symmetry elements (a) and stereographic projection (b) of the trigonal trapezohedral class 32

regular "hexagonal" prism. This designation is usually given to this form, although the six faces are not really related through a 6-fold repetition. One face is obtained from the other through rotation around a 2-fold rather than a 6-fold axis. Therefore, it can in reality just as well be considered a combination of equally developed positive and negative trigonal prisms. If we move the projection point from this border position inward along the connecting line to the center, either a positive or negative rhombohedron results. Faces represented by a point lying at the center of the projection form a pinacoid {0001} with its parallel opposing face.

Fig. 56. Left-handed trigonal trapezohedron   Fig. 57. Right-handed trigonal trapezohedron

Quartz (Fig. 58) usually displays faces of the hexagonal prism m {10$\bar{1}$0}, the positive rhombohedron r {10$\bar{1}$1} and the negative z or r' {01$\bar{1}$1}, the trigonal dipyramids s {11$\bar{2}$1} and s' {2$\bar{1}\bar{1}$1}, (shown in Fig. 59 with s_l and s_r) and the trapezohedron x {51$\bar{6}$1}. Fig. 59 shows the position of these points in stereographic projection, designating positive and negative and right- and left-handed forms. If the faces of both rhombohedra are equally developed, they give the impression of a hexagonal pyramid. A very careful study of face development usually shows that each set of three alternating faces belong together. Steep rhombohedra whose projection points lie very close to the primitive circle, produce the common striations found on the prism faces of quartz. A rhombohedron whose projection points would fall on the primitive circle, would be a hexagonal prism. The varied development of positive and negative rhombohedral faces can be dependent upon growth or dissolution phenomena. The latter, in the case of quartz, can be brought about artificially, either with caustic potash (Fig. 60) or hydrofluoric acid. These figures show that two adjacent faces of the so-called

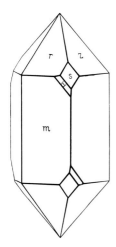

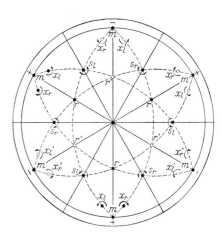

Fig. 58. Right-handed quartz. $m(10\bar{1}0)$, $r(10\bar{1}1)$, $z(01\bar{1}1)$, $s(11\bar{2}1)$, $x(51\bar{6}1)$

Fig. 59. Stereographic projection of the common faces of quartz. ● positive, ○ negative, ⌒ right, ⌒ left forms

hexagonal prism are not related to each other by a 6-fold axis. Etch figures are also important technologically, because with their help it can be established externally whether a crystal is homogeneous, or whether it consists of several crystals intimately intergrown. Such intergrowths, called twins, will be referred to later (p. 98).

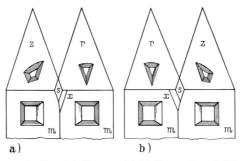

Fig. 60a and b. Difference in the etch figures of (a) left-quartz and (b) right-quartz. Etching agent is in both cases alkali carbonate. (After LIEBISCH)

As has already been noted, there are in this class both left- and right-handed forms. The ability of a substance to form both left- and right-handed crystals is called *enantiomorphism*. It is related to the symmetry of the crystal and is encountered only in those crystals which possess neither a center nor plane of symmetry. In the case of quartz the Si and O atoms are spirally arranged, right-handed quartz having left-spiralling screw axes, and left-handed quartz, right. The 2-fold axes are polar, that is to say, opposing directions are not equivalent. Related to the symmetry are two additional properties of quartz, its optical activity (p. 142) and piezoelectric behavior (p. 118), both of which we shall encounter later.

Quartz is a useful crystal on account of its piezoelectric behavior (oscillator quartz) and is an important raw material because of its excellent transparency in the ultraviolet (quartz spectrograph). Smaller crystals are used in the production of quartz glass. Optically clear specimens are called rock crystal. Violet amethyst, which was at one time considered as a protection from drunkedness, finds use as a semi-precious stone. The word, probably of pre-Hellenic origin, is related to the Greek word *methyein*, meaning to become drunk, and the negative prefix *a*. Madeira topaz, quartz topaz, and genuine topaz quartz are names for yellow to yellow-brown (Madeira wine) colored quartzes, usually produced by heating amethyst or dark-colored smoky quartz. Chalcedony is quartz which has grown in fibrous form perpendicular to the 3-fold axis, along the [10$\bar{1}$0] or [11$\bar{2}$0] axes. Quartz, fibrous parallel to *c*, also occurs and is called quartzin. Agate consists of chalcedony and finely crystalline quartz intermixed. In addition to quartz the important mineral cinnabar, HgS, crystallizes in the class 32.

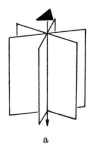
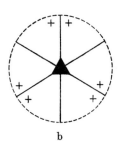
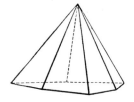

a   b

Fig. 61 a and b. Symmetry elements (a) and stereographic   Fig. 62. Ditrigonal pyramid
projection (b) of the ditrigonal pyramidal class 3*m*

The next class which we shall study has a polar 3-fold axis. Accordingly, electrical effects occur along this axis upon heating: the crystal becomes positively charged at one end, negatively at the other. The charged ends then attract light particles. This *pyroelectric effect* (see p. 118) was first discovered in the mineral tourmaline, a sodium aluminum borofluorsilicate. This property led to the Dutch designation of this mineral as "Aschentrekker". Plates cut perpendicular to the 3-fold axis are also piezoelectric. The class exemplified by tourmaline is derived by combining the 3-fold axis with a plane of symmetry so that the axis lies in the plane (Fig. 61). This actually creates three equivalent symmetry planes intersecting each other at an angle of 60°. The general form is a ditrigonal-pyramid (Fig. 62). The class is called the *ditrigonal-pyramidal*, with the symbol 3*m*.

It is usually the case with tourmaline that several ditrigonal-prisms occur, so that a cross section of a crystal resembles a triangle with convex-curved sides. The polarity of the 3-fold axis is rendered observable in many specimens of tourmaline by the form development (Fig. 63). The "red silver ores" proustite Ag$_3$AsS$_3$ and pyrargyrite Ag$_3$SbS$_3$ also belong to this class.

The addition of 2-fold axes as the angle bisectors of the symmetry planes of class 3*m*, leads to the *ditrigonal-scalenohedral* class, 32/*m* or $\bar{3}$*m* (Fig. 64). The

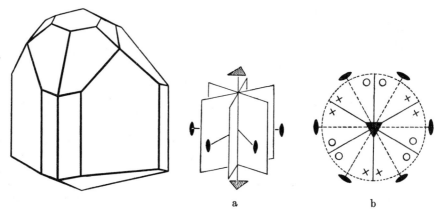

Fig. 63. Tourmaline. Combinations of {10$\bar{1}$0}, {10$\bar{1}$1}, {11$\bar{2}$0}, {02$\bar{2}$1}, {32$\bar{5}$1}

Fig. 64 a and b. Symmetry elements (a) and stereographic projection (b) of the ditrigonal scalenohedral class 3 m

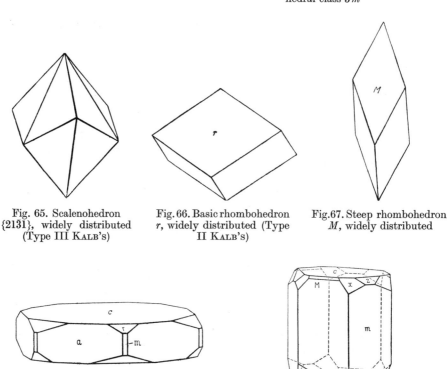

Fig. 65. Scalenohedron {21$\bar{3}$1}, widely distributed (Type III KALB's)

Fig. 66. Basic rhombohedron r, widely distributed (Type II KALB's)

Fig. 67. Steep rhombohedron M, widely distributed

Fig. 68. From Maderanertal. (After NIGGLI, KÖNIGSBERGER, PARKER)

Fig. 69. From St. Andreasberg. (After SANSONI)

common and form-rich mineral calcite ($CaCO_3$) crystallizes in this class. The scalenohedron, to which the class owes its name, is a closed form in which the six faces on the upper and bottom ends of the crystal lie together in pairs (Fig. 65). Additional common forms and combinations are illustrated in Figs. 66—71. While the examples in Figs. 65—67 show only simple forms, the calcite crystals in Figs. 68—71 consist of combinations of several forms. The general aspect of a

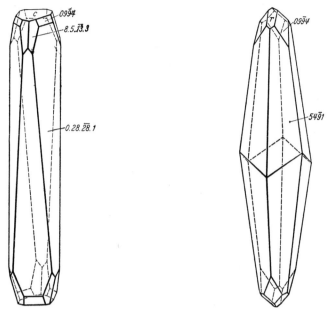

Fig. 70. From St. Andreasberg. (After Thürling)   Fig. 71. From St. Andreasberg. (After Thürling)

Figs. 65—71. Forms of calcite. $c\{0001\}$, $r\{10\bar{1}1\}$, $a\{11\bar{2}0\}$, $m\{10\bar{1}0\}$, $M\{40\bar{4}1\}$, $z\{08\bar{8}7\}$, $x\{8324021\}$

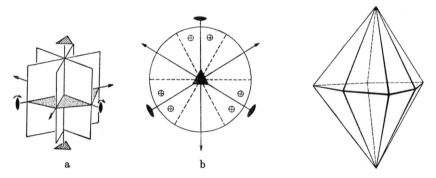

a   b

Fig. 72a and b. Symmetry elements (a) and stereographic projection (b) of the ditrigonal dipyramidal class $\bar{6}m2$ Fig. 73. Ditrigonal dipyramid

crystal is usually referred to as its *habit*. Thus the habit of calcite in Fig. 68 is *tabular*, in Fig. 69 is *compact columnar*, in Figs. 70 and 71 *columnar* to *acicular*. The habit of crystals whose dimensions are approximately equal in all directions is called *isometric*.

The elements As, Sb, Bi, as well as the minerals corundum (Al_2O_3) and hematite (Fe_2O_3), crystallize in the class $\bar{3}2/m$. Varities of blue corundum are called sapphire; the red variety, ruby. Fine-grained corundum is known as emery.

If we now add a horizontal symmetry plane to the classes $3m$ or 32, we derive the *ditrigonal-dipyramidal* class, $\bar{6}m2$ (Figs. 72 and 73), in which only the very rare mineral benitoite $BaTi[Si_3O_9]$ crystallizes.

 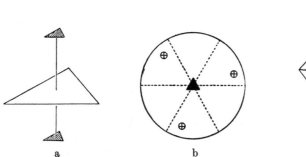 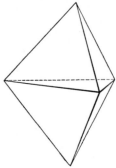

Fig. 74a and b. Symmetry elements (a) and stereographic projection (b) of the trigonal dipyramidal class $\bar{6}$

Fig. 75. Trigonal dipyramid

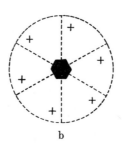 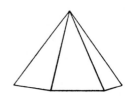

Fig. 76a and b. Symmetry elements (a) and stereographic projection (b) of the hexagonal pyramidal class 6

Fig. 77. Hexagonal pyramid

 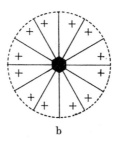

Fig. 78a and b. Symmetry elements (a) and stereographic projection (b) of the dihexagonal pyramidal class $6mm$

Fig. 79. Dihexagonal pyramid

As mentioned earlier, theoretically one would expect a crystal class resulting from the combination of a 3-fold axis and a perpendicular plane of symmetry, but no representatives are known. The corresponding class would be called the *trigonal-dipyramidal*, with the symbol $\bar{6}$ (Figs. 74 and 75).

The symbols of these last two classes ($\bar{6}m2$ and $\bar{6}$) have been written using a 6-fold inversion axis. Therefore, frequently they are not grouped with the trigonal, but with the hexagonal classes. However, when we recall that a $\bar{6}$ axis is equivalent to $3/m$, and if, in the assignment of morphology we wish to emphasize clearly and prominently the 3-fold symmetry, we will then place them among the trigonal classes. However, this assignment is still arbitrary, and for a variety of reasons one might prefer to group them among the hexagonal classes. This concludes the discussion of the trigonal classes, and we can now proceed to those containing 6-fold axes.

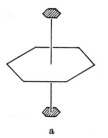

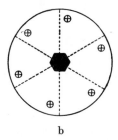

a

b

Fig. 80a and b. Symmetry elements (a) and stereographic projection (b) of the hexagonal dipyramidal class $6/m$

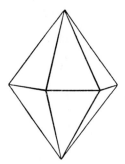

Fig. 81. Hexagonal dipyramid

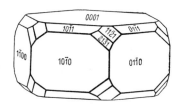

Fig. 82. Apatite

The Hexagonal Classes. The simplest hexagonal class is the *hexagonal pyramidal*, 6 (Figs. 76 and 77) containing only a 6-fold axis. Nepheline, $Na[AlSiO_4]$, a common constituent of basaltic rocks, crystallizes in this class. In nepheline about one-fourth of the sodium is usually replaced by potassium.

If we first add a symmetry plane parallel to the 6-fold axis, we create actually six equivalent symmetry planes intersecting each other at an angle of 30°. This is the *dihexagonal-pyramidal* class, $6mm$ (Figs. 78 and 79). A form of ZnS, wurtzite, crystallizes in this class.

If we combine a horizontal symmetry plane with a 6-fold axis, we derive the *hexagonal-dipyramidal* class, $6/m$ (Figs. 80 and 81), in which the most important phosphate mineral, apatite, $Ca_5(F, OH, Cl)(PO_4)_3$ (Fig. 82) crystallizes.

By combining a 2-fold axis perpendicular to the 6-fold axis, we derive the *hexagonal-trapezohedral* class, 622 (Fig. 83). The hexagonal trapezohedron corresponds to the trigonal one we met earlier, but has 2×6 rather than 2×3 faces. Again right- (Fig. 84) and left-handed (Fig. 85) forms occur. "High" quartz, the SiO_2 modification stable between 575 and 870° C at atmospheric pressure, belongs to this class according to most existing information. Upon cooling, "high" quartz inverts into several individuals of "low" quartz without the original crystal losing its integrity (twinning p. 96ff., also p. 62).

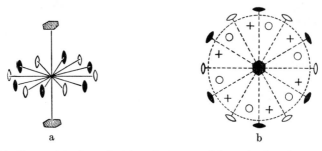

a   b

Fig. 83a and b. Symmetry elements (a) and stereographic projection (b) of the hexagonal trapezohedral class 622

If we now add a center of symmetry to this last class or to the class $6mm$, we create the highest symmetry possible in the hexagonal system, the *dihexagonal-dipyramidal* class $6/m\,2/m\,2/m$, abbreviated $6/mmm$ (Figs. 86 and 87). In this class crystallizes the mineral beryl, $Be_3Al_2[Si_6O_{18}]$ (Fig. 88), known as the semi-precious blue-green gem aquamarine, or as the green gem emerald. The green variety of beryl has been especially highly prized since antiquity. In the Middle Ages thin plates of beryl were used in the peepholes of holy shrines, explaining the derivation from the German word, *Brille*, meaning eye glasses.

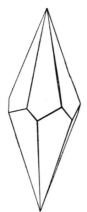

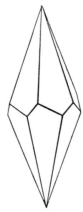

Fig. 84. Right-handed hexagonal trapezohedron

Fig. 85. Left-handed hexagonal trapezohedron

The types of form occurring in this class are indicated and numbered in the stereographic projection (Fig. 89) 1. pinacoid $\{0001\}$; 2. hexagonal prism, I. orientation $\{10\bar{1}0\}$; 3. hexagonal prism, II. orientation $\{11\bar{2}0\}$; 4. dihexagonal prism $\{hki0\}$; 5. hexagonal dipyramid, I. orientation $\{h0\bar{h}l\}$; 6. hexagonal dipyramid, II. orientation $\{hh\overline{2h}l\}$; 7. dihexagonal dipyramid $\{hkil\}$.

The last twelve classes (trigonal and hexagonal) are sometimes subdivided in a different fashion. The classes 6, $6/m$, 622, $6mm$, $6/mmm$, $\bar{6}$, and $\bar{6}m2$ are sometimes grouped together into a hexagonal system, whereas the classes 3, $\bar{3}$,

32, $3m$, $\bar{3}2/m$, are grouped together as the *trigonal rhombohedral system*. In the latter either hexagonal or rhombohedral coordinate axes (p. 14) are used. For all twelve of these classes, when referred to hexagonal coordinates, it is sufficient in characterizing axial parameters to denote the ratio $a:c$. In the case of rhombohedral coordinate axes, it is necessary to indicate the angle which the three axes make with each other.

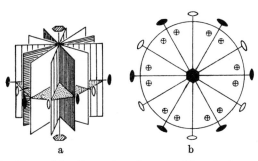

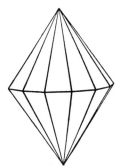

Fig. 86a and b. Symmetry elements (a) and stereographic projection (b) of the dihexagonal dipyramidal class $6/mmm$

Fig. 87. Dihexagonal dipyramid

The Tetragonal Classes. The next seven classes are distinguished by a 4-fold rotation axis and are grouped together as the tetragonal system. A single 4-fold axis is characteristic of the *tetragonal pyramidal* class 4 (Figs. 90 and 91), of which wulfenite, $Pb[MoO_4]$, may be a member.

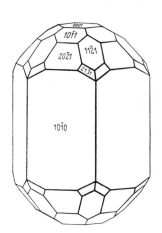

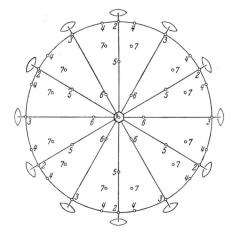

Fig. 88. Beryl

Fig. 89. Stereographic projection of the forms of the class $6/mmm$. 1. $\{0001\}$, 2. $\{10\bar{1}0\}$, 3. $\{11\bar{2}0\}$, 4. $\{hk\bar{i}0\}$, 5. $\{h0\bar{h}l\}$, 6. $\{hh\overline{2h}l\}$, 7. $\{hk\bar{i}l\}$

If a horizontal symmetry plane is added, the *tetragonal dipyramidal* class, $4/m$ (Fig. 92) results. The mineral scheelite ($CaWO_4$) (Fig. 93) is a member of this class.

If the mirror plane is placed vertically, it is repeated again after 90°, in accordance with the four-fold symmetry. As a result of the symmetry two additional symmetry planes occur midway between the former two. This class is called the *ditetragonal-pyramidal*, $4mm$ (Figs. 94 and 95). Thus pairs of faces reoccur in tetragonal repetition. An example of this class is the laboratory product $AgF \cdot H_2O$.

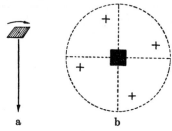
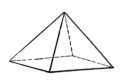

Fig. 90a and b. Symmetry elements (a) and stereographic projection (b) of the tetragonal pyramidal class 4

Fig. 91. Tetragonal pyramid

If we combine the tetragonal rotation axis with a 2-fold axis at right angles to it, a second equivalent 2-fold axis must occur at 90° to the first by virtue of the symmetry. If we study the resulting symmetry, it is easily seen that two

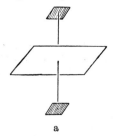

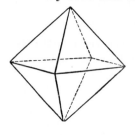

Fig. 92a and b. Symmetry elements (a) and stereographic projection (b) of the tetragonal dipyramidal class $4/m$

Fig. 93. Scheelite, tetragonal dipyramid

additional 2-fold axes must occur, bisecting the angles between the first pair (Fig. 96). The general form is called the tetragonal trapezohedron. In this case also there are both left- (Fig. 97) and right-handed (Fig. 98) forms. The class is

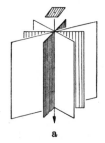
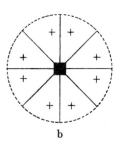
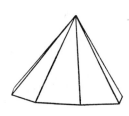

Fig. 94a and b. Symmetry elements (a) and stereographic projection (b) of the ditetragonal pyramidal class $4mm$

Fig. 95. Ditetragonal pyramid

called the *tetragonal trapezohedral* and has the symbol 422. $NiSO_4 \cdot 6 H_2O$ crystallizes in this class.

If we add to the classes 422 or $4mm$ a center of symmetry, or to the class $4/m$ a horizontal 2-fold axis, additional symmetry elements appear, resulting in the most highly symmetrical tetragonal class, $4/m\,2/m\,2/m$, abbreviated $4/mmm$, the *ditetragonal dipyramidal* class (Fig. 99). The general form is the ditetragonal dipyramid $\{hkl\}$, (Fig. 100), which possesses eight paired faces on the upper as

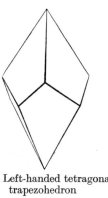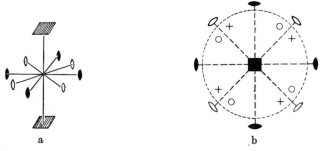

Fig. 96a and b. Symmetry elements (a) and stereographic projection (b) of the tetragonal trapezohedral class 422

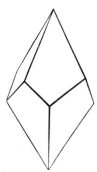

Fig. 97. Left-handed tetragonal trapezohedron

Fig. 98. Right-handed tetragonal trapezohedron

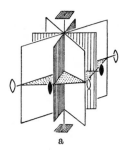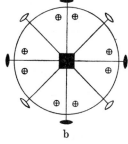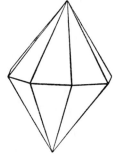

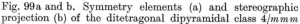

Fig. 99a and b. Symmetry elements (a) and stereographic projection (b) of the ditetragonal dipyramidal class $4/mmm$

Fig. 100. Ditetragonal dipyramid

well as on the bottom side of the crystal. In addition to these we find the following forms in this class, as illustrated in the stereographic projection in Fig. 101: the pinacoid $\{001\}$; the prisms I. $\{110\}$ and II. orientations $\{100\}$; ditetragonal prism $\{hk0\}$; tetragonal dipyramids I. $\{hhl\}$ and II. orientation $\{h0l\}$. Representing this class is the common mineral zircon ($ZrSiO_4$), which is prized as a gemstone — especially the blue variety produced by heating the brown variety (hyacinth) (Fig. 102). Other important minerals are vesuvianite, $Ca_{10}(Mg, Fe)_2Al_4$

$(OH)_4[SiO_4]_5[Si_2O_7]_2$ (Fig. 103), rutile and anatase (both varieties of TiO_2), and cassiterite (SnO_2).

Two additional classes are distinguished by tetragonal inversion axes. One such axis alone (Fig. 104) leads to a closed form consisting of four faces and

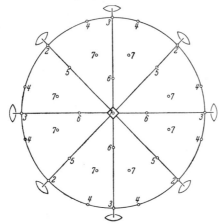

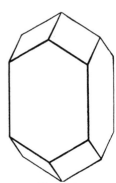

Fig. 101. Stereographic projection of the forms of the class $4/mmm$. 1. {001}, 2. {110}, 3. {100}, 4. {$hk0$}, 5. {hhl}, 6. {$h0l$}, 7. {hkl}

Fig. 102.
Zircon. {100}, {111}

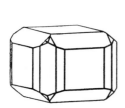

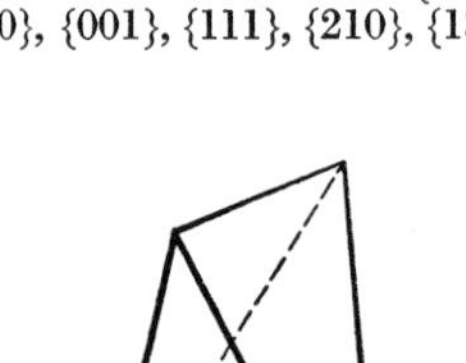

Fig. 103. Vesuvianite. {110}, {100}, {001}, {111}, {210}, {132}

Fig. 104a and b. Symmetry elements (a) and stereographic projection (b) of the tetragonal disphenoidal class $\bar{4}$

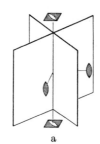

Fig. 105.
Tetragonal disphenoid

Fig. 106a and b. Symmetry elements (a) and stereographic projection (b) of the tetragonal scalenohedral class $\bar{4}2m$

called the *tetragonal disphenoid* (Fig. 105), after which the class is named. The class symbol is $\bar{4}$. A member of this class is the very rare mineral cahnite, $Ca_2B(OH)_4[AsO_4]$.

If we add to the tetragonal inversion axis either a perpendicular 2-fold axis or a symmetry plane parallel to the 4-fold axis, two mirror planes parallel to the rotation axis and two 2-fold rotation axes perpendicular to it appear (Fig. 106). The general form is the tetragonal scalenohedron in which, as in the trigonal variety, paired faces above and below oppose each other rotated 90° with respect to each other. As in the case of the rhombohedron, positive (Fig. 107) and negative scalenohedra (Fig. 108) can be distinguished. In this *tetragonal scalenohedral* class, $\bar{4}2m$, are found disphenoids $\{hhl\}$ (Fig. 109 shows $\{111\}$ and $\{332\}$), as well as prisms I. $\{110\}$ and II. $\{100\}$ orientations, dipyramids II. orientation $\{h0l\}$ and the pinacoid $\{001\}$. This class is represented by the mineral chalcopyrite ($CuFeS_2$) (Fig. 109), the most abundant copper mineral.

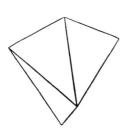

Fig. 107. Positive
tetragonal scalenohedron

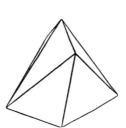

Fig. 108. Negative
tetragonal scalenohedron

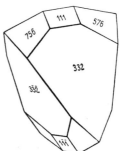

Fig. 109. Chalcopyrite

The Cubic Classes. All of the possible combinations of 2-fold rotation axes and mirror planes with a single 3-, 4-, or 6-fold rotation axes have been exhausted with the classes already enumerated. If we now attempt to combine with each other several axes which have higher than two-fold symmetry, we note that this is only possible when we arrange four 3-fold axes along the directions of the corner diagonals of the cube. We observe further that a 4-fold axis occurs perpendicular to each cube face of the same cube. Since each of these axes penetrates two cube faces, there are in all three 4-fold axes. We shall now concern ourselves with these arrangements. We shall group together the five remaining crystal classes into the *cubic system*. The corresponding crystals are related to orthogonal coordinate axes. The unit faces intersect all three axes equally so that no further statement is necessary, other than to call the crystal cubic.

The Hermann-Mauguin symbols for cubic crystals are formulated in the following manner: the kind of symmetry axis parallel to the cube edge is designated in the first position (it does not necessarily have to be a 4-fold axis, as we shall see); in the second position the kind of symmetry axis parallel to the corner diagonal of the cube (3 or $\bar{3}$); and in the third position the axes parallel to the edge diagonals. The same symmetry plane notation suffices as with the preceding crystal classes. We are able to recognize immediately from the Hermann-Mauguin symbols that we are dealing with a cubic crystal when 3 or $\bar{3}$ occurs in the second position.

The lowest cubic symmetry occurs when only the four 3-fold axes along the cube-diagonals are assumed. With this combination of 3-fold axes, three 2-fold axes appear parallel to the edges of the cube and bisecting the angles between the 3-fold axes. No 4-fold axes are found in the geometrical cubic shape itself. Likewise neither symmetry planes nor a center of symmetry appear (Fig. 110). The projection point of the general form occurs at 2×3 positions on the upper hemisphere with a like number on the lower hemisphere. The corresponding form is a dodecahedron (Greek dodeca, 12; hedra, plane), called a pentagonal dodecahedron (Fig. 111). In order to distinguish it from other pentagonal dodecahedra, we shall refer to it by another common name, tetartoid. In projection each of three pentagonal planes is arranged around the projection point of the tetrahedron (see p. 49). The symbol for this *tetratoidal* class is 23. In this class belong the mineral ullmanite (NiSbS), very rarely occurring as well-developed crystals, sodium chlorate and sodium bromate, both of which are optically active and piezoelectric (p. 142 and 118).

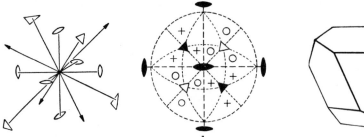
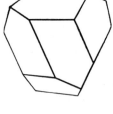

Fig. 110a and b. Symmetry elements (a) and stereographic projection (b) of the tetartoidal class 23

Fig. 111. Tetartoid

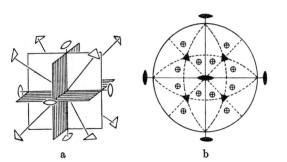
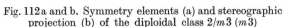
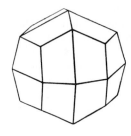

Fig. 112a and b. Symmetry elements (a) and stereographic projection (b) of the diploidal class $2/m3$ ($m3$)

Fig. 113. Diploid (disdodecahedron)

If a horizontal symmetry plane is then added, the number of faces is doubled and they appear on both the upper and lower ends of the crystal. At the same time two additional mirror planes appear, and the 3-fold axis becomes a 6-fold inversion axis (Fig. 112). A center of symmetry also occurs. The corresponding general form is a disdodecahedron (Fig. 113), composed of 24 faces. In order to differentiate it from other 24-faced forms, it is also commonly called a diploid, referring to the occurrence of its faces in pairs. The $2/m3$ or $m3$ class is named after the diploid. In it crystallizes one of the most common minerals, pyrite (FeS$_2$), whose morphology was thoroughly described as far back as 1725 by HENCKEL, in his monograph, "Die Pyritologie". Because pyrite occurs in many forms, and because crystals are readily found, we shall briefly enumerate its possible forms (Fig. 114). In the diploid $\{hkl\}$ three irregular four-sided faces are distributed around each 3-fold axis. Depending on which of the 24 parts of the projection one starts from, either positive or negative forms (7$^+$ or 7$^-$) are obtained. In the case of face location (6), we obtain again 24 faces, which are trapezoids. This form is called, therefore, the trapezohedron (Fig. 138). It is illustrated by the form $\{hhl\}$ with $h < l$.

Also in the case of face position (5), we get 24 faces, but now these are isosceles triangles. The resulting form is called the trisoctahedron, $\{hhl\}$ with $h > l$ (Fig. 136). Points lying on a symmetry plane (4) are repeated twelve times forming a form bounded by pentagons and called the pentagonal dodecahedron $\{hk0\}$ (Fig. 131). This form is often called the pyritohedron, because of its common occurrence on pyrite. The pentagons are not regular, or else the body would have 5-fold axes. In the case of the pentagonal dodecahedron, positive (4$^+$) and negative (4$^-$) forms can be distinguished. If one places the projection point at the center of the symmetry plane, that is to say, 45° from the 2-fold axis, a twelve-faced form (3) is obtained bounded by rhombi. This form is the rhombic dodecahedron $\{110\}$ (Fig. 130). The positions of the points of emer-

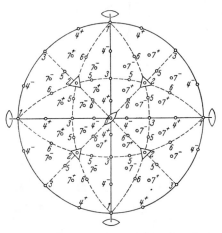

Fig. 114. Stereographic projection of the forms in class $2/m\bar{3}$ 1. $\{100\}$, 2. $\{111\}$, 3. $\{110\}$, 4. $\{hk0\}$, 5. $\{hhl\}$, $h>l$, 6. $\{hhl\}$, $h< l$, 7. $\{hkl\}$. —— symmetry planes and axes; ---- zones

gence of the 3-fold axes correspond to the octahedron $\{111\}$ (2) (Fig. 134); the points of emergence of the 2-fold axis, to the cube $\{100\}$ (1).

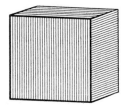

Fig. 115. Pyrite cube with striations

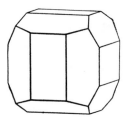

Fig. 116. Pyrite. $\{100\}$ and $\{hk0\}$

In pyrite the combination of $\{100\}$, $\{110\}$, $\{111\}$, and $\{hk0\}$ is particularly common. Often cubes are found whose faces are striated in the manner shown in Fig. 115. The striations indicate that these crystals lack the 4-fold axes as well as the diagonal symmetry planes, which are encountered in classes of higher symmetry. The striations correspond to the directions of horizontal and vertical edges of the pentagonal dodecahedra (pyritohedra) which result from alternating growth after $\{100\}$ and $\{hk0\}$, especially $\{210\}$ (Fig. 116).

The combination of the pentagonal dodecahedron $\{210\}$ and the octahedron $\{111\}$ (Fig. 117) gives a 20-faced body illustrated in Fig. 118, if the faces of both forms are of the proper size. This looks very similar to the icosahedron, the regular body with 5-fold axes. The twelve pentagonal dodecahedral faces, however,

Fig. 117. Pyrite. {111} and {210}

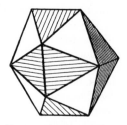

Fig. 118. Pyrite. Pseudo-icosahedron, {111} and {210} striated after {321}

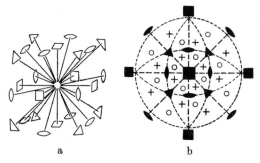

a   b

Fig. 119a and b. Symmetry elements (a) and stereographic projection (b) of the gyroidal class 432

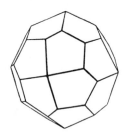

Fig. 120. Gyroid

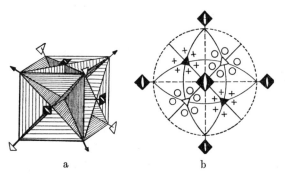

a   b

Fig. 121a and b. Symmetry elements (a) and stereographic projection (b) of the hextetrahedral class $\bar{4}3m$

Fig. 122. Hextetrahedron

are not equilateral, but rather isosceles triangles and frequently appear dull from fine striations after {421}, while the equilateral triangles of the octahedral faces are brilliant.

If we insert into the class 23 a diagonal 2-fold axis instead of the vertical symmetry plane, this axis is repeated six times, three times around each 3-fold axis. The three 2-fold axes of the class 23 become 4-fold axes (Fig. 119). The general form is again a twenty-four-faced one bounded by pentagons, the *pentagonal icosotetrahedron* (Fig. 120), more commonly called a *gyroid* and after which the class is named. The class symbol is 432 or 43. The forms are the same

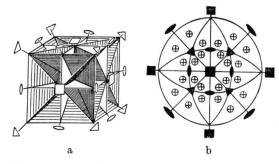

a

b

Fig. 123.
Sphalerite. {111}, {100}

Fig. 124a and b. Symmetry elements (a) and stereographic
projection (b) of the hexoctahedral class $4/m\,\bar{3}\,2/m$ ($m\,\bar{3}\,m$)

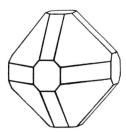

Fig. 125. Hexoctahedron

Fig. 126. Galena. {100}, {110}, {111}

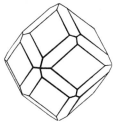

Fig. 127.
Fluorite. Cube {100} with hexoctahedron

Fig. 128.
Garnet. {110} and {112}

as in class $m3$, except that $\{hk0\}$ is now also a twenty-four-faced form, the tetrahexahedron (Fig. 132).

On the basis of their outward crystalline form some crystals of sal ammoniac (NH_4Cl) belong to this class. On the basis of its inner atomic structure the β form of manganese, which is stable between 150° and 850° C, is also a representative of this class.

If a diagonal symmetry plane is introduced into the class 23, it is repeated six times. The 2-fold axes become 4-fold inversion axes (Fig. 121). The general form after which the class is named is the *hextetrahedron* (Fig. 122). The class is called the *hextetrahedral* with symbol $\bar{4}3m$. {111} is here the tetrahedron (Fig. 133), $\{hhl\}$ with $h > l$ the deltoid dodecahedron (deltohedron) (Fig. 135), and $\{hhl\}$ with $h < l$ the tristetrahedron (Fig. 137). Sphalerite (ZnS) (Fig. 123), a common and the most important zinc-bearing mineral, belongs here.

The introduction of a center of symmetry to class $\bar{4}3m$ or 432, as well as the introduction of a diagonal symmetry plane to class $m3$, results in the highest crystal symmetry obtainable by any combination of symmetry elements (Fig. 124). This class, which is represented by the 48-faced form, the hexoctahedron (Fig. 125), has the symbol $4/m\ \bar{3}\ 2/m$ or $m3m$ and is called the *hexoctahedral*. In this class many metals such as gold, silver, and copper crystallize, as do many important minerals. As examples we can mention magnetite (Fe_3O_4), which forms octahedra and rhombic dodecahedra, and galena (PbS) which occurs as cubes frequently modified by octahedra and rhombic dodecahedra (Fig. 126).

In all classes

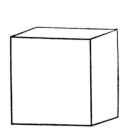

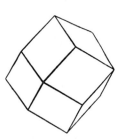

Fig. 129. {100} Cube (hexahedron)   Fig. 130. {110} Rhombic dodecahedron

In the classes:

23 and $m\bar{3}$ $\bar{4}3m$, 432 and $m3m$

$\{hk0\}$

Fig. 131.   Fig. 132.
Pentagonal dodecahedron (pyritohedron)   Tetrahexahedron

Figs. 129—138. Summary of the occurrence of special forms in the cubic system

Fluorite (CaF_2), which usually crystallizes as cubes and always exhibits octahedral cleavage, is occasionally modified by the hexoctahedron at the cube corners (Fig. 127). Garnet, (Mg, Fe^{+2}, Mn^{+2}, Ca)$_3$ (Al, Fe^{+3}, Cr^{+3})$_2$ [SiO_4]$_3$, commonly crystallizes as the rhombic dodecahedron or the trapezohedron (Fig. 128). Diamond probably also belongs in this class. Leucite K[$AlSi_2O_6$] crystallizes usually with {112} as its diagnostic form.

All of the forms of the cubic system, with the exception of the general $\{hkl\}$ forms respectively of all five of the cubic classes, are enumerated diagramatically in Figs. 129—138.

Additional Symbols and Names for the 32 Crystal Classes. In addition to the Hermann-Mauguin symbols utilized here, there it another symbolism in use that goes back to Schoenflies. We shall not deal with it further here, since today the Hermann-Mauguin symbols are in most general use. Since it is necessary to have some familiarity with them in order to understand the crystallographic literature, the reader is referred to Table 2 in Appendix A, in which the Schoen-flies symbols are also tabulated.

In naming the 32 crystal classes, we have used the name of the most general form, as recommended by GROTH. There are still other names in use whose derivation is based on the reasoning that one can proceed in each crystal system from the class of highest symmetry and systematically eliminate symmetry

In the classes:

23 and $\bar{4}3m$ $m\bar{3}$, 432 and $m3m$

{111}

Fig. 133. Tetrahedron

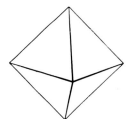

Fig. 134. Octahedron

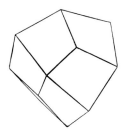

{hhl}
(h > l)

Fig. 135. Deltoid dodecahedron
(deltohedron)

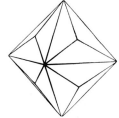

Fig. 136. Trisoctahedron

{hhl}
(h < l)

Fig. 137. Tristetrahedron

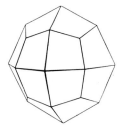

Fig. 138. Trapezohedron

elements, thereby decreasing the number of faces of the general form. The most highly symmetrical class in each system is called the *holohedral*. Pertinent details are again referred to in Appendix A in Table 2.

With these observations we have concluded the formal discussion of crystallography. This is a field which frequently causes the beginner special difficulty. Many people have a very poorly-developed three-dimensional perception. Anyone who wants to concern himself seriously, however, with the architecture of the solid state, that is, with crystal structure, must develop his three-dimensional perception to a very high degree. This is accomplished only through practice, particularly by using models from which recognition of symmetry elements and the corresponding faces can be learned. Apart from its educational value, the knowledge of the 32 crystal classes and their corresponding forms constitutes the foundation for the description of minerals, for the investigation of crystal growth, and for the understanding of physical phenomena, such as

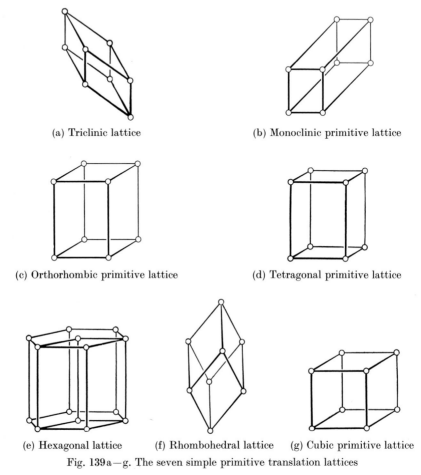

(a) Triclinic lattice   (b) Monoclinic primitive lattice

(c) Orthorhombic primitive lattice   (d) Tetragonal primitive lattice

(e) Hexagonal lattice   (f) Rhombohedral lattice   (g) Cubic primitive lattice

Fig. 139a—g. The seven simple primitive translation lattices

mechanical and optical behavior. The view that it is sufficient to know a little bit about structure, but that it is unnecessary to become familiar with crystal morphology, hinders deep penetration into these problems. The knowledge of the crystal classes is a prerequisite for the understanding of crystal structures.

5. Space Groups

The 14 Translation Lattices (Space Lattices). The most convenient way to build up a periodic point arrangement in space is to start with a point, and by means of translations in three directions (which naturally may not lie in the same plane), and repetition of this process to the newly created point, to produce a simple lattice (see Fig. 16). Such a lattice consists as it were of parallelopipeds stacked one upon the other, at whose corners points occur. Such a parallelopiped is called an *elementary* or *unit cell*. The magnitude of the three translations and the angles between them can assume different values. Careful study leads to the conclusion that only 14 symmetrically different point arrangements can be obtained in this manner. Seven of these (Fig. 139), comprise the most highly symmetrical unit cells, containing points only at their corners. Since each point belongs equally to eight unit cells coming together at a common corner, each unit cell contains only one point. The lattice is said to be *simple primitive*. In

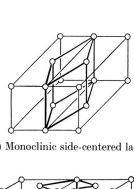

(a) Monoclinic side-centered lattice

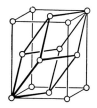

(b) Orthorhombic body-centered lattice

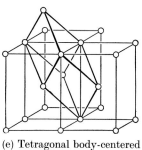

(c) Orthorhombic side-centered lattice

(d) Orthorhombic face-centered lattice

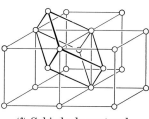

(e) Tetragonal body-centered
lattice

(f) Cubic body-centered
lattice

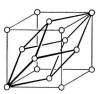

(g) Cubic face-centered
lattice

Fig. 140a—g. The seven multiple translation lattices

particular cases space lattices are known in which the most highly symmetrical unit cell contains two points. These are called *doubly primitive* (Fig. 140a—c, e and f); in addition there are those which contain four points, called *quadruply primitive* (Fig. 140d and g).

Space lattices are classified as triclinic, monoclinic, orthorhombic, tetragonal, hexagonal, rhombohedral, and cubic, based on their coordinate axes. In the case of multiple primitive lattices, it is necessary to indicate whether the most highly symmetrical unit cell is body centered, face-pair centered, or fully face centered. In order to avoid confusion, it should be emphasized that those lattices which

are usually described as multiple primitive can be produced by means of three
translations of a primitive unit cell; the geometrical form of this cell has then,
however, a lower symmetry than the lattice considered as a point arrangement
in space. It is indicated in Fig. 140 how the point arrangement is obtained through
simple translation. The rhombohedral lattice can be considered as an interpenetration of hexagonal lattices and vice versa; then a triply primitive lattice
must be used. These 14 space lattices are also called Bravais lattices after
BRAVAIS in France, who promulgated them in 1850. The German, FRANKEN-
HEIM, had concerned himself with these lattices as early as 1835, but their
complete derivation was first published by him in 1855.

The Way to the 230 Space Groups. These space lattices were historically the
first space groups. From their number alone it can be seen that they cannot
explain the symmetry of all 32 crystal classes. They represent rather the seven
most highly symmetrical classes of each system $\bar{1}$, $2/m$, mmm, $4/mmm$, $\bar{3}\,2/m$,
$6/mm\,m$, $m3m$.

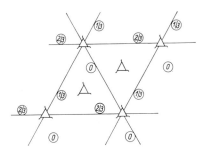
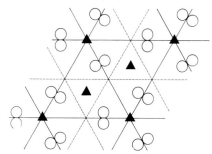

Fig. 141. Symmetry elements of a space
group containing only 3 fold screw axes

Fig. 142. Symmetry elements of a space
group with 3-fold axes, symmetry planes,
and glide planes

In order to build up point arrangements in space to which the lower symmetry
classes also correspond, one must turn to another constructional principle,
utilizing operations other than translations for the generation of repetition. To
this end one investigates the geometric possibilities of periodic two-dimensional
patterns (for example, wallpaper and fabrics). In so doing we meet again as
symmetry elements all of those which we already know from the macrosymmetry
of the crystal, and in addition screw axes, glide planes (see p. 21), and translations. Just as one can discern from the symmetry elements of the macrocrystal
only a finite number of combinations (the 32 crystal classes), so can we recognize
only a finite number of symmetry possibilities for spatial patterns—230 which
are called the *space groups*. These encompass the symmetry of all the crystal
classes. Usually several space groups constitute each crystal class. This cannot
be discerned macroscopically, since the magnitudes of the translations involved
in screw axes and glide planes are so small (order of magnitude: several Å). As a
result these appear macroscopically like ordinary axes or symmetry planes.

Two examples of space groups are illustrated in Figs. 141 and 142. In Fig.
141 only 3-fold screw axes are indicated; in Fig. 142, 3-fold rotation axes,
symmetry planes, and glide planes. Particles which lie on a symmetry center,
a symmetry axis, or a symmetry plane must satisfy their symmetry; particles
which lie between the symmetry elements or on a screw axis or glide plane need
have no unique particle symmetry. As a result it is possible to build up highly
symmetrical arrangements from quite asymmetrical particles. The experimental

investigation of crystals with X-rays, with which we shall later become acquainted, has revealed, however, that the lattice constituents of crystals, at least, very frequently possess high individual symmetry.

While the study of the symmetry of periodic three-dimensional arrangements is quite modern (the first derivations of the 230 space groups were given by FEDEROV in 1890 and by SCHÖNFLIESS in 1891), mankind has, during that period for which we have a historical record, concerned himself with two-dimensional arrangements in the design of ornaments. The symmetry of these arrangements can be systematically understood. There are only 17 planar space groups. Two examples of old Egyptian designs (Figs. 143 and 144) show how strongly

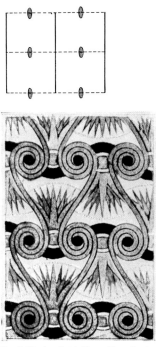

Fig. 143. Ancient Egyptian design
(after PRISSE D'AVENNES from Speiser)

Fig. 144. Ancient Egyptian design
(after PRISSE D'AVENNES from Speiser)

geometrical requirements are fulfilled and how great is their variation. Furthermore, planar symmetry is also important in the case of crystals. Not only the symmetry of natural crystal faces, but especially the symmetry discerned by the use of etch figures, is used to recognize the crystal class. We have already noted this in the case of dolomite and quartz.

The symmetry details of the 230 space groups are amply described in numerous reference works. A summary table is included here in the Appendix (p. 352). We shall not concern ourselves with them here, but want only to learn the manner in which they are described.

Space Lattice Description. We consider the 230 space groups as an enlargement of the 14 Bravais lattices, that is, as if a group of points were derived from one lattice point, or what is the same, from interpenetrating Bravais lattices. If we want to describe such a space lattice we need first of all to know that principle by means of which the translation is repeated. We need to know the parameters of the unit cell, that is, the lattice dimensions, a, b, c, and the interaxial angles α, β, γ, and its translation group. Secondly it is necessary to know the pattern of points (motif) that replace the Bravais points. It must be specified how many atoms occur in the unit cell and how they are arranged, by noting their coordinates with respect to the coordinate axes of the unit cell. As with face indices, the coordinates are written in order with respect to the a-, b-, and c-axes. Thus the translation group alone is sufficient for describing the cubic body-centered lattice. It can, however, also be described as two interpenetrating simple cubic lattices, whose origins have the coordinates 0, 0, 0, and $\frac{1}{2}$, $\frac{1}{2}$, $\frac{1}{2}$. If one wishes to describe the cubic face-centered lattice as simple penetrating cubic lattices, a base of four points, $0\,0\,0$, $0\frac{1}{2}\frac{1}{2}$, $\frac{1}{2}0\frac{1}{2}$, $\frac{1}{2}\frac{1}{2}0$, is needed. The NaCl lattice is a penetration of two cubic face-centered lattices with the origins for Na, $0\,0\,0$, and Cl $\frac{1}{2}\frac{1}{2}\frac{1}{2}$. The following point positions are taken up with respect to a simple cubic lattice.

$$\text{Na } 0\,0\,0; \mid \tfrac{1}{2}\tfrac{1}{2}0; \mid \tfrac{1}{2}0\tfrac{1}{2}; \mid 0\tfrac{1}{2}\tfrac{1}{2};$$
$$\text{Cl } \tfrac{1}{2}\tfrac{1}{2}\tfrac{1}{2}; \mid 0\,0\tfrac{1}{2}; \mid 0\tfrac{1}{2}0; \mid \tfrac{1}{2}0\,0.$$

II. Crystal Chemistry

1. Ionic Bonding

Ionic Radii. Our previous discussion has shown the symmetries which are possible in point arrays and how they are related to crystal form. We are now familiar with the geometric framework into which the collective crystal world can be arranged. We now want to inquire further as to what relationships exist between the kinds of particles — atoms or molecules — and their crystal structural arrangement. Why, for example, do crystals of the three compounds BN, ZnS, and NaCl each possess a unique structure and crystallize in different classes? Chemists and mineralogists have concerned themselves with these questions for more than 100 years. In the beginning, attempts were made to establish some universal generalities, by collecting data from as many kinds of crystals as possible. This approach culminated in 1919 with the publication of P. VON GROTH's "Chemische Kristallographie". His first volume was published in 1906. This is a book which even today is an important reference work, especially in the field of organic crystallography. In it is compiled all that was known at that time about the crystal forms of the elements and their compounds. It was not possible in this way, however, to organize the enormous volume of data according to some unifying concept. An important principle was revealed around 1920, when the first crystal structures were experimentally determined. Different investigators, especially V. M. GOLDSCHMIDT and H. G. GRIMM, attempted to explain the spatial arrangement of particles in terms of their volume requirements. They recognized that crystal structure was dependent upon the size relationships of the building blocks. They experimented systematically, synthesizing crystals, substituting first one and then the other constituent atom. This proved to be an extremely fruitful method. It was soon suggested that these particles, atoms and ions, were essentially spherical, and that their "effective radii" could be calculated. In the case of structures which consist of only one element it is possible to calculate directly the atomic radii, if the arrangement is known and the assumption made that the atomic spheres are in contact or as close together as possible. It is more difficult to determine atomic radii in crystals composed of several chemical elements. An important step forward was taken in 1922, when WASASTJERNA first calculated from refractometric data that the ionic radii of F^{1-} and O^{2-} were 1.33 and 1.32 Å respectively. These data were immediately used by V. M. GOLDSCHMIDT to derive empirically the ionic radii of many other elements. As soon as the radius of oxygen became known, the radii of the metallic ions could be calculated from the structures of their oxides. In 1927 Pauling calculated another set of ionic radii on the basis of wave mechanics. Both sets of ionic radii in most cases show very good agreement. In Table A 7, p. 358 in the Appendix, GOLDSCHMIDT's ionic and atomic radii are tabulated. With increasing atomic number, the atomic and ionic radii[1] decrease in the horizontal rows of the periodic table; in the vertical rows on the other hand they increase. Thus it is noted in Table A 7 that ionic radii decrease in the horizontal row from Na^+ (0.98 Å) to S^{+6} (0.34 Å), but increase from Li^+ (0.78 Å) to Cs^+ (1.65 Å). With increasing positive ionic charge the radius decreases; for trivalent positively charged manganese the radius is 0.91 Å, for tetravalent manganese 0.70 Å, and for the septavalent ion, only 0.52 Å. Negative charge increases the radius, since electrons are added to the original shells. Chemical bonding by means of electrostatic forces is called *ionic* or *heteropolar bonding*.

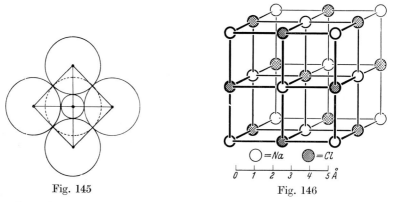

Fig. 145   Fig. 146

Fig. 145. Octahedral 6-fold coordination in cross section; above and below the dashed circle are two additional spheres

Fig. 146. NaCl structure. Each type of ion is octahedrally coordinated

Radius Ratios and Coordination Number. With the help of this simple representation of spherical ions, one can understand a surprising number of phenomena in the crystal world. We begin with the question of how such oppositely charged particles group themselves. We start by assuming that ions are rigid and that arrangement is energetically most favorable, when each ion is surrounded by as large a number of neighboring ions as possible. In this way the average distance between oppositely charged particles is kept as small as possible. The likely arrangement depends then on the relative size of atoms in a compound and on the relative numbers of ion species. The size relationships of two ions are expressed by the *radius ratios* R_A/R_B, where R_B is taken as the radius of the larger ion. Frequently chemical compounds with the same atomic proportions are grouped together and related to a type compound. Thus the substances NaCl, CsCl, MgO, ZnS, AsS, etc. are AB type compounds; CaF_2, FeS_2, SiO_2, H_2O, etc. are AB_2 types; the compounds $CaCO_3$, $PbCO_3$, $CaTiO_3$, $MgSiO_3$ are ABC_3 types.

For a given radius ratio it is possible to arrange six B spheres around a sphere A, as is shown in cross section in Fig. 145. The centers of the B spheres lie at the corners of an octahedron with all of them in contact with A. We say that the *coordination polyhedron* around the A sphere is an octahedron. In general the coordination polyhedron is that polyhedron formed by connecting the centers of the coordination neighbors with one another. An example of a structure with

---

[1] Here we are referring to ionic radii for the highest possible valence state, that is, for example, S^{6+} and not S^{2-}.

octahedral coordination is NaCl (Fig. 146). For the case described above it follows then:

$$R_A + R_B = R_B \cdot \sqrt{2}$$

$$\frac{R_A}{R_B} = \sqrt{2} - 1 \approx 0.41 .$$

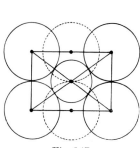

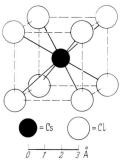

Fig. 147

Fig. 148

Fig. 147. Central cross section of 8-fold cubic coordination parallel to {110}. Additional spheres lie above and below the dashed circles. The ratio of the shorter side of the rectangle to the diagonals is $1:\sqrt{3}$

Fig. 148. CsCl structure

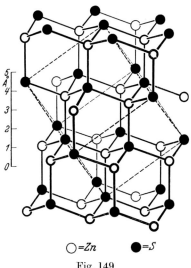

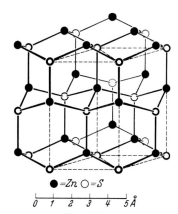

○=Zn ●=S

Fig. 149

Fig. 150

Fig. 149. Sphalerite structure. Both types of atoms are tetrahedrally coordinated. The cubic unit cell is oriented with the 3-fold axis vertical

Fig. 150. Wurtzite structure

If the A atom is made smaller, maintaining the size of B, it can no longer be in contact with six spheres. Another arrangement becomes energetically more favorable, namely that one with four B's around A, in which the centers of the B spheres lie at the corners of a tetrahedron. The ideal value for the radius ratio in such a case is $R_A/R_B = \sqrt{\frac{3}{2}} - 1 \approx 0.22$. If on the other hand A is increased in size, the six B spheres remain in contact with it, but can no longer remain in contact with each other. As soon as the radius of A is sufficiently large that eight spheres can coordinate about it, 8-fold cubic coordination results. The radius ratio in this case, as can be deduced from Fig. 147 is:

$$\frac{R_A}{R_B} = \sqrt{3} - 1 \approx 0.73.$$

Fig. 148 shows an example of this coordination in the CsCl structure. Octahedral coordination is exhibited by the NaCl structure (Fig. 146), tetrahedral coordination in the sphalerite structure (Fig. 149). This last structure is not purely ionic (see p. 82) and strictly speaking does not belong here. A very similar structure

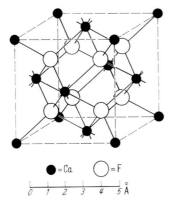

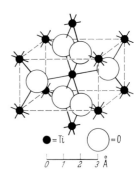

● = Ca   ○ = F

0 1 2 3 4 5 Å

● = Ti   ○ = O

0 1 2 3 Å

Fig. 151. Fluorite (CaF$_2$) structure. Each Ca ion surrounded by eight F; each F by four Ca

Fig. 152. Rutile (TiO$_2$) structure

which likewise possesses fourfold coordination, is that of wurzite (Fig. 150). Wurtzite is also a form of ZnS, crystallizing, however, not like cubic sphalerite, but in the dihexagonal pyramidal class[1]. In the sphalerite structure the Zn atoms and the S atoms each form a cubic face-centered lattice; in wurtzite each type of atom forms a hexagonal lattice. No really pure ionic compounds crystallize with either of these structural types. Perhaps most nearly approaching an ionic structure with tetrahedral coordination is BeO, which has the wurtzite structure.

We can assume, therefore, that the grouping together of ions obeys such simple geometrical relationships. These determine the *coordination number*, the number of nearest neighbors. The limiting radius ratios just deduced, are applicable naturally not only to $A B$-type compounds, but generally. In the case of $A B_2$ compounds, each A ion has twice as many neighbors as each B ion. If eight B's surround each A, four A's surround each B. A is, then, cubically (8-fold) and B tetrahedrally coordinated, as in the fluorite structure (Fig. 151). In a crystal structure of the type $A B_2$, if the A ion is octahedrally coordinated by 6 B ions, each B ion must in turn have 3 A neighbors.

One would expect that this would be realized ideally, by three octahedra linked together at a common B ion and with 3 A ions around B forming an

---

[1] Besides wurtzite there are still several other atomic arrangements for ZnS. Their differences from wurtzite are only trivial energetically. In all of the ZnS structures, the Zn is tetrahedrally coordinated by four S atoms, and vice versa.

equilateral triangle. Actually this ideal arrangement does not occur. Instead the coordination in such a structure is always somewhat distorted. Such is the case for the three TiO_2 modifications, rutile (Fig. 152), anatase, and brookite. Cassiterite, SnO_2, has the same structure as rutile.

Important representatives of $A B_2$ compounds with tetrahedral coordination about A, and 2-fold coordination about B, are the SiO_2 modifications, quartz, tridymite, cristobalite, coesite, and keatite. The latter is known only as a synthetic product. In these the SiO_4-tetrahedra are linked through corners, so that each oxygen is shared between two SiO_4-tetrahedra. Linkage occurs, however, only through corners — the tetrahedra do not share edges! The known SiO_2-modifications differ from each other only in the geometry of the SiO_2 framework. The SiO_4 tetrahedra are linked together in the same manner in all of them[1] (see discussion of tectosilicates, p. 74). As an example, high cristobalite is illustrated in Fig. 153.

Cuprite is another example of an $A B_2$ compound. This structure can be described as an interpenetration of a body centered O- and a face centered Cu-lattice. A summary of the theoretical coordination relationships for $A B$ and $A B_2$ compounds is given in the following Table 3:

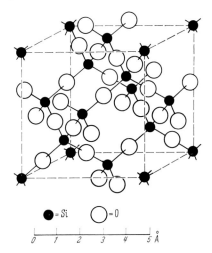

Fig. 153. High-Cristobalite (SiO_2) structure

Table 3. *Coordination relations and limiting radius ratios*

Arrangement of B around A	Limiting radius ratio	$A B$ compounds		$A B_2$ compounds	
		coord.-number	example	coord.-number	example
Tetrahedral	0.22	4	ZnS	4 and 2	SiO_4
Octahedral	0.41	6	NaCl	6 and 3	TiO_2
Cubic	0.73	8	CsCl	8 and 4	CaF_2

Deviations from Theory. Let us now attempt to confirm these simple geometrical considerations by arranging the X-ray determined structure types of simple compounds according to increasing cationic and anionic radii. This has been done in Table 4 for the alkali halides. It can be seen that strict conformity to simple geometric principles is not adhered to.

The coordination relations of other compounds of divalent cations, are given in Tables 5 and 6. Numerous exceptions to theory are noted here also. The reasons are varied. The ionic radii used for calculation and those appearing in Tables 4, 5, and 6 are valid only for 6-fold coordination. With 8-fold coordination, the effective ionic radii become about 3% greater, as in the alkali halides. As noted in Table 6,

---

[1] The recently synthesized and discovered mineral stishovite, which forms at very high pressure (above about 120,000 atm.), is a modification of SiO_2 in which the silicon is coordinated octahedrally by six rather than the usual four oxygens. It has the rutile structure.

Table 4. *Coordination relationships of the alkali-halides*

	Li+ 0.78	Na+ 0.98	K+ 1.33	Rb+ 1.49		Cs+ 1.65	
F- 1.33	6	6	6	6		6	
Cl- 1.81	6	6	6	8[a]	6	8	6[b]
Br- 1.96	6	6	6	6		8	
I- 2.20	6	6	6	6	8[c]	8	
$R_A/R_B < 0.41$		R_A/R_B between 0.41 and 0.73				$R_A/R_B > 0.73$	

[a] At low temperatures ($-190°$ C).
[b] At temperatures above $445°$ C.
[c] At high pressures ($4{,}500$ kg/cm²; $25°$ C).

Table 5. *Coordination relationships of divalent cations. Formula type A B*

	Be2+ 0.34	Mg2+ 0.78	Zn2+ 0.83	Cd2+ 1.03	Ca2+ 1.06	Hg2+ 1.12	Sr2+ 1.27	Pb2+ 1.32	Ba2+ 1.43	Ra2+ 1.52	
O²⁻ 1.32	4'	6	4'	6	6	A	6	A	6		
S²⁻ 1.74	4	6	4; 4'	4; 4'	6	A; 4	6	6	6		$R_A/R_B > 0.73$
Se²⁻ 1.91	4	6	4	4; 4'	6	4	6	6	6		
Te²⁻ 2.03	4	4'	4	4	6	4	6	6	6		
$R_A/R_B < 0.41$		R_A/R_B between 0.41 and 0.73									

Table 6. *Coordination relationships of divalent cations. Formula type A B₂*

	Be2+ 0.34	Mg2+ 0.78	Zn2+ 0.83	Cd2+ 1.03	Ca2+ 1.06	Hg2+ 1.12	Sr2+ 1.27	Pb2+ 1.32	Ba2+ 1.43	Ra2+ 1.52	
2F- 1.33	4	6	6	8	8	8	8	A; 8*	8	8	
2Cl- 1.81	4	6s	4	6s	6de	②	8	A	A		$R_A/R_B > 0.73$
2Br- 1.96		6s	4	6s	6de	②	A	A	A		
2I- 2.20		6s	4	6s	6s	4s		6s	A		
$R_A/R_B < 0.41$		R_A/R_B between 0.41 and 0.73									

s Layer structure; 4' wurtzite type; ② Molecular structure; *A* special type; 6 *d e* distorted rutile type; * only at high temperatures.

for the compounds of certain metals (Zn, Hg) and some anions, the disagreement is especially bad. Here the influence of other types of bonding asserts itself. This effect will be discussed later in more detail. In general, however, when considering the same anion, coordination number around the cation increases with increasing effective cation radius.

Pauling's Rules. In the previous discussion we have used only the radius ratio, that is the size relationships of rigid ionic spheres, in order to explain different structural types. This is naturally a very approximate procedure. The more proper way to consider crystals with electrostatic bonding is to inquire about the energy which is released when ions come together into crystals. Of all the possible geometrical arrangements, that one occurs, at least at low temperatures where vibrations and other motions of the crystal can be neglected, which results in greatest release of energy. This is also the most stable arrangement. One can calculate this released energy (electrostatic lattice energy, see p. 166), but the procedure is usually very laborious. Often one can resort to PAULING's *Rules* (PAULING, 1929), which suggest qualitatively the requirements for electrostatic bonded atomic arrangements with most favorable energy relationships. Because of their importance, they will be stated here:

1. Around every cation, a coordination polyhedron of anions forms, in which the cation-anion distance is determined by the radius sums, and the coordination number by the radius ratio.

2. In a stable coordination structure the total strength of the bonds which reach an anion from all neighboring cations, is equal to the charge of the anion.

3. Sharing of edges, and especially faces, between two coordination polyhedra lowers the stability of the coordination structure. This effect is large for cations of high charge and small coordination number, and is especially large when the radius ratio approaches the lower limiting value for the polyhedron.

4. In a crystal which contains different cations, those with high charge and small coordination number tend not to share elements of their coordination polyhedra.

5. The number of essentially different kinds of constituents in a crystal tend to be small (Rule of Parsimony).

PAULING's first rule treats structures from the same view point as our previous discussion. Rules 2—4 give the qualitative conditions for the energetically most favorable linkage of such polyhedra. For rule 2 it is still necessary to explain what is meant by the "bond strength" between cations and anions. This is equivalent to the charge on the cation divided by the number of neighbors in the coordination polyhedron. As an example, the fluorite structure (Fig. 151) will serve to make this clear. In CaF_2 each Ca^{2+} is surrounded by eight F^{1-} ions; the bond strength is consequently $\frac{2}{8} = \frac{1}{4}$. Since each F^{1-} ion is surrounded by four Ca^{+2} ions, $4 \times \frac{1}{4} = 1$ "bond strength" contributions result, equal to the charge on the F^{1-} ion.

Polymorphism. Since vibration of lattice constituents changes with temperature, an ionic arrangement which is thermodynamically more favorable at low temperature need not be stable at higher temperatures. Thus CsCl, which, in agreement with its radius ratio of 0.91, possesses at room temperature a structure with 8-fold coordination, transforms at about 460° C into the NaCl-type structure, with octahedral coordination. The nitrates, carbonates, and borates in Table 7 show very clearly that, with increase in cationic radius, a structural change takes place, and that in the case of a single compound both structural types are possible at the transition point. This structural change for a given compound is called *polymorphism*, and the different structural types are called polymorphs or structural modifications.

The calcite structure is most easily described as a deformed NaCl structure, with one cube-diagonal (3-fold axis) standing perpendicular and with the Cl^- ions replaced by triangular CO_3 groups lying in planes perpendicular to the

Table 7. *Borate, carbonate, and nitrate structure types*

Formula	Cation radius	Formula	Cation radius	Formula	Cation radius	Structure type
		$MgCO_3$	0.78			
		$FeCO_3$	0.83			
		$ZnCO_3$	0.83			Calcite
$ScBO_3$	0.83	$MnCO_3$	0.91	$LiNO_3$	0.78	
$InBO_3$	0.92	$CdCO_3$	1.03	$NaNO_3$	0.98	
YBO_3	1.06	$CaCO_3$	1.06	KNO_3	1.33	
$LaBO_3$	1.22	$CaCO_3$	1.06	KNO_3	1.33	
		$SrCO_3$	1.27			Aragonite
		$PbCO_3$	1.32			
		$BaCO_3$	1.43			

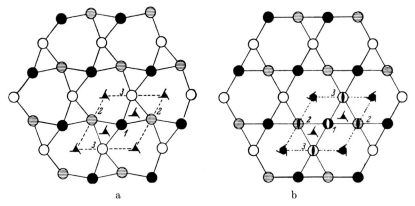

a   b

Fig. 154a and b. Projection of the Si atoms in the quartz structure on (0001) (a) below and (b) above 575°C. The different atoms (white, cross-hatched, black) are distinguished by different projection elevations; each about 1.80 A apart. (STRUNZ)

3-fold axis. The aragonite structure is similarly derived from the NiAs structure (p. 88) which will be described later. In the calcite structure the Ca^{2+} ions are surrounded by six oxygens atoms; in aragonite, by nine.

Polymorphism implies that with the same chemical substance, differences in structural type can occur as a function of external conditions, such as pressure and temperature. Depending on the magnitude of the geometrical variation, one can differentiate the following: *polytypism*, in which different structural types are met, as previously discussed; *polysyngonism*, in which only slight changes in structure are encountered, as exemplified by the transition of high to low quartz (Fig. 154)[1]; a third and less important subdivision, in which the structural type is completely retained, but in which the structure still undergoes physical change is called *polytropism*. The difference in physical behavior results from the fact that chemically strongly bound complexes in the structure begin to rotate (or at least distribute themselves statistically over several orientations) above

---

[1] According to recent investigations by ARNOLD, high quartz is distinguished from low quartz in that the former consists of the tiniest domains with the structure of low quartz, which are twinned after the Dauphine law (see p. 98).

a certain temperature. An example is the NO_3 group in $NaNO_3$ at 280° C (Fig. 155). It is also manifest by lattice constituents exchanging places in the structure, without changing structural type. Such examples are referred to later (p. 185). According to the degree of structural change during such transformations, the coherence of the crystal may be either preserved or lost. As can be observed with

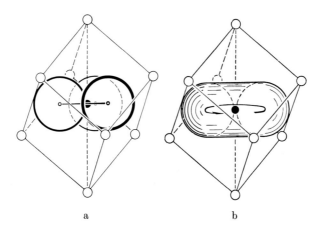

a   b

Fig. 155. (a) Portion of the $NaNO_3$ structure at 25° C. NO_3 group sits within rhombohedron. (b) Same view at 280° C. NO_3 group rotating around N. (After BARTH)

small crystals of $K_2Cr_2O_7$ under the polarizing microscope, the whole crystal unfolds into a new structure upon heating to 237° C. The crystal can be observed breaking up into several fragments. In the case of KNO_3, on the other hand, the aragonite structure transforms into the calcite structure upon heating to 128° C, and the crystal disintegrates in the process. If a transformation results upon cooling as well as heating, it is reversible or enantiotropic (Gr. enantioi, opposite; tropos, direction). In the case of $CaCO_3$ at atmospheric pressure, only the transformation from aragonite to calcite, taking place at approximately 400° C, can be observed. In order to observe the transformation from calcite to aragonite, higher pressures (approx. 3,000 atmospheres) are necessary. This can be accomplished very simply by grinding calcite powder vigorously and for a long time in a mortar (BURNS and BREDIG; DACHILLE and ROY). Transformation in the solid state results as a rule in the production of individual nuclei of the new modification, which then grow (solid state reaction). Additional discussion of the influence of temperature and pressure on the occurrence of particular structural types will be given later in the discussion of one-component systems (p. 183). Frequently in the case of polymorphic phases, the phase which is stable under normal conditions is designated as the α-modification; that which is stable at higher temperatures as the β-modification; then follows the γ-modification, etc. Since these designations are not completely universal, one often uses, for substances with two modifications over different temperature ranges, the appropriate expressions, high- or low-temperature modifications.

Isomorphism. Table 7 shows also, that the members of each of the two carbonate groups have the same structure. The phenomenon of chemically different substances possessing the same structure, as well as the concept of

polymorphism, was discovered at the beginning of the 19th century by EILHARD
MITSCHERLICH. Following the suggestion of BERZELIUS, he called this phenomenon
isomorphism. Until the introduction of X-ray structure investigation, this concept

Table 8. *Camouflage*

Element	Ion radius	Element	Ion radius
Ge^{4+}	0.44	Si^{4+}	0.39
Ga^{3+}	0.63	Al^{3+}	0.57
Ni^{2+}	0.78	Mg^{2+}	0.78
Hf^{4+}	0,87	Zr^{4+}	0.86

was based only on the similarity of external crystalline form, ascertained primarily
through angular measurements of crystals. Crystal structural determinations
have in many cases corroborated the views based on morphological studies, in
many cases not. Thus earlier, zircon, $ZrSiO_4$, and rutile, TiO_2, were considered
by GROTH to be isomorphous. As a matter of fact, by appropriate choice of
orientation, both crystal forms assume quite similar parameters, but their
structures are different. While in the rutile structure each Ti is surrounded by
six O, and each O by three Ti, in the case of zircon, Si has four and Zr eight O
as nearest neighbors.

Table 9. *Capture*

Element	Ion radius	Element	Ion radius
Ti^{4+}	0.64	Nb^{5+}	0.64
Ce^{3+}	1.18	Th^{4+}	1.10
Fe^{2+}	0.83	Sc^{3+}	0.83
Na^+	0.98	Ca^{2+}	1.06
Ca^{2+}	1.06	Y^{3+}	1.06
K^+	1.33	$\begin{cases} Sr^{2+} \\ Ba^{2+} \end{cases}$	1.27 1.43

Miscibility in the solid state was once regarded as an especially certain
criterion of isomorphism. One referred also to "impfisomorphism" (induced
isomorphism) when one form of a crystal grew from another, and so this concept
became increasingly vague. Today the view is taken that even different structural
types, can be miscible, and so important distinctions must be suggested by
appropriate terminology. Two substances with the same structural type are
called *isotypes*; with similar type, *homotypes*; and with differing type, *heterotypes*.
Miscibility in the solid state infers the same completely random distribution of
constituents as does miscibility in fluids. Miscibility will be discussed more fully
later (p. 90 and 195). In the case of miscibility in the solid state, one differen-
tiates, as with fluids, between complete and limited miscibility. Independent of
the degree of miscibility, one speaks of isomorphic miscibility in isotypic structures,
homomorphic in similar structures, and heteromorphic in dissimilar structures.
An example of the latter is the complete miscibility of $MgCl_2$ and LiCl (see p. 91).

The representation of ions as rigid spheres also enables us to understand the
formation of *mixed crystals*. For the occurrence of isotypism it is sufficient that

radius ratios are equal, but miscibility requires approximately equal absolute values of ionic radii. Introduction of foreign ions into a crystal can only take place if they fit rather well in the structure. The extent to which the radius of the foreign ion can deviate from the ideal depends on temperature and the type of structure.

Camouflage and Capture. The accommodation of foreign ions into a crystal structure plays an important role in geochemistry. Many elements, like gallium, form their own compounds only rarely. They almost always fit into compounds of other substances. When substitution of equivalent ions is involved, the process is referred to as "camouflage". Table 8 shows some examples.

If a lower valence ion is replaced, one refers to the "capture" of the higher valence ion in the structure of the lower valence one. Thus monazite, $CePO_4$, captures tetravalent thorium in place of trivalent cerium. The charge balance is maintained by substituting an equivalent amount of divalent Ca for Ce, or by substituting $[SiO_4]^{4-}$ groups for a portion of the $[PO_4]^{3-}$ groups. Some examples of pairs of elements with equal or similar ionic radii, but with different valence, are assembled in Table 9.

We shall come back again later to this business of capture in the discussion of multicomponent systems (p. 195). However, it may be mentioned here that chemical laws, in addition to geometric considerations, must be fulfilled in the construction of crystals

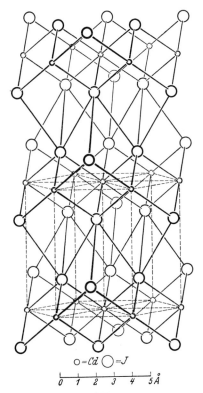

$o = Cd$ $\bigcirc = J$

Fig. 156. CdI_2 structure

Fig. 157. Transition from ionic- to covalent bonding through polarization. (After K. Fajans from Hedvall)

2. Transition to Other Bond Types

Polarization, Layer Lattices. The representation of ions as rigid spheres is very appropriate and useful for many purposes, but it also has its limitations. As we have already noted in the discussion of coordination number, bond types other than ionic also assert themselves. As we have seen in Table 6, CdF_2, along with most of the series of alkaline earth halides, crystallizes with the calcium fluoride structure. If in CdF_2, with $R_A/R_B = 0.77$, the anion is replaced by I, the value of R_A/R_B becomes 0.47, and we should expect six-fold coordination, instead

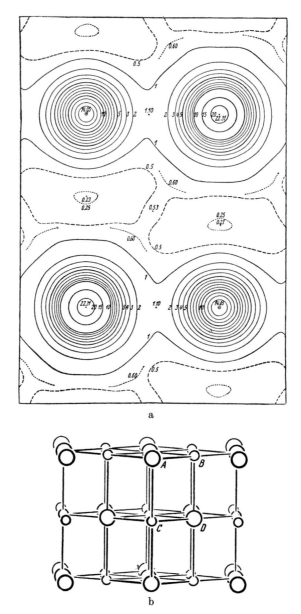

a

b

Fig. 158. (a) Electron density in NaCl projected on (110) at 100° C. (From BRILL, GRIMM, HERMANN, PETERS.) Numbers indicate number of electrons per sq. $\mathring{A}$. in the projection (b) NaCl structure projected approximately parallel to [110]. The atoms designated as A and D correspond to Cl$^-$, those as B and C are Na; in (a) the former have maximum electron densities of 22.31 e.$\mathring{A}^{-2}$, — the latter 14.05 e.$\mathring{A}^{-2}$

of eight-fold. Actually the Cd in CdI$_2$ has octahedral coordination. Even so this compound does not crystallize with the rutile-structure, but with the atomic arrangement shown in Fig. 156, as a typical "layer" structure. It is concluded from this arrangement that the I^{1-} ions are not rigid, but are deformed. This phenomenon is called *polarization*. The polarization hypothesis was not originally introduced in crystal chemistry to explain structural anomalies, but was discovered much earlier in studies of liquids. As a result of polarization, the centers of ionic positive charge are displaced with respect to the centers of negative charge. The magnitude of the polarizability can be calculated from spectral or refraction data. The degree of polarizability increases with ionic radius and is especially strong in the case of ions with complex electron structure. $Cd(OH)_2$ forms a layer structure of the same type as CdI_2, although the "ionic radius" of $(OH)^{1-}$ is equal to that of F^{1-}. One can imagine that a small cation such as Cd^{2+}, when it is brought near a large ion like I^{1-}, with only weakly-bound outer electrons, would pull the electron cloud of the larger anion toward itself. If the electrons are so strongly attracted that they end up belonging equally to both ions, we pass from strictly ionic bonding, to homopolar or covalent bonding (Fig. 157).

Ionic (heteropolar or polar) bonding depends on the electrostatic attraction of oppositely charged particles, upon Coulombic forces. In pure ionic bonding the electron density between two oppositely charged ions falls to zero. This can be shown experimentally by means of electron density maps calculated from X-ray data. Fig. 158 shows an electron density map for NaCl. Valence bonding (homopolar or covalent bonding) depends on chemical valence forces, and involves mutual sharing of electrons between atoms.

The layer structures represent, therefore, a sort of transition from ionic to covalent structures. In such layer structures mechanical coherence between atoms within the layers is stronger than between layers, so that the layers can easily cleave apart. The micas are typical and widely distributed minerals with layer structure.

Transitions between ionic and covalent bonds occur quite frequently. Pauling attempted to estimate the proportion of ionic bonding in such intermediate states. Table 10 gives some of his values that are especially important for minerals.

Table 10. *Proportion of ionic bonding.* (After PAULING)

	F	O	Cl	Br	I
Al, Be	79	63	44	35	22
Si	70	50	30		

Complex Ions. Intermediate states between ionic and covalent bonding are especially common in complex ions. In these the individual constituents are

Table 11. *Shape of complex anions*

Formula type	Shape	Examples
BX	linear	O_2^{2-}; CN^-;
B_3, BX_2, BXY	linear angular	N_3^-; CNO^-; CNS^- ClO_2^-; NO_2^-
BX_3	planar trigonal pyramidal	CO_3^{2-}; NO_3^- [a] PO_3^{3-}; SO_3^{2-}; ClO_3^-
BX_4	tetrahedral	SiO_4^{4-}; AlO_4^{5-}; AsO_4^{3-}; PO_4^{3-}; SO_4^{2-}; BeF_4^{2-}; ClO_4^-; MnO_4^-; BF_4^-; MoO_4^{2-}; WO_4^{2-}; IO_4^-
	planar	$Ni(CN)_4^{2-}$; $PtCl_4^{2-}$; $CuCl_4^{2-}$
BX_4	octahedral	SiF_6^{2-}; $TiCl_6^{2-}$; $PtCl_6^{2-}$; $PbCl_6^{2-}$

[a] Latest investigations indicate that in $Ba[NO_3]_2$ the $[NO_3]^-$ group is distorted to a flat pyramid.

5*

predominantly covalently bonded together, while entire radicals are linked ionically by means of cations. In Table 11 the shapes of these complex ions are indicated.

Just as all carbonates and nitrates contain planar CO_3^{2-} or NO_3^{1-} groups, so the SO_4^{2-} group occurs in all sulfates. In the latter, four oxygens are situated at the corners of a tetrahedron, with the sulfur atom at its center. The S-O distance measures about 1.48 ± 0.02Å.

Among the sulfate minerals, the structure of barite, $BaSO_4$, has a certain similarity to that of NaCl. Ba^{2+} ions occur at the positions of the Na^{1+} ions in NaCl, and the Cl^{1-} ions are replaced by the sulfate groups. Thus each Ba^{2+} ion is surrounded by six SO_4^{2-} groups at approximately equal distances. The coordination number of oxygen around barium is twelve. The mineral celestite, $SrSO_4$, is an isotype of barite. Anhydrite, $CaSO_4$, crystallizes however, with a different structure.

Crystal Chemical Formulae. In previous discussion we have already mentioned the importance of coordination number in relation to the construction of crystals. Consequently it is useful in crystal chemical discussions to include the coordination numbers and other important features of the structure in a *crystal chemical formula*. We shall follow the suggestions of MACHATSCHKI and write the coordination number in brackets to the right of and above each element; in addition we place before the formula $\overset{3}{\infty}$, $\overset{2}{\infty}$, or $\overset{1}{\infty}$, according to whether we are dealing with a three-dimensional, a sheet, or a chain-structure. Following the formula, the crystal system is abbreviated. Some examples of structures which we have already discussed may clarify this. In NaCl, for example, each Na^{1+} is coordinated with six Cl^{1-} and each Cl^{1-} with six Na^{1+} octahedrally. Linkage occurs in a like manner in all three directions in space. The crystal system is cubic. The crystal chemical formula thus reads:

$$\overset{3}{\infty} Na^{[6]} Cl^{[6]} c.$$

The following structural formulae are thus self-explanatory: $\overset{3}{\infty} Zn^{[4]} S^{[4]} c$ (sphalerite), $\overset{3}{\infty} Zn^{[4]} S^{[4]} h$ (wurtzite), $\overset{3}{\infty} Cs^{[8]} Cl^{[8]} c$ (cesium chloride), $\overset{3}{\infty} Ti^{[6]} O_2^{[3]} t$ (rutile), $\overset{3}{\infty} Si^{[4]} O_2^{[2]} trig$ (quartz), and $\overset{2}{\infty} Cd^{[6]} Cl_2^{[3]} h$ (cadmium chloride). As a simplification in the following discussion, $\overset{3}{\infty}$ will always be omitted, the type of linkage only being indicated when we are dealing with a layer- or chain-structure. In addition we shall usually designate only the coordination number around the cations.

Structures of the Silicates. Structural research in the case of the silicates finally brought organization to an extraordinary abundance of empirical information. All silicate minerals contain SiO_4-tetrahedra in which the Si-O distance measures about 1.63 ± 0.03 Å. The SiO_4-group has a -4 charge. Within this group the Si-O-bonding is assumed to be about 50% ionic (see Table 10). In the case of silicates, an oxygen of the SiO_4^{4-} tetrahedra is rarely replaced by an hydroxyl group. One such case is the rare mineral afwillite, $Ca_3^{[7]} [Si^{[4]} O_3 (OH)]_2 \cdot 2H_2O\, m$.

The silicates are classified according to the manner in which SiO_4-tetrahedra are linked to one another. If the tetrahedra are independent, having no common linking oxygen, and bound through cations to one another, as in the case of zircon with Zr^{4+}, they are referred to as *nesosilicates*. Olivine, the mixed crystal

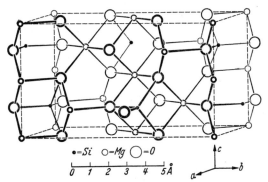

Fig. 159. Olivine structure (nesosilicate)

series between $Mg_2^{[6]}[SiO_4]or$ and $Fe_2^{[6]}[SiO_4]or$ (Fig. 159), has such a structure. Further examples are the garnets which are almost always mixed crystals of the following end-members:

pyrope	$Mg_3^{[8]}Al_2^{[6]}[SiO_4]_3 c$
almandine	$Fe_3^{[8]}Al_2^{[6]}[SiO_4]_3 c$
spessartite	$Mn_3^{[8]}Al_2^{[6]}[SiO_4]_3 c$
grossularite	$Ca_3^{[8]}Al_2^{[6]}[SiO_4]_3 c$
andradite	$Ca_3^{[8]}Fe_2^{[6]}[SiO_4]_3 c$
uvarovite	$Ca_3^{[8]}Cr_2^{[6]}[SiO_4]_3 c$

Melanite is a Ti-bearing garnet, similar to andradite, in which the Ti^{4+} probably substitutes for Fe^{3+} with simultaneous charge compensation e.g. by partial substitution of Na^{1+} for Ca^{2+}.

Of the three modifications of Al_2SiO_5, kyanite and andalusite are quite clearly nesosilicates. In both there are two kinds of Al^{3+} ions; one-half is coordinated octahedrally by six O; the other half in kyanite has likewise 6 fold-, but in andalusite, 5 fold-coordination. Thus the structural formula for kyanite is $Al_2^{[6]}O$ $[SiO_4]tr.$, and for andalusite, $Al^{[6]}Al^{[5]}O[SiO_4]or$. It should be noted that 5-fold coordination is very rare for Al^{3+}. In the structure of the third modification of Al_2SiO_5, sillimanite, half of the aluminium is again coordinated by six oxygens; the other half, however, has tetrahedral coordination, like silicon. The Si and Al are not randomly distributed over tetrahedral sites, but are ordered. The crystal chemical formula for this mineral, emphasizing the mutual tetrahedral association of Si and Al, is:

$$\overset{1}{\infty} Al^{[6]}[Al^{[4]}Si^{[4]}O_5]or, \quad \text{or} \quad Al^{[6]}Al^{[4]}O[SiO_4]or.$$

Additional nesosilicates are topaz, $Al_2^{[6]}F_2[SiO_4]or$, sphene, $Ca^{[7]}Ti^{[4]}O$ $[SiO_4]m$, and staurolite. The latter very probably crystallizes monoclinic, but with only very slight deviation from orthorhombic symmetry. Its structure, which is closely related to that of kyanite, gives the following formula, $Fe_2^{2+[4]}$-$Al_9^{[6]}O_7(OH)[SiO_4]_4 m$.

In silicates $[SiO_4]^{4-}$ tetrahedra can be linked also through oxygens. In minerals linkage through tetrahedral "corners", rather than "edges" and "faces", is known. If in this way small, discrete units occur in the structure, the silicate is referred to as a *group silicate* (sorosilicate). Groups of two tetrahedra characterize thortveitite, $Sc_2[Si_2O_7]m$. Vesuvianite (idocrase) also contains such groups, as well as individual tetrahedra. Its structural formula is $Ca_{10}(Mg, Fe)_2Al_4(OH)_4$-$[SiO_4]_5[Si_2O_7]_2t$. According to recent structural determinations, the mineral epidote is a further example. Its stoichiometric formula is $Ca_2(Al, Fe)_3HSi_3O_{13}$, but, according to the structural determination, the crystal chemical formula is written $Ca_2^{[6-8]}(Al, Fe)_3^{[6]}O(OH)[SiO_4][Si_2O_7]m$. As in vesuvianite, isolated SiO_4-tetrahedra are found along with Si_2O_7 groups.

More often several silicate tetrahedra link together through corners forming rings. Such silicates are called *ring silicates* (cyclosilicates). Rings of three tetrahedra, are found in benitoite, $Ba^{[6-12]}Ti^{[6]}[Si_3O_9]trig.$

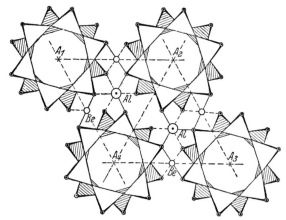

Fig. 160. Beryl structure with $[Si_6O_{18}]^{12-}$ rings

Beryl, $Al_2^{[6]}Be_3^{[4]}[Si_6O_{18}]h$, (Fig. 160) is built from groups of six tetrahedra, which likewise are joined into rings. Each tetrahedron shares an oxygen with two adjacent ones, giving 18 oxygens instead of 24, in the silicate rings.

In tourmaline, a widely distributed mineral whose chemical composition is quite complex, Si_6O_{18} rings form the characteristic building motif. Its formula is $(Ca, Na)(Al, Mg, Fe^{2+}, Fe^{3+}, Mn, Li, Cr^{3+}, \ldots)_9^{[6]}[B^{[3]}O_3]_3[Si_6O_{18}](OH, F)_4$ *trig.* In a few rare minerals $(Si, Al)_{12}O_{30}$ groups are found, in which two Si_6O_{18} rings are joined together, forming a double ring, bonded through six oxygens.

Cordierite likewise contains hexagonal rings; their tetrahedral sites, however, are only $^2/_3$ occupied by Si and $^1/_3$ by Al. Its crystal chemical formula, emphasizing the ring structure, is $(Mg, Fe^{2+})_2^{[6]}Al_2^{[4]}Si^{[4]}[Si_4Al_2O_{18}]$ *or.* Reformulation as $(Mg, Fe^{2+})_2^{[6]}[Si_5Al_4O_{18}]or$, indicates that it can be classified also as a framework structure (p. 74).

As the next silicate group we observe those with contiguous tetrahedra strung out in rows into infinitely long chains and ribbons (inosilicates). Chains are formed when each tetrahedra in a row shares an oxygen with a tetrahedron on each side. These chains continue indefinitely to the terminal boundaries of the individual crystal. In the case of the chains shown in Fig. 161 the X-ray measured distance from one silicon to the silicon in the second adjacent tetrahedron is about 5×10^{-7} mm. Thus a fragment of a crystal 1 mm long would contain about 4,000,000 tetrahedra. The Si:O ratio rapidly approaches the value 1:3 with growing chain length, as can be ascertained easily by simple calculation. Such $_\infty^1[SiO_3]^{2-}$ chains occur in minerals of the pyroxene group. Diopside, $CaMg[Si_2O_6]$, is a member in which the chains are bound together by Ca^{2+} and Mg^{2+} ions.

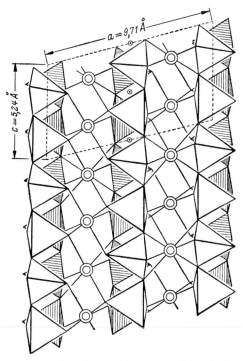

Fig. 161. Diopside structure; projected on (010). Plain and hatched tetrahedra separated $b/2$ from each other. (After SCHIEBOLD)

The pyroxenes can be subdivided into the following groups:

I. Monoclinic pyroxenes with very little or no Al in tetrahedral coordination:

diopside	$\overset{1}{\infty} Ca^{[8]} Mg^{[6]} [Si_2O_6] m$
hedenbergite	$\overset{1}{\infty} Ca^{[8]} Fe^{[6]} [Si_2O_6) m$
jadeite	$\overset{1}{\infty} Na^{[8]} Al^{[6]} [Si_2O_6] m$
aegirine	$\overset{1}{\infty} Na^{[8]} Fe^{[6]} [Si_2O_6] m$
clinoenstatite	$\overset{1}{\infty} Mg_2^{[6]} [Si_2O_6] m$
spodumene	$\overset{1}{\infty} Li^{[6]} Al^{[6]} [Si_2O_6] m$

II. Augite: In this mineral up to one-fourth of the Si is replaced by Al, and it is likewise a monoclinic mixed crystal of the general formula $\overset{1}{\infty} (Ca, Na)^{[8]}$ (Al, Fe, Mg, Ti, ...) $^{[6]} [(Si, Al)_2O_6] m$.

III. Orthorhombic pyroxenes: mixed crystals between enstatite. $\overset{1}{\infty} Mg_2^{[6]}$-$[Si_2O_6] or$, and a hypothetical end member $Fe_2[Si_2O_6]$ ("ferrosilite"). Mixed crystals with about 20 mole percent $Fe_2[Si_2O_6]$ are common as the mineral called bronzite. Iron-rich members (with about 50 mole percent $Fe_2[Si_2O_6]$) are called hypersthene. Orthorhombic pyroxenes with a higher iron content are rather rare.

Earlier the names pyroxene and augite were used synonymously for the entire mineral group. More recently, the name pyroxene has been adopted for use as the group name, and augite to designate a sub-group of special pyroxenes, as we have done above.

If two chains are linked together, so that one-half of the tetrahedra of each chain share an oxygen with one-half of the tetrahedra of the other chain, ribbons or double chains occur, which are characteristic of the important amphibole group. The Si:O ratio is 4:11; and the formula for the silicate ribbon is $\overset{1}{\infty}[Si_4O_{11}]^{6-}$. Within each of these silicate units the amphiboles contain in addition an OH-group, which can also be replaced by F. There are numerous species distinguished according to the linking cationic species present.

I. Monoclinic amphiboles with little or no Al in tetrahedral coordination:

tremolite	$\overset{1}{\infty}Ca_2^{[8]}Mg_5^{[6]}(OH)_2[Si_8O_{22}]m$
actinolite	$\overset{1}{\infty}Ca_2^{[8]}(Mg, Fe)_5^{[6]}(OH)_2[Si_8O_{22}]m$
glaucophane	$\overset{1}{\infty}Na_2^{[8]}Mg_3^{[6]}Al_2^{[6]}(OH)_2[Si_8O_{22}]m$
riebeckite	$\overset{1}{\infty}Na_2^{[8]}Fe_3^{2+[6]}Fe_2^{3+[6]}(OH)_2[Si_8O_{22}]m$
cummingtonite	$\overset{1}{\infty}(Mg, Fe)_7^{[6]}(OH)_2[Si_8O_{22}]m$

II. Hornblende: Monoclinic mixed crystals of the amphibole group in which usually every fourth tetrahedron contains Al instead of Si.

III. Orthorhombic amphiboles: Mixed crystals of the two end members $Mg_7(OH)_2[Si_8O_{22}]$ and $Fe_7(OH)_2[Si_8O_{22}]$; they are called anthophyllite. It should be mentioned that, analogous to the pyroxenes, the names amphibole and hornblende were earlier synonymous. Today amphibole is generally used as a major group name and hornblende in the restricted sense as defined above.

Hornblende proper frequently contains more than two ions of the size class of Na^{1+} and Ca^{2+} per formula unit. These "excess" cations, along with potassium ions, are situated in interstices in the structure of $Ca_2Mg_5(OH)_2[Si_8O_{22}]$.

Pyroxenes and amphiboles can be differentiated macroscopically by means of their different cleavage. This occurs in both mineral groups parallel to {110}, but the angles (110)−(1$\bar{1}$0) for pyroxenes and amphiboles are markedly different. In addition the cleavability of amphiboles is clearly better than that of pyroxenes. Fig. 162 shows, in cross section perpendicular to [001], how the cleavage is related to structure.

A further example of a chain silicate is wollastonite, $\overset{1}{\infty}Ca_2^{[6]}Ca^{[7]}[Si_3O_9]tr$. The $\overset{1}{\infty}[SiO_3]^{2-}$ chains in this case are quite different from those of the pyroxenes. Only every fourth tetrahedron in a chain has the same orientation. Accordingly the lattice constants in the chain direction have approximately one and one-half times the value of pyroxenes. Wollastonite occurs primarily in contact metamorphosed limestones.

If chain after chain is joined together in infinite repetition in one plane, we arrive at sheet structures or phyllosilicates. These two-dimensional articulated six-fold rings are the building motifs for many common silicates. The Si:O ratio is 2:5, with each tetrahedron sharing three of its oxygens with three other tetrahedra.

The most important members of the natural layer silicates are mica-like minerals. The fundamental structural units are pseudo-hexagonal $\overset{2}{\infty}[Si_2O_5]^{2-}$ layers, which contain also OH^- or F^-. Two major groups of layer silicates can be differentiated. In the one case, two $\overset{2}{\infty}OH[Si_2O_5]^{3-}$ layers are bonded together by a layer of octahedrally coordinated cations. In pyrophyllite, $\overset{2}{\infty}Al_2^{[6]}(OH)_2$-$[Si_4O_{10}]m$, this intermediate layer consists of Al ions, which are coordinated by four O and two OH (Fig. 163). By the intercalation of water between such layer silicate packets, the important clay mineral montmorillonite results, whose structure will be described later (p. 95). If, in the pyrophyllite structure, $3 \, Mg^{2+}$ occur in place of $2 \, Al^{3+}$, we arrive at the structure of talc, $\overset{2}{\infty} Mg_3^{[6]}(OH)_2[Si_4O_{10}]m$.

If one fourth of the Si is replaced by Al in the tetrahedral sheet, the layer packet $Al_2(OH)_2[AlSi_3O_{10}]^{1-}$ becomes negatively charged. In the aluminous mica, muscovite (Fig. 164), the packets are held together by K^+-ions; in a like manner, they are held together by Na^+ in paragonite. In phlogopite, three Mg^{2+} occur in the octahedral layer in place of two Al^{3+}. In dark-colored biotite, a part of the Mg is replaced by Fe. In natural crystals, (OH) is partly replaced by F.

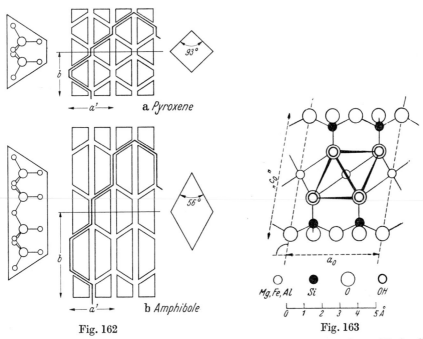

Fig. 162

Fig. 163

Fig. 162. Relationship of cleavage to the structure of pyroxene and amphibole. Cross section perpendicular to c-axis (from WARREN). According to the cleavage paths indicated here the coordination polyhedra of the 6-fold-coordinated cations would be disrupted. It is by no means certain that the cleavage takes this exact path

Fig. 163. Pyrophyllite structure. Montmorillonite is constructed from such layers, which are superimposed along the c-axis without crystallographic orientation. Periodicity perpendicular to layers varies from $10-20$ Å, depending on adsorbed water content

The formula for biotite is, therefore, $\overset{2}{\infty} K(Mg, Fe)_3^{[6]}(OH, F)_2[Si_3AlO_{10}]m$. Pure fluorphlogopite is produced synthetically from a melt. As HENDRICKS has shown, one can regard mica as an intergrowth of one or more silicate packets, rotated or translated with respect to each other in different directions, but in a regular manner, and stacked one upon the other. Several building motifs can be embodied in a single crystal. Micas are elastically flexible. Chlorites and brittle-micas are, on the other hand, plastically deformed upon bending. An example of a *brittle-mica* is *margarite*, $CaAl_2(OH)_2[Al_2Si_2O_{10}]$, in which two Si are replaced by Al and the alkali ions by alkaline earths.

In the chlorites, biotite-like $\{(Mg, Al, Fe)_3^{[6]}(OH)_2[(Si, Al)_4^{[4]}O_{10}^{x-}]\}$ double layers, which as a whole are negatively charged, are held together by brucite-like $\overset{2}{\infty} (Mg, Fe, Al)_3^{[6]}(OH)_6^{x+}$ layers with positive charge.

In the other major layer silicate group, only one tetrahedral and one octahedral layer are combined together. Kaolinite, $\overset{2}{\infty} Al_2^{[6]} (OH)_4 [Si_2O_5] t\, r$ (Fig. 165), an important clay mineral, belongs here. The quite rare minerals dickite and nacrite have the same chemical formula as kaolinite, but differ structurally from this mineral in the manner in which the "kaolinite" layers are superimposed.

Serpentine, with a kaolinite-like structure, corresponds rather exactly to the formula $\overset{2}{\infty} Mg_3^{[6]} (OH)_2 [Si_2O_5]$. Its relation to kaolinite is similar to that between talc and pyrophyllite. Since, however, the "magnesium hydroxide" layer does not have exactly the same dimensions as the Si_2O_5 layer, — it is somewhat too

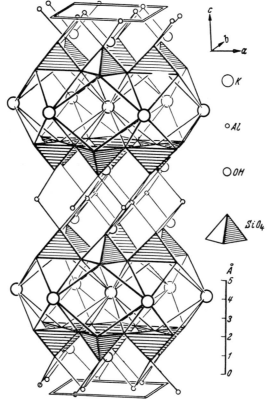

Fig. 164. Muscovite structure, $\overset{2}{\infty} K^{[6+6]} Al_2^{[6]} (OH)_2 [AlSi_3O_{10}] m$

large — it is deformed, either into a tubular structure (in which case one speaks of fibrous serpentine or chrysotile), or into the corrugated structure displayed by platy serpentine or antigorite. The atomic arrangement of chrysotile is not three-dimensionally periodic and accordingly does not correspond to a typical crystal structure. In the case of antigorite well-ordered crystals are extremely rare. Usually the structure is strongly distorted.

Finally, if, in a structure each tetrahedron shares each of its oxygens with four adjacent tetrahedra, a framework structure or *tectosilicate* results. The (Si, Al):0 ratio is now 1:2. The most important representatives are the feldspars which can be crudely subdivided into the K-feldspars, $\overset{3}{\infty} K[Al^{[4]}Si_3^{[4]}O_8]$, and into the mixed crystal series plagioclase, with the end members albite,

$\overset{3}{\infty}$ Na[Al$^{[4]}$Si$_3^{[4]}$O$_8$] and anorthite $\overset{3}{\infty}$ Ca[Al$_2^{[4]}$Si$_2^{[4]}$O$_8$]. In the case of the K-feldspars we can distinguish two modifications based on their structure and optics: a monoclinic modification, sanidine (Fig. 166), and a triclinic, but distinctly pseudomonoclinic modification, microcline. The two forms of KAlSi$_3$O$_8$ differ in construction primarily in that in sanidine the Si and Al atoms are randomly

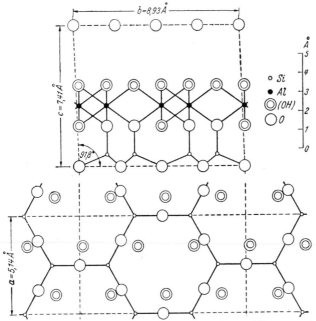

Fig. 165. Kaolinite structure. (After BRINDLEY and ROBINSON)

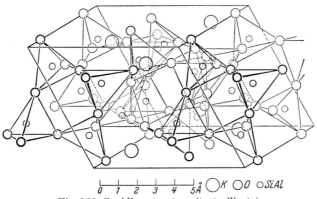

Fig. 166. Sanidine structure (tectosilicate)

distributed over the centers of the tetrahedra, while in microcline they are ordered. The lowering of symmetry from monoclinic to triclinic is connected with this ordering. Sanidine is the high temperature modification (its stability field lies somewhat above 700° C). Microcline is the low temperature modification (it is stable at normal temperatures). The transition between the two modifications does not take place, however, at a precise temperature, or as easily as the transition encountered in the case of quartz. On the contrary, the transition is exceedingly sluggish. This is not surprising, since a much more drastic rearrangement in structure is necessary than that encountered in the inversion between high and low quartz. In order for sanidine to invert to microcline, or vice versa, the Si and Al atoms in the framework must be able to change places, which requires a high activation energy. Thus it is not surprising that the high temperature modification of K-feldspar, sanidine, is preserved in rocks, whereas high quartz is not. This is true, for example, in trachytes, where crystals were cooled too suddenly for the transition to microcline to take place. Although microcline is found in rocks, it is usually finely polysynthetically twinned, like plagioclase, after both the "albite" and "pericline" laws (see p. 97). It has been inferred that the crystals first formed as monoclinic and that later transformation took place which led to this fine microcline grid twinning. This does not necessarily mean that the presence of a particular feldspar is indicative that it formed within its stability field, for example, above about 700° C. Under certain circumstances it may have grown metastably at a lower temperature. This is very important to remember when attempting to make genetic inferences. Orthoclase is an optically and morphologically monoclinic species of K-feldspar which occurs in intrusive rocks. According to its form development and optical constants, it is a completely different K-feldspar from sanidine. X-ray investigations have shown that orthoclase is not a distinct phase, as are sanidine and microcline. From the structural standpoint, it is a transition state between these two modifications, with intermediate states of ordering of Si and Al and submicroscopic twinning.

With the plagioclases we must distinguish also, as with the K-feldspars, between high and low temperature members. This was first recognized from careful optical studies (for example, A. KOEHLER). Here also the high temperature modification of plagioclase has a statistical distribution of Si and Al in its framework, and the low temperature modification an ordered distribution. The relation, ships here are still more complicated than with the K-feldspars. This is because-in the plagioclase "mixed crystal series", the one end-member (anorthite), relative to the other (albite), has a doubled unit cell. There occurs for $NaAlSi_3O_8$ below the melting point a third monoclinic high temperature modification (monalbite) in addition to the triclinic low temperature modification (common albite) and the triclinic high temperature modification (analbite). It is assumed that in monalbite, as well as in analbite, the Si and Al are statistically distributed over the tetrahedral sites. Transformation from pure monalbite to analbite takes place with the ease of high to low quartz inversion, and it can be concluded that this is connected only with deformation of the lattice, not with its rearrangement. As a result of the reversibility of this transformation, potassium free monalbite does not occur as a mineral.

Mixed crystal formation between K-feldspar and anorthite is very limited and of little mineralogical importance. On the other hand K-feldspar can accept larger amounts of the albite "molecule" into its structure. There is at high temperature a complete mixed crystal series between sanidine and monalbite. If members of this series, whose compositions do not lie close to that of the end members, are cooled slowly, unmixing to Na-rich and K-rich components takes place in the solid state. Such unmixed or exsolved K-Na feldspars are called *perthites*. It is customary to speak of these as perthites if, in one individual with predominant K-feldspar (host), an exsolved Na-feldspar phase (guest) occurs ("albite-spindles"); in the corresponding opposite case one speaks of *anti-perthite*.

With the plagioclases also there is limited miscibility at low temperatures. Unmixing can occur under certain circumstances (for example, sufficiently slow cooling). This leads not only to separation of two feldspars near to the end members in composition, but also to other especially stable members.

Such an example is plagioclase with about 5—20% anorthite. One can recognize "low temperature crystals", which can be shown to be unmixed by X-ray investigation. One component is essentially pure albite, the other a plagioclase with about 25% anorthite. The unmixing is always on an extremely fine scale and frequently produces an iridescent play of colors. Such plagioclase is referred to as *peristerite*.

The picture given here of the feldspars is still deficient in many points, but should suffice for a first impression of the extent of the existing problems. That the framework structure of the feldspars results from the three-dimensional linkage of SiO_4 and AlO_4 tetrahedra through the corners, was first recognized by MACHATSCHKI on the basis of general silicate constructional principles. Important studies by BARTH followed. The first structural determination of a member of this mineral family, that of sanidine, was carried out by W. H. TAYLOR in 1933. F. LAVES and his co-workers, as well as others, have concerned themselves in recent years with the very important concept of order-disorder phenomena in feldspars. Much of this discussion has followed his work.

The *feldspathoids* belong also to the tectosilicate group. These minerals occur in place of, or frequently along with, the feldspars, in alkali and aluminum rich eruptive rocks. The most important of these are the morphologically cubic leucite, $\overset{3}{\infty} K[AlSi_2O_6]$ and the hexagonal-pyramidal nepheline, $\overset{3}{\infty} Na[AlSiO_4]h$; in the latter one-fourth of the sodium is frequently replaced by potassium, in such a way that the Na^+ ions and K^+ ions are not randomly distributed, but lie ordered in the cavities of the $\overset{3}{\infty} [AlSiO_4]^-$ framework. The correct formula for this nepheline is, therefore, $\overset{3}{\infty} Na_3K[Si_4Al_4O_{16}]h$.

Additional members of the tectosilicate group are pollucite, $Cs[AlSi_2O_6]H_2Oc$, a rare cesium silicate, and the *zeolites*, open-packed aluminosilicate structures in whose pores in the structure, loosely bound water as well as alkali and alkaline earth ions are situated (see p. 79). Examples of naturally occuring zeolites are the fairly common minerals analcite, $\overset{3}{\infty} Na[AlSi_2O_6] \cdot H_2Oc$ and natrolite, $\overset{3}{\infty} Na_2[Al_2Si_3O_{10}] \cdot 2H_2Oor$.

The various SiO_2 modifications also have three-dimensional framework structures of SiO_4 tetrahedra. These are quartz, tridymite, cristobalite, and keatite and the high pressure modification coesite. The stability fields of quartz, tridymite, cristobalite, and coesite will be dealt with later (see p. 186).

The highest pressure modification of SiO_2, stishovite, has a rutile-type structure (see p. 51), not a $\overset{3}{\infty} [Si^{[4]}O_2]$-framework structure.

A beautiful example, illustrative that the formula-type $[(Si, Al)^{[4]}O_2]^{x-}$ does not necessarily indicate a three-dimensional framework structure, is exhibited by the hexagonal modification of $Ca[Al_2^{[4]}Si_2^{[4]}O_8]$. This phase has the same chemical formula as anorthite. A structural determination has shown that the Al as well as Si is tetrahedrally coordinated by four oxygens and that these are linked through corners. However, the structure is not a tectosilicate, but is more closely related to the micas. If one superimposes two Si_2O_5 sheets, so that apical oxygens are common to both sheets, a two-dimensional infinite double layer $\overset{2}{\infty} [Si^{[4]}O_2]$ occurs. The hexagonal modification of $Ca[Al_2Si_2O_8]$ contains such double layers as its usual structural unit, except that one-half of the Si ions are replaced by Al. To maintain charge balance, Ca^{2+} ions occur between these double sheets, and link them together in a manner analogous to the micas.

Model Structures. It has often been mentioned that in silicates Si can be replaced in part by Al, if corresponding additional cation substitution is provided for to maintain electrical neutrality. There are also isotypes of silicate compounds in which all of the Si is replaced by Al or another element, in particular by P and As. Thus xenotime, $Y^{[8]}[PO_4]$, has the zircon structure, triphyllite, $Li(Fe, Mn)PO_4$, the olivine structure, berzeliite, $NaCa_2Mg_2[AsO_4]_3$, the garnet structure, and berlinite, $AlPO_4$, as well as $AlAsO_4$, the quartz structure. Synthetic aluminum and iron compounds, isotypic to garnet are known, such as $Y_3^{[8]}Al_2^{[6]}[AlO_4]_3c$ and $Y_3^{[8]}Fe_2^{[6]}[FeO_4]_3c$. The possibility of compounds with very different composition having the same or very similar structural types, can be utilized to build model structures. Li_2BeF_4 can serve as a model for $Zn_2[SiO_4]$, willemite. Table 12 shows that lattice parameters of these two compounds are

Table 12. *Example of a model structure.* (After V. M. GOLDSCHMIDT)

	Zn_2SiO_4	Li_2BeF_4
Ionic radii in Å	Zn^{2+} 0.83 Si^{4+} 0.39 O^{2-} 1.32	Li^{1+} 0.78 Be^{2+} 0.34 F^{1-} 1.33
Lattice dimensions in Å (based on rhombohedral axes, α)	8.63 Å 107°45′	8.15 Å 107°40′
Symmetry	rhombohedral	
Habit	prismatic	
Cleavage: 10$\bar{1}$0 0001	} observed	good clear
Birefringence Index of refraction	+ rather low (~ 0.02) ~ 1.7	+ very low (~ 0.006) ~ 1.3
Hardness	5.5	3.8
Melting point °C	1,509.5	~ 470
Solubility in water	insoluble	easily soluble

quite similar. Those physical properties of fluoroberyllates, such as melting point, optics, and hardness, which depend on the charge of the lattice constituents, are corresponding diminished with lower charge. Such models can be technically useful. For example, in order to draw conclusions about compounds which might have very high melting points, this approach has been fruitfully applied in cement research. We shall at this point go no further into the relation between crystal structure and physical properties, but shall refer to this later in the appropriate discussion of crystal physics.

Structural (OH). In concluding our discussion of the silicates, we should make mention of the hydroxyl and water content of crystals. Hydroxyl-containing layers play an important role in many silicates. In our discussion of the CdI_2 structure, we have already referred to the strong polarizability of the OH ion. In most hydroxides, such as $Ca(OH)_2$, this leads to the formation of layer lattices. $Ca(OH)_2$ has a layer structure analogous to CdI_2 (see Fig. 156), in which the oxygen ions occupy the positions of the I atoms in CdI_2. Hydrogen atoms have been shown from neutron diffraction (see p. 160) to be only 0.96 Å distant from the oxygen nucleus and so arranged that they are as far distant as possible from the calcium ions. In this way each oxygen is surrounded by the tetrahedral coordination of one hydrogen and three calcium ions from the CdI_2 type cation layer. Many hydroxides of divalent elements, such as $Mn(OH)_2$, $Co(OH)_2$, $Mg(OH)_2$ (brucite) and others, have the same or at least very similar structure. In crystal structures the hydrogen can cause oxygens to approach each other more closely than is customary. Diaspore, $Al^{[6]}O(OH)$ or (Fig. 167) is an example in which hydrogen is located, practically on the connecting line between two oxygens but not midway between them. The O—O separation is only 2.65 Å, compared to the O—O distance in MgO of 2.98 Å. Such an OH—O interaction is called a *hydrogen bond*. Gibbsite (hydrargillite), $Al^{[6]}(OH)_3 m$ (Fig. 168), a common constituent of bauxite, in addition to the above mentioned hydroxides, possesses a typical layer structure. So does the fibrous iron ore goethite, α-FeO(OH). The rarer mineral lepidocrocite, γ-FeO(OH), has a different orthorhombic structure.

Structural Water (H_2O). The crystals with which we have been concerned above are hydroxides or substances which contain hydroxyl groups and it would be incorrect to write the formula for diaspore as $Al_2O_3 \cdot H_2O$. There are, however, many crystals which contain water molecules as such. We can divide these into two different groups.

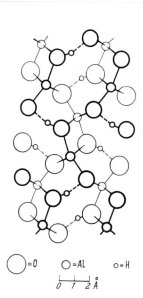

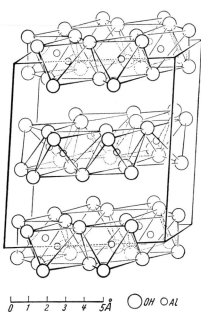

$\bigcirc = O$ $O = Al$ $o = H$

0 1 2 Å

Fig. 167. Atomic arrangement in diaspore. The light and dark circles are actually located in separate planes; the distance between these planes is 1.42 Å

0 1 2 3 4 5 Å $\bigcirc OH$ $O Al$

Fig. 168.
Gibbsite (hydrargillite) structure

In one group, water cannot be driven off without destroying the crystal structure. This becomes evident microscopically from the development of turbidity or opacity in the crystal. All of those compounds which are customarily designated as hydrous salts belong to this group. Examples are chalcanthite, $CuSO_4 \cdot 5H_2O$, and *natron*, $Na_2CO_3 \cdot 10H_2O$. One refers in this connection to *crystal water*. Often all or at least a greater part of the crystal water is especially strongly bound to the cation and called, therefore, *cation water*. An example is

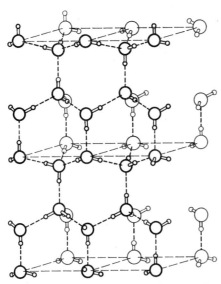

bischofite, $MgCl_2 \cdot 6H_2O$, in which the six water molecules form an octahedral complex with the magnesium. Therefore, its crystal chemical formula should be written $[Mg^{[6]}(H_2O)_6]Cl_2m$. In chalcanthite only four of the five water molecules are cation water. These four form a square planar complex with copper, giving the structural formula $[Cu^{[4]}(H_2O)_4]$-$SO_4 \cdot H_2O tr$. In gypsum, $CaSO_4 \cdot 2H_2O$, each Ca^{2+} is coordinated by six oxygens of the sulfate groups and two water molecules. The atomic arrangement forms well defined layers parallel to (010). This plane is also a perfect cleavage plane. The individual two-dimensional layers have the same formula as the complete mineral, $CaSO_4 \cdot 2H_2O$. The layers are held together by means of hydrogen bonds.

Fig. 169. Arrangement of H_2O molecules in ice. The distance between oxygen atoms is 2.76 Å. (From PAULING)

In the other group of hydrous crystals, the water can be driven off without the structure breaking down. Such crystals are called *zeolites*. In them the water is bound loosely to the walls of canals in a framework structure. The zeolites are almost without exception silicates. In zeolites the water can be removed by heating and can also be replaced by other molecules, such as alcohols, NH_3, and Hg. These fit into holes in the structure without essentially changing the atomic arrangement of the framework. Many zeolites, because of this property, are of technical interest as "molecular sieves". In addition to the water in zeolites, loosely bound cations, usually alkali ions or Ca^{2+}, are situated in the canals. These can be readily exchanged by other ions, giving them the important property of cation exchange. We have already on page 77 become familiar with two examples of zeolites.

In this connection a few words should be devoted to ice. Its structure is illustrated in Fig. 169. We can describe the geometric arrangement of the oxygens in ice, by indicating that in a wurtzite-type lattice (Fig. 150) the positions of Zn as well as the S atoms are occupied by oxygen. Geometric similiarity also occurs relative to the structure of tridymite. If we place Si at the positions of the oxygen in ice and O at the positions of hydrogen (the latter being at the same time moved to the midpoint between two Si atoms), we arrive at the ideal tridymite structure. Ice forms a molecular structure containing the same H_2O molecules as in water or in water vapor. The O—H distance measures somewhat less than 1.00 Å, as it does in the OH group. The H—O—H angle is close to the tetrahedral angle, namely 104°. While the arrangement of the oxygens is strictly periodic, this is not the case for the hydrogen atoms, since the H_2O molecules are oriented randomly over different possible orientations. The H atoms lie on or near the connecting line between two oxygen atoms, as shown in Fig. 169.

3. Covalent Bonding

In the foregoing examples we have been concerned with ionic or predominantly ionic bonding. We have, however, repeatedly mentioned that this form of

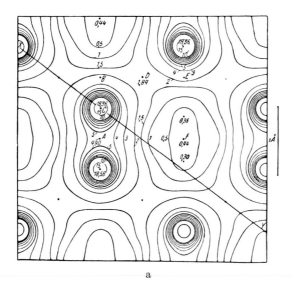

a

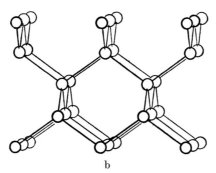

b

Fig. 170. (a) Electron density in diamond, in e.Å^{-2} projected almost parallel to [110] corresponding to a temperature of 5,000°. (From BRILL, GRIMM, HERMANN, PETERS.) (b) Diamond structure in analogous orientation near [110]

bonding does not always occur in its purest form, but that there are transitions, especially to covalent bonding. We can say the same of homopolar or covalent bonding. This form of bonding is displayed in its purest form by diamond, $\overset{3}{\infty}C^{[4]}c$. Its structure is that of sphalerite, in which the Zn as well as the S positions are occupied by equivalent C atoms, each C atom being surrounded tetrahedrally by four others. Accordingly the lattice constant a_0 decreases from 5.40 Å (ZnS) to 3.57 Å. Fig. 170a shows that the electron density is high between the C atoms arranged in non-planar puckered six-fold rings. As indicated in Fig. 170a, the electron density along the line from atom C to the underlying atom does not decrease as much (namely to 4.90 e.Å^{-2} at point A) as along the line to the atoms above to the right and left (1.84 e.Å^{-2} at point D). This is, however, an effect of the projection, as can be readily seen by comparison with Fig. 170b. In the void spaces in the structure the electron density drops off essentially to zero. This structure and bonding is typical also of the other elements of the fourth row of the period table, Si, Ge, and Sn (gray tin). The four valence electrons are always distributed toward the corners of a tetrahedron, toward neighboring atoms, so that two electrons are contributed for each atom. It is, however, not necessary for an equal number of bonding electrons to be provided by both atoms. It is sufficient that both together contribute four. An example is sphalerite, ZnS, already mentioned on p. 58, in which the atomic positions of the diamond structure are occupied half by Zn and half by S, so that each S is surrounded by four Zn and vice versa. Additional examples are CuBr, ZnSe, GaAs, AgI, CdTe, and InSb. In some of these compounds the influence of metallic bonding is asserted, while others like sphalerite (see p. 67) form transitions to ionic bonding.

We have already referred (p. 68) to the contribution of covalent bonding in complex ions or radicals. Covalent bonding is especially important in organic chemistry, for it is this type of bonding which is effective within organic molecules. In recent years very important contributions have been made by application of X-ray structural investigations. We cannot go into these in detail here. In addition to the exact determination of inter-atomic distances and angles, which is just as critical in organic as in inorganic chemistry for elucidating questions of bonding, crystal structure analysis is becoming also increasingly important in the constitutional elucidation of organic molecules. The determination of structural arrangements of extremely complex proteins has already been highly successful.

4. Intermolecular Bonding

In many crystals forces are active, analogous to those which occur between molecules in fluids. The resultant bonding is referred to as *van der Waals* or *intermolecular bonding.*

The elements of the VI and VII rows of the periodic table form inorganic molecular crystals exhibiting intermolecular bonding. A rule has been established for the structures of these semi- and non-metallic elements, which states that each element has in its structure as many neighboring atoms in nearest coordination as there are electrons lacking in the octet of the outer electron shell. If the number of electrons is n, then the number of neighbors is $(8-n)$. According to this "octet rule" I should have only one neighbor, and in fact the I structure is built of I_2 diatomic molecules. If we indicate the outer eight electrons by means of dots, we obtain the picture:

$$\ddot{:}\ddot{I}\!:\!\ddot{I}\ddot{:}$$

Each I atom is then surrounded by an octet of electrons as in the inert gases. In the iodine molecule we are dealing with covalent bonding. These diatomic molecules are held together in the solid state by means of intermolecular forces.

In the case of selenium and tellurium, where two electrons are lacking in the octet, essentially infinite structural chains result:

$$\ldots\ldots:\ddot{Se}:\ddot{Se}:\ddot{Se}:\ddot{Se}:\ddot{Se}:\ldots\ldots,$$

in which each Se atom shares an electron pair with two others: $\overset{1}{\infty}\,[Se^{[2]}]\,h$. In the case of orthorhombic sulfur, chains of eight members are bent into puckered

S_8 rings. In As, which has three missing electrons, a layer structure occurs. The structure can be considered also as a simple cubic structure which has been stretched along a cube diagonal. Of the six neighbors of each As atom, three are more strongly bonded to it and hence form layers perpendicular to the three-fold axis, that is, parallel to (0001). The crystal-chemical formula is $\overset{2}{\infty} As^{[3]}h$. The same structure is less clearly expressed with antimony and bismuth. With four missing electrons, we get a three-dimensional structure with four-fold coordination, like diamond, which can only be bonded together by covalent bonding. This is the type of bonding existing *within* the diatomic molecules, chains, rings, and ribbons. These units are in turn held together by means of intermolecular or van der Waals forces, which in the case of Se, Te, As, Sb, and Bi show transition to metallic bonding.

5. Metallic Bonding

Pure Metals. We come now to another form of bonding, the *metallic bond*. It has been concluded from the electrical conductivity of metals (RIECKE, 1898), that essentially free and mobile electrons occur between positive metal ions in metal crystals. These free electrons act as a kind of electron gas. Electron density determinations have established this hypothesis in the case of Mg. Although metals play only a subordinate role as minerals, we shall briefly discuss the types of metal structures because of their great importance in understanding the nature of crystals. Let us recall the coordination structures of ionic compounds of the type $A B$. There the highest coordination number was eight, as in cesium chloride. A higher mutual coordination is geometrically impossible in $A B$-type compounds. However, if the crystal is built of only one type of element, a twelve-fold coordination can be attained. The crystal structure with 12-coordination corresponds to the closest packing of like spheres. A planar arrangement of close

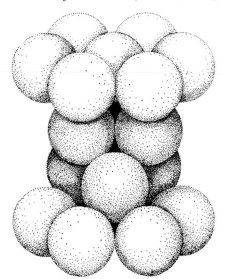

Fig. 171. Cubic closest packing, formed from planar packed layers stacked along the diagonals of a cube

packed spheres has each sphere in contact with six others. In order to propagate closest packing in three dimensions, we must superimpose such closed packed planar layers one upon the other so that spheres in one layer always lie in the depressions in the adjacent layer. In superimposing a third layer one has two choices of orientation. We can place it either over those depressions which cause the spheres in the third layer to lie directly over those of the first layer, or the third layer can be placed over an alternate set of depressions. If, during the stacking of layers, the fourth layer is the first to lie directly over the initial layer (Fig. 171), such packing is called, *cubic closest packing*. It corresponds to a cubic face-centered lattice (Fig. 140g, p. 51) which, because of our method of construction, stands with one of its cube diagonals perpendicular to the layers. Fig. 172 shows that the closest packed planar layers are parallel to the octahedral plane. In cubic closest packing the coordination polyhedron is the cubooctahedron (Fig. 173).

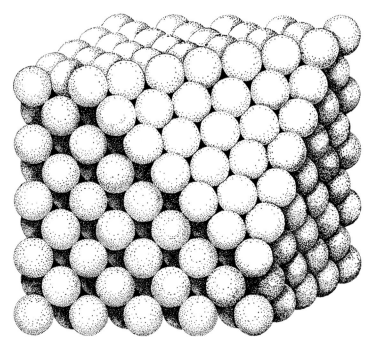

Fig. 172. Cubic closest packing, showing the face-centered nature of the resulting lattice.

That arrangement, in which it is the third superimposed layer which first lies directly over the initial layer, is called *hexagonal closest packing* (Fig. 174). By means of other repetitions of close packed layers many "close packed" types can arbitrarily be produced. The cubic and the normal hexagonal closest

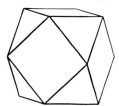

Fig. 173. Cubooctahedron

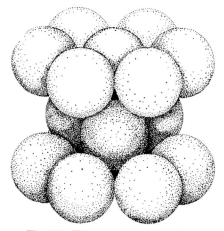

Fig. 174. Hexagonal closest packing

packing are widely distributed in metals. The following metals crystallize in cubic closest packing:

Ag, Al, Au, αCa, αCe, αCo, Cu, γFe, Ir, βLa, αNi, Pb, Pd, βPr, Pt, αRh, βSc, Sr, Th, αTl, Yb.

Hexagonal closest packing can also be described as two interpenetrating hexagonal lattices with the axial ratio $c_0 : a_0 \sim 1.63$. The following metals crystallize with this arrangement:

Be, βCa, Cd, βCe, βCo, Cp, βCr, Dy, Er, Gd, Hf, Ho, αLa, Mg, Nd, βNi, Os, αPr, Re, Ru, αSc, Tb, Tc, αTi, βTl, Tm, Y, Zn, αZr.

Almost all of the remaining metals crystallize with a cubic body-centered lattice (Fig. 140f, p. 51) with the coordination number 8:

Ba, αCr, Cs, Eu, αFe, K, Li, Mo, Na, Nb, Rb, βRh, Ta, βTi, V, W, βZr.

In the two types of closest packing, 74.1% of space is filled; in the cubic body-centered structure it is somewhat less, but always more than in the simple cubic atomic arrangements annotated in Table 13.

Table 13. *Space filling of packing of spheres*

Arrangement	Shortest interatomic distance (a = lattice constant)	Space filling in %	Coordination number
Cubic closest	$\dfrac{a}{2}\sqrt{2}$	74.1	12
Hexagonal closest	$a\,(c:a = 1.633)$		
Cubic body-centered	$\dfrac{a}{2}\sqrt{3}$	68.1	8
Simple cubic	a	52.4	6

Comparison of the packing arrangements of Table 13 with the structures of metals indicates that there is apparently a tendency for the most highly symmetrical structures to form and for space to be filled as completely as possible.

Alloys. Similar tendencies are also prevalent among the metal alloys, which are technically so important. If two metals are melted together, the two metals may not mix in the solid state, but instead separate into pure crystals of each of the constituents (see p. 188). However, the original metals may not separate out of the melt, but instead form alloys. In this case there are two possibilities. The first is that mixed crystals form. These are to be expected when the atomic radii are sufficiently similar and similar bonding properties prevail. Mixed crystals have arbitrary and non-constant chemical composition and the two constituents are randomly distributed in the structure. True mixed crystals are formed, for example, when we melt together gold and silver. In nature gold is almost always silver-bearing. If the silver content reaches more than 25%, the natural alloy is called electrum. The other possibility of changing the constituents of metals is by the formation of a compound between the two partners. This is a common occurrence in the case of ionic crystals, such as salts, because each compound corresponds to a definite stoichiometric composition. In the case of metal compounds, in a certain sense transitional states occur between compounds and mixed crystals, since the crystals which form often have no exactly defined chemical formula, but vary in their composition, showing a considerable latitude therein.

Following LAVES, we shall refer in metallic systems to mixed crystals when one of the partners accepts the other into its structure, and to a compound when a new structure is formed. This is also a crystallographic and non-chemical definition of a compound. Often a compound state exists only over a definite temperature range. Gold and copper, for example, behave like true mixed crystals in all proportions only at higher temperatures, and with random distribution of the two kinds of atoms in a cubic-face-centered lattice. Upon sudden cooling, this arrangement is retained. If cooling takes place slowly, the atoms arrange themselves into a phase with the composition $AuCu_3$, so that a "superstructure" is formed with Cu at the cube corners and Au at the centers of the faces. $AuCu_3$ is a compound and behaves electrically and mechanically quite different from the suddenly cooled mixed crystal. Upon heating, and the addition of energy, the energetically most favorable state disappears and the disordered state corresponding to the mixed crystal appears. Such relations are common among intermetallic phases. With ionic and covalent compounds, on the other hand, the structural order is as a rule maintained up to the melting point.

The Hume-Rothery Rule. We shall now mention two important generalizations with regard to compound formation in metallic systems. The Hume-Rothery rule states that the structural type depends on the ratio of the number of valence electrons to the number of atoms in the compound. The metals of the VIII group of the periodic table must be considered as having zero valence electrons. The three structural types which occur are indicated in Table 14, along with some examples.

Table 14. *Hume-Rothery compounds*

Lattice type	Cubic body-centered	Hexagonal closest packing	Cubic, 52 atoms in the cell
Metallographic designation	β-phase	ε-phase	γ-phase
Valence electrons: atoms	$3:2$	$7:4$	$21:13$
Examples	$CuZn$	$CuZn_3$	Cu_5Zn_8
	$CuBe$	Cu_3Sn	Cu_9Al_4
	$AgMg$	Au_3Sn	$Cu_{31}Sn_8$
	$NiAl$	Ag_5Al_3	Fe_5Zn_{21}
	Cu_3Al		Ni_5Cd_{21}
	Cu_5Sn		

The Hume-Rothery rule is not without exceptions, and it has as yet no satisfactory theoretical explanation.

The diamond structure can be considered, from a purely formal standpoint, as a special case of this rule. The ratio of valence electrons to atoms is $4:1$.

Laves Phases. While the above-mentioned compounds depend upon the number of valence electrons, other groups are formed exclusively by geometric relationships. These are compounds of the type AB_2, and are designated as "Laves phases". More than 60 such compounds are already known. Three types may be differentiated having the $MgCu_2$, $MgZn_2$, and $MgNi_2$ structures. Of these $MgCu_2$ merits detailed description (Fig. 175). The structure exhibits atomic properties which, from an energetic standpoint, could not occur in normal ionic compounds.

In $MgCu_2$ the Mg atoms are surrounded by twelve Cu atoms (four Mg atoms are located at only about 4% greater distance). The structure is, however, constructed so that each Cu atom has as nearest neighbors other Cu atoms, and six additional dissimilar neighbors (Mg) are found at about a 17% greater distance. The Cu—Cu distance in $MgCu_2$ is 2.49 Å, quite similar to that in elemental Cu (2.55 Å). Also the Mg—Mg distance is not very different from that in metallic Mg. The geometric arrangement of the Cu atoms is like that in elemental Cu except that a portion of the Cu atoms is missing. The structure has an additional noteworthy geometrical property: if one imagines it to be built of spheres which are so large that they are in mutual contact, one obtains two separate assemblages of spheres; namely, an assemblage of Cu spheres touching one another and a second assemblage of Mg spheres touching one another. The Cu and Mg are always in contact with like atoms, not with each other. The structural formula is ∞^3 Mg$^{[12 \, Cu + 4 \, Mg]}$Cu$_2^{[6Cu+6Mg]}$ c; the coordination polyhedron around the Cu is an icosahedron (see Fig. 118, p. 46), whose corners are occupied half by Cu, half by Mg. This type of structure frequently occurs in intermetallic compounds with metallic radius ratios $R_A/R_B \approx 1.20$. Just as the Cu arrangement in MgCu$_2$ is similar to cubic closest packing, so does Mg Zn$_2$ possess analogous similarities to hexagonal closest packing. Here the Zn atoms possess in part this atomic arrangement. MgNi$_2$ displays a sort of mixed structure between MgCu$_2$ and MgZn$_2$.

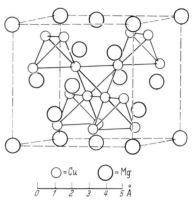

Fig. 175. MgCu$_2$ structure. The array of Cu-atoms is emphasized which occurs when the Cu spheres are in mutual contact. The Mg spheres are in contact with each other forming an arrangement with the diamond structure

Transition to Other Bond Types. Just as there are transitions between ionic and covalent bonding, there are also transitions between metallic and ionic or covalent bonding. When metals of the first three groups of the periodic table form compounds with those of the IV to VII groups, these show, in spite of their metallic appearance, transition to ionic bonding. For example, these compounds are soluble in liquid NH$_3$ and possess a noticeable electrical conductivity in solution. They act in NH$_3$ as normal salts do in water. Examples of such compounds are Mg$_2$Sn and Mg$_2$Pb, which crystallize with the fluorite structure. Thus they are also structurally similar to ionic compounds.

A structural type which is not found among purely ionic compounds is that of NiAs, niccolite. This structure can be most simply described as a hexagonal close packing of As atoms in which the Ni atoms are intercalated in the interstices. In a close packed array there are two kinds of interstices, those with

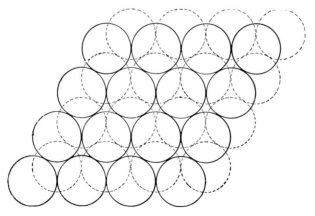

Fig. 176. Two superimposed close packed layers showing octahedral and tetrahedral interstices

octahedral and those with tetrahedral coordination. As can be discerned immediately from Fig. 176, the number of octahedral sites is equal to the number of packed spheres; the number of tetrahedral sites is twice this number. In NiAs all of the octahedral interstices formed from the hexagonal closest packing of As atoms are occupied by Ni. While in cubic closest packing the atoms in octahedral sites are arranged likewise in a cubic close packed array, in the structure of NiAs the octahedral sites lie in chains in the direction of the hexagonal axis (Fig. 177). It can be demonstrated that along this chain direction metallic bonding occurs between Ni atoms, while the coherence between the As- and Ni-atoms may be dependent predominantly upon covalent bonding.

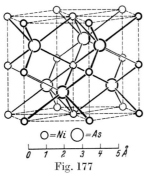

$\bigcirc = Ni$ $\bigcirc = As$

0   1   2   3   4   5 Å

Fig. 177

Fig. 177. NiAs structure

Fig. 178. $\overset{1}{\infty} Sb_2^{[3]} S_3$ double chains in stibnite (schematic); the hatched Sb atoms lie above the plane of the drawing, the non-hatched Sb below. The S atoms lie in the plane. Actually the planes of the two $\overset{1}{\infty} Sb^{[3]} S_2$-chains which form the double chain are approximately perpendicular to each other

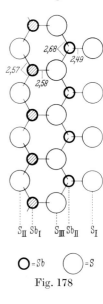

$S_{II} Sb_I$ $S_{III} Sb_{II}$ S_I

$\bigcirc = Sb$ $\bigcirc = S$

Fig. 178

This sort of accommodation of Ni atoms in the interstices of a close packed network helps us to understand an unusual phenomenon exhibited by pyrrhotite, FeS. It has long puzzled analytical chemists and mineralogists, that in this mineral the stoichiometric ratio Fe:S is not exactly 1:1. Accordingly we find in older mineralogical books, compositional descriptions such as $Fe_{10}S_{11}$, as well as others. It was formerly believed that an excess of S could be accommodated in the structure (to 6%), but X-ray investigations have indicated that a deficiency of Fe actually occurs. The S packing, therefore, remains stable even when not all the octahedral sites are filled with Fe. Unlike the NiAs type, stoichiometric FeS at room temperature is easily deformed and possesses a larger unit cell. In addition, iron sulfides of composition $Fe_{1-x}S$ ($x \leq 0.15$) occur as superstructures of the ideal NiAs structure, as a result of an ordered arrangement of the Fe atoms and the vacancies in the structure.

Another important sulfide structure is that of stibnite, Sb_2S_3. Its structure is very much more complicated than that of NiAs. We can best perceive its structure if we first consider only those Sb—S distances which are less than 2.70 Å. Each Sb atom is coordinated by three S atoms in a pyramid in which the average S—Sb—S angle is 90°. The SbS_3 pyramids are linked together into $\overset{1}{\infty} [Sb_2^{[3]}S_3]$ ribbons, as illustrated in Fig. 178. Two such ribbons lie together in the structure in such a manner that one S_I of one chain and two Sb_{II} of a second chain always approach at a distance of 2.82 Å. This is not much greater than the greatest distance within the double chain itself (2.68 Å) and certainly must indicate weak chemical bonding. By emphasizing this additional bonding, the structure can be viewed as consisting of quadruple ribbons in which one half of the Sb atoms possess a pyramidal 3-fold S coordination and the other half a $(3+2)$ coordination. The antimony with $[3+2]$ coordination sits approximately at the center of the base of a square pyramid formed by S atoms. The crystal chemical formula is, therefore, $\overset{1}{\infty} Sb^{[3]}Sb^{[3+2]}S_3$ or.

Molybdenite, $\overset{2}{\infty} Mo^{[6]}S_2 h$, crystallizes with a typical layer structure, with covalent bonding within the layer. The coordination polyhedron is, however, not an octahedron, as we have always imagined 6-fold coordination, but a trigonal prism.

The pyrite structure, $Fe^{[6]}[S_2]c$, is geometrically derived from the NaCl structure, in that Fe atoms are fitted into the positions of sodium ions and dumbbell-shaped S_2 molecules into the positions of the chlorine ions. As a result, the usual symmetry planes of the NaCl lattice are destroyed and only glide planes parallel to the cube faces remain. Morphologically these appear as normal symmetry planes. The bonding is predominantly covalent with a definitely metallic contribution.

6. Summary of Bond Types

In summary we want to make clear again that there are not only the pure ionic, covalent, intermolecular, and metallic bond types in crystals, but, as we have seen, also various deviations therefrom. These deviations are manifest in two different ways.

First of all there are transitions between the main bond types themselves. For example, transitions between ionic and covalent bonding are found in the Si—O bonding in silicates and probably in the Zn—S bonding in sphalerite. Transitions between metallic and covalent or ionic bonding occur in NiAs, niccolite, or in PbS, galena. The crystal structure of PbS corresponds to NaCl, but the metallic luster of PbS shows that the bonding cannot be purely ionic.

In addition to transitions between bond types, different bond types occur in crystals at different locations within the same crystal. A distinct example of this is displayed by orthorhombic sulfur. Within the S_8 rings covalent bonding prevails; between these rings, van der Waals bonding. In silicates we find that the Si—O bond is transitional between ionic and covalent. Linking Si—O assemblages together are cations which, in many cases (Na^{1+}, K^{1+}, Mg^{2+}, Ca^{2+}, Ba^{2+}, as well as others) exhibit essentially electrostatic bonding. In pyrite, FeS_2, the S—S distance in the S_2 group is almost exactly the same as in the S_8 molecule, namely about 2.1 Å, indicating that the S—S bond is covalent. Based on its electrical conductivity it must be concluded that metallic bonding is prevalent in the structure of pyrite.

The problems of chemical bonding are still far from being completely solved. Unfortunately the usual structure determination gives only interatomic distances and thus infers only indirectly the type of bonding. It is of great importance, therefore, to combine crystal structural results with other physical methods (electrical conductivity, absorption spectroscopy, magnetic measurements, etc.), to discern the true nature of bonding within crystals.

7. Crystal Structures as Packed Spheres

In our discussion of metals, as well as the NiAs-type structures, we have referred to the closest packing of spheres. This concept can be put to good advantage also to describe a number of other structural types, especially if we allow a certain amount of distortion from ideal packing. The NaCl structure can be described as cubic closest packed, in which all octahedral sites are occupied. In the ideal case the A ions (atoms) would be in contact with the B ions (atoms) and the B ions likewise in contact with each other. The radius ratio R_A/R_B would be exactly 0.41. In NaCl itself the radius ratio is 0.54. The Cl ion packing is expanded, contrary to the ideal case. In addition to a series of halides, oxides, and sulfides (NaBr, MgO, MgS), TiC, TiN, ZrC and ZrN possess this type of structural packing. In the latter, N or C is situated in the octahedral sites in the cubic closest packed array of Ti or Zr. If only one half of the octahedral sites are occupied and in layers parallel to an octahedral face, the $MgCl_2$-type structure results. The "cubic close packing" of the anions is rhombohedrally distorted in this structure. In an analogous manner the CdI_2-type structure is derived from a hexagonal close packed array. Sometimes only a fourth of the octahedral interstices are occupied, as in Mn_4N and Fe_4N. Formally the CaF_2 structure can be described, by noting that the Ca^{2+} ions form a cubic face centered lattice, corresponding to cubic close packing, with the F^- ions situated in the tetrahedral sites. It is to be noted, however, that the Ca^{2+} ions cannot be in contact with each other, since the F^- ions are much too large to fit into the interstices of a close packed array of Ca^{2+} ions. This description fits much better the structure of Li_2O, crystallizing analogous to CaF_2, except that cations and anions have exchanged places (antifluorite structure) giving the structural formula $Li_2^{[4]}O^{[8]}c$. The small Li^+ ions sit in the tetrahedral interstices of a cubic close packed O^{2-} array. If, in a cubic close packed array, only one-half of the tetrahedral sites are occupied, with retention of the highest possible symmetry, the ZnS (sphalerite) structure results. In order to avoid misunderstanding, it should be expressly stated that this arrangement, involving like size spheres in contact with each other is not closest packing, but quite open packing. A hexagonal close packing with half of the tetrahedral sites filled corresponds to the structure of wurtzite (ZnS).

If both types of interstices in a cubic close packed array are occupied by cations, we can arrive at the spinel-type structure, $Mg^{[4]}Al_2^{[6]}O_4c$. Here one-eighth of the tetrahedral sites, corresponding to one-fourth of the oxygen ions, are filled by Mg, and one-half of the octahedral sites by Al. It is noteworthy that the smaller Al-ions are situated in the octahedral, and the larger Mg-ions in the tetrahedral interstices.

Olivine, $(Mg, Fe)_2^{[6]}[SiO_4]or$, can be considered to a first approximation as a somewhat deformed and expanded hexagonal close packed array of oxygen. In it the densest packed planes lie in the plane (010). The Si atoms are found in the tetrahedral sites, which are one-eighth occupied, and the Mg or Fe ions occupy half of the octahedral sites.

8. Deviations from Ideal Crystals

Defects. While the geometric theory of 230 space groups pictures the crystal as a completely ordered structure, the previous discussion of real structures, has already shown that this ideal picture is not quite correct.

In mixed crystals we have insisted that a random distribution of constituents occurs. This alone implies disorder. The example, FeS, illustrates a further kind of disorder, namely incomplete occupancy of equivalent lattice points. In this structure the Fe atoms are not periodically repeated on the atomic scale. In the spinels it has been shown that, in addition to the normal spinel mentioned earlier, there is also a second type of cation distribution which has been found, for example, in $MgGa_2O_4$. In this spinel one-half of the Ga^{3+} ions are situated in tetrahedral sites; the remainder along with the Mg^{2+} ions are situated in the octahedral sites, and indeed the two types of ions are not situated in definite locations, but are randomly distributed. The appropriate crystal chemical formula is as follows: $\overset{3}{\infty} Ga^{[4]}(Ga, Mg)_2^{[6]}O_4 c$. The same phenomenon is found with magnetite, $\overset{3}{\infty} Fe^{3+[4]}(Fe^{3+}, Fe^{2+})_2^{[6]}O_4 c$. The spinels form mixed crystals with the γ-modification of Al_2O_3. This, like spinel, possesses cubic closest packing.

The unit cell contains 32 O ions. In place of the 24 cation sites per unit cell of spinel (16 Al 8 Mg), in γ-Al_2O_3 there are $21^1/_3$ Al accommodated in the octahedral and tetrahedral sites. In three unit cells only 64 of a possible 72 sites are occupied by Al, and purely at random without geometric order. The solid solution between $MgAl_2O_4$ and γ-Al_2O_3 is thus easily explained.

The mixed crystals between $MgCl_2$ and LiCl, already mentioned on p. 64, can likewise be considered as a cubic clos-est packing of chlorine ions. In the $MgCl_2$ structure half of the octahedral inter-

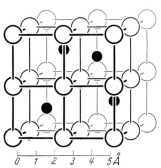

Fig. 179. CaF_2 structure emphasizing the primitive cubic arrangement of the F^- ions

stices are unoccupied. By the addition of two Li in place of one Mg, mixed crystals occur, until, upon sufficient replacement by Li, the crystal of formula Li_2Cl_2 results. Conversely the $MgCl_2$ structure can be visualized as being derived by subtraction of two Li in $Li_2Cl_2(LiCl)$ and replacement by one Mg.

Such view can also be taken of structures which are not close packed. As an example, we can consider the mixed crystal between CaF_2 and YF_3. The CaF_2 structure can be considered also as a simple cubic array of F ions, in which a Ca ion is situated at the centers of alternate F cubes (Fig. 179). If the Ca^{2+} is replaced by Y^{3+}, additional F appears in the empty alternate F lattices.

As these examples show, crystals which display disorder phenomena can be classified into two types: those with disordered random distribution of constituents throughout the entire crystal, *substitution crystals*; and those with disordered vacancies. Both kinds of disorder can be simultaneously present in the same crystal. The manner in which vacancies are produced can be classified still further as taking place either by addition, $MgCl_2{\rightarrow}Li_2Cl_2$, or by subtraction, $Li_2Cl_2{\rightarrow}MgCl_2$.

Another concept has been introduced by SCHOTTKY and WAGNER. They showed that crystals with a clearly stoichiometric formula must have defects (vacant sites) at all temperatures above absolute zero. Their number increases with increasing temperature and diminishes with decreasing temperature. Here also substitution, addition, and subtraction can be distinguished. These defects must be postulated in order to explain certain optical and electrical phenomena and, in part, also reaction in the solid state. To denote the magnitude of departure from ideality it is informative to mention MOTT and GURNEYS' conclusions, based on measurements of electrical conductivity. In AgCl at 250° C, they find that 0.02% of the ions are in interstitial lattice positions; at 350° C, 0.1%. The effects of SCHOTTKY-WAGNER defects are in part identical with and indistinguishable from those of the above mentioned type. In the latter case we are dealing, at least in part, with defects which are not stable at absolute zero.

The phenomenon of defects in crystals has been intensively studied in recent years. Results already demonstrate clearly that the prototype of regularity, the crystal, can also show gradation of random order. The proviso of the genuinely homogeneous discontinuum is not strict, but on the atomic scale is only randomly fulfilled.

Regular Intergrowths. Additional deviations from ideal construction are manifest by the intergrowth of several individuals. For a mixed crystal we have established the requirement that the distribution of atoms, ions, and molecules

a   b   c

Fig. 180a—c. Distribution of black and white squares, (a) statistical (random), (b) Deviation from random toward chess board pattern, (c) deviation toward segregation of larger black and white domains. (From LAVES)

shall be random: components exhibit no preferential locations, and no segregation of one or the other end members occurs. In addition to such true mixed crystals, there are also certain cases in which the components segregate into larger domains, a kind of tiny crystallite. Fig. 180a shows a random distribution of equal numbers of black and white squares, such as would be obtained, for example, by throwing dice. Fig. 180b shows a distribution which is non-random and approaches the ordered pattern of a chessboard; in Fig. 180c the non-random distribution tends toward a segregation of larger black and white domains.

Intermixing of components can range from a random distribution to intergrowths completely visible to the naked eye. In this case also it is informative to illustrate the principle utilizing the concept of close packed spheres. As mentioned previously, in the structure of γ-Al_2O_3, oxygens are cubic closed packed and interstices are occupied by Al. If in addition we insert Mg ions in some of the tetrahedral interstices, $MgAl_2O_4$ occurs at a certain point, and a mixed crystal between γ-Al_2O_3 and $MgAl_2O_4$ is formed. Such mixed crystals, in which the chemical formula as well as the structural type of the end member do not correspond, are called anomalous mixed crystals. The name is poorly chosen because it does not properly imply the phenomenon to which it is related. If, in the example just alluded to, ions in the tetrahedral and octahedral sites were randomly distributed, one would speak, in spite of the different formula types of the end members, of a homogeneous mixed crystal. When, however, larger domains are formed which correspond to the end members, intercalation of one crystal form in another results (see Fig. 180c). Frequently the intergrowth is oriented crystallographically with respect to the host crystal. Intergrowths can occur by unmixing in the solid state. However, it is not necessary that this happen.

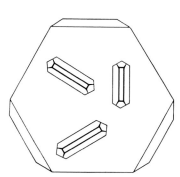

Fig. 181. Intergrowth of rutile and hematite. (After SEIFERT)

Fig. 182. Overgrowth of potassium iodide on muscovite

Fig. 182

For a long time it has been known that two different kinds of crystals can grow together in a regular arrangement. Intergrowths of rutile and hematite (Fig. 181) are very common. Beautiful overgrowths can easily be produced experimentally by allowing a drop of aqueous KI solution to evaporate on a fresh muscovite mica cleavage surface. The octahedral faces of the cubic KI and the corresponding lattice plane possess trigonal symmetry, the mica cleavage plane, pseudohexagonal symmetry. Since their dimensions are rather similar, the KI crystals grow with the octahedral face oriented on the basal plane of the mica. In this way triangular crystals are formed as a result of controlled crystallization. The triangular crystals are oriented parallel demonstrating the preferred orientation of the regular intergrowth.

Non-oriented intergrowths also occur very frequently. Here the relation of the boundary surface tension (see also p. 244), determines whether a foreign body is included or shoved aside during growth ("self-refining capacity"). Such foreign bodies, be they different crystals, drops of fluid, or gas bubbles, are called inclusions. They occur probably down to submicroscopic size also.

Imperfections. In addition to the defect phenomena already mentioned, a series of observations leads to the far-reaching supposition that natural and at least many artificial crystals exhibit other imperfections. The "parketting" of crystal faces has been known for a long time by crystallographers (Fig. 183). This can sometimes be discerned by the naked eye. More often, during goniometric measurements, it is noticeable by multiple or distorted signals. As early as BECKE, the formation of etch figures was attributed to cracks and breaks in crystal surfaces. VON LAUE, only a year after his discovery of X-ray diffraction, had expressed the opinion that the fluorite crystal investigated by himself and TANK[1] was "ein Konglomerat vieler nicht mit der nötigen Genauigkeit zusammengesetzter Stücke". Based on strength investigations, W. VOIGT, as early as 1919, had referred to the importance of thermal and mechanical inhomogenieties in crystals. In 1920 GRIFFITH attempted to explain the deviations of experimental strength properties from those to be expected theoretically by external or internal

Fig. 183. Fluorite with parkette surface

cracks. In the field of strength of materials, the question of imperfection in crystals has been considered often, especially by SMEKAL. So much seems to be certain, that even if we exclude cracks formed as a result of mechanical action, crystals still form from subindividuals. The size of these constructional units varies from that of the mosaic particles deduced by DARWIN from X-ray reflections (10^{-4} to 10^{-7} cm), to the parketting noticeable with the naked eye. These sub-units are rotated with respect to each other by trivial amounts, without being confined to a definite direction of rotation. An appropriate picture is probably that of the branches of a tree which are tightly connected (*Ver-zweigungs-* or BUERGER'S *lineage struc-ture*). The comparison suffers in as much as it cannot be demonstrated that the diameters of the blocks decrease in any particular direction as do the branches of a tree; the increase or decrease of the size of the blocks is irregular. The coherence of such a lineage crystal is so great that, upon cleaving, the crystal does not break up into individual blocks, but instead an almost smooth surface is produced in which, if the dimensions are sufficiently large the building blocks, can be made visible by means of reflection or interference phenomena. Imperfections have a great influence on many strength properties (see p. 107 and 111) and on reactions in the solid state.

Such departures from ideal crystals are easily produced during natural growth with its many accidents (see p. 171). In the laboratory it is possible to suppress gross departures by means of suitable experimental methods. To what extent it is possible within the sub-microscopic dimensions to purposely create imperfections is still controversial. It must be noted in discussing these questions that part of the phenomena ascribed to imperfections may be traced back to the defect phenomena mentioned above. By especially careful elimination of all sources of error, it appears possible to obtain crystals which are at least very largely free of imperfections. Even so one must clearly recognize that natural and most artificial crystals, are not without imperfections. The presentation which was developed in the first chapter was, therefore, only an expedient, giving the mathematically ideal relations. With each application we must consider how far we may idealize. Because of the many departures from ideal crystals, it is

[1] "An aggregate of many pieces piled together without the necessary precision".

appropriate to speak of "real crystals". However, it appears important to distinguish as far as possible between defects and imperfections.

Disorder can become even greater and result in transitions to *mesophases*, as mentioned on page 6. In the case of layer structures, the layers may be superimposed one over the other in more or less disordered fashion. In the important clay mineral *montmorillonite* (Fig. 163, p. 73), layer packets are stratified in a disordered fashion, so that only the (001) planes are parallel; more general (*hkl*) lattice planes are rotated arbitrarily with respect to those in the neighboring packet. The distance from the centers of contiguous layer packets varies with increasing water content from about 10 to 20 Å. Organic liquids can produce still greater periodicities. These inner silicate surfaces lead to an ex-

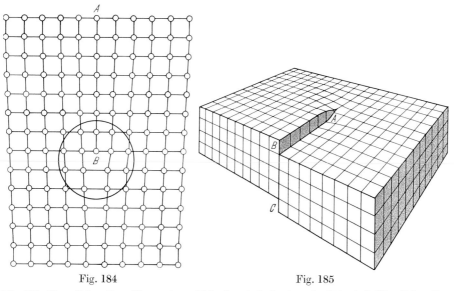

Fig. 184   Fig. 185

Fig. 184. Step dislocation. The region within the circle is strongly distorted. The dislocation line runs perpendicular to plane of diagram
Fig. 185. Screw dislocation. Dislocation line emerges at *A*. At some distance from the dislocation line, at about *B—C* the lattice is essentially undistorted. (From READ)

ceptionally high adsorption capacity for the mineral. In the *kaolinite*-group also there are representatives with disordered stacking sequences; these are referred to as "fireclay" minerals.

Dislocations. In recent years variations from ideal crystal construction have been revealed which are called *dislocations*. These are very important for a proper understanding of many crystal physical phenomena (for example plastic deformation, p. 101 and crystal growth, p. 162). In Fig. 184 a simple and also quite theoretical example of this is given. It shows a primitive cubic lattice with the plane of the drawing parallel to (001); the atoms of the planar net above and below the plane of the drawing lie exactly above and below the indicated points. It can be seen that in the upper half of the drawing, an additional lattice plane has been included, which ends in the crystal at *B*. Around *B* the lattice is strongly distorted and the distortion is continued perpendicular to (001) equally in both directions. This is called a *dislocation line*. This is not a line in the mathematical sense, but indicates the locus of greatest lattice distortion. This form of dislocation is called a *step dislocation*.

In addition to step dislocations, *screw dislocations* are important. In this type of dislocation the lattice planes are so deformed that they are wound like a spiral staircase around a dislocation line (Fig. 185). The pitch of the spiral is sometimes only one or a few translation distances (therefore from a few to about 20 Å), but may be up to several hundred Ångströms in magnitude.

Step- and screw dislocations represent cases in which the dislocation line is a straight line. There are, however, frequent dislocations in which the dislocation line is irregular and more difficult to characterize. Quite generally the dislocation line delineates especially energetic regions in the crystal.

Twinning. In discussing imperfections in crystals, we assumed that the growth results in almost parallel domains whose angular variation from the ideal undistorted lattice is very slight. There is still another form of intergrowth of crystals of the same substance. In these the mutual positions of the individual crystal domains are quite dissimilar. They are, however, related by crystallographically oriented symmetry elements. Obviously these symmetry elements

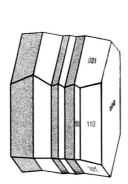

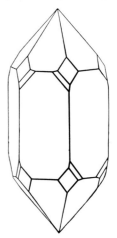

Fig. 186. Albite twin. (After RAAZ-TERTSCH)   Fig. 187. Quartz twin (Brazil law) (idealized)

may not coincide in kind and orientation with those characteristic of a single crystal of the substance, since only a parallel repetition would result. Such regular intergrowths of the same sort of crystal are called *twins*.

There are two kinds of such symmetrical arrangements which we can observe. In the first case the individual crystals lie as if reflected across a simple crystal plane, the *twin plane*. Often this plane is at the same time the growth plane, or *composition plane*, as it is in the case of albite twinning (Fig. 186), twin plane (010). Twinning after the albite law is not confined to albite itself, but is exceedingly common among all members of the plagioclase group. In contrast to this example, twins are known for which the twin plane and composition plane do not coincide, but in which the latter is an irregular and bent and buckled surface. The two contiguous crystals can even penetrate one another as in quartz twins (Fig. 187). In this case the twin plane is a prism plane (11$\bar{2}$0), and the left- and right-handed trapezohedra lie symmetrically with respect to it (Brazil law). In practice, the Brazil twins of quartz are only rarely recognizable from the morphological development. More frequently the individual twinned units alternate in layers, as is seen clearly by optical study. It is noted that in Brazil twinning right and left-handed quartz alternate with each other.

In the second case the individual crystals are rotated 180° with respect to each other around a simple rational edge direction, the *twin axis*. An example is offered again by albite twinned according to the pericline law (Fig. 188).

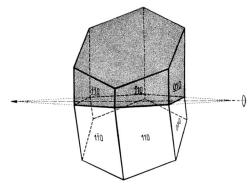

Fig. 188. Pericline twin

The twin axis is [010]; the composition plane is the so-called "rhombic section". This is a plane whose position does not correspond to rational indices, but rather is determined by the dimensions of the crystal and the position of the twin axis.

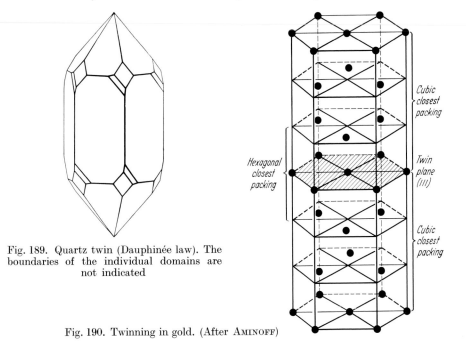

Fig. 189. Quartz twin (Dauphinée law). The boundaries of the individual domains are not indicated

Fig. 190. Twinning in gold. (After AMINOFF)

As is the case with the albite law, the pericline law is common to all plagioclases. Since the position of the "rhombic section" varies with anorthite content, it can serve to denote the composition of the plagioclase. MÜGGE was able to show in the case of anorthite that the formation temperature of such minerals can be deduced from the deviation of the position of the composition plane calculated theoretically

from the axial ratios and thus be used as a "geologic thermometer". The basis
for this is that the axial ratios of the crystal change with temperature and with
it the position of the "rhombic section". The latter is, however, established by
the formation temperature of twinning and cannot then be further changed.
Penetration twins frequently occur in quartz in which the twin axis coincides with

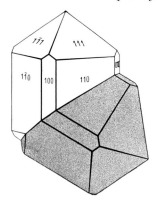

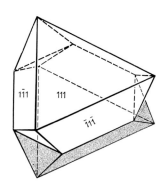

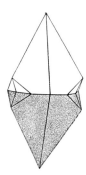

Fig. 191. Cassiterite twin
("elbow twin")

Fig. 192. Spinel twin after (111).
(After Raaz-Tertsch)

Fig. 193. Calcite
twin after (0001)

[00.1] (Dauphinée law, Fig. 189). These twins have, with ideal development, the
morphological symmetry 622, the symmetry ascribed to high quartz (see p. 37).
In agreement therewith is the fact that, as shown in Fig. 189, the right trapezohedral faces are repeated every 60° (not every 120°, as in low quartz).

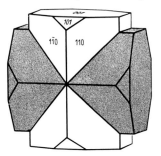

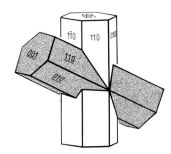

Fig. 194. Staurolite twin after (032).
(After Raaz-Tertsch)

Fig. 195. Staurolite twin after (232).
(After Raaz-Tertsch)

The origin of twinning results essentially from two mechanisms. In the case
of *growth twinning* it may be assumed likely that some particles (ions, atoms, or
molecules) of the initial lattice structure do not continue the normal mode of
growth, but go on to build a related structure, so that at the transition point an
atomic arrangement occurs, that is energetically not quite the most favorable
for the regular further development of the structure. It corresponds, however,
to the next most favorable energetically and to that structure which is geometrically best. As Fig. 190 shows, the transition layer between the two twins
can often be considered as a change in modification. Gold crystallizes, for example,
in cubic closest packing. The transition zone has the structure of hexagonal
closest packing which upon growth changes to cubic packing again. In 1911

MÜGGE had considered the transition layer between individual twins as a thin plate of a different modification.

From the formation of growth twins it is appropriate to single out the formation of *polysynthetic twins*, in which very small (frequently microscopic) twin laminae occur, repeated over and over. They commonly form by the transformation of a higher symmetry modification into one of lower symmetry, if both modifications are structurally similar, often by cooling a crystal of a high temperature modification.   *134 344*

We have already become acquainted with polysynthetic twinning in the case of microcline (p. 76). The plagioclases also are twinned polysynthetically, as a rule after the albite and pericline laws. The formation of polysynthetic twins by mechanical deformation is dealt with later (p. 101).

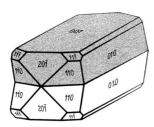

Fig. 196. Orthoclase, Manebach twin.
(After RAAZ-TERTSCH)

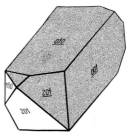

Fig. 197. Orthoclase, Baveno twin.
(After RAAZ-TERTSCH)

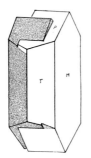

Fig. 198. Orthoclase, Carlsbad twin

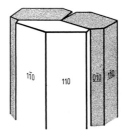

Fig. 199. Aragonite triplet.
(After RAAZ-TERTSCH)

Twins occur frequently in nature. They are especially characteristic of many minerals in addition to the feldspars and quartz already mentioned. For example, cassiterite, SnO_2, whose twinning was used by miners in the Middle Ages for identification, forms the characteristic "elbow" twin shown in Fig. 191. The twin plane is (101). Other examples are the spinel twin, twinned after the octahedron in the class $m3m$ (Fig. 192), and the common twinning in gypsum after (100). In pyrite crossed twinning occurs with a rhombic dodecahedral plane as the twin plane. In the $2/m3$ crystal class of pyrite, no symmetry planes occur parallel to {110}, as is the case on the other hand in the most highly symmetrical cubic classes. Thus, this direction can serve as a twin plane in pyrite. Calcite forms twins after the basal pinacoid (0001) (Fig. 193) and after the rhombohedron (01$\bar{1}$2). Renowned are the cross-shaped twins of the class $2/m\,2/m\,2/m$, exemplified morphologically by staurolite [Fig. 194 after (032) and Fig. 195 after (232)],

which gave rise in the past to legends concerning their origin. As the true
symmetry of staurolite, according to recent work, is monoclinic, although distinctly
pseudo-orthorhombic, the twinning in reality is very complicated. Important
for diagnostic purposes is the twinning of the feldspars. We have mentioned
already the pericline and albite laws for plagioclase (Fig. 188 and 186). In ortho-

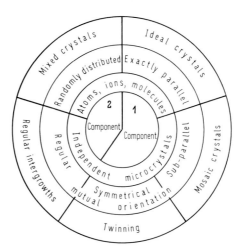

Fig. 200. Schematic representation of the forms of intercalation in crystalline matter

clase, crystallizing according to its macrosymmetry in the class $2/m$, the (010)
plane cannot be a twin plane, since it is a symmetry plane. Here we find the planes
(001) (Manebach law, Fig. 196) and (021) (Baveno law, Fig. 197) as twin planes.
Carlsbad twinning (Fig. 198) can be characterized just as well by the planar law
(100) as the axial law [001]. Not uncommonly, twinning produces an apparent
false symmetry. For example, in Fig. 199 the triplet of orthorhombic aragonite,
twinned after (110), appears almost hexagonal.

Summary. In summarizing these different modes of intercalation of foreign
and like individuals, we can illustrate them in the following schematic diagram
(Fig. 200).

III. Crystal Physics

1. Plastic Deformation

General. Twinning of crystals occurs not only during growth, but can be accomplished also by means of mechanical deformation. Thus we begin to concern ourselves with the field of crystal physics, a borderline area between physics, crystallography, and mineralogy in its most restricted sense. As is true of every interdisciplinary field, the resulting overlap of ideas is desirable and beneficial. The researcher who approaches the subject from pure physics is accustomed to drastic simplification of concepts in order to work out fundamental relationships. The mineralogist, on the other hand, who deals with natural crystals, must always keep in mind the great variability which nature affords. The two approaches complement each other. In this introduction crystal physics will be considered from the viewpoint of the mineralogist. We shall especially consider and keep in the foreground of our interest those matters which are considered important, either for the understanding of processes in the earth's crust, or in aiding us in the understanding of different kinds of crystals.

Mechanical Twinning (simple shear). If a calcite crystal is fixed in the direction [12.0] between the jaws of a vice and carefully compressed, polysynthetic

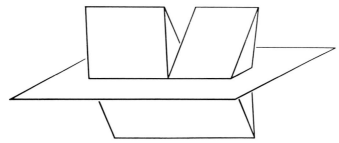

Fig. 201. Pressure twinning in calcite; the reference plane corresponds to (01$\bar{1}$2)

(01$\bar{1}$2) twins are formed. If a cleavage rhomb of calcite is carefully pressed on the [$\bar{1}$2.1] edge with a knife, a portion of the crystal can be easily deformed without breaking (Fig. 201). The angle of the cut does not influence the size of the notch which is produced. The plane along which the gliding takes place is called the *glide plane*; the direction of movement, the *glide direction*. Both are independent of the direction of stress and both are characterized by simple indices. It is characteristic of this form of deformation that the magnitude of the displacement is proportional to the interplanar spacing of the twin plane.

Such deformation is called *simple gliding*. It occurs also in isotropic media under definite types of stress and is, therefore, important in processes of rock metamorphism. Many rocks can be considered as isotropic in a first approximation.

Let us consider a sphere which is deformed through shearing into a triaxial ellipsoid of equal volume[1]. In deformation to the triaxial ellipsoid, one diameter of the sphere coincides with the ellipsoidal axis (c) and becomes shorter, a second becomes longer (a) and a third (b) remains the same length. In Fig. 202 the latter is oriented perpendicular to the plane of the drawing. The other two ellipsoidal axes, a and c, lie in the plane of the drawing. The shearing takes place from left to right. If the volume and the magnitude of b do not change during deformation,

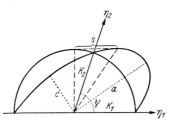

Fig. 202. Simple shear; cross section through a sphere and its deformation ellipsoid; k_1 trace of the glide plane of first circular section; η_1 glide direction; k_2 trace of second circular section; η_2 direction of greatest angular change; S magnitude of the shear

$r^2 = a \cdot c$. In order to describe the shearing process the following nomenclature is used. Each triaxial ellipsoid has two central circular sections. One is the glide plane or the first circular section k_1. The shear plane stands perpendicular to it and parallel to the shear direction η_1, therefore lying in the plane of the drawing. The second circular section, k_2, cuts this plane along the line η_2 which specifies that direction, of all possible directions of deformation, which is most markedly rotated from the initial position, that is around the angle $[180° - 2\,\psi]$; η_1 and η_2 are symmetrical with respect to a, the longest axis of the deformation ellipsoid.

The magnitude of the shear S is given by the distance traversed during deformation by a point at a unit distance from the plane k_1. If ψ is the angle between the two circular sections, $\tan \psi = 2/S$.

In isotropic materials the circular sections assume different positions depending upon the pressure relationships. The amount of deformation (the magnitude of S) varies with the magnitude of the mechanical stress. In the case of crystals, on the other hand, definite glide planes occur in the lattice and deformation takes place only along these planes. In addition, S does not depend on the applied pressure. As soon as the applied stress becomes great enough for the deformation mechanism to be initiated, the same value of S is assumed. Data for k_1, k_2, and S are tabulated for some metals and minerals in Table 15. Figs. 203 and 204 illustrate important differences between the positions of the glide planes in calcite $(01\bar{1}2)$ and in dolomite $(02\bar{2}1)$. The traces of twin lamellae on the surfaces of a cleavage rhomb of calcite (Fig. 203) run parallel to the edges and longer face diagonals; in the case of dolomite (Fig. 204), on the other hand, they are parallel only to the two face diagonals. These differences serve as important criteria in distinguishing calcite and dolomite. The formation of pressure twinning can be considered to be similar to twinning which results during growth. In both cases the lattice is rearranged under external influences. In a transition zone bordering the glide planes a different modification, or really another ordered state, of the lattice is produced.

Translation Gliding. Glide twinning is one means by which plastic deformation of crystals takes place. Another possibility is gliding that takes place in a manner

---

[1] A triaxial ellipsoid is a closed form in which any arbitrarily oriented cross-sectional plane is an ellipse — in two special positions the ellipsoidal sections degenerate to circles. It has the same symmetry as the orthorhombic dipyramidal class (see p. 28). The 2-fold axes coincide with the three major axes. The equation for a triaxial ellipsoid, whose major axes a, b, and c coincide with the usual coordinate axes is $\left(\dfrac{x}{a}\right)^2 + \left(\dfrac{y}{b}\right)^2 + \left(\dfrac{z}{c}\right)^2 = 1$.

Table 15. *Some examples of simple shear*

Crystal	Crystal class	1st circular section, k_1	2nd circular section, k_2	Amount of shear S
α-Iron	$m\,3\,m$ (cubic body centered)	(112)	(11$\bar{2}$)	0.707
Zinc	$6/m\,m\,m$ (hex. closest packing	(10$\bar{1}$2)	(10$\bar{1}$2)	0.143
Arsenic	$\bar{3}\,2/m$	(01$\bar{1}$2)	(0$\bar{1}$11)	0.256
Antimony		(01$\bar{1}$2)	(0$\bar{1}$11)	0.146
Bismuth		(01$\bar{1}$2)	(0$\bar{1}$11)	0.118
Rutile, TiO_2	$4/m\,m\,m$	(101)	($\bar{1}$01)	0.908
		(101)	(301)	0.190
Dolomite, $CaMg(CO_3)_2$	$\bar{3}$	(02$\bar{2}$1)	(0$\bar{1}$11)	0.588
Calcite, $CaCO_3$	$3\,2/m$	(01$\bar{1}$2)	(0$\bar{1}$11)	0.694
Soda niter, $NaNO_3$		(01$\bar{1}$2)	(0$\bar{1}$11)	0.753
Hematite, Fe_2O_3		(0001)	(02$\bar{2}$1)	0.634
		(10$\bar{1}$1)	($\bar{1}$012)	0.205
Aragonite, $CaCO_3$	$m\,m\,m$			0.130
Saltpeter, KNO_3		(110)	(130)	0.041
Carnallite, $MgCl_2 \cdot KCl \cdot 6\,H_2O$				0.048
Anhydrite, $CaSO_4$		(101)	($\bar{1}$01)	0.228

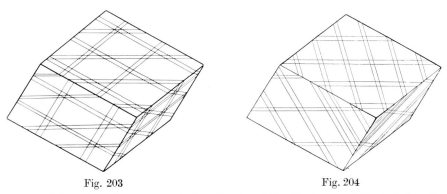

Fig. 203   Fig. 204

Fig. 203. Orientation of pressure twin lamellae in calcite; the traces of the twin lamellae parallel to the rhombohedral edges are not morphologically prominent; they can be observed, however, under the polarizing microscope

Fig. 204. Orientation of pressure twin lamellae in dolomite

similar to the sliding of individual cards in a deck of cards one over the other. This is referred to as mechanical translation, or translation gliding.

Parts of a crystal are displaced with respect to one another along a crystallographically defined plane, the *translation glide plane*. The glide direction is not arbitrary in this plane, but the movement takes place only in certain crystallographically defined directions, the *translation glide direction*. The magnitude of the translation depends not only on the mechanical properties of the crystal, but also on the magnitude of the applied stress. Translation takes place only along unique planes, so that the distance which an arbitrary point traverses in the crystal, unlike twin gliding, is not proportional to the distance between glide planes. With translation gliding twinning does not occur, but instead the two parts of the crystal always remain parallel, and crystal lamellae of varying thickness are mutually displaced. Mechanical deformation by translation gliding is more common than by twin gliding. Deformation by translation gliding can be illustrated with reference to the halite (NaCl) lattice. Fig. 205 shows a view of the NaCl lattice with the dodecahedral plane (110) indicated as the translation glide plane. If one part of the crystal is moved relative to another in the direction of the arrow [110], a Cl⁻ ion will always lie adjacent to a Na⁺ ion. Therefore, positive and negative ions always lie opposite one another and the unity of the lattice is always maintained. On the other hand, if one attempts to deform

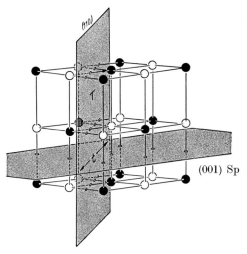

Fig. 205. Translation gliding and cleavage (sp.) in sodium chloride

the crystal perpendicular to the above direction, along translation direction [001], the crystal cleaves, for now, during deformation, likecharged ions are brought into juxtaposition. In NaCl (001) translation planes can occur also when the glide direction coincides with a cubeface diagonal [110]. Octahedral (111) planes can also serve as glide planes. Glide directions are always those which allow Na⁺ ions to "glide" on Cl⁻ ions. The migration of dislocations (see p. 95) through a crystal plays an important role in the actual atomic mechanism of translation gliding.

Sufficiently thin NaCl crystals (2—4 mm thick) can be deformed easily by bending. In this case individual layers glide over one another in a manner analogous to bending a ream of paper. Warming in hot water makes the crystal sufficiently plastic to be deformed in this way. The water dissolves and heals cracks which form, so that fracture does not so easily occur. The easy deformability of NaCl was of considerable importance in the genesis of the north German salt deposits. As a result of relatively slight tectonic pressure, layers of salt were extensively squeezed into folds. Translation gliding plays a very important role also in the deformation of metals. In sheet metal rolling, for example, the individual crystals which form the sheet are deformed by gliding. Glacier ice also flows slowly downhill, because the ice crystals are deformed under the pressure of the overlying ice. The translation glide plane in the hexagonal ice crystal is the (0001). In the case of kyanite, and especially in the case of BaBr₂ · 2H₂O, the glide direction is unidirectional, the translation taking place only in one direction and not in the opposite one. These examples are noted in Table 16, which also gives a summary of translation gliding, in some metals and minerals. It is important to note that in the case of most simple structures, translation glide planes are the most densely populated lattice planes and the glide directions the most densely populated lattice lines in the crystal. These are denoted by d in Table 16. If several glide planes or directions occur, they are designated with decreasing population density as d_1, d_2, etc. In simple ionic structures the lattice rows which correspond to glide directions are usually occupied by like ions, as was indicated above in the case of NaCl. In more complex structures these generalizations break down because lattice rows of different population density can occur parallel to one another.

Table 16. *Examples of translation gliding*

Substance	Crystal class	Translation	
		plane T	direction t
Aluminum Copper Silver Gold	$m3m$ (cubic face centered)	(111)d	[$\bar{1}0\bar{1}$]d
α Iron	$m3m$ (Cubic body centered)	(101)d (112) (123)	[$11\bar{1}$]d
Diamond	$m3m$	(111)d_2[a]	[$10\bar{1}$]d
Magnesium Zinc Cadmium	$6/mmm$ (hex. close packed)	(0001)d	[$11\bar{2}0$]d
Halite, NaCl	$m3m$ (NaCl type)	(001)d_1 (110)d_2 (111)d_3	[$1\bar{1}0$]d
Sylvite, KCl Periclase, MgO Galena, PbS		(110)d_2 (001)d	[110]d
Ice I, H_2O	$6/mmm$[b]	(0001)	
Dolomite, $CaMg(CO_3)_2$	3	(0001)	[$\bar{1}2\bar{1}0$]
Aragonite, $CaCO_3$ Anhydrite, $CaSO_4$	mmm	(010) (001)	[100] [010]
Barite, $BaSO_4$		(001) (011) (102) (010)	[100] and [010] [0$\bar{1}$1] [010] [100]
Stibnite, Sb_2S_3		(010)	[001]
Mica group Gypsum, $CaSO_4 \cdot 2\,H_2O$	$2/m$	(001) (010)	[110] [001]
$KClO_3$; $BaBr_2 \cdot 2\,H_2O$		(001) (100)	[100] unilateral [001] unilateral
Kyanite, $Al_2O(SiO_4)$	$\bar{1}$	(100)	[001] unilateral

[a] Most densely populated lattice plane is (110), but the layer packet of two (111) planes is more densely populated, see Fig. 210.

[b] For statistical distribution of the orientation of H_2O molecules (see p. 80).

Theory of Plastic Deformation. If we investigate the stresses which lead to plastic deformation, say by stretching a metal crystal in a tensile test, and then plot the stress as ordinate against the magnitude of the elongation as abscissa, curves are obtained like those shown in Fig. 206. At low stress the deformation is insignificant until, at some definite stress, very significant plastic deformation sets in (shear stress law). This critical stress is called the *elastic limit* of the crystal. It is, as Fig. 206 shows, strongly dependent on the orientation of the translation glide planes relative to the tension direction. The amount of elongation (strain) is always very much less in ionic crystals than in the case of the cadmium metal crystal illustrated.

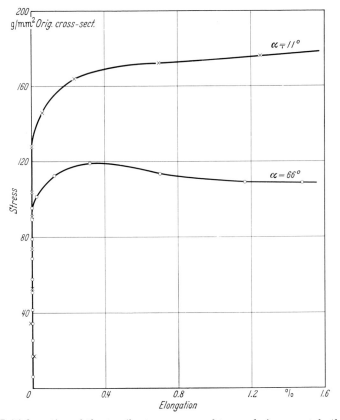

Fig. 206. Initial portion of the tensile stress curves of two cadmium crystals (from SCHMID-BOAS); α is the angle between the translation glide plane and the direction of tension at the start of the test; AQ initial cross section

Experimentally determined values for the elastic limit are always much lower than those calculated from crystal lattice forces. This stems in part from the fact that the theoretical values apply only at absolute zero. At higher temperatures, as R. BECKER and OROWAN have shown, energetically rich sites occur locally in the lattice. As a result the additional tensile stress necessary for deformation is lower than that which is necessary at absolute zero. This is reminiscent of the phenomena associated with Schottky-Wagner defects (p. 91) and infers some interrelationship. This explanation is not sufficient, however, for at very low temperatures, too, differences between calculated and observed stresses are still considerable. It must be assumed, that in addition, imperfections influence the deformation process. An imperfect crystal possesses stresses at the boundaries of the mosaic blocks, if we assume the branching structure proposed by BUERGER. It can be demonstrated, following the suggestion of TAYLOR, that by imposing an external tensile stress upon such local stresses, jumps of individual atoms over their potential barriers are induced. Dislocations are propagated from atom to atom in the lattice by a sort of chain reaction. A relatively small impulse is necessary, of the order of 0.01 to 0.001 that of the stress calculated from lattice forces. Then the dislocation migrates through the crystal until the process comes to a standstill at a barrier (foreign atom, inclusion, other imperfection, mosaic block boundaries).

Imperfections, in particular dislocations, are also very important in explaining the phenomenon of *hardening* which plays a particularly important role in metal working. At the beginning of deformation the tensile stress is smaller than required by theory, but it increases during the course of deformation. The crystal becomes hardened. During plastic deformation the imperfections are mobilized and influence one another with commensurate increase in strength. If appropriate energy is supplied by heating, the strength decreases again since the initial state is partially restored. Deformation at low temperature is called cold working, at higher temperatures, hot working. In our later discussion of rock metamorphism (p. 319) we shall encounter similar processes involving rocks.

2. Strength Properties

Cleavage. Having dealt with the plastic behavior of crystals, we now want to examine those processes which are related to cohesion of a crystal, and during which its breaking point is exceeded. Determination of compressive, tensile, and bending strengths is technologically of considerable importance. In crystals these strength properties are directionally dependent. In many crystals the loss of cohesion takes place by fracturing along definite, well-defined planes, that is, along *cleavage planes*. Cleavage planes in crystals always correspond to those with small rational indices. Cleavability is governed by symmetry. If a cubic crystal cleaves along (100), it cleaves just as well along (010) and (001).

The cleavability of mica is fairly well known to all of us. In fact the technical use of mica depends on the fact that very thin cleavage flakes can be pro-

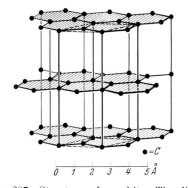

Fig. 207. Structure of graphite. The distance between two adjacent C-atoms within a layer is 1.42 Å; the distance between layers is 3.40 Å

duced from it. We can easily rationalize the perfect cleavage of mica on structural grounds, if we recall that mica has a layer-type lattice. In the case of a layer structure the coherence within layers is strong, for example, as a result of covalent bonding; between the layers it is weak, resulting from intramolecular bonding. It is easy to conclude that the excellent cleavage should take place between mica units. Graphite, $\overset{2}{\infty} C^{[3]}h$ (Fig. 207) also has such a layer-type lattice. The technical utilization of graphite is also dependent upon its excellent cleavage. We are

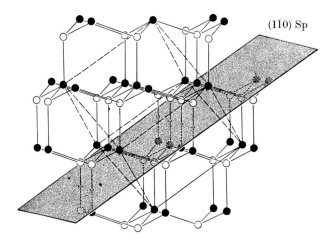

Fig. 208. Structure of sphalerite showing cleavage plane (sp.)

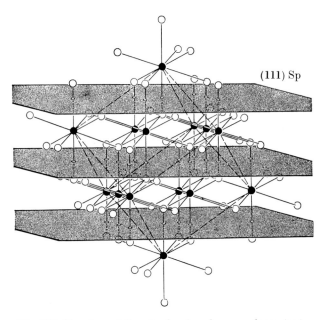

Fig. 209. Structure of fluorite showing cleavage planes (sp.)

able to write with a pencil on paper, because the graphite aggregate is easily abraded into individual structural layers, which are left behind on the rough surface of the paper. The use of talc as "powder" is related to the adsorption of moisture on the very large surface area which results from the fine sub-division of talc crystallites into tiny sheet-like cleavage particles.

With ionic crystals like NaCl, cleavability can be rationalized as was done by J. STARK, and as we have already done in discussing the phenomenon of translation gliding (Fig. 205). It can be noted that, during deformation, posi-

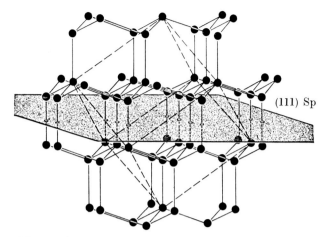

Fig. 210. Structure of diamond showing cleavage plane (sp.)

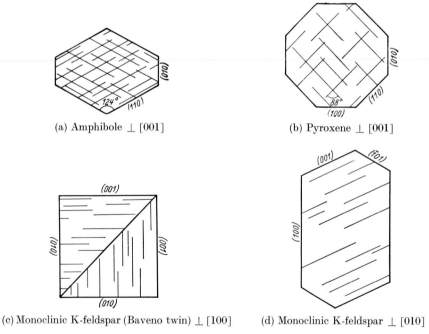

(a) Amphibole ⊥ [001]   (b) Pyroxene ⊥ [001]

(c) Monoclinic K-feldspar (Baveno twin) ⊥ [100]   (d) Monoclinic K-feldspar ⊥ [010]

Fig. 211a—d. Cleavage traces in crystal cross sections

tively charged ions along the cleavage planes are continually brought into juxta-position with other positively charged ions. In this way the coherence, which is essentially due to electrostatic attraction, is destroyed. Whether the cleavage mechanism is actually as depicted by this model, is by no means certain. It is generally true, however, that almost without exception, ionic crystals cleave so that the cleavage fragments formed are electrically neutral. This can be illustrated easily, for example, in the case of NaCl with its {100} cleavage, or for sphalerite, which cleaves perfectly along {110} (Fig. 208). To explain the perfect octahedral {111} cleavage of fluorite we refer to (Fig. 209). Here the atomic arrangement of CaF_2 is illustrated, but in this case the diagram differs from Figs. 151 and 179 in that the cube diagonal is oriented vertically. It can be clearly seen that, parallel to the octahedral planes, series of layers F-Ca-F, F-Ca-F etc. are repeated. Atomic planes containing only negatively charged fluorine ions are continuous. Between two such fluorine planes bonding is very weak. It is apparent, however, that the prerequisite of electrical neutrality of cleavage planes does not provide a complete solution to the problem of cleavage in ionic crystals. It can be noted that in NaCl, separation along {110} also produces electrically neutral parts, yet NaCl does not possess dodecahedral cleavage. There are similar discrepancies when considering dodecahedral cleavage in fluorite. In diamond the cleavage does not take place along {110}, as in sphalerite, but along {111} instead. In this purely covalent lattice the minimum bonding forces are decisive (Fig. 210). The cleavage planes are those planes which involve the smallest number of bonds per unit area.

Cleavage is an important diagnostic aid in the identification of minerals, proving useful also in microscopic investigations. In Fig. 211a—d crystal sections showing cleavage traces are illustrated for a few important crystals. In many crystals cleavage is poorly developed. This is the case, for example, with quartz. If one crushes a quartz crystal with a hammer, it is broken generally into small pieces with conchoidal fracture. This is the manner in which glass is fractured. Careful statistical studies by v. ENGELHARDT have shown in this case that definite preferred fracture directions develop as would be expected for a crystalline material. In the case of quartz these directions vary with temperature. At room temperature the fracture surfaces lie in part close to the rhombohedron r, inclined 45—65° to the c-axis, and in part steeper faces are formed at 70—75° inclination to the c-axis (see p. 32).

Compression-, Tensile-, and Bending-Strength. Compression-, tensile-, and bending-strengths are likewise directionally dependent, as Table 17 shows. For

Table 17. *Strength properties of quartz.* (After BERNDT and NIGGLI)

	$\| c$		$\perp c$	
	average kg/cm²	maximum kg/cm²	average kg/cm²	maximum kg/cm²
Compression strength	25,000	28,000	22,800	27,400
Tensile strength	1,160	1,210	850	930
Bending strength	1,400	1,790	920	1,180

simple structures like NaCl, the tensile strength can be calculated from the lattice energy (p. 166). The theoretical values lie around 20,000 kg/cm², far above the observed values, which vary between 20—200 kg/cm². These results have led to lively discussion during the last 30 years. It is certain that imperfections in the crystal cause the low strength values. The question as to whether they are due to mechanical damage, grooves or real small-scale imperfections is still not resolved, although in many cases probably all are involved. By dissolving away the external surface of a crystal during or just before the tensile test, the strength, based on the cross-sectional area, is increased. Very thin specimens give experimentally the theoretical strength, as Fig. 212 shows.

Hardness. Our previous discussion of strength properties was concerned with properties that have been clearly and quantitatively defined. The study of crystal hardness has been much more qualitative, in spite of its technological importance. The metallograph measures hardness by making an imprint of a rounded or pyramidal stylus on a plane surface, providing what is essentially a measure of plastic deformation (e.g. indentation hardness with Knoop indenter).

Mineralogists, on the other hand, have utilized a *hardness scale* established by Mohs in 1812. This is so conceived that a mineral with a certain hardness will scratch one of lesser hardness. This hardness scale (Table 18) is quite useful in the identification of minerals. Since gem stones are for the most part characterized by high hardness values, this property can be useful for their identification. Thus most true gems can be easily distinguished from glass imitations if they can be scratched by quartz, which is of inferior hardness to most gem minerals.

Scratching is accomplished by penetration of the point of a crystal or crystal aggregate into the face of another crystal. In this way easily deformed material will be plastically deformed, while brittle materials are broken or fractured.

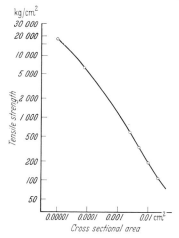

Fig. 212. Tensile strength of NaCl crystals whose outer surfaces are etched away, in relation to the cross sectional area. (After Stranski)

Deformation and fracture can also occur consecutively. For a given mineral the *scratch hardness* is different on different crystal faces, and is also dependent on direction on a single face. For brittle crystals the influence of cleavage is often clearly recognizable here. This is apparent in the data reproduced in Fig. 213 a—c. The scratch hardness can be measured with very simple apparatus (Seebeck, 1833). The crystal is mounted on a small carriage so that the face under investigation is oriented horizontally. A weighted stylus is placed in contact with the crystal face. The carriage with the mounted crystal is pulled away from under the stylus by means of a pulley with appropriate weights attached. The counter

Table 18. *Scratch, indentation and abrasion hardness*

Mineral	Scratch hardness, after Mohs	Knoop indentation hardness (U.S. Bur. of Standards)	Abrasion hardness, after Rosiwal
Talc	scratched by fingernail scratched by knife	—	0.003
Halite	scratched by fingernail scratched by knife	32	1.25
Calcite	scratched by knife	135	4.5
Fluorite	scratched by knife	163	5
Apatite		360—430	6.5
Orthoclase	scratches window glass	560	37
Quartz	scratches window glass	$\perp c$ 710, $\parallel c$ 790	120
Topaz	scratches window glass	1,250	175
Corundum	scratches window glass	nat. 1,400—1,450 syn. 1,650—2,000	1,000
Diamond	scratches window glass	6,200—6,500	9,000

weight just necessary to cause the stylus to scratch is taken as the hardness value. Such relative hardness values are indicated in Fig. 213a—c, as plotted on different crystal faces. The dependence of scratch hardness on cleavability infers that a correlation exists between hardness and structure. Generally one might predict

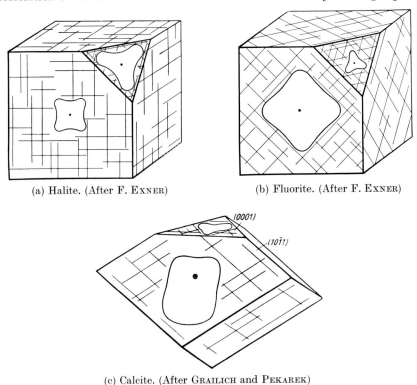

(a) Halite. (After F. Exner)   (b) Fluorite. (After F. Exner)

(c) Calcite. (After Grailich and Pekarek)

Fig. 213a—c. Dependence of scratch hardness on cleavage direction

such interdependence and expect that hardness would be greater, the closer the atoms are to each other, and the higher their charge. Experience confirms this assumption, as V. M. Goldschmidt was able to show. We shall call attention first to the relation between hardness and interionic distance for the alkali halides crystallizing with the NaCl structure (Table 19).

Table 19. *Dependence of scratch hardness on cation-anion separation*

	LiF	NaF	LiCl	LiBr	NaCl	NaBr	KCl	KI
Interionic distance (Å)	2.02	2.31	2.57	2.75	2.81	2.98	3.14	3.53
Scratch hardness	3.3	3.2	3.0	2.5	2.5	2.4	2.3	2.2

We can see here clearly, that in cases of equal valence and structure, the hardness decreases with increasing interatomic distance of the constituent atoms. If we vary the valence, maintaining the same structural type and like interatomic distances, the hardness increases with increasing charge (Table 20). Finally we can observe the effect on hardness of different structures with constant interatomic separation and equal valence (Table 21). Comparing pairs of such compounds it is noted that the substance with the sphalerite or wurtzite-type structure is always less hard than the corresponding NaCl-type.

The scratch hardness of a mineral is always temperature dependent as would be expected. The data in Tables 19—21 were obtained at room temperature. Ice near its melting point has a scratch hardness of $1\frac{1}{2}$—2; glacial ice from Greenland, measured at $-44°C$, has a hardness of 4; at the temperature of solid carbon dioxide ($-78.5°C$) the hardness is 6.

Table 20. *Dependence of scratch hardness on valence (sphalerite structure, equal interatomic distances)*

	CuCl	ZnS	GaP	Si-Si	CuI	ZnTe	GaSb
Valence	1	2	3	4	1	2	3
Interatomic distance (Å)	2.34	2.35	2.35	2.35	2.62	2.64	2.64
Hardness	2.5	4	5	7	2.4	3	4.5

Table 21. *Dependence of scratch hardness on structure (interatomic distances and valence constant)*

Structure type	Halite	Sphalerite	Wurtzite	Valence
Substance	NaF	CuCl		
Interatomic distance (Å)	2.31	2.34		1
Hardness	3.2	2.5		
Substance	NaCl		AgI	
Interatomic distance (Å)	2.81		2.81	1
Hardness	2.5		1.5	
Substance	CaO	BeTe		
Interatomic distance (Å)	2.4	2.43		2
Hardness	4.5	3.8		
Substance	BaO		CdTe	
Interatomic distance (Å)	2.77		2.80	2
Hardness	3.3		2.8	

Abrasion Strength. A third form of hardness is abrasion hardness. This should more properly be called abrasion strength (v. ENGELHARDT). If different minerals are abraded under completely identical conditions, different weight losses are obtained, depending on hardness. Relative abrasion hardness values are given in Table 18 for minerals of the hardness scale, along with the comparable scratch hardness values. Abrasion strength is a quantitative measure of complex processes. The emery or silicon carbide grains which are customarily used for abrasion material cause plastic deformation, but in addition they penetrate the surface of the crystal and tear out small fragments. Therefore, since work is carried on in opposition to the surface tension, abrasion strength is also dependent upon the abrasion fluid. Thus the abrasion hardness of quartz in octyl alcohol is only half as great as in water. Abrasion hardness can, therefore, be used to measure the relative surface energies of a crystal.

Percussion and Pressure Figures. A phenomenon based on plastic deformation, but during which the strength modulus of a crystal is exceeded, is the formation of percussion figures. If a needle is driven with a sharp blow into a cube face of NaCl, the crystal splits along the face diagonals and forms in addition striations parallel to the cube edges (Fig. 214). The cracks as well as the striations stem from translation gliding along dodecahedral planes.

Even more complex are similar relationships exhibited by mica. If one presses, with a well rounded glass probe of about 3 mm diameter, on a mica flake underlaid by a pliable base, a flexure figure (Fig. 215a) is first formed. This is a triple-rayed star within an approximately triangular border; the figure usually is indicative of the monoclinic symmetry of the mica. If one presses harder, a pressure figure (Fig. 215b) is formed. This is a six-rayed star, but is not always clearly developed. The borders of the flexure figure correspond approximately to

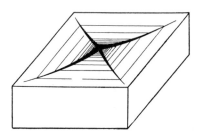

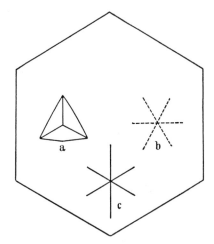

Fig. 214. Percussion figure for halite

Fig. 215. (a) Flexure figure; (b) pressure figure; (c) percussion figure of micas

the directions of the rays in the pressure figure and are presumably associated with translation gliding. The cracks of the flexure figure correspond to those of the percussion figure and are probably fault cracks. While flexure and pressure figures can only be produced with large mica flakes, percussion figures can be obtained from mica crystals of only a few millimeters diameter. The percussion figure, shown in Fig. 215c, illustrates a six-rayed star, revealing the pseudo-hexagonal structure of mica. The cracks run parallel to the edges which the cleavage plane {001} makes with the prism {110} and the pinacoid {010}. The crack developed parallel to {010} is usually somewhat longer and is called the guide-ray. It runs parallel to the crystallographic a axis and thus serves to establish crystallographic orientation of mica crystals, when no crystal faces are present other than the cleavage face, as is usually the case.

3. Elastic Behavior

Free Thermal Dilatation. We shall discuss further some of those physical phenomena in crystals which result in change in shape. In this case, however, the shape is not permanently changed as in plastic deformation, but instead the crystal recovers its original shape as soon as the distorting force is removed. A simple example of this is free thermal dilatation, which is observed when a crystal is uniformly heated or cooled. Although a spherical-shaped amorphous body expands upon heating, its spherical shape is maintained. The expansion of a crystal however, is directionally dependent (anisotropic), and generally a triaxial ellipsoid is formed from a sphere. The symmetry of the space lattice is maintained. Point rows remain point rows, and if they were originally parallel they remain so. Only the distances between lattice points and the angles between lattice rows are changed (Fig. 216). Geometrically this form of deformation is called *homogeneous deformation*.

Upon homogeneous deformation of a triclinic crystal, no relationship is found between the orientation of the dilatation ellipsoid and the original crystallographic axes. In the case of monoclinic crystals, as a result of the preservation of symmetry, one of the three axes of the ellipsoid must coincide with the two-fold axis of the crystal or with the normal to its plane of symmetry. Following conventional notation for monoclinic crystals, this axis is the b axis (see p. 14 and 22).

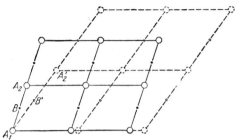

Fig. 216. Homogeneous deformation of a planar lattice

However, it is not possible to predict which of the ellipsoid axes this will be, nor how the other two axes are oriented within the ac-plane. In the orthorhombic system the three ellipsoid axes coincide with the three crystallographic axes, giving rise to six possible orientations of the dilatation ellipsoid. In trigonal, tetragonal and hexagonal crystals (see p. 14 and 29), again in compliance with symmetry, two or three major axes of the ellipsoid must be of equal length. Thus the triaxial ellipsoid is actually a rotation ellipsoid, produced by the rotation of an ellipse around one of its major axes. Finally, in the cubic system the symmetry is so high that the triaxial ellipsoid degenerates to a sphere. During homogeneous deformation, a cubic crystal behaves like an isotropic body.

In Table 22 and 23 some numerical values are given, representative of crystal dilatation during heating. λ_1, λ_2, and λ_3 are the coefficients of expansion measured

Table 22. *Linear expansion coefficients (λ) and temperature coefficients (α)*

Orthorhombic crystals	$\lambda_1 \cdot 10^6$	$\alpha_1 \cdot 10^8$	$\lambda_2 \cdot 10^6$	$\alpha_2 \cdot 10^8$	$\lambda_3 \cdot 10^6$	$\alpha_3 \cdot 10^8$
Aragonite	9.90	0.64	15.72	3.68	33.25	3.36
Topaz	4.23	1.42	3.47	1.68	5.19	1.82

Hex. and tetrag. crystals	$\lambda_1 \cdot 10^6$	$\alpha_1 \cdot 10^8$	$\lambda_2 \cdot 10^6$	$\alpha_2 \cdot 10^8$	Cubic crystals	$\lambda \cdot 10^6$	$\alpha \cdot 10^8$
Quartz	6.99	2.04	13.24	2.38	Diamond	0.6	1.44
Calcite	25.57	1.60	−5.7	0.83	Halite	38.59	4.48
Beryl	−1.52	1.14	0.84	1.32	Sylvite	35.97	5.14
Brucite, $Mg(OH)_2$	44.7		11.0		Fluorite	17.96	3.82
$Ca(OH)_2$	33.4		9.8		Copper	16.17	1.82
AgI	−2.26	−4.26	−0.10	1.38			
Sb	17.3	1.34	8.3	−0.94			
Bi	15.37	3.1	10.48	2.08			
Mg	27		24				

in the direction of the ellipsoidal axes. They indicate the relative increases in elongation for a temperature increase of 1°C. A NaCl sphere of 1 cm radius expands $38.59 \cdot 10^{-6}$ cm or $0.386\ \mu$ with a 1° temperature increase. In the tetragonal and hexagonal systems λ_1 is measured parallel to the 3-, 4-, or 6-fold axis and λ_2 perpendicular to it. Since the coefficients of expansion change with temperature, temperature coefficients, α_1, α_2, and α_3, must be given also. If λ_1^0 is the expansion coefficient at 0°C, then at t, $\lambda_1^t = \lambda_1^0 + \alpha_1 \cdot t$. As indicated in the table by means of minus signs, certain crystals contract upon heating, either in all directions or along one major direction. Values not designated as negative indicate expansion. The thermal expansion of a crystal is related to its structure.

Table 23. *Some additional data for the expansion coefficients of low symmetry minerals*

		$\lambda \cdot 10^6$
Anorthite	$\perp$ (001)	6.0
	$\perp$ (010)	1.6
Mica (Phlogopite)	$\perp$ (001)	14.9
Diopside	$\perp$ (100)	6.6
	$\perp$ (010)	15.5

Layer structures have smaller coefficients of expansion within the layers and larger values perpendicular to them [$Ca(OH)_2$, $Mg(OH)_2$]. Close packed structures, such as Mg, or approximately close-packed structures, like topaz, show little directional dependence. Calcite has a greater expansion along the c-axis than perpendicular to it. A more detailed discussion of structural control is still not possible. Thermal expansion differs, depending upon the type of crystal and direction within individual grains in a rock, and is important in considering mechanical weathering of rocks (p. 243).

If a crystal is heated on a goniometer, it is observed that the interfacial angles change. From such angular measurements it is possible to calculate the axial ratios of the deformation ellipsoid. This was first pointed out by E. MITSCHERLICH in 1823. In addition to *linear coefficients of expansion*, one uses also the "cubic", or better the volumetric coefficient, the increase, α, of the volume V_0 to volume V_1, upon heating to 1°C.

$$V_1 = V_0(1 + \alpha).$$

Uniform (hydrostatic) Compression. It is possible to compress a crystal by applying uniform pressure, just as it is possible to induce crystal expansion and contraction by means of uniform heating or cooling. The same relationships apply here as with free thermal dilatation. A spherical cubic crystal remains a sphere. In the tetragonal and hexagonal systems a rotation ellipsoid is formed, and in the remaining systems a triaxial ellipsoid. These ellipsoids differ from those for thermal dilatation for all crystal classes in their dimensions; for monoclinic and triclinic crystals also as to the orientation of the axes. Only in cubic crystals can the thermal expansion be compensated completely by uniform pressure. The measurement of compressibility is also expressed analogous to thermal expansion through coefficients. If we designate V_p as the volume of a crystal under pressure P and V_{p+1} as the volume under the pressure $P+1$, we obtain the equation for the volume decrease per unit of pressure and the volumetric compressibility coefficient k:

$$V_{p+1} = V_p(1 - k); \qquad k = \frac{V_p - V_{p+1}}{V_p}.$$

Table 24. *Some examples of volumetric compressibility coefficients;* $k \cdot 10^6 (0-30°C)$

Li	8.6	Graphite	< 3.0	Feldspars	1.1—1.8
Na	14.2	Quartz	2.62	Calcite	1.36
K	23.2	Garnet	0.59	Aragonite	1.50
Rb	32.8	Olivine (fayalite)	0.87	Pyrite	0.70
Cs	36.4	Augite	~ 1.0	Marcasite	0.79
Au	0.577	Hornblendes	~ 1.3	Sphalerite	1.26
Cu	0.719	Mica	2.2	Wurtzite	1.31
Diamond	0.16				

Table 24 gives a summary of some values for k. Here it is apparent that compressibility correlates directly in the case of the alkali metals with their atomic volumes. Among the silicates, the nesosilicates have the lowest values, whereas framework and layer silicates, such as micas, give higher values. In the case of polymorphic substances one would expect the least dense modification to be the most compressible; in the case of calcite ($d = 2.71$) and aragonite ($d = 2.95$ g/cm³), the situation is reversed.

The correlation between ionic radius, structural type, and compressibility is especially noteworthy for the alkali halides listed in Table 25. Those salts with the NaCl structure illustrate the correlation with ionic radius. The values for CsCl, CsBr, and CsI are not directly comparable to the other values in the table, since these three halides crystallize with the CsCl, rather than the NaCl structure.

The dependence on structural type is shown especially well by considering *linear compressibility*. Although only a few data are available for minerals, such data are included in Table 26 along with some values for metals and other compounds. As was the case for thermal

Table 25. *Volumetric compressibility coefficients* $k \cdot 10^6$ *of the alkali halides at 30° C*

	F	Cl	Br	I
Li	1.50	3.34	4.23	5.89
Na	2.07	4.182	4.98	6.936
K	3.25	5.53	6.56	8.37
Rb		6.52	7.78	9.39
Cs	4.155	5.829	6.918	8.403

expansion, the reference surface for tetragonal and hexagonal crystals is a rotation ellipsoid; for triclinic, monoclinic, and orthorhombic crystals, a triaxial ellipsoid.

The linear compressibility coefficients are either measured directly or calculated from elastic constants. In Table 26 the values given have meanings analogous to those used for expressing thermal expansion. Therefore, if p is the value for pressure,

$$k = k_0 + \alpha \cdot p.$$

k_1 represents, as before, values parallel to the major axes, k_2 perpendicular to it.

Table 26. *Linear compressibility coefficients for some tetrag. and hex. crystals (mostly at 0—12,000 kg/cm²)*

	$k_1 \cdot 10^6$	$\alpha_1 \cdot 10^{12}$	$k_2 \cdot 10^6$	$\alpha_2 \cdot 10^{12}$
Be	0.220	$- 0.70$	0.282	$- 1.67$
Mg	0.9842	$- 6.51$	0.9845	$- 9.19$
Zn	0.35	$- 7.68$	0.157	$- 0.75$
Sb	1.648	$- 20.5$	0.5256	$- 4.56$
Bi	1.592	$- 11.1$	0.6620	$- 4.30$
NaNO₃	2.436	$- 23.5$	0.709	$- 5.88$
Calcite, CaCO₃	0.882		0.273	
Quartz, SiO₂	0.718		0.995	
Rutile, TiO₂	0.105		0.190	

Be and Mg, with hexagonal-close packing, show essentially no anisotropy; in the case of Zn, with $c:a = 1.86$ and representing a transition between a normal and layered structure, the anisotropism is clear, and with Bi and Sb, which have definite layer structures, very pronounced. $NaNO_3$ is much more compressible perpendicular to the plane of the NO_3 groups than in the direction parallel to it, in accordance with its structure.

Pyroelectricity. Upon homogeneous deformation the phenomenon of pyro-electricity (pyr, Greek, fire) is encountered in crystals with a polar major axis. When such a crystal is heated or cooled, alternate ends of this axis become oppositely charged. We have already mentioned tourmaline (see p. 33) as a typical example. This phenomenon was recognized long ago by LINNÉ (1747) and AEPINUS (1756). To demonstrate this property, one usually utilizes the fact that oppositely charged ends of the crystal attract small, charged particles. If a cooling crystal is dusted with a mixture of sulfur and red lead, which in turn has been charged by passing it through a fine cotton sieve, the yellow sulfur becomes negative from the friction, the red lead powder positive, and each is attracted by electrostatic attraction to the appropriate end of the crystal. It is also possible to measure the potential developed between the two ends of the crystal by means of sensitive measuring instruments. This effect is confined to the classes $1, 2, m, mm2, 4, 4mm, 3, 3m, 6$, and $6mm$. Detection of pyroelectricity can be used to establish the appropriate crystal class in the case of crystals which have imperfect morphological form development. It is necessary, however, to be very cautious about such conclusions.

Piezoelectricity. If a crystal is not uniformly heated, stresses occur which can cause the development of electrical charges. One can accomplish this also by applying pressure along a polar direction. This direction need not coincide with a polar axis of symmetry. This phenomenon is called piezoelectricity (piezein, Greek, to press). It was discovered in 1880 by the brothers J. and P. CURIE. M. G. LIPPMANN concluded the following year that the opposite effect of alternating contraction or expansion of a crystal must be effected by applying alternating electrical potentials. For many crystals this property has attained great technological importance. It is not confined to the classes that exhibit pyro-electricity, but can occur in all those classes in which polar directions are possible, that is those without a center of symmetry. Only the class 432 has such high symmetry that in spite of the absence of a center of symmetry, no piezoelectric phenomenon can occur. This was pointed out by W. VOIGT long ago. To the pyroelectric classes can be added also the classes $222, \bar{4}, \bar{4}2m, 422, 32, 622, \bar{6}, \bar{6}m2, 23$ and $\bar{4}3m$.

Quartz is technologically the most important naturally occurring piezoelectric crystal. It exhibits this effect in the direction of its polar 2-fold axis. Since its atomic arrangement is also polar in this direction, it can be demonstrated that compression causes a predominantly positive charge to develop on one side, and a negative charge on the other. As a result of left-right twinning the effect is cancelled. Oscillator quartz is used for the control of radio transmission, as a time and pressure measurer, and for the generation and reception of sound waves of exceptionally high frequency (ultrasonic waves). It should be recalled that a true pyroelectric effect cannot occur in the crystal class of quartz. Piezoelectric investigations are of general importance in determining whether a crystal has a center of symmetry.

Theory of Unilateral Stress. The theory of unilateral stress is considerably more complex than that of uniform deformation. We can take as an example a crystal rod which is stretched. The elastic elongation is proportional to the stress, for example, an attached weight (Hook's law).

$$\frac{\Delta l}{l} = \alpha S .$$

Here Δl is the elongation and l the total length of the crystal rod, S the tensile stress (force per unit area). α is a proportionally constant, termed the extension modulus. Its reciprocal, $1/\alpha = E$, is the elastic modulus. In a crystal the elastic modulus is likewise dependent upon direction. In order to describe the elastic properties of a crystal, six equations are necessary which, in the general case of the triclinic crystal, contain 21 constants. The higher the symmetry, the simpler the equations. Even so, in the cubic system three constants are necessary for complete characterization.

4. Crystal Optics of Visible Light

Introduction. For the mineralogist the most important area of crystal physics is optics, involving the wave length range of visible light ("ordinary" light) as well as X-radiation. Those phenomena which involve ordinary light are treated from the point of view of a continuum, for in this way they are much more simply described. We may use the notion of a continuum, because the wave lengths of ordinary light are very large compared to the lattice distances in crystals. For example, the wave length of red light is $6{,}400 - 7{,}500 \cdot 10^{-8}$ cm, whereas the distance between two C atoms in diamond is $1.54 \cdot 10^{-8}$ cm. When considering X-ray optics, the wave lengths are the same order of magnitude as the lattice spacings. For example the wave length of Cu K_α radiation is $1.54 \cdot 10^{-8}$ cm. Thus in this case matter must be considered as a discontinuum. Both optical concepts are indispensible tools to the mineralogist. Anyone who, like the chemist, wants to study laboratory prepared crystals or, like the geologist and soil scientist, wants to identify minerals accurately or, like the petrologist, to study the structure of rocks, must master the fundamentals of both optical concepts. In addition these concepts are used in other sciences, especially metallurgy and structural study areas. These concepts have been advanced through this work.

a) Optically Isotropic Substances

Refraction. We shall begin with ordinary light and consider refraction first. In *optically isotropic*, weakly adsorbing media, such as gases, liquids, glasses, and cubic crystals, like NaCl, sphalerite, and diamond, Snell's law of refraction is applicable. According to this, the ratio of the propagation velocity of light in a medium A to its velocity in a denser medium B which it encounters after crossing an interface, is equal to the ratio of the sines of the angle of incidence (α) at the interface and the angle of refraction (β) in B.

$$\frac{\text{Light velocity in } A}{\text{Light velocity in } B} = \frac{\sin \alpha}{\sin \beta} .$$

The reciprocals of the light velocities, referred to the velocity of light in a vacuum, are called the *refractive indices*, n_A and n_B. Therefore,

$$\frac{\sin \alpha}{\sin \beta} = \frac{n_B}{n_A} .$$

In the following discussion and diagrams, the light beam used in experiment will always be represented by a single ray. Refraction studies are normally investigated with reference to air and, since n_A is close to unity, ($n_{air} = 1.0003$) $\sin \alpha / \sin \beta$ gives the refractive index of the substance B.

Total Reflection. If we consider a case in which the light passes from the medium B, with the higher refractive index, into A, and gradually increase the angle β, a value of β is sooner or later reached, depending on the magnitude of n_B, at which no more light passes into A. This value of β is called the limiting angle of *total reflection*. Diamond owes a considerable part of its brilliance to the phenomenon of total reflection. An appropriately cut diamond (brilliant cut), because of its high index (2.4), totally reflects a great deal of light from the underside of the crystal (Fig. 217). Accordingly the under surfaces of the diamond appear mirrored, as if silvered.

Reflection. In addition to the light reflected internally by a diamond, additional light is reflected from the surface. Together these produce the "brilliance" of the skillfully cut diamond. That portion of the light reflected from the surface is that which is only weakly absorbed in the case of colorless or weakly colored substances. The greater the index of refraction of the reflecting substance, the greater the reflectivity. Some data are given in Table 27. For perpendicular incidence and weak adsorption the formula

$$R = \frac{(n-1)^2}{(n+1)^2}$$

applies. R is the relecting power and represents that percentage of the incident beam which is reflected. For oblique incidence a more complex formula applies.

Luster. Luster is an important diagnostic property for mineral identification. It depends, in the case of perfectly planar surfaces, on the reflecting power of the crystal. With minerals one distinguishes between those with *adamantine luster* (therefore, high index of refraction) and *vitreous luster*. Minerals which strongly adsorb visible light reflect it much more strongly than diamond. They are said to have *metallic luster*. An example is silver, which reflects 95 % of the light at perpendicular incidence. The luster also depends on the detailed surface structure, in addition to the index of refraction, and on the adsorption power, giving rise to variations in luster described as waxy, pearly, silky, etc.

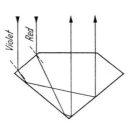

Fig. 217. Refraction of light in diamond (brilliant cut)

Streak. In addition to luster the "streak" of minerals is used for identification. A fine mineral powder is produced by rubbing the specimen on an un-glazed porcelain plate. Colorless minerals give a white streak, resulting from complete scattering of light. Colored minerals, especially those with metallic luster, frequently give colored streaks, because tiny particles distributed in thin layers on a white surface, still transmit light differentially for those wave lengths which are not too strongly adsorbed.

Dispersion. Returning again to diamond, we notice that it has an additional property which makes it especially popular as a gem stone, — its play of colors. This is because the index of refraction of diamond is different for different wave lengths; that is, it exhibits dispersion. The difference between the indices of refraction for wave lengths $\lambda = 0.397$ and $\lambda = 0.760\ \mu$ is 0.0628 for diamond. This is approximately five times the dispersion for water, and three times that for ordinary glass. This dispersion is particularly noticeable if we consider the case in which light emerges from the diamond into air as shown in Fig. 218a. The violet light $(0.397\ \mu)$ emerges, just grazing the surface, whereas the red light $(0.760\ \mu)$ emerges at an angle of 13°. The angle of incidence here is 24°. By re-

Table 27. *Percent light reflected*

Angle of incidence		0°	70°
Diamond	$(n_D = 2.42)$	17	27
Grossularite	$(n_D = 1.75)$	$7^1/_2$	21
Glass	$(n_D = 1.50)$	4	17
Water	$(n_D = 1.33)$	2	13

ducing the angle to 20° (Fig. 218b), the dispersion of the two rays is now only 2° 13'. Play of colors and brilliance together cause the characteristic "fire" of diamond.

Index of Refraction Determination by the Immersion Method. Determination of index of refraction by prism methods and by means of total reflection, as discussed in many physics texts, will not be considered here. Likewise, it will not be possible to go into the different methods of producing monochromatic light. Here we shall consider only that method of index determination which has been adopted for microscope work and which has proven especially convenient and accurate. This is the immersion method.

If a fragment of a transparent, isotropic crystal or glass is immersed in a liquid of the same index of refraction, it cannot be distinguished from the surrounding medium, when using monochromatic light, and if the surfaces of the fragment are very clean. In incandescent (white) light, the indices of refraction

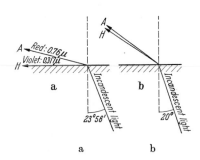

Fig. 218a and b. Dispersion upon emergence of white light from diamond into air. (a) Angle of incidence 24°. (b) Angle of incidence 20°

for all the different wave lengths are never exactly the same. As a result of dispersion the object appears with slightly colored borders. If the indices of refraction of the object and the immersion medium are very different, the grain stands out prominently, that is, it shows *relief*. This is because surface irregularities scatter the light. In addition such a grain (under the microscope) exhibits a bright border of light. If the barrel of the microscope is raised, the bright line appears to migrate into the medium of higher index of refraction. This line is called the *Becke line* after its discoverer. It provides us with a very convenient means of determining whether the grain or the immersion medium has the higher index of refraction. This behavior can be applied also to anisotropic crystals, as will be shown later (p. 130). To explain the Becke line let us observe Fig. 219, which illustrates the refraction relationships for a fluorite cleavage fragment, $n = 1.435$, immersed in water, $n = 1.333$. With perpendicular, as well as obliquely incident light, the light is bent predominantly into the crystal, because of its higher index of refraction. Total reflection occurs in part, but this is by no means a necessary requisite, nor is it necessary that the interface be vertical. A complete explanation of the phenomenon would require consideration of diffraction as well as refraction. Increased illumination on the inner border of the higher-index medium results from the converging rays. As the focal plane of the microscope is raised, it appears as if the Becke line migrates inward in this case; lowering it moves the Becke line outward.

b) Optically Anisotropic Substances

The Discovery of Double Refraction. We have discussed thus far only simple refracting or optically isotropic substances. The majority of crystals behave differently, showing double refraction. This was first observed by ERASMUS BARTHOLINUS, a descendent of a Danish academic family. His publication dates from 1669, the same year in which his countryman STENO published the law of constancy of interfacial angles. The first sentences of his treatise are so characteristic of the genuine delight of a scientist with a new observation, that they shall be quoted from the translation by MIELEITNER:

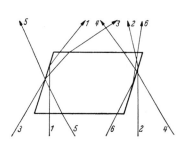

Fig. 219. Refraction conditions of a fluorite fragment in water. *1, 2,* illumination by a parallel beam; *3, 4,* illumination with a convergent beam; *1, 3, 5* illumination of the left and *2, 4, 6* right edges with convergent beam

"Diamonds are reknown to all peoples and manifold are the joys which such treasures as precious gems and pearls bring, but they serve only for pomp and adornment of finger and neck. On the other hand, he who prefers for enjoyment the knowledge of rare phenomena will, I hope, have no less joy in a new form of body, a transparent crystal which was brought to us recently from Iceland, and belongs perhaps to the greatest wonders which nature has created."

He describes then a cleavage rhomb of calcite. If we also examine such a piece, and allow a narrow beam of light to fall on it, we observe that within the crystal the light is broken up into two beams. In 1679 CHRISTIAN HUYGENS gave a plausible explanation for this phenomenon, suggesting that two light waves are transmitted in the crystal. HUYGENS thought in terms of longitudinal waves, and thus could only explain a portion of the observed phenomenon. His wave theory was not accepted because the Newtonian corpuscular theory was in vogue at the time. Complete explanation on the basis of wave theory first came, when, in the year 1808, MALUS looked through a calcite rhomb into an open window of the Luxemburg Palace in Paris. He noted that the two images produced change in brightness as the crystal is rotated. He concluded from this that the light corpuscles were somehow one-sided or polar, and called the phenomenon polarization. This observation of MALUS led the Englishman YOUNG (first in a letter to ARAGO in 1817) to establish a wave theory for light based on transverse waves. Interference phenomena can be shown for longitudinal as well as transverse waves, but only the latter can exhibit polarization perpendicular to the direction of propagation. Polarization means then, that from a whirl of transverse waves vibrating in all directions, those are "sifted" out, which vibrate only in one direction. Thus some crystals exhibit two phenomena which are not characteristic of amorphous bodies, like liquids or glass. These are double refraction and polarization.

Wave Normals. As we observe the refracted light in anisotropic crystals, it becomes apparent that SNELL's law is not completely valid. For one of the refracted rays the expression $\dfrac{\sin \alpha}{\sin \beta} = \dfrac{C_A}{C_B}$, is no longer constant; indeed it is no longer necessary that the refracted rays lie in the plane of incidence. If we turn our attention however, from propagation velocities in the direction of the light rays, to directions of the *wave normals*, we find that SNELL's law is in fact valid. In isotropic bodies ray directions and wave normal directions coincide, but this is not generally the case in crystals. In an anisotropic medium, $\dfrac{\sin \alpha}{\sin \beta} = \dfrac{(C_A)_w}{(C_B)_w}$ applies for wave normal velocities. Since in this case the wave normal transmission velocity in the crystal, $(C_B)_w$, is dependent on direction, $\dfrac{\sin \alpha}{\sin \beta}$ is no longer constant.

In optically isotropic media, refraction relationships can be illustrated, using the representation of Huygenian wave fronts. For anisotropic crystals a more complex surface must be substituted for the spherical wave front. Its form

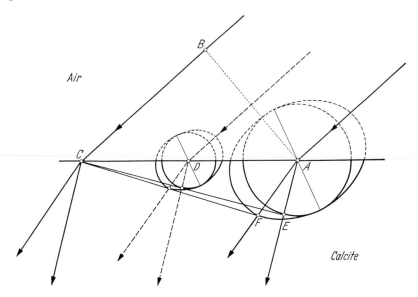

Fig. 220. Refraction of monochromatic light at the air-calcite interface. A wave front of the light incident at the right intersects the calcite interface earlier at A than at C, since the ray at C must travel the additional distance BC. The drawing shows the optical relations at the instant the ray reaches C. By this time at A the light, which has been broken up into two components, has moved along paths defined by the ray velocity surfaces shown. The line connecting the points of intersection of the two surfaces is the $[00.1]$ direction. The dotted extensions of the ray velocity surfaces in calcite have no significance in air. They are shown only to assist in clarifying the shapes of the surfaces. At all points between A and C light rays are scattered to develop ray velocity surfaces. These become smaller and smaller toward C as the time interval becomes shorter. CE and CF represent the wave fronts of the ordinary and extraordinary waves respectively. The directions of propagation of these waves are perpendicular to their corresponding wave fronts. The directions of propagation of the corresponding rays are AE and AF

depends upon the crystal symmetry, as well as other factors. For calcite it consists of a sphere and an oblate rotation ellipsoid (an ellipse rotated around its shorter axis) which coincide at two points. The line connecting these two points coincides with the direction of the three fold axis in calcite. The refraction relationships at the calcite-air interface are illustrated in Fig. 220. These optical surfaces have a rather more complex form in crystals of lower symmetry (orthorhombic, monoclinic, triclinic). Mathematically this surface is represented by a quadratic equation. There are always two wave fronts associated with each ray direction, and vice versa (Figs. 221 and 222). Mastery of the optical processes in crystals is easier, when we note the wave normal directions instead of ray directions.

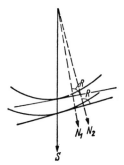

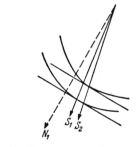

Fig. 221. The two wave normals (N_1 and N_2) corresponding to the ray direction (S)

Fig. 222. The two ray directions (S_1 and S_2) corresponding to the wave normal (N_1)

In this way we can describe all of the phenomena which are important to us. In the following discussion, when we speak of direction of propagation, we shall always be referring to the wave normal velocities and likewise to the refractive indices of the wave normals.

The Indicatrix. The light associated with each of the two waves transmitted in our calcite crystal is not polarized in the same directions. The vibration directions of the two waves are perpendicular to each other and both vibration directions are perpendicular to the wave normal. This is true of all double refracting (anisotropic) crystals. In order to describe the behavior of light in such crystals, we shall consider a graphical three-dimensional plot of the indices of refraction in the vibration directions of the corresponding waves. This gives us, so to speak, an orthogonal system of coordinate axes. One axis is represented by the wave normal; the other two axes are the vibration directions. The lengths of the vibration axes represent the indices of refraction of the two waves. If we insert this axial system into the center of an anisotropic, transparent crystal and allow the wave normal to assume all possible orientations, the ends of the index axes describe a triaxial ellipsoid. This is a body which we have already encountered (see p. 102) in discussing mechanical deformation of a sphere and free thermal dilatation (p. 114). In optics this solid figure is called an *indicatrix* or index ellipsoid (Fig. 223). Cross-sectional planes in the indicatrix are generally ellipses. Let us imagine now a crystal into whose interior the surface of the ellipsoid is somehow engraved. If we remove an infinitely thin wafer perpendicular to a wave normal, the lengths of the radii of the ellipse give the indices of refraction of the two waves associated with the wave normal. The directions of the radii represent their vibration directions.

The indicatrix has three *principal sections*, which are also its planes of symmetry. The intersections of the three planes define the longest, shortest and intermediate axes and, therefore, the highest (n_γ), lowest (n_α), and intermediate (n_β) indices of refraction[1]. If the wave normal coincides with the n_γ axis, the elliptical section perpendicular to it contains n_α and n_β. The *birefringence* of this plate is $n_\beta - n_\alpha$. If we now incline the wave normal to the n_α line, in the plane con-

---

[1] The major indices of refraction n_α, n_β, and n_γ are also designated in the literature as α, β, and γ or as n_x, n_y, n_z.

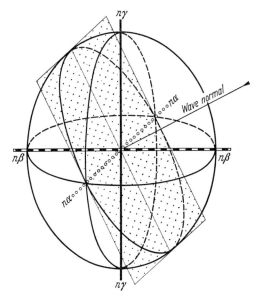

Fig. 223. Biaxial indicatrix showing randomly oriented elliptical section

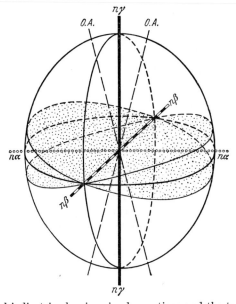

Fig. 224. Biaxial indicatrix showing circular sections and the two optic axes OA

taining n_α and n_γ (Fig. 224), we obtain an ellipical perpendicular cross section. One radius is again n_β; the other radius is now larger than n_α, and continues to increase with increasing inclination, until the wave normal finally attains a position where it takes on the value of n_β. The cross section is then no longer an ellipse, but instead a circle with radius n_β. Such a circular section would also have been obtained if we had originally inclined the wave normal toward the opposite side in the $n_\gamma - n_\alpha$ plane (Fig. 224). A circular section implies that the two waves associated with the wave normal have the same index of refraction. In the direction perpendicular to the circular section, no double refraction occurs. The crystal behaves like an isotropic body. These two special directions are called the *optic axes*, and such crystals are called *optically biaxial*. The term "optic axis" is unfortunate in that the beginner must always take care to distinguish between optic axes and ellipsoidal axes. There is also some danger in confusing them with crystallographic axes.

The orientation of the indicatrix (optic orientation) with respect to the crystallographic axes depends on the crystal symmetry, as was mentioned earlier in discussing the ellipsoid formed during free thermal dilatation (p. 114). The triaxial ellipsoid itself (p. 115) has the symmetry mmm, with three mutually perpendicular symmetry planes and three orthogonal 2-fold axes. In triclinic crystals it is not possible to predetermine which optical orientation the indicatrix will assume. The orientation will be governed by the symmetry restrictions, which in this system is no more than a center of symmetry. In a monoclinic crystal either the two-fold axis must coincide with an ellipsoidal axis or the symmetry plane of the crystal with one of the principal sections of the indicatrix. It is easy to see, that within these limits, an infinite number of optic orientations are possible. In an orthorhombic crystal, however, there are only six possible optical orientations, and one of these must be appropriate in an individual case. In addition to optical orientation, note must also be taken of the form or shape of the indicatrix, and, related to it, the angle between the optic axes. Both the shape and optic angle change with wave length as well as with temperature. For monochromatic red light, the optic angle is different than for blue light. In the trigonal, tetragonal and hexagonal systems the triaxial ellipsoid becomes a rotation ellipsoid. Thus only one circular section is present. The crystal is *optically uniaxial*, that is, it behaves as if isotropic in only one direction. The optical axis coincides with the major crystallographic axis (3-, 4-, or 6-fold) of the crystal. In the cubic system, finally, the indicatrix is a sphere so that only one index of refraction is necessary to characterize the crystal. There are no unique vibration directions.

For uniaxial crystals the major refractive indices are designated as ω and ε, the Greek letters for the Latin expressions for ordinary (ordinarius) and extraordinary (extraordinarius) waves. In order to understand this method of notation, we shall consider once again a ray of light obliquely incident on the face of a calcite cleavage rhomb ($10\bar{1}1$). The birefringence (double refraction) causes the incident ray to be resolved into two rays within the crystal (Fig. 220). If we rotate the crystal around the face normal, one of the two rays in the crystal responds to this rotation as it would in an isotropic crystal. This ray and its associated wave are called the ordinary. On the other hand the direction of transmission of the other ray changes as the crystal is rotated, and indeed the ray itself rotates around the ordinary. This ray and its associated wave are called the extraordinary. In optically uniaxial crystals the index of refraction of the ordinary wave is always constant. The indicatrix is a rotation ellipsoid with an infinite number of symmetry planes passing through the rotation axis. Each such plane is called a principal plane. The axes of the ellipse coinciding with a principal plane represent the refractive indices ω and ε. Depending on the shape of the uniaxial indicatrix, two kinds of uniaxial crystals can be differentiated. If the rotation axis is greater than the diameter of the circular section (Fig. 225), that is, if $\varepsilon > \omega$, the crystal is uniaxial *positive*. Quartz and rutile are examples. Crystals for which $\varepsilon < \omega$ (Fig. 226) are uniaxial *negative*. Calcite and apatite are typical examples.

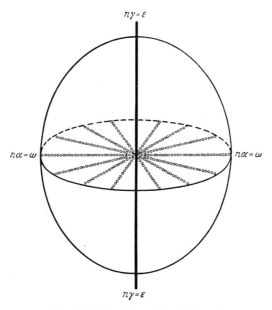

Fig. 225. Uniaxial positive indicatrix

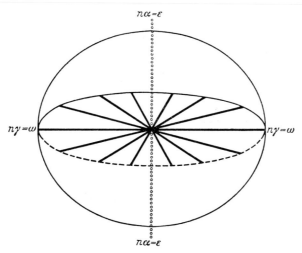

Fig. 226. Uniaxial negative indicatrix

One distinguishes between optically positive and negative biaxial crystals also. If the angle between optic axes (around n_γ) is less than 90°, the crystal is said to be biaxial positive; when greater than 90°, biaxial negative. The index direction which bisects the acute optic angle is called the *acute bisectrix*. That which bisects the obtuse angle, the *obtuse bisectrix*. According to the definition of a biaxial positive crystal, n_γ must be the acute bisectrix, and n_α the obtuse bisectrix. In negative crystals the situation is reversed; n_α is the acute bisectrix, n_γ the obtuse. The angle between the optic axes is the *optic angle* and is designated as $2V$. By convention in biaxial positive crystals this is the angle around n_γ, in negative crystals, around n_α, so that $2V$ is always less than, or at most, equal to 90°. If by chance the optic angle is exactly 90°, the biaxial crystal is *optically neutral*. The n_β axis of the indicatrix is the *optic normal*. As the optic angle of a positive indicatrix becomes smaller and smaller, the indicatrix approaches the shape of a positive uniaxial indicatrix and the two circular sections merge into one. As the angle about n_α becomes smaller, the indicatrix becomes a negative rotation ellipsoid whose rotation axis is n_α.

The optic angle is also an important parameter for identification. It is more sensitive than the indices of refraction to changes in the shape of the indicatrix. The $2V$ is related to the major indices of refraction n_α, n_β, and n_γ, by the following expression:

$$\tan V = \frac{n_\gamma}{n_\alpha} \sqrt{\frac{n_\beta^2 - n_\alpha^2}{n_\gamma^2 - n_\beta^2}}.$$

For very low birefringence, the following expression can be used:

$$\tan V \cong \sqrt{\frac{n_\beta - n_\alpha}{n_\gamma - n_\beta}}.$$

In both cases the optic angle about n_γ is calculated. If $(n_\gamma - n_\beta) > (n_\beta - n_\alpha)$, $V < 45°$, and the crystal is positive. If $(n_\gamma - n_\beta) < (n_\beta - n_\alpha)$ it is negative. The optic axes always lie in the $n_\alpha n_\gamma$ plane. This plane is called the *optic plane*.

Polarizers. Up to now we have only considered crystal optics from the theoretical standpoint. Let us now take a look at the phenomena which are important for the investigation of crystals by means of the polarizing microscope. Such an instrument is different from an ordinary microscope in that devices are included for producing polarized light. The simplest method of doing this is by reflection, for example, from a glass plate. The light observed by MALUS in looking through a calcite crystal was polarized by reflection. In 1815 BREWSTER showed that polarization by reflection is most complete when the reflected and refracted rays are perpendicular to each other. If α is the grazing angle and n the index of refraction of the reflecting substance:

$$\frac{\sin \alpha}{\sin (90° - \alpha)} = \tan \alpha = n.$$

The vibration direction of the reflected ray is in the plane perpendicular to the reflecting surface (Fig. 227). Sets of glass plates were used as polarizers in the Noerrenberg polarization apparatus, which was for a long time the only polarizer available for light beams of large diameter.

A second way of producing polarized light is to utilize the double refracting property of a crystal and eliminate one of the doubly diffracted rays produced in some unique direction of propagation. This can be accomplished by differential *absorption*. In strongly absorbing crystals the two waves are not only refracted by different amounts, but they may be absorbed to a markedly different extent. If, in a crystal plate, only visible light is transmitted in one vibration direction, and only ultraviolet, for example, in the other direction, the crystal can serve as a polarizer for visible light. In many tourmaline crystals the ordinary ray is completely absorbed and only the extraordinary rays are transmitted, somewhat reduced in intensity. A tourmaline plate cut parallel to the 3-fold axis, lets only the light of the extraordinary ray through. Its vibration direction lies parallel to the optic axis, corresponding to the general optical properties of uniaxial crystals. Earlier such tourmaline plates were actually used as polarizers. It is possible to produce only very narrow beams of polarized light with these crystals, since there are no large usable tourmaline crystals. In addition the extraordinary ray is always colored. Even if it were possible to find a tourmaline crystal in which the extraordinary ray was very slightly diminished, it would still appear

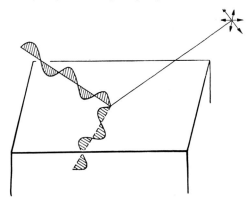

Fig. 227. Polarization of light by reflection and refraction in an isotropic medium

colored because both waves are important for the total impression of the absorption phenomenon. The adsorption properties of iodocinchonidine-sulfate, called herapathite after its discoverer HERAPATH (1852), are more favorable than those of tourmaline. From this substance it is possible to produce thin crystal plates of several centimeters size. It is now possible to produce thin transparent sheets of parallel oriented herapathite crystals embedded in plastic (polaroid). These have such fine optical properties that they have essentially replaced the early calcite polarizers for use in mineralogical microscopes.

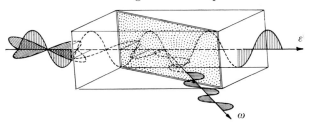

Fig. 228. Ray paths in the Nicol prism

A third way to produce polarized light depends again on use of a double refracting crystal. In this case the phenomenon of *total reflection* is used. For this calcite is used. In Na-light the index of refraction of the ordinary wave is 1.658 and the major index for the extraordinary wave is 1.486. A calcite prism is cut so that the incident light produces extraordinary waves having the index $\varepsilon' = 1.54$. The prism is cut in half along a diagonal face and the two halves recemented with Canada balsam, $n \sim 1.54$. The inclination of the faces was so chosen that the ordinary wave, whose index is always equal to 1.658, is totally reflected in passing from calcite into the Canada balsam, whereas the extraordinary wave passes through this interface (Fig. 228). This form of polarizer was first described in 1828 by NICOL. Today other cutting orientations as well as other cementing agents are used. The principle, however, remains the same.

An Anisotropic Plate in Parallel and Polarized Light. Let us now observe a plate cut from a crystal in an arbirtary orientation and illuminated by polarized light. The elliptical section of the indicatrix gives the vibration directions of the two waves and their indices of refraction, n_α' and $n_\gamma' (n_\alpha' < n_\gamma')$. In order to determine the indices of refraction of the plate by means of the Becke line method (p. 121), we must first orient n_α' with its vibration direction parallel to the vibration direction of the polarizer. Then only light vibrating in this direction passes through the plate, and it has the index n_α'. To determine n_γ', the procedure must be repeated, reorienting the crystal so that n_γ' is parallel to the polarizer. This procedure can be demonstrated, using an aggregate of aragonite crystals imbedded in Canada balsam $(n \sim 1.54)$. The aragonite crystals are elongated parallel to the c axis $(n_\alpha$, parallel $c = 1.530$, n_β, parallel $a = 1.682$, n_γ, parallel $b = 1.686)$. It is observed that in one orientation aragonite has a significantly higher index than Canada balsam; in the other direction it is a little lower. Using the Becke line method, one can estimate also the differences in indices between two crystals of different minerals in contact, for example, quartz and feldspar. To do this, the orientation of the indicatrices of both grains must be taken into account.

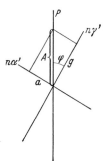

Fig. 229. Wave amplitude in a birefringent plate illuminated by polarized light with vibration direction P and amplitude A

An additional phenomenon very important for mineral identification can be discerned by use of the polarizer. This is *pleochroism*. In anisotropic crystals the two perpendicular vibrating waves are absorbed to varying degrees. Thus all anisotropic crystals are pleochroic to some extent, but the differences in absorption do not in all cases lie in the narrow spectral region to which our eye is sensitive. An especially beautiful example of pleochroism is exhibited by cordierite, as was mentioned early in the introduction to this book. A cube of cordierite is cut with the cube faces parallel to the three principal sections of the indicatrix. If we orient the three major vibration directions parallel to the polarizer one after the other, we see that when n_α is parallel to the polarizer, the crystal appears yellow, when n_γ is parallel it is blue, and when n_β green. Other minerals with strong pleochroism are tourmaline, biotite, amphiboles and epidote.

We have considered thus far only the two cases in which one of the two vibration directions in the plate lies parallel to that of the polarizer. We should consider also the random rotation of the crystal plate with respect to the vibration direction of the polarizer. If A is the amplitude of the wave transmitted through the polarizer, and ϕ the angle between the n_γ' direction and the vibration direction of the polarizer, and g and a the amplitudes of the two waves in the crystal plate (Fig. 229), then

$$g = A \cos \phi \quad \text{and} \quad a = A \sin \phi.$$

It is seen at once that, when $\phi = 0°$, $g = A$ and $a = 0$, and for $\phi = 90°$, $a = A$ and $g = 0$. Between these two extremes, which involve planar polarization, the two waves combine by phase shifts to form elliptically polarized waves. The combination of two waves of unequal amplitude vibrating perpendicular to one another and with $\lambda/4$ path difference to form elliptically polarized light is shown in Fig. 230. Waves of equal amplitude combine under like conditions to form circular polarized light (Fig. 231). The polarization state of light after passing through polarizer and crystal plate depends, therefore, on the orientation of the plate relative to the polarizer. In addition the birefringence must be taken into account. This is equal to the difference in the two indices of refraction, $n'_\gamma - n'_\alpha$. In addition the thicker the plate, the greater the path difference of the two waves. The product of the crystal thickness, d, and its birefringence $(n'_\gamma - n'_\alpha)$ is called the *retardation*.

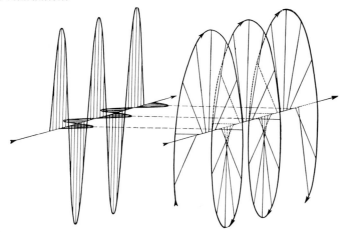

Fig. 230. Combination of two transverse waves of unequal amplitude, vibrating perpendicular to one another and with a path difference of $\lambda/4$. (From POHL)

If we observe a crystal plate of uniform thickness (for example, a mica cleavage sheet) which gives a phase difference of $\lambda/4$ in polarized light (Fig. 232), elliptically polarized light is produced by rotation between $\phi = 0°$ and $\phi = 45°$; at $\phi = 45°$ circularly polarized light, and between $45 - 90°$ elliptically polarized light

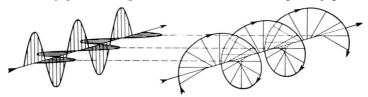

Fig. 231. Combination of two transverse waves of equal amplitude vibrating perpendicular to each other and with a path difference of $\lambda/4$. (From POHL)

is produced again. At $90°$ the ellipses degenerate to a straight line, and no light vibrating in the n'_α direction comes through the plate. Only light vibrating in the n'_γ direction, which is then oriented parallel to the polarizer, comes through. In this experiment the relative amplitudes have been changed by rotating the plate, and the phase difference has been kept constant. At $\phi = 45°$ the amplitudes of the two waves are equal. We shall now consider a case in which the phase difference is varied. To do this a wedge-shaped quartz crystal, cut parallel to its optic axis, is gradually inserted above the polarizer in the $45°$ position (Fig. 233). The phase difference increases with increasing wedge thickness. Parallel polarized light is produced at phase differences of $0, \lambda/2, 2\lambda/2, 3\lambda/2, 4\lambda/2$, etc. and vibrates perpendicular to the polarizer at uneven multiples of $\lambda/2$ and parallel to it at even multiples.

A Birefringent Plate between Crossed Polarizers. Let us now consider an additional polarizer, an "analyser", installed above a crystal plate, with its

9*

vibration direction perpendicular to that of the polarizer. Let us observe the uniform crystal plate in monochromatic light as we did in the first example above (Fig. 232). When the crystal plate with constant phase difference is rotated, darkness occurs at $\phi = 0°$, $90°$, $180°$, etc. The plate becomes dark four times during complete rotation and is bright in between. Maximum brightness occurs

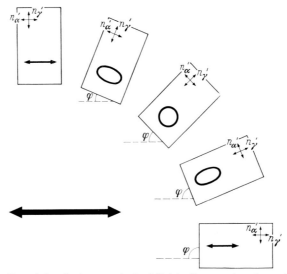

Fig. 232. Polarization state of planar polarized light after passing through a crystal plate which produces a retardation of $\lambda/4$. The orientation of the plate with respect to the vibration direction of the incident light is varied corresponding to the angle φ. The heavy arrow gives vibration direction of incident light

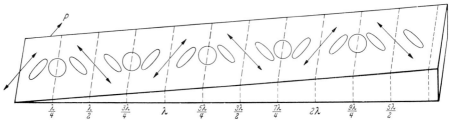

Fig. 233. Vibration directions in a quartz wedge in polarized monochromatic light. By comparison with Fig. 234 the directions shown here correspond to red light with $\lambda \sim 656$ mμ

at $\phi = 45°$, $135°$, $225°$, etc. When a quartz wedge instead of the uniform plate is inserted between crossed polarizers in the $45°$ position, darkness occurs at the places where the phase differences are 0, λ, 2λ, etc. The light, as it emerges from the wedge, is vibrating perpendicular to the vibration direction of the analyzer. At $\lambda/2$, $3\lambda/2$, $5\lambda/2$, etc., however, maximum brightness is observed. Here the vibration direction of the wedge coincides with that of the analyser. These observations are described in the basic formula of FRESNEL:

$$A = A_0 \sin 2\phi \sin \pi \frac{d(n'_\gamma - n'_\alpha)}{\lambda_0}.$$

A is the amplitude of light emerging from the analyser, A_0 of the light from the polarizer, ϕ the rotation angle which we have used already, d the plate thickness, $(n'_\gamma - n'_\alpha)$ the birefringence of the plate and λ_0 the wave length in vacuum (essentially equal in air). The formula is usually written in quadratic form, since the light intensity is proportional to the square of the amplitude. It can be seen at once from the formula that when $\phi = 90°$, $2\phi = 180°$, etc., the amplitude A becomes zero. This is also the case when $d(n'_\gamma - n'_\alpha) = \lambda$, 2λ, 3λ, etc. At $\phi = 45°$, 135°, etc., the value for $\sin 2\phi$ attains its maximum value, 1.

If the quartz wedge is illuminated with white light, the maxima of brightness and darkness occur at different places for different wave lengths. This is illustrated in Fig. 234 for blue, green, and red light. As a result of extinction of certain wave lengths through *interference*, bright interference colors occur, which correspond to those which are exhibited as Newton rings in thin films and which like them are distributed in *orders*. In Fig. 235 interference colors exhibited by different minerals in white light are shown and related to d and $(n_\gamma - n_\alpha)$. The values of birefringence of the minerals shown are based on $(\varepsilon - \omega)$ for uniaxial crystals and $(n_\gamma - n_\alpha)$ for biaxial crystals for sodium light ($\lambda = 589$ mμ). With the help of this

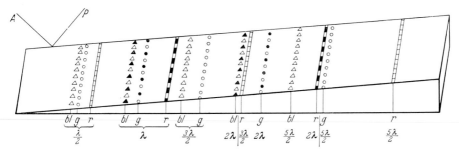

Fig. 234. The quartz wedge in white light, between crossed Nicols

△△ Brightness for blue light
▲ Darkness for blue light } $\lambda = 4341$ Å

○○ Brightness for green light
● Darkness for green light } $\lambda = 5330$ Å

□□ Brightness for red light
▬ Darkness for red light } $\lambda = 6563$ Å

table (Fig. 235), the retardation can be determined from the interference color of the crystal plate in the 45° position between crossed polarizers. If the birefringence of the mineral in the direction of transmission is known, the thickness of the specimen can be determined from the interference color. This approach is used in the preparation of thin sections. A rock specimen is cut just thin enough for the quartz which is present to show its maximum first order white interference color (the quartz exhibiting this color is cut parallel to its optic axis). Under these conditions the thin section has the standard thickness of 30 μ. Conversely, in a thin section of known thickness (determined from the maximum interference color of quartz), the birefringence of a mineral can be estimated from the interference color. This is an extremely important diagnostic aid in petrography.

Determination of the vibration directions of n'_α and n'_γ in a mineral grain is also important for identification. It is only necessary to rotate the specimen between crossed polarizers until complete darkness is obtained. Then the vibration directions in the grain are parallel to those of the polarizer and analyser. The ocular of the mineralogical microscope is equipped with cross-hairs which serve to indicate these directions at a glance. The vibration directions of n'_α and n'_γ

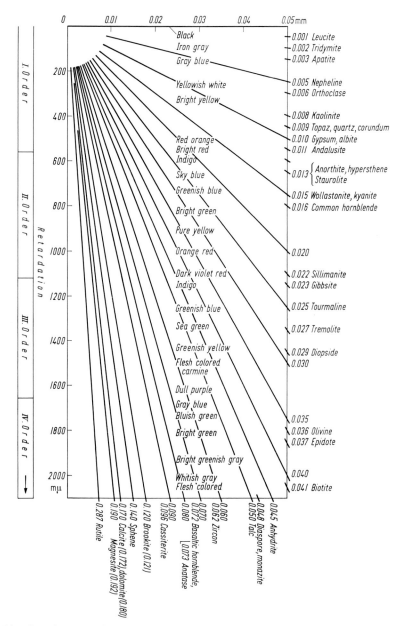

Fig. 235. Interference colors of minerals for maximum birefringence in relation to plate thickness

are found during rotation to lie in the positions of darkness. These positions are called *extinction positions*. A crystal of anhydrite, which cleaves along (100), (010), and (001), always shows perpendicular sets of cleavage cracks. The crystal shows extinction when the two cleavage directions parallel the vibration directions of the crossed polarizers. It is possible to use anhydrite to test whether the vibration directions of the polarizers are parallel to the cross hairs of the ocular, and to adjust the microscope accordingly. All uniaxial crystals when lying on a prism face show extinction parallel to the major axis. They are said to show *parallel extinction* to this direction. Quartz crystals elongated along [00.1] or apatite needles show this sort of parallel extinction. Parallel extinction with respect to zonal or cleavage directions occurs also in biaxial crystals. Platelets of monoclinic sanidine developed after P {001} exhibit parallel extinction relative to M {010} cleavage traces. {110} cleavage fragments of clinopyroxenes exhibit inclined extinction against [001]. It is important in describing extinction directions to indicate the reference direction.

It is very important to be able to ascertain the high index vibration direction in the crystal plate under consideration. To do this the crystal is oriented in the 45° position between crossed polarizers. A second accessory birefringent plate, for which the directions of n_α'' and n_γ'' are known, is placed in the 45° position between the crystal and the analyser. If n_γ' of the specimen is parallel to n_γ'' of the accessory plate, the retardation is increased and the interference colors rise toward higher orders. The sample appears as if it were thicker. If n_γ' and n_α'' are parallel, the sample appears thinner and lower interference colors occur. It has proved especially useful to use a cleavage plate of gypsum, which gives a first order red interference color (retardation 550 mμ). Such a *gypsum plate* causes samples with very low retardation to exhibit a second order blue interference color as a result of addition. By subtraction, first order yellow interference colors results. Since these are very noticeable color changes and result from slight changes in retardation, the gypsum plate is sometimes called the *sensitive tint plate*. With crystals of high birefringence, a *quartz wedge* is used instead of the gypsum plate. By subtraction the birefringence is compensated. When sample and quartz wedge both cause the same phase difference, complete extinction occurs. It is possible to measure the birefringence quantitatively with a calibrated quartz wedge if the thickness of the sample is known. The *rotation compensator* is used almost exclusively today for measurement of birefringence. The most distinctive of these is the Berek compensator. It consists essentially of a plane-parallel plate of calcite cut perpendicular to its optic axis. This is inserted into the accessory slot, located between the objective and analyzer, in the barrel of the polarizing microscope. It is inserted in the 45° position. In addition the calcite plate can be rotated around an axis in the insertion direction. This rotation direction lies in the plane of the plate. Thus the plate can be oriented perpendicular to the microscope axis, producing no phase difference, because the calcite is "isotropic" when viewed along its optic axis. By inclining the Berek plate, increasing phase difference is produced, and the birefringence of the sample can be compensated. The magnitude of the rotation angle necessary to accomplish compensation is related to the phase difference, and the compensator is calibrated accordingly.

The locations of vibration directions in a birefringent plate are given by the major axes of the ellipsoidal section which the plane perpendicular to the wave normal forms with the indicatrix. If the characteristics of the indicatrix are known, the vibration directions of the waves associated with a specific wave normal can be constructed very simply with the help of a stereographic projection. The method was introduced by FRESNEL.

As an example, we will determine for a plagioclase of about 72% anorthite the inclined extinction angle of M (010) cleavage traces on the plane P (001) (Fig. 236). We place the pole of P (001) at the center of a stereographic projection and plot the pole of plane M (010), as well as the optic axis directions A_1 and A_2, corresponding to independently measured values. The pole of the great circle through A_1 and A_2 gives the vibration direction of n_β, and the bisectors of the optic angles give the vibration directions of n_α and n_γ. Since this plagioclase is optically positive, n_γ is the acute bisectrix. According to the construction of FRESNEL, the vibration directions of the waves propagated perpendicular to P are found as follows: P is joined to A_1 and A_2. The bisector of the angle A_1PA_2 gives the vibration directions sought. Therefore n_γ' lies in that sector of the projection in which n_γ lies, and n_α' in that which also contains n_α. We now draw

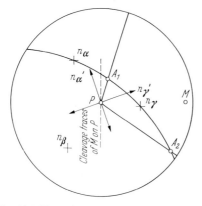

in the trace of the common edge between $P(001)$ and $M(010)$, that is, the trace of the M cleavage on P, which is the normal to the zone $M-P$. The angle which this direction makes with the vibration direction of n_α' is the extinction angle sought.

The observation of specimens in parallel polarized light, using only the polarizer, is sometimes incorrectly described as "polarizers parallel" or "Nicols parallel". This error is especially common in labeling microphotographs. Two polarizers, oriented with vibration directions parallel, are not used in crystal optics studies, except under very specialized circumstances. With the second

Fig. 236. Fresnel construction of the vibration directions in stereographic projection

analyser, the two waves which pass through the crystal plate would be forced to interfere, as they are also with crossed polarizers. Different interference colors are obtained, however, which are complementary to those obtained with crossed polarizers.

Fig. 237. Universal stage. (Firm Zeiss)

The Universal Stage. A great deal of important information on optic orientation of a crystal can be determined with the polarizing microscope. Much more information can be obtained, using a *universal stage*. Many rotation devices have been used, especially by C. KLEIN in conjunction with the microscope. Although v. FEDEROV described in 1893 the first universal stage suited for the study of thin sections, only relatively recently has the universal stage been adapted for generally wide usage. A variety of universal stages are manufactured by numerous firms (Fig. 237), and with these a specimen can be measurably rotated around 3—5 axes. In this way the principal planes of the indicatrix can be oriented perpendicular to the microscope axis. The orientation of the optic axes can be determined by seeking the directions of "isotropism". In the case of biaxial crystals the optical angle can be measured then by suitable rotation. In a rock thin section the directions of the optic axes of quartz grains, for example, and their orientation with respect to rock structures, such as foliation, can be determined. Such information is especially important in petrofabric studies.

The Conoscope. The *conoscopic method* provides another approach to studying the optical properties of a crystal plate in different directions. The strongest possible convergent beam of polarized light is allowed to fall on the plate. A strong condenser in the sub-stage illumination apparatus is used for this. A high-power lens must also be used in the objective. Each of the light waves traveling through the crystal in a conical bundle traverses a different path length. Accordingly interference takes place like that which occurs with a quartz wedge. An interference figure, occurring in the upper focal plane of the objective, is observed through the analyser. It is only necessary to remove the ocular of the microscope to view this interference figure. In order to avoid the effects of disturbing scattered light, a pin-hole aperture is inserted in place of the ocular. In many microscopes an accessory lens is also used, which can be inserted into the optical path (Bertrand or Amici lens). This forms with the ocular a small microscope through which the interference figure can be observed at low magnification. When the polarizing microscope is modified in this manner it is called a conoscope (konos, Gr., cone). In order to avoid a common misconception, it should be noted that the light path of the conoscope is the same as in the ordinary microscope (orthoscope) at the same magnification. The only difference is that in one case an interference picture of the light is observed, in the other case a picture of the specimen.

If a plate of a uniaxial crystal cut perpendicular to the optic axis is illuminated in the conoscope, using a monochromatic cone of light, maximum brightness occurs along those directions where phase differences $\Gamma = \lambda/2$, $3\lambda/2$, $5\lambda/2$, etc. prevail. The loci of these directions lie on a set of coaxial concentric cones. In the focal plane of the objective the figures of equal phase difference are concentric circles. Between the bright circles, at $\Gamma = 0$, λ, 2λ, etc., darkness occurs. The

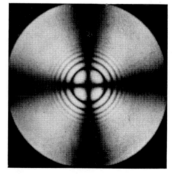

Fig. 238. Conoscopic figure of a calcite plate parallel to (0001) in monochromatic light. The vibration directions of the polarizer and analyser run left and right and up and down. (From LIEBISCH)

thicker the plate and the greater its birefringence, the closer together the circles lie. In this system of concentric circles ε' always vibrates radially, and ω tangentially to a circle. Wherever the two vibration directions are parallel to those of the crossed polarizers, darkness prevails, analogous to extinction positions in orthoscopic work (p. 134). As a result the interference figure with monochromatic light shows light and dark rings and a black cross, whose arms are parallel to the vibration directions of the polarizers. The arms of the cross are narrow and sharp near the center and become broader and more diffuse towards the edge of the interference figure (Fig. 238). The arms of the cross are also called *isogyres*.

In white light the dark cross is also formed, but the interference rings become colored, with the interference colors rising from the center outward, in the sequence shown by the quartz wedge. As the specimen is rotated around the axis of the microscope, the interference figure is not altered. By means of an accessory

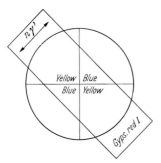

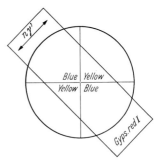

Fig. 239. Color distribution in an optic axis figure for a uniaxial positive crystal with 1st order red gypsum plate inserted

Fig. 240. Color distribution in an optic axis figure for a uniaxial negative crystal with 1st order red gypsum plate inserted

plate it is easy to establish whether ω or ε' has the greatest index of refraction and thus determine the optic sign. The first order red gypsum plate is introduced between specimen and analyser so that its vibration directions are at $45°$ to the polarizer. In the case of a positive crystal, if the gypsum plate is introduced in the NW quadrant of the field, n'_γ of gypsum is parallel to ε' of the sample, and the interference color rises to blue near the center of the figure, in the NE and SW quadrants. In the other two quadrants a first order yellow interference color is observed (Fig. 239). For optically negative crystals, the opposite effects are noted (Fig. 240).

If a uniaxial crystal plate is not cut perpendicular to the optic axis, at small angles of inclination the axial cross is observed to be displaced toward the edge of the interference figure. At higher angles of inclination only the arms of the cross are seen to migrate from time to time across the field of view during rotation. Sections parallel to the optic axis exhibit an enlarged dark cross that breaks up very quickly into two segments upon rotation of the specimen. This is, loosely speaking, a biaxial interference figure with an "optic angle" of $180°$.

With a biaxial crystal with small optic angle, in sections cut perpendicular to the acute bisectrix, the same interference colors are observed around the points of emergence of the two optic axes. These are the *isochromatic curves*. Close to the axes they are concentric circles but, with rising interference color they change first to oval shaped curves and at some definite point[1] into a figure-eight shaped curve, in which the crossover point of the "eight" intersects the point of emergence of the acute bisectrix. At still higher interference colors, the isochromatic curves are "dumbbell" shaped. Fig. 241 shows the spatial distribution

---

[1] This depends on the optic constants of the crystal and its thickness.

of curves of equal phase difference for monochromatic light. The isogyre cross is not shown. It appears only when n_β lies parallel to one of the vibration directions of the polarizers (*normal position*). Contrary to optic uniaxial crystals, the two arms of the cross are not equal. That one which parallels the vibration direction n_β is broader; the other arm is narrower and, in addition, is restricted at the

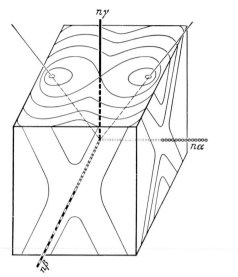

Fig. 241. Curves of equal path difference for a biaxial crystal in monochromatic light between crossed Nicols with conoscopic illumination

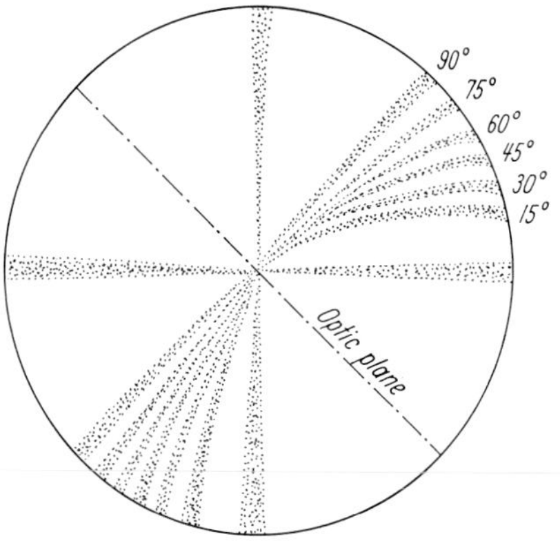

Fig. 242. Relationship of isogyre curvature to optic angle (2 V) in biaxial optic axis figure. (After WRIGHT, based on average $n = 1.60$)

points of emergence of the optic axes. If the crystal is rotated from the normal position, the cross opens into two hyperbola, which converge again to a cross when rotated a full 90°. The separation of the two axes can be measured with an optical micrometer. This distance, in conjunction with an instrumental constant (MALLARD'S constant) determined from a test crystal of known optic angle, can be used to calculate the optical angle, 2 E, in the air. The crystal optic angle 2 V is then found according to the formula

$$\sin V = \frac{\sin E}{n_\beta}.$$

In sections perpendicular to one of the optic axes, the optic angle can be estimated from the curvature of the isogyre as indicated in Fig. 242.

The optic sign of a biaxial crystal can be determined with the help of an accessory plate in a manner similar to uniaxial crystals. To do this the optic orientation of the crystal must be taken into account. Figs. 243 and 244 should assist in these considerations for sections cut perpendicular to the acute bisectrix.

The differentiation of uniaxial and biaxial crystals by conoscope observation of sections strongly inclined to bisectrices and optic axes is not always possible. The combination of conoscope and universal stage is especially useful in this respect (H. SCHUMANN, 1937).

As already mentioned (p. 126), there is an appropriate indicatrix for each specific wave length and temperature. The dependence on wave length of the

optic angle, and with it the form of the indicatrix, is especially well illustrated
by the extreme case of the orthorhombic mineral, brookite (TiO_2). This mineral
frequently occurs in thin platelets developed after (100). If a brookite crystal is
placed under the conoscope and illuminated with blue and then with red light,
it is observed that the optic plane for red light is perpendicular to that of blue

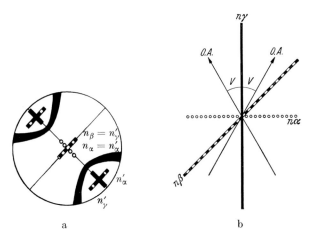

Fig. 243a and b. Biaxial positive crystal. (a) Orientation of the vibration directions in acute
bisectrix figure; (b) orientation of optic angle in indicatrix

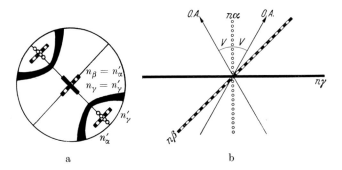

Fig. 244a and b. Biaxial negative crystal. (a) Orientation of the vibration directions in acute
bisectrix figure; (b) orientation of optic angle in indicatrix

light. Fig. 245 shows that brookite is "uniaxial" at $\lambda \sim 0.55\,\mu$. The different
orientations of optic axes in relation to wave length is diagnostically important,
even when the effect is very much less than that exhibited by brookite. *Dispersion
of the optic angle* is indicated in the tables of appendix III B. $r > v$ means that the
optic angle in red light is greater than in violet light. In this case the isogyres,
relative to the acute bisectrix, are bordered blue on the outside and red on the
inside, being complementary to the relationships of the optic axes.

The change with temperature of the optic angle of gypsum was studied as
early as 1826 by MITSCHERLICH. At room temperature the optic plane coincides
with the plane of symmetry of the monoclinic crystal. Upon heating, the optic
angle becomes smaller and smaller and at $90-91°$ C is zero for the visible wave

lengths. For Na light ($\lambda = 0.589$ mμ) the arms of the isogyres close at 90.9° C (TUTTON, 1913). For this special wave length and temperature gypsum behaves like an optically uniaxial crystal. Upon further heating the optic angle opens again, but now the optic plane is perpendicular to the plane of symmetry of the crystal.

Strain Birefringence. Isotropic bodies can exhibit birefringence when they are mechanically stressed. This can be easily demonstrated by bending a glass rod between crossed polarizers. When the stress is released, the birefringence disappears. This phenomenon is used with models of engineering structures, made of transparent isotropic materials such as glass or plastic, to investigate strain distribution caused by mechanical stress. Lenses in microscope objectives are sometimes so permanently strained that they are birefringent and not usable for work involving polarized light. Stresses occur also during the rapid cooling of glass, causing birefringence. The birefringence frequently shown by diamonds is probably related to such strain birefringence. Certain gels, for example, $SiO_2 \cdot x H_2O$, develop strain birefringence upon drying.

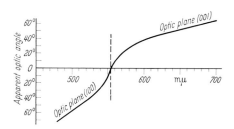

Fig. 245. Change of optic angle and the orientation of optic plane as related to wave length in brookite. (After data from ARNOLD.) The acute bisectrix n_γ is parallel to [010]

A crystal, whose optical behavior does not correspond to its symmetry is called optically anomalous. Included here are crystals, like leucite and boracite, which sometimes occur as multiple twins of a birefringent modification exhibiting the external form of a higher temperature cubic modification. Other crystals show anomalies, caused by the inclusion of a mixed crystal component. In the case of cubic crystallizing alum, birefringence can arise from mixing chromium alum with potassium aluminum alum experimentally during growth. Whether the resulting birefringence is always due to stress phenomena is not quite certain. It could be that such inclusion, if regularly ordered, is caused by form birefringence.

Form Birefringence. Cylindrical or disk-shaped isotropic particles, whose thicknesses and inter-particle separations are small in relation to the wave length of light, can exhibit birefringence as a result of their arrangement alone. An aggregate of parallel-arranged, isotropic rodlets behaves as if it were an optically positive uniaxial crystal. A parallel stack of disk-shaped particles, behaves like a negative uniaxial crystal. The magnitude of the birefringence depends on the difference between the refractive indices of the particles and their enveloping medium. This so-called form birefringence changes, therefore, with immersion liquid. If we designate the indices of the particles and immersion medium as n_1 and n_2 respectively, and their relative volumes as m_1 and m_2 ($m_1 + m_2 = 1$), the birefringence for rod-shaped particles is a follows:

$$\varepsilon^2 = m_1 n_1^2 + m_2 n_2^2$$

$$\omega^2 = n_2^2 \frac{(m_1 + 1) n_1^2 + m_2 n_2^2}{(m_1 + 1) n_2^2 + m_2 n_1^2}$$

$$\varepsilon^2 - \omega^2 = \frac{m_1 m_2 (n_1^2 - n_2^2)^2}{(m_1 + 1) n_2^2 + m_2 n_1^2}.$$

For disk-shaped particles:

$$\varepsilon^2 = \frac{n_1^2 \cdot n_2^2}{m_1 \, n_2^2 + m_2 \, n_1^2}$$

$$\omega^2 = m_1 \, n_1^2 + m_2 \, n_2^2$$

$$\varepsilon^2 - \omega^2 = - \frac{m_1 \, m_2 \, (n_1^2 - n_2^2)^2}{m_1 \, n_2^2 + m_2 \, n_1^2} \; .$$

In the case of birefringent rod- or disc-shaped particles, their individual birefringence is superimposed on the form birefringence. This is important for some mineral aggregates. An example is chalcedony, which is composed of quartz fibers which have grown perpendicular to the c-axis. Waves with the lower index of refraction vibrate parallel to the direction of fiber elongation. Chalcedony, therefore, exhibits a lower birefringence than quartz, because of the superimposed form birefringence.

Crystal Structure and Birefringence. Form birefringence can be applied as a very rough rule of thumb to crystals, in as much as they too, in a sense, are composed of chains or layers of atoms. Thus layer lattices are in general optically negative. There are exceptions, however, such as $Mg(OH)_2$ (brucite) and $Al(OH)_3$ (gibbsite), as well as many chlorites. In these minerals the dipole character of the OH groups apparently determines the birefringence. Carbonates and nitrates with their CO_3^{2-} and NO_3^{1-} groups, are optically negative when these groups lie parallel to one another in the crystal structure. The higher index of refraction lies in the plane of the complex group. Calcite, magnesite, aragonite, and others are such examples. There are many crystals with chain structures, like selenium and cinnabar (HgS). In cinnabar screwlike $\cdots -Hg-S-Hg-S-\cdots$ chains run parallel to its 3-fold axis. This mineral, like most pyroxenes (especially the Fe-poor varieties), is optically positive. The same is true of calomel in which elongate $Cl-Hg-Hg-Cl$ molecules are always preferentially oriented parallel to the 4-fold axis of the crystal. Crystals which are close-packed in more than two directions should exhibit weak or no birefringence. Very noteworthy exceptions are compounds of titanium (rutile, sphene) and iron (hematite, in contrast to corundum). The relation between structure and optical properties is based on the idea that light is transmitted more slowly in the direction of densest layering, but there are so many exceptions that strong *a priori* adherence is not to be expected. It is possible though to calculate the birefringence in some cases and this has been done especially by P. P. EWALD, M. BORN and W. L. BRAGG. Such calculations are tedious and lie beyond the scope of this introduction.

c) Optically Active Crystals

There is an additional property which sometimes complicates optical behavior. In certain crystals, just as with some liquids, the vibration direction of the plane polarized light is rotated a definite amount, proportional to length of the optical path through the substance. The angle of rotation α increases regularly with increasing optical path, d; $\alpha = k \cdot d$. This phenomenon is known as optical activity. It occurs in the very common mineral quartz, as well as numerous others. For quartz the rotary power has been determined to be $\alpha = 21°45'/mm$ for sodium light. In order to explain the rotation it can be assumed that every linear polarized vibration can be considered as the resultant of two circular polarized vibrations with opposing sense of rotation. In optically active substances the indices of refraction and, therefore, the transmission velocities of these two polarized waves are different, that is, they show a sort of birefringence. Hence the resultant vibration direction is rotated.

This birefringence is best observed in "isotropic" directions; in quartz in the direction of the c-axis, in monoclinic sucrose in the direction of the two optic axes, and in cubic $NaClO_3$ in all directions. In directions inclined to the optic axes the two waves are elliptically polarized with opposing vibration directions. Since the magnitude of the rotation along the c-axis in quartz is $21°45'/mm$ for sodium light, optical activity cannot be observed in thin sections which are only about $1/30$ mm thick.

Optical activity can be observed in 15 of the 32 crystal classes. A crystal must not possess a center of symmetry for it to occur. The classes in which optical activity occurs are enumerated in Table 6 of the appendix III A. It should be noted further that it is possible for a substance to exhibit optical activity in the crystalline state without exhibiting it in aqueous solution. $NaClO_3$ is such an example.

d) Strongly Absorbing Crystals

Methods of Observation. The optical relationships of strongly adsorbing minerals are considerably more complex than those of transparent crystals. The

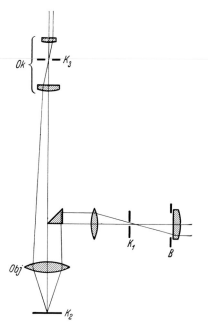

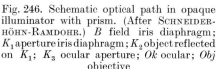

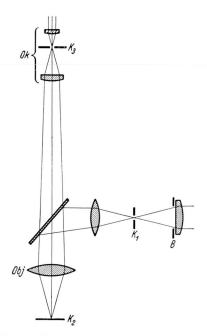

Fig. 246. Schematic optical path in opaque illuminator with prism. (After SCHNEIDER-HÖHN-RAMDOHR.) B field iris diaphragm; K_1 aperture iris diaphragm; K_2 object reflected on K_1; K_3 ocular aperture; Ok ocular; Obj objective

Fig. 247. Schematic optical path in opaque illuminator with glass plate. (After SCHNEIDER-HÖHN-RAMDOHR.) B field iris diaphragm; K_1 aperture iris diaphragm; K_2 object reflected on K_1; K_3 ocular aperture; Ok ocular; Obj objective

most important of the opaque minerals are the ore minerals, which are opaque even in thin section. They are studied microscopically by using incident light. With a small totally reflecting prism placed in the optical path, the specimen is illuminated vertically (Fig. 246). In order to investigate very fine structure at high magnification, a glass plate is used instead of the prism (Fig. 247). The illuminating device is called an *opaque illuminator*, and it is mounted in the tube of the microscope. Since the illumination passes through the opaque illuminator and the microscope tube, a microscope is often used in which the sample is focused, not by raising and lowering the microscope barrel, but by adjusting the microscope stage. Such a microscope is called an ore microscope. In the last 40 years ore microscopy has become more important. It is based to a large extent on studying the appearance of minerals and their behavior when polished and etched. A great wealth of data has been collected, but we cannot discuss this in any more detail here.

Theory. The determination of optical constants of opaque substances is still in its infancy, because optical relationships for strongly absorbing bodies are extremely complex. In addition to the refractive index, the *absorption coefficient* plays a significant role. If A_0 is the amplitude of the incident light of wave length λ_0 in vacuum, and A the amplitude of light that has traversed a distance d in the crystal, the following relationship applies:

$$A = A_0 \cdot e^{-2\pi k \frac{d}{\lambda_0}}.$$

k is a constant, the *absorption coefficient*. Occasionally the absorption index $\varkappa$ is used. This is related to λ_1, the wave length in the crystal. Frequently the product of $\varkappa$ and the index of refraction n is utilized. If $\varkappa/\lambda_1$ is substituted in the formula for k/λ_0, since $\lambda_0/\lambda_1 = n$, $n\varkappa = k$. Through the involvement of the absorption coefficients, a general second order surface, serves as a reference in place of the indicatrix. The radial vectors of this surface are complex refractive indices, that is, composed of real and imaginary numbers $n' = n - i \cdot k$ $(i = \sqrt{-1})$. We can no longer deal with perceptual bodies like ellipsoids, but must deal with the appropriate optical phenomena purely by calculation.

Triclinic, monoclinic, and orthorhombic crystals have three major indices of refraction and three major adsorption coefficients. Their directions do not generally correspond. In the trigonal, tetragonal, and hexagonal classes, reference surfaces of the refractive indices as well as the adsorption coefficients are rotation ellipsoids, both having a common rotation axis. In cubic crystals both surfaces are spheres. It must be expressly noted, however, that even in the cubic system, SNELL's law is only valid when the light has perpendicular incidence. The index of refraction n_i is dependent on the angle of incidence, i, in air, according to the following relationship:

$$n_i^2 = \tfrac{1}{2}\left(n^2 - k^2 + \sin^2 i + \sqrt{4n^2 k^2 + (n^2 - k^2 - \sin^2 i)^2}\right).$$

For reflection at perpendicular incidence, the reflecting power R, that portion of the light reflected (BEER, 1854), is as follows:

$$R = \frac{(n-1)^2 + (nk)^2}{(n+1)^2 + (nk)^2}.$$

e) Fluorescence and Discoloration Halos

We shall conclude our discussion of optics involving visible light by considering briefly the phenomenon of *fluorescence*. This is important in mineral identification and promises to be of even greater importance in the future. By fluorescence, a substance radiated with short wave length light reemits light of longer wave length. Ultraviolet light is used to demonstrate this property. This is commonly produced by means of a mercury-quartz glass lamp, and filtered through a screen transparent only to ultraviolet light. It is sufficient to use an ordinary arc lamp with such a filter. Quartz optics are necessary for transmission. Fluorescence of minerals is usually caused by impurities, which usually occur in only trace amounts. Common examples are the inclusion of small amounts of rare earths for Ca^{2+} in fluorite or of Mn^{2+} for Ca^{2+} in calcite. Their detection can have important geochemical significance, and is often used in identifying locality of origin. Fluorescent substances can be detected in very low concentrations. For example, as little as 0.00026 cm^3 of petroleum can be detected in 1 cm^3 of sand.

Another interesting phenomenon is the occurrence of *discoloration halos*. These occur frequently in biotite, and less often in amphiboles, cordierite, tourmaline, fluorite, spinel, and garnet. Dark zones, which are disk-shaped in cross-section, occur around inclusions of radioactive minerals such as zircon, monazite, and orthite. They sometimes form distinct rings as in the fluorite from Woelsendorf. The discoloration of the original mineral is the result of emission of alpha-particles in the inclusions. From the ring diameter it is possible to determine the radius of action of the alpha rays and from this the radioactive element. The time duration of the effect can be estimated from the magnitude of the discoloration and from this the age of the mineral. The discoloration halos of anisotropic minerals are often pleochroic. These are referred to as *pleochroic halos*. They are seen very distinctly around zircon inclusions in cordierite. The cordierite, which is normally colorless in thin-section, is pleochroic in bright yellow tones around the zircon inclusions.

5. X-ray Optics

Introduction. So far we have concerned ourselves only with that very narrow range of wave lengths to which our eye is sensitive. Fig. 248 summarizes the entire wave length region important to optics. Space does not permit detailed

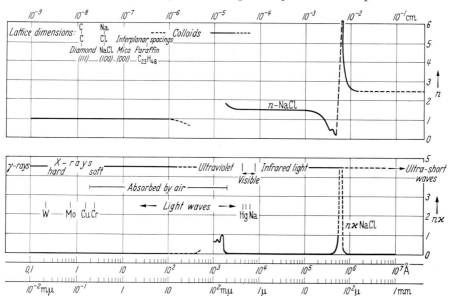

Fig. 248. Summary of the optical wave length region. (n and $n\varkappa$ curves from Pohl)

discussion of the phenomena associated with the ultraviolet and infra-red regions. At the present time these are of relatively limited importance as far as mineralogy is concerned, although absorption measurements in the infrared region are becoming increasingly important. They provide significant information e.g. concerning the bonding of hydrogen in crystals. We shall consider instead in some detail the very short wave length region, the X-ray spectrum. X-rays are of fundamental importance for the determination of crystal structures, as well as for the identification of minerals. X-ray methods have been especially useful in the study of very fine-grained minerals not amenable to study by microscopic methods, and are an important tool also for textural studies of rocks.

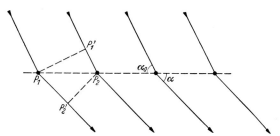

Fig. 249. Diffraction from a linear lattice

The Laue Equations. The X-ray interference in crystals was first discovered in the year 1912 by v. LAUE. Simultaneously he proved the wave character of X-rays and the existence of atoms and opened the way to the extremely important and flourishing field of crystal structure analysis. Space does not permit us to go into the methods of production of X-rays. Appropriate details can be obtained from the standard physics references. In order to understand the phenomenon of X-ray interference by crystals, we shall consider first of all the case in which a monochromatic X-ray beam is incident upon a linear lattice and is scattered by the individual lattice points (atoms) (Fig. 249). The path difference between the rays scattered at two adjacent points in some arbitrary direction is $P_1 P_2' - P_1' P_2$. In order that the individual waves constructively reinforce one another in the direction selected, the path difference must be expressed in whole multiples, h_1, of the wave length, $h_1 \lambda$. The number h_1 indicates whether the zero, first, second, third, etc. order of diffraction is being considered. If the distances $P_1 P_2'$ and $P_1' P_2$ are related to the repeat period a^1 and the angle α of the scattered and angle α_0 of the incident beam, measured with respect to the lattice direction, we obtain the following so-called Laue equation:

$$a(\cos \alpha - \cos \alpha_0) = h_1 \lambda.$$

This equation is used also for visible light in grating spectroscopy, and from it λ can be determined when the other parameters are known.

This Laue equation explains why in visible light no analogous interference occurs with crystal lattices. The greatest path difference is obtained at angles corresponding to grazing incidence and scattering. Then the path difference is almost equal to $2(P_1 - P_2) = 2a$; thus $h_1 \lambda \leq 2a$. If a is equal to $2 \cdot 10^{-8}$ cm, then λ may be no greater than $4 \cdot 10^{-8}$ cm, if at least the first order is to occur. As we know visible light has much longer wave lengths (Fig. 248).

---

[1] In this chapter we shall use a, b, and c for identity periods (lattice constants) rather than a_0, b_0, and c_0 in order to simplify presentation of formulae.

Fig. 250 is a three dimensional diagram indicating the different diffraction cones produced by monochromatic X-rays at perpendicular incidence to the linear lattice. Diffraction associated only with a one-dimensional lattice is not of great importance from a mineralogical standpoint. One dimensional lattices are not represented as minerals, although asbestos shows certain diffraction effects which are one-dimensional in character.

Proceeding further, let us consider two linear point lattices, intersecting at some arbitrary angle, say 70°. If they are radiated simultaneously by monochromatic X-rays perpendicular to the plane defined by the two point rows, a diffraction pattern as shown in Fig. 251 would be obtained on a film placed perpendicular to the incident beam. This consists of two families of hyperbolae which represent the intersections of the two sets of diffraction cones and the recording film. If both the intersecting linear lattices are repeated by translations in a plane, a planar lattice or grating is produced. In the resulting diffraction pattern the intensities at the hyberbolae intersections (Fig. 251) are always greater than between these points. Such grating spectra are obtained by electron diffraction from thin mica sheets.

As a final step, if we stack the individual planar lattices one upon the other, a space lattice is produced. If the direction of the incident beam in our experiment coincides with the stacking direction, the point rows lying in this new direction produce a third set of interference cones. These intersect a film placed perpendicular to the incident beam in concentric circles. The two original point rows again produce the two families of hyperbolae (Fig. 252). In the case illustrated in Fig. 252, the three families of curves never intersect at a common point. Accordingly a three-dimensional periodic pattern (crystal lattice) with monochromatic radiation produces cooperative scattering in only certain directions. These are those which by coincidence would correspond to the intersection of three diffraction curves in Fig. 252 at common points.

There are two experimental approaches for satisfying the conditions for diffraction from space lattices:

1. The use of polychromatic (white[1]) X-rays. In this case, in experiments such as those just described, for certain select wave lengths the three sets of curves intersect occasionally, satisfying the conditions for cooperative interference. In Fig. 253, this situation is illustrated using the analogy of visible light.

2. The use of monochromatic X-rays. The crystal must be rotated. Diffraction takes place in certain specific orientations with respect to the incident X-ray beam.

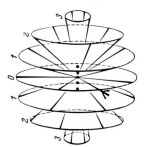

Fig. 250. Diffraction cones from a linear lattice. (After BIJVOET)

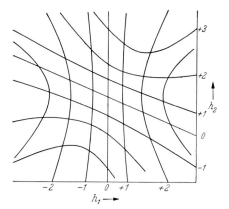

Fig. 251. Grating spectrum. (After EWALD)

_____
[1] With reference to visible white light which is polychromatic.

10*

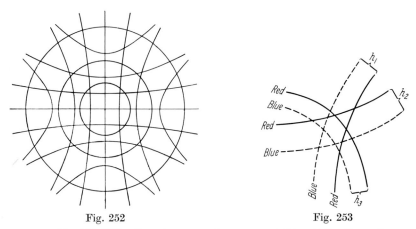

Fig. 252   Fig. 253

Fig. 252. Diffraction phenomena from a space lattice. (After EWALD)

Fig. 253. Intersection of the three diffraction cones of Fig. 252 for several wave lengths of polychromatic light. For yellow light the three curves intersect at a common point. (After EWALD)

Mathematically the diffraction directions for a three-dimensional lattice are derived from the conditions for diffraction for each of three linear lattice rows. The approach is to solve simultaneously three Laue equations, one for each of the three linear lattices, in order to ascertain the conditions necessary for reinforcement of scattered waves from the three linear lattices. The following are the three appropriate Laue equations:

$$\left.\begin{array}{l} a\,(\cos\alpha - \cos\alpha_0) = h_1\,\lambda \\ b\,(\cos\beta - \cos\beta_0) = h_2\,\lambda \\ c\,(\cos\gamma - \cos\gamma_0) = h_3\,\lambda. \end{array}\right\} \tag{1}$$

b, β, β_0 and c, γ, γ_0 are analogous to the terms a, α, α_0 used above in the first Laue equation. The lattice dimensions $a, b,$ and c are crystal constants. If λ as well as α_0, β_0 and γ_0 are held constant, generally $\alpha, \beta,$ and γ do not give whole numbers for $h_1, h_2,$ and h_3; the three equations are not simultaneously solved and diffraction maxima are not produced. Only by varying λ, can this happen. v. LAUE used X-rays with a broad range of wave lengths in his first experiments, and thus obtained interference maximum, even with a stationary crystal. Fig. 262 on p. 158 shows a typical *Laue photograph*.

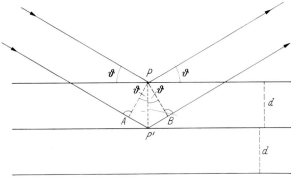

Fig. 254. Geometrical derivation of the Bragg equation. Note that $\overline{AP'} = \overline{P'B} = d \sin\theta$

The Bragg Equation. By using monochromatic rather than polychromatic X-rays the angle of incidence and thus α_0, β_0, and γ_0 can be varied and brought into coincidence. In this way W. H. BRAGG and W. L. BRAGG, soon after LAUE's discovery, determined the first crystal structures. They showed that X-ray diffraction can be viewed as taking place by "reflection" from lattice planes in the crystal. If d represents the interplanar spacing, and θ the angle between the lattice plane and the incident X-ray beam, the path difference, Γ, from two scattering points, as shown in Fig. 254, is equal to $2d \sin \theta$. Thus in order for constructive interference to occur, the path difference must equal whole multiples of the wave length, thus,

$$n \, \lambda = 2d \sin \theta . \tag{2}$$

From this Bragg equation it is seen that either λ or θ must be varied if diffraction is to occur from a given plane of atoms. By analogy with visible light optics the angle θ is frequently called the angle of reflection. If we imagine a crystal, radiated by monochromatic X-rays, oriented with the incident X-ray beam essentially parallel to the lattice plane, we see that no diffraction takes place from this lattice plane. If we rotate the crystal about an axis lying in the lattice plane, and perpendicular to the X-ray beam, a reflection occurs as soon as the Bragg conditions are fulfilled for a value of $n = 1$. Upon further rotation the reflection is extinguished again until rotation brings the plane to an angle whose sine is double the value of the sine of the angle at which the first reflection occurred. A further reflection occurs when $\sin \theta = 3 \cdot \dfrac{\lambda}{2d}$, etc.

Interrelation of the Bragg and Laue Equations. In order to relate these two expressions, the interplanar spacing d of the Bragg equation is expressed in terms of the lattice constant a, and the crystallographic (MILLER) indices of the reflecting plane. For a cubic lattice, the simplest case, which we shall only consider,

$$d = \frac{a}{\sqrt{h^2 + k^2 + l^2}} \cdot \qquad \text{Therefore,} \qquad \sin \theta = \frac{n \, \lambda}{2a} \sqrt{h^2 + k^2 + l^2} ,$$

or in quadratic form:
$$\sin^2 \theta = \frac{\lambda^2}{4a^2} [(n \, h)^2 + (n \, k)^2 + (n \, l)^2]. \tag{3}$$

We obtain from the Laue equations for a cubic lattice, by squaring, and noting that $a = b = c$ and that $\cos^2 \alpha + \cos^2 \beta + \cos^2 \gamma = 1$:

$$2 - 2(\cos \alpha \cdot \cos \alpha_0 + \cos \beta \cdot \cos \beta_0 + \cos \gamma \cdot \cos \gamma_0) = \frac{\lambda^2}{a^2} \cdot (h_1^2 + h_2^2 + h_3^2).$$

Within the parentheses on the left side, we can substitute $\cos \chi$; χ is the angle between the incident and diffracted X-ray beams. Therefore:

$$1 - \cos \chi = 2 \sin^2 \frac{\chi}{2} ,$$

so that,
$$\sin^2 \frac{\chi}{2} = \frac{\lambda^2}{4a^2} (h_1^2 + h_2^2 + h_3^2). \tag{4}$$

This equation permits us to relate χ to λ and to the orders of diffraction, h_1, h_2, and h_3. If we now compare Eqs. (3) and (4), we see that $\chi = 2\theta$; this is called the *Bragg angle*. We can also conclude this from Fig. 254, if we extend the reflected ray downward. The Laue indices are equal to the product of the Miller indices (cleared of a common denominator) and the order of diffraction n of the Bragg formula. Therefore:

$$h_1 = n \, h; \quad h_2 = n \, k; \quad h_3 = n \, l.$$

In structural studies, the Laue indices or the enlarged Miller indices are always inferred when using the symbols h, k, l. The beginner must make special note of this. Fig. 255 clarifies this relationship further. In the cross section through a space lattice, $2a$ and $3b$ are the intercepts of the trace of a macroplane through p and q. Its Miller indices are therefore $h = 3$ and $k = 2$. In the space lattice additional parallel planes lie between the points of the coordinate axes, with points which also scatter according to the Bragg relationships. It can be seen that these planes cut the x-axis at intervals of $a/3 (= a/h)$ and the y-axis at $b/2 (= b/k)$. They likewise have the Miller indices $h = 3$, $k = 2$.

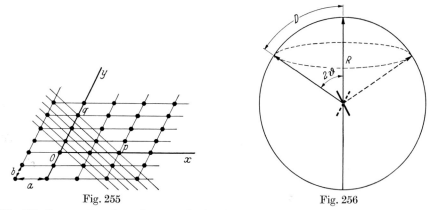

Fig. 255. Cross section through a space lattice; intercepts of the plane pq: $Op = 2a$; $Oq = 3b$; $h = 3$; $k = 2$; the family of planes repeat at distances a/h and b/k. (After BIJVOET)

Fig. 256. Origin of a powder pattern

The Powder Diffraction Pattern. We now want to consider how diffraction can be used for structure determination. Of the numerous X-ray methods we shall describe only two in detail, namely, the powder (DEBYE-SCHERRER) method and the rotating crystal method. In the powder method, a sample consisting of many very small crystalline particles is exposed to monochromatic X-rays. The crystals are randomly oriented, thus affording all possible angles of incidence which correspond to the available interplanar distances. Because of the random orientation, a given reflecting plane does not diffract in a single direction, but instead its locus lies on the surface of a cone whose semi-apical angle is equal to 2θ for that particular plane. This is very easily visualized, if one imagines a reflecting lattice plane and rotates the crystal around an axis, represented by the incident beam. This is indicated in Fig. 256 for a single lattice plane. All of the additional lattice planes form cones of reflection also, as is true also for the second and higher orders. On a photographic plate oriented perpendicular to the incident beam at some definite distance from the specimen, a family of concentric circles is produced. Usually a cylindrical film is used, with the sample under study located in the axis of the cylindrical film. The sample (powdered) is frequently placed in an X-ray transparent glass capillary. Using a cylindrical film, and with the X-ray beam perpendicular to the axis of the film, the diffraction pattern produced when the film is flattened after exposure consists of concentric ellipses. With the very narrow film strips ordinarily used in X-ray powder cameras, sections of the ellipses resemble arcs of circles symmetrically distributed with respect to the $0°\ 2\theta$ reference point (where the undiffracted or primary beam intersects the film). This arrangement of the film around the sample has the advantage that all diffracted rays are registered, including those in the back-reflection region, that is, at $2\theta > 90°$. In order to determine the angle θ, the distance $2D$, between two corresponding diffraction arcs, is measured. D divided by the camera radius R gives (Fig. 256) the angle 2θ in radians. In degrees therefore:

$$\frac{D}{R} \cdot \frac{360}{2\pi} = 2\theta.$$

Frequently cameras are used with a diameter such that the D value in millimeters is equal to the θ value in degrees. If D is set equal to θ, it follows then that:

$$360/2\pi = 2R = 57.33 \text{ mm}.$$

In order to determine the parameters of the space lattice, the lattice constants, from the measured values, the interplanar spacings of the Bragg equation must be related to the indices of the corresponding planes. That is to say, the diffraction pattern must be indexed. We shall consider the general case of a crystal with orthogonal coordinate axes, that is, a crystal which is either cubic, tetragonal, or orthorhombic. For the interplanar spacing d_{hkl} of a plane (hkl) in the orthorhombic system with lattice constants a, b, c;

$$d_{hkl} = \frac{1}{\sqrt{\left(\frac{h}{a}\right)^2 + \left(\frac{k}{b}\right)^2 + \left(\frac{l}{c}\right)^2}}.$$

If this value for d is substituted in the Bragg equation, and the entire expression squared, then:

$$\sin^2 \theta = \frac{\lambda^2}{4} \left(\frac{n^2 h^2}{a^2} + \frac{n^2 k^2}{b^2} + \frac{n^2 l^2}{c^2}\right).$$

For a cubic crystal for which $a = b = c$, the expression is simplified as follows:

$$\sin^2 \theta = \frac{\lambda^2}{4a^2} (n^2 h^2 + n^2 k^2 + n^2 l^2).$$

If we set $\lambda^2/4a^2$ equal to m:

$$\sin^2 \theta = m (n^2 h^2 + n^2 k^2 + n^2 l^2).$$

The $\sin^2\theta$ value for each line in the diffraction pattern is determined and the common factor m is sought. The residual term must represent the sum of the squares of the indices or their multiples. The interpretation of a powder pattern of NaCl is explained in Fig. 257. From $m = 0.01865$ it follows that for CuK_α radiation (1.54 Å), $a = 5.64$ Å.

Use of Powder Diffraction Patterns. It is relatively easy to index and interpret cubic crystals using powder patterns. It is only a little more difficult to do the same with tetragonal and hexagonal crystals. With crystals of lower symmetry, indexing and interpretation in this way is particularly unwieldy and difficult, so that other methods are used. However, for all crystals the powder method offers the advantage that the interplanar spacings d can easily be determined from the $\sin\theta$ values $\left(d = \frac{\lambda}{2\sin\theta}\right)$. By comparison with the powder patterns of known minerals and artificial crystals, unknown crystalline substances can be relatively easily and unequivocally identified. This is particularly important when dealing with very fine-grained substances for which microscopic methods are inadequate.

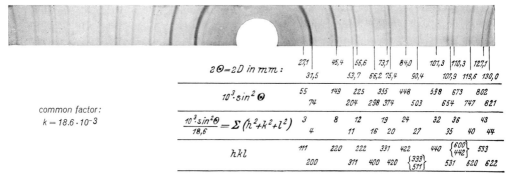

$2\Theta = 2D$ in mm:

| | 27,1 | 45,4 | 56,6 | 73,1 | 84,0 | 107,3 | 110,3 | 127,1 |
| 31,5 | | 53,7 | 56,2 | 75,4 | 90,4 | 107,9 | 119,6 | 130,0 |

$10^3 \cdot \sin^2\Theta$

| | 55 | 149 | 225 | 355 | 448 | 598 | 673 | 802 |
| 74 | | 204 | 298 | 374 | 503 | 654 | 747 | 821 |

common factor:
$k = 18.6 \cdot 10^{-3}$

$$\frac{10^3 \cdot \sin^2\Theta}{18,6} = \Sigma\,(h^2 + k^2 + l^2)$$

| | 3 | 8 | 12 | 19 | 24 | 32 | 36 | 43 |
| 4 | | 11 | 16 | 20 | 27 | 35 | 40 | 44 |

hkl

| | 111 | 220 | 222 | 331 | 422 | 440 | $\begin{Bmatrix}600\\442\end{Bmatrix}$ | 533 |
| 200 | | 311 | 400 | 420 | $\begin{Bmatrix}933\\511\end{Bmatrix}$ | 531 | 620 | 622 |

Fig. 257. Interpretation of a powder pattern of NaCl (Θ here corresponds to θ and k to m)

In this way it has been possible to obtain important information for the very fine-grained mineral constituents of clays and soils. X-ray identification is also used with advantage in the important field of mineral synthesis. In this case very fine-grained reaction products are usually formed, and identification must be carried out with very small amounts of sample. By means of the powder method it is possible to distinguish mechanical mixtures, chemical compounds, and mixed crystals. Mechanical mixtures of two oxides, for example, give the superimposed diffraction patterns of each of the pure oxides. If a single chemical compound occurs, however, it gives a characteristic diffraction pattern that can be distinguished from those of the starting materials. In the case of mixed crystals the diagram is representative of a single structure, whose d values and lattice parameters lie intermediate between those of the two end members.

The powder method provided an additional very important contribution soon after its introduction by DEBYE and SCHERRER in 1917. This was the indication that some colloids are crystalline. Even today one finds a tendency to equate the colloidal and the amorphous states, even though powder diffraction studies have shown that there are crystalline as well as amorphous colloids. In the mineral world, almost all colloids are crystalline. The natural globular-shaped, so-called mineral gels are actually aggregates of crystals. The most important exceptions are the volcanic glasses and the silica gels. The latter, when they occur in their present form as *opal* have often been transformed into more or less very fine-grained, and often poorly ordered, cristobalite. An amorphous body, a gas, liquid, or glass, gives only one or very few diffuse rings when irradiated with X-rays in the manner of the Debye-Scherrer method. This can be explained by considering the behavior of crystals during pulverization: as the particles in a powder become smaller and smaller, the interference maxima become broader and more diffuse, and the X-ray diffraction pattern approaches that of a truly amorphous body.

From the line broadening the particle size can generally be calculated. For very thin specimens and parallel X-ray beam, the following approximation is valid:

$$A \sim \frac{\lambda}{\beta \cdot \cos\theta}\,,$$

where β represents the angular width at half peak intensity, and A the edge dimension of a cube-shaped particle.

The photographic method is not always used to register X-ray diffraction patterns. Frequently, and to an increasing extent, a geiger counter or similar device is employed.

Fiber Diagrams. If a substance is not sufficiently pulverized, the circular arcs on the diffraction pattern become spotted. By means of simple geometrical considerations the non-random orientation of the crystallites can be determined. Fig. 258 explains how this can be done. ε is the angle between the center line of

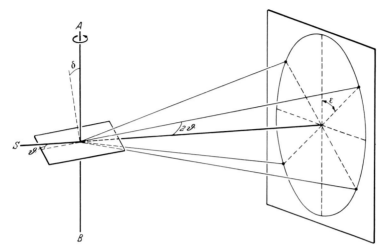

Fig. 258. Determination of crystal orientation

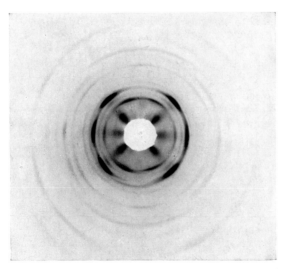

Fig. 259. Fiber pattern of chalcedony from Olomuczan. Fiber perpendicular to X-ray beam, CuK$_\alpha$ radiation

the X-ray photograph and the line joining the diffraction maximum with the center of the pattern. δ is the angle between the face normal to the reflecting plane and the fiber direction. Accordingly, $\cos \varepsilon = \dfrac{\cos \delta}{\cos \theta}$. The lattice planes involved are found most easily with the help of a stereographic projection.

If the particles exhibit a preferred orientation, as do the crystallites in rolled or extruded metals, the diffraction spots are not randomly distributed, that is, the diffraction rings do not show uniform darkening throughout their length. Instead regions of maximum darkening occur along the diffraction rings. Textured rocks, such as slates, exhibit this sort of preferred orientation of their mineral constituents. Mineral aggregates occur in nature in which one unique zone direction lies more or less parallel in all crystallites. An example is chalcedony, a subparallel aggregate of quartz crystals which have grown fibrous along [11.0]. Fig. 259 shows an X-ray fiber diagram of such a crystalline aggregate. Fiber diagrams are also produced by animal and plant fibers, stretched rubber, etc.

For all powder patterns, it is important to note that a specific wave length is used. The radiation selected must be one which does not cause the specimen to fluoresce by exciting its own characteristic radiation, as this produces a highly undesirable background. In order to estimate the exposure time, it is important to keep in mind that the scattering power of an atom is proportional to the number of electrons it contains. When used wisely the powder method is extremely versatile and especially useful in petrography.

Structure Determination. In order to carry out a complete structure determination, the absolute size and shape of the unit cell must first be determined. To do this rotating single crystal methods, as well as the powder method are used; the latter most frequently with cubic, tetragonal, and hexagonal crystals. The latter method will be considered first. This we have already done for NaCl (p. 151 and Fig. 257). The constant $m = \lambda^2/4a^2 = 0.0186$. Therefore for $\lambda = 1.54$ Å, $a = 5.64$ Å.

In order to calculate the number of formula units per unit cell, it is best to proceed as follows. It is basic that the mass of the unit cell must be a multiple of the absolute mass of the chemical unit formula. Therefore,

$$V \cdot \varrho = MW \cdot 1.660_8 \cdot 10^{-24} \cdot Z.$$

$V = $ Unit cell volume in cm³
$\varrho = $ Density of crystal in g/cm³
$MW = $ Molecular weight (in chemical sense)
$1.660_8 \cdot 10^{-24} = $ Factor to convert molecular weight to absolute mass units
$Z = $ Number of formula units per unit cell.

For NaCl: $V = a^3 = (5.64 \cdot 10^{-8})^3$ cm³   or $(5.64)^3 \cdot 10^{-24}$ cm³, $\varrho = 2.16$ g/cm³, MW $= 58.45$.

Therefore, for NaCl:

$$Z = \frac{(5.64)^3 \cdot 10^{-24} \cdot 2.16}{58.45 \cdot 1.660_8 \cdot 10^{-24}} \approx 4.$$

There are four formula units in the unit cell of NaCl.

To proceed further with the structure determination, we make use of the macroscopic symmetry as represented by the crystal class on the one hand, and the intensities of the X-ray reflections on the other. These depend on different factors. The scattering powers of the different elements are very different. As a rule of thumb, it can be noted that the atomic scattering power is approximately proportional to the number of electrons in the atom or ion. Thus for K^+ and Cl^-, the scattering factors are essentially equal; for Na^+ and Cl^-, distinctly different. The differences in intensities for individual reflections, which arise through interference, are especially important in structure determination.

We shall consider first the CsCl structure. It can be considered as consisting of two cubic primitive lattices, one consisting only of Cs^+, the other of Cl^- ions. The two lattices are displaced with respect to each other by one-half the cube diagonal. This is equivalent to a displacement of one-half unit translation in all three translation directions. If we place a Cs^+ ion at the origin of the unit cell, the coordinates of the Cl^- ion are $\frac{1}{2} \frac{1}{2} \frac{1}{2}$. The phase difference of the waves scattered from the "Cs-lattice" and from the "Cl-lattice", with indices hkl measured in radians, is $2\pi \cdot \frac{1}{2}(h+k+l)$. When $(h+k+l)$ is an even number the two waves reinforce each other constructively. When $(h+k+l)$ is odd, the two waves interfere destructively and subtraction occurs. Since the vibration amplitudes of the Cs-scattered and Cl-scattered waves are not equal, at even values of $(h+k+l)$, the resultant wave has large amplitude, at odd values of $(h+k+l)$, small amplitude. If we designate the amplitudes of the Cs-scattered waves as f_{Cs} and that of the Cl-scattered wave as f_{Cl}, then the resultant amplitude S is

and

$$S = f_{Cs} + f_{Cl} \quad \text{for} \quad (h+k+l) \text{ even}$$

$$S = f_{Cs} - f_{Cl} \quad \text{for} \quad (h+k+l) \text{ odd.}$$

S is called the *structure factor* (also designated as F).

The structure of tungsten, which has a cubic body-centered lattice, can be considered as also based on the CsCl structure. The sites of the Cs as well as the Cl ions are occupied by W. The lattice constants are, of course, different. The W atoms located at the two lattice points of the original CsCl lattice, have equal scattering power. For planes for which $(h+k+l)$ is even, $S = 2f_W$. For planes for which $(h+k+l)$ is odd, $S = f_W - f_W = 0$.

The cubic face-centered lattice can be considered as being composed of four cubic primitive lattices. If one is chosen as the basic lattice, the other three are derived by translating each of them one-half the face diagonal from the first. If we place one of the sites of one primitive lattice at the origin, we obtain, as with the body-centered lattice, the phase differences for the other three lattices (in radians),

$$2\pi \cdot \tfrac{1}{2} \cdot (h+k); \quad 2\pi \cdot \tfrac{1}{2} \cdot (k+l); \quad 2\pi \cdot \tfrac{1}{2} \cdot (l+h).$$

Therefore, four waves with equal amplitudes combine and exhibit these phase relations. If the three indices hkl are either all odd or all even for each of the four waves, the phase difference is a whole multiple of 2π and constructive interference and large resultant amplitude arises. If the indices are mixed odd and even, then two of the phase differences are an even multiple of 2π, and two an odd multiple, or vice versa. Thus extinction occurs. This can be summarized as follows:

$$S = 0 \quad \text{for } h, k, l \text{ mixed,}$$

$$S = 4A \quad \text{for } h, k, l \text{ all even, or all odd.}$$

The absence of reflections with mixed indices can be observed in the powder photographs of all cubic face-centered metals.

We want now to consider a somewhat more complex case, the NaCl structure. It can be described as one in which the Na^+ ions form a cubic face-centered lattice and the Cl^- ions likewise. The two lattices are displaced with respect to each other by one-half the cube diagonal, as were the two lattice points in a body centered lattice. Since it can be considered as a partial face-centered lattice, reflections with mixed indices are absent. For the remaining reflections, with hkl unmixed, the interference properties of the body centered lattice are applicable. Therefore reinforcement occurs when $(h+k+l)$ is even, extinction when $(h+k+l)$ is odd. If we consider the NaCl pattern (Fig. 257) the data given in Table 28 can be deduced from it. All reflections with mixed indices are absent.

Multiplicity factors are listed in one column of Table 28. These are important in determining intensities of X-ray reflections. Each crystal of the class $m3m$ possesses three equivalent sets of cube lattice planes, four sets of octahedral planes, six sets of dodecahedral planes, twelve sets of trapezohedral planes, etc.

Table 28. *Intensities, indices, and multiplicity factors for a NaCl powder pattern*

Observed intensity	Multiplicity factor	Indices	Comments
weak	4	111	diminished
very strong	3	200	intensified
very strong	6	220	intensified
very weak	12	311	diminished in spite of high mult. factor
very strong	4	222	intensified
strong	3	400	intensified, low mult. factor
very weak	12	331	diminished, like (311)
very strong	12	420	intensified, high mult. factor
very strong	12	422	intensified, high mult. factor

Since each $\bar{h}\,\bar{k}\,\bar{l}$ lattice plane is parallel to the hkl plane of a form, the multiplicity factor of a hkl lattice plane is only half as great as the number of faces of the corresponding holohedral crystallographic form. The intensity of a reflection in a powder pattern is proportional to the multiplicity factor of its lattice plane. Both effects, the multiplicity factor and structure factor are superimposed. In addition the intensities decrease systematically to $\theta \approx 50°$ and then increase again. Upon the two discontinuous intensity factors, structure factor and multiplicity factor, continuous factors related to changing θ are superimposed, influencing the intensity. In addition to the atomic scattering factors already mentioned, these continuous functions are the polarisation, Lorentz, and temperature factors. For an exact evaluation of intensities, these must be taken into account. A detailed discussion of these is beyond the scope of this discussion. There are additional geometrical and absorption factors which would have to be considered also.

We have seen that in the case of a body-centered translation group (structure of tungsten), all reflections with $h+k+l=2n+1$ are missing; in the case of a completely face-centered translation group, all reflections with mixed indices are absent. These mathematically regular absences are called *systematic extinctions*. They assist in determining not only the translation group (space lattice), but also indicate the presence or absence of glide planes and screw axes, and thus assist in determining the space group. Thus systematic extinctions are of great importance in X-ray crystal structure analysis.

Rotating Crystal Methods. It is convenient to index diffraction patterns, in the manner illustrated here for NaCl, only in the case of very highly symmetrical crystals. It is more convenient and often imperative to use single crystal rotation methods. In principle the same experimental arrangement can be used as for the powder method. A single crystal is substituted for the polycrystalline powder, and it is rotated around one of its zone axes, usually a crystallographic axis. Each lattice plane in the zone is gradually brought into reflecting position at the appropriate angle of incidence by rotation. Each produces a single diffraction spot on the film. All of the reflections from planes in this zone lie on a line which coincides with the intersection of a plane perpendicular to the rotation axis and the film. If the zone axis is the c-axis, all reflections from this zone will lie on this layer line on the film and have the indices $hk0$. This line of intersection on the film is called the equator or zero-layer line. The hkl reflections likewise form series of spots on the film, distributed on additional layer lines which extend parallel to the equator at some definite distance from it. Thus the $hk2$ reflections lie on the 2nd layer line, etc. The identity period in the rotation direction can be determined from the distance between a layer line and the equator. The rotation method is illustrated schematically in Fig. 260. A rotation diagram of a garnet crystal rotated around [001] is reproduced in Fig. 261. Several layer lines are seen in addition to the equatorial line. In order to find the repeat distance, a, in the rotation direction, the following equation is used: p is the distance between the respective layer line and the equator, μ is the layer line angle, h is the order number (index) of the layer line and R the camera radius:

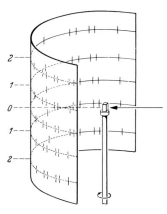

Fig. 260. Schematic diagram of a rotating crystal diffraction pattern

$$\tan \mu = \frac{p}{R}; \qquad a = \frac{h\,\lambda}{\sin \mu}.$$

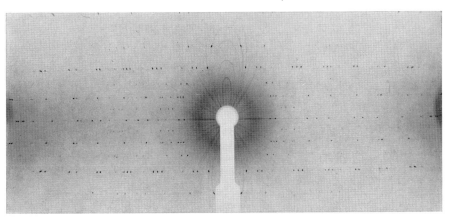

Fig. 261. Rotating crystal photograph of pyrope, $Mg_3Al_2(SiO_4)_3$, around [001] (reduced)

An example of such a calculation, using data taken from the original photograph from which Fig. 261 was reproduced, is summarized in Table 29. The wave length used was $\lambda = 1.539\,\text{Å}$.

If separate rotation patterns are taken around the three crystallographic axes, the unit cell parameters are obtained. These values can then be more accurately determined from calibrated powder patterns.

In the case of both powder and single crystal methods, some of the reflections from different lattice planes coincide, because they have the same angle of diffraction. A unique evaluation of X-ray extinctions is not always possible in

such cases. For complete interpretation this must be known, however, in order
to determine the appropriate structure factors. For this reason X-ray gonio-
meters are used in which not only the crystal is rotated, but also the film is
simultaneously translated in a definite direction. In this way the diffraction

Table 29. *Calculation of a_0 parameter from a single crystal rotation pattern. (Synthetic pyrope,*
$Mg_3Al_2(SiO_4)_3$ *around [001])*

Layer line (order number h)	p (mm)	tg μ	sin μ	$a = \dfrac{h \cdot \lambda}{\sin \mu}$
1	3.8	0.1326	0.1316	11.72 Å
2	7.9	0.2757	0.2658	11.60 Å
3	12.5	0.4363	0.3998	11.57 Å
4	18.1	0.6318	0.5340	11.55 Å
5	25.8	0.9005	0.6691	11.52 Å

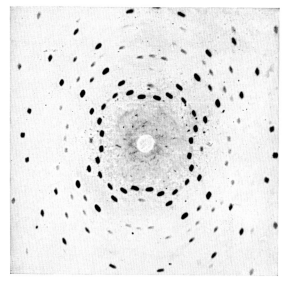

Fig. 262. Laue photograph of garnet in [001] direction. In general each diffraction spot
originates from a different wave length

maxima are spread out so that each reflection corresponds to a single hkl plane,
and the resulting array of spots can be very easily interpreted. The X-ray goniometric methods, using perpendicular or inclined incidence of the X-ray beam as
developed by WEISSENBERG, BUERGER, and MENZER are especially important.
We cannot treat them in further detail here.

In this summary it should further be stated that determination of crystal structures by X-rays alone is frequently extremely difficult. Therefore supplementary
information is of very considerable importance. Atomic and ionic radii, packing
densities, coordination schemes, the principle of electrostatic neutrality (lines of
force should be as short as possible), optical properties (indices of refraction,
birefringence), magnetic and cohesion properties, and other information provide
considerable assistance in crystal structure analysis.

The Laue Method. The procedure used originally by v. LAUE involved a stationary crystal irradiated by X-rays of different wave lengths. An array of diffraction spots is produced (Fig. 262). The Laue photograph gives a pattern indicating the crystal symmetry in the direction of X-ray transmission and is

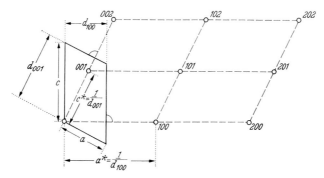

Fig. 263. Relation between the unit cell lattice (solid lines) and the reciprocal lattice (dashed lines). The reciprocal lattice continues in all directions

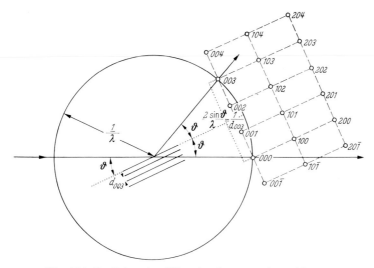

Fig. 264. Conditions for diffraction from a reciprocal lattice

still used for symmetry studies of crystals. However, for crystal structure analysis, monochromatic methods are much more suitable. Under usual circumstances X-ray photographs indicate that a given lattice plane reflects equally from both sides of the plane (G. FRIEDEL, 1913). The effect is to introduce an apparent center of symmetry. Therefore it is not possible to ascertain by means of X-ray diffraction alone whether a crystal direction is polar or not, that is, whether or not a crystal has a true center of symmetry. The exception to this situation occurs when the crystal contains atoms with an X-ray adsorption edge lying near to that for the radiation used. Then the symmetry of crystals with enantiomorphic forms can actually be determined. An example of such an enantiomorphic structure is that of right and left-handed quartz. It has been shown that the morphologically defined right-quartz contains left-spiralling screw axes (p. 32).

The Reciprocal Lattice. In X-ray crystallography it is frequently convenient to derive an imaginary lattice from the direct lattice of the crystal. The axes of this imaginary lattice are parallel to the directions of the face normals of the unit cell and the repeat distances along its axes are the reciprocals of interplanar lattice spacings. This imaginary lattice is called a reciprocal lattice (Fig. 263). The reciprocal lattice has been extensively used because with its help the diffraction relationships of single crystal diffraction patterns can be easily understood. This is shown for a two-dimensional case in Fig. 264. It can be seen that the real lattice plane is in a position to satisfy the Bragg diffraction conditions, when its corresponding point in the reciprocal lattice (whose origin is at $0, 0, 0$) lies on a circle of radius $1/\lambda$ (reflecting circle). In three dimensions we do not use a circle of reflection but the corresponding *Ewald sphere of reflection*, of radius $1/\lambda$.

If the lattice planes in a crystal are not spaced periodically in one direction, that is, if they have one-dimensional disorder, the X-ray reflections are not sharp in all directions. Accordingly the reciprocal lattice points are smeared out perpendicular to the disordered planes, sometimes continuously from one reciprocal lattice point to the next.

Fourier Synthesis. The manner of crystal structure determination discussed so far depends upon trial and error methods. After the lattice parameters and unit cell symmetry have been determined and the number of formula units per unit cell calculated, a structure compatible with the symmetry and intensity relations is proposed. Fourier synthesis is an important resource in modern crystal structure determination. It takes its name from the analysis of a periodic function by Fourier series. It is possible by means of Fourier methods to determine extremely complex structures and to do so with much greater accuracy than was possible earlier with the methods previously described. By the use of special and very careful methods of measurement, it is possible to determine the electron density at all points in a crystal (see Figs. 158a and 170a).

Electron Diffraction. An additional diffraction method utilizes electron beams to produce diffraction patterns. It has been known in theory since DE BROGLIE (1924), and from experiments by DAVISSON and GERMER (1927), that electrons can be diffracted like light waves. Electrons with mass m and velocity v behave like waves with wave length $\lambda = \dfrac{h}{mv}$, where h is PLANCK's constant. If velocity is expressed in terms of an accelerating potential in volts applied to the electrons, we obtain the expression:

$$\lambda = \sqrt{\frac{150}{v}} \ \text{Å}.$$

At 63 V, waves would be produced of wave length equal to that of CuK_α radiation. Usually much more energetic electrons are used.

The diffraction of electrons is fundamentally different from that of X-rays, in that the electron beams are not only influenced by the electron shells of an atom, but also by its nucleus. The diffracted intensity is about 10^8 greater than with X-rays, but they are also much more strongly adsorbed. They are transmitted through only very thin layers.

Neutron Diffraction. Excited neutrons are diffracted like other elementary particles by crystal lattices. Neutrons produced in an atomic pile do not all have the same velocity. Their wave lengths extend over a large range. "Thermal" neutrons, which are those which through numerous collisions are in thermal equilibrium with their surroundings, have their most frequent velocities corresponding to a wave length of 1.3 Å. Thus in a continuous spectrum, the wave lengths of the neutrons have a maximum at just that wave length most convenient for structural analysis. For comparison we can recall that the most frequently used X-radiation for structure determination is that of $CuK_\alpha (\lambda = 1.54$ Å$)$. By means of reflection from a crystal and appropriate collimation, a narrow beam of monochromatic neutrons can be produced and used for diffraction experiments.

It is especially important from the mineralogical standpoint that the position of hydrogen atoms in crystals can be accurately determined by neutron diffraction. Because of the very low atomic scattering power of hydrogen, this is possible by means of X-rays only when the other atoms present in the crystal have low atomic numbers (to perhaps 20). Even in these favorable cases the hydrogen can be only inaccurately located. Knowledge of the positions of hydrogen are of fundamental importance to the crystal chemistry of hydroxides, OH containing salts, and hydrated salts.

Electron Microscopy. We can only briefly mention the important field of electron microscopy. It is an important supplementary aid for studying very fine-grained minerals, such as the clay minerals. It reveals primarily information about the size and shapes of small particles. It is possible to obtain electron diffraction patterns from the same samples being viewed in the electron micro-scope. Lattice contacts can be determined in much the same way as from X-ray powder patterns.

IV. Crystal Growth and Dissolution

1. Geometrical Relationships

Introduction. In the preceding discussion we have dealt with a series of physical properties of crystals and have seen in the last chapter how the atomic structure of crystals can be determined with the help of X-ray optics. We have yet to discuss the most sensitive expression of crystal structure, the phenomena of crystal growth and dissolution. The occurrence of natural planar bounded bodies was the starting point of crystallography and the origin of such bodies still remains one of its most important problems. In spite of all the research that has been carried out, there is still much uncertainty about the mechanisms of crystal growth.

Growth Velocities. The problem can be approached from different directions. We will first consider the geometric approach. Why is it that a given cubic crystal sometimes crystallizes as cubes, sometimes as dodecahedra and sometimes as octahedra ?

The law of constancy of interfacial angles tells us that the faces of the crystal can be displaced parallel to themselves. We shall assume that a crystal grows by means of such parallel displacement of its faces and that each form has a definite displacement (or growth) velocity, unrelated to its size and boundaries. This growth velocity, for a given structure, is dependent only on external conditions. These velocities can be measured on growing crystals in the laboratory. SPANGENBERG determined the following values (Table 30) for potassium alum at 30° C and 0.5% supersaturation.

Table 30. *Relative growth velocities during growth of potassium alum*

Form	{111}	{110}	{001}	{221}	{112}	{012}
Growth velocity	1	4.8	5.3	9.5	11.0	27.0

If we want to study the concurrent development of all possible faces, a sphere fashioned from a crystal is used as the initial body. It is observed during a growth experiment that planar surfaces develop at certain places on the sphere. Other points first remain curved or become rough until these points also gradually are over-grown by the faces which first appeared. Simple geometric considerations show that those faces survive which have the lowest growth velocities. In Fig. 265 the relationships are shown for alum in a section parallel to (110). The curved and rough initial state is omitted, and the (hhl) forms indicated in Table 30 are drawn tangent to the sphere so that they form a polyhedron. Several growth stages are indicated after equal time intervals, corresponding to the growth velocities given in Table 30. Already after the first stage, the faces (112) and (221) are no longer present. Their growth velocities are so great that they would lie far outside the crystal. By the second stage (110) has also disappeared. The face (001) becomes smaller and smaller. It would have disappeared by stage six which, however, is not shown in the drawing.

Whether a face persists during growth or disappears depends upon the ratio of its displacement velocity to that of the other faces. This will be illustrated by the simple example of growth of a crystal consisting of a dodecahedron and a

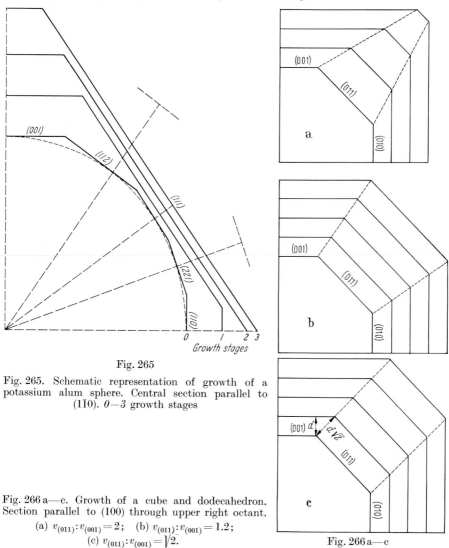

Fig. 265

Fig. 265. Schematic representation of growth of a potassium alum sphere. Central section parallel to (1$\bar{1}$0). $0-3$ growth stages

Fig. 266 a—c. Growth of a cube and dodecahedron. Section parallel to (100) through upper right octant.

(a) $v_{(011)} : v_{(001)} = 2$;   (b) $v_{(011)} : v_{(001)} = 1.2$;

(c) $v_{(011)} : v_{(001)} = \sqrt{2}$.

Fig. 266a—c

cube. In Fig. 266a the velocity ratio, is $v\{011\} : v\{001\} = 2$. The face (011) gradually disappears. The lines connecting the face intersections converge. In Fig. 266b they diverge, and in this case both faces persist upon further growth and in fact enlarge. In this case the displacement velocity is $v\{011\} : v\{001\} = 1.2$. It is easy to see that parallel interfacial boundaries would occur when $v\{011\} : v\{001\} = \sqrt{2}$. The size of (011) remains constant during growth. This case is illustrated in Fig. 266c.

11*

Dependence on External Conditions. Definite forms whose growth velocities are small survive as the end product of growth of a spherical crystal. These considerations assist in explaining the characteristic forms of crystals, if the additional assumption is made that growth velocities are dependent upon external conditions, especially the magnitude of supercooling and supersaturation of the solution constituents, and perhaps also temperature and pressure. An example showing the temperature influence was described by EAKLE for crystallization of potassium iodate. It crystallizes as a monoclinic crystal, forming pseudocubic forms. Between 10 and 20° C it grows as "cubes", but with increasing temperature the cube is modified by "rhombododecahedron" until, at 70° C, this form occurs exclusively. To what extent the degree of supersaturation shares in this effect requires further investigation.

$NaClO_3$ crystallizes as cubes from pure solutions at room temperature. However, if SO_4^{2-} ions are added to the solution, say by addition of Na_2SO_4, tetrahedra form. $S_2O_3^{2-}$ ions serve as even more effective solution constituents. Even at concentration ratios of $ClO_3^- : S_2O_3^{2-}$ as low as $1000/1$ the cube is eliminated as the growth form (BUCKLEY). Urea, $CO(NH_2)_2$ is another example, known for a long time to be an effective ingredient for form modification of NaCl. While NaCl crystallizes from aqueous solutions by evaporation in air (therefore at not too great a supersaturation) exclusively in the form $\{100\}$, the addition of urea to the solution causes octahedra to appear. At very small urea concentrations the octahedra occur in combination with the cube; at higher concentrations the octahedron occurs alone. Similar form modification is affected by additions of $CdCl_2$ or $PbCl_2$. A very large number of other inorganic and organic substances have very little or no effect on form development of NaCl. Thus the property involved here is very specific and as yet unpredictable for individual substances.

Fibrous Growth. Geometric considerations lead also to an explanation of fibrous growth. We must distinguish here between minerals which grow fibrous because of their structure, for example the chain silicates, and those whose fibrous growth is a consequence of external growth conditions, as is sometimes the case for quartz and calcite. We shall be concerned here with only the latter. Let us consider a situation in which many small crystals are lying close together on a substrate and in random orientation. Crystal growth from each of these nuclei is initiated simultaneously and the supply of growth material is available only from above. Fig. 267 represents a section through such a cluster of crystals as would be easily produced experimentally and viewed through the side walls of a cylinder. Of the six nuclei represented, nuclei 2 and 3 are almost completely eliminated following growth stage I. Following stage II crystal 6 has completely disappeared and crystals 1 and 5 have become insignificant. During stage III crystal 1 is gone and 5 has almost disappeared. Nucleus 4, oriented most favorably, has become more and more prevalent and finally continues to grow all by itself.

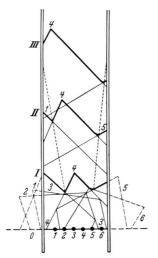

Fig. 267. Fibrous growth (after GROSS and MOELLER). *1, 2, 3, ...* nuclei; *I, II, III* growth stages

Thus a selectivity of nuclei occurs. In addition to the orientation of the nucleus, this selectivity depends on the face growth velocities. Those nuclei succeed in this competition for which the greatest growth velocities occur perpendicular to the substrate. The lateral boundary of such a fiber is not a crystal plane. It is formed by the junction of two growth directions and is planar only if the temperature and concentration do not vary during growth.

Fibrous growth develops especially distinctly where crystals can grow from a central nucleus outward in all directions. This can be demonstrated easily in two dimensions by seeding a supercooled melt of salicylic acid phenyl ester with a cluster of nuclei. In three dimensions, spherical radially fibrous crystal aggregates, spherulites, form under such conditions. It is also common for the nuclei to be situated not at the center of the sphere, but on the surface of a cavity. In such cases the crystals grow radially inward toward the center of the cavity. In all of these cases the growth directions are those directions of greatest face growth velocity.

Dissolution. The same geometrical considerations apply to dissolution as to growth of crystals. However, it must be noted that dissolution of a crystal from within is the converse of the usual crystal growth (displacement of the crystal-solution interface outward from the point of origin). These relationships can be studied by boring a crystal and dissolving it from within through the bore canal. If we have a small hollow cavity at the start (say in an alum crystal), we can utilize Fig. 265 again to illustrate the process involved. As solution progresses the planes with the smallest growth velocities must be left to predominate. In this way a polygonal cavity results which is identical in form to a normal crystal, a so-called negative crystal. Such negative crystals occur frequently in minerals. By producing them artificially, it can be observed that their forms are influenced by solution constituents just as is the case for normal crystal growth. Since in this case naturally no introduction of the solution constituents into the crystal is possible, it is possible to ascertain clearly the influence of growth velocities alone, without the effects of form modification due to introduction of solution impurities into the lattice (FRIEDEL).

A solid sphere which is dissolved from the outside behaves quite differently. In this case those faces with greatest growth velocities should persist and finally dominate. The following must be considered. There are relatively few planes of low growth velocity, namely those faces with low indices that would persist during growth. In contrast to these, there occurs on a sphere theoretically an infinitely large number of planes with high dissolution velocities. The formation of a large number of faces close to one another creates the impression of curved faces and in fact such solution forms are produced by dissolution of a spherical crystal.

A crystal behaves similarly during degradation by a chemical reaction. Again the growth velocities are unequal for different face orientations. Also the relative reaction of different faces depends on the solution or reaction reagent.

Table 31. *Reaction velocities of fluorite plates of different orientations with HCl*
(d = 1.108 g/cm^3; 96°C) and concentrated boiling Na$_2$CO$_3$ solution; μ in minutes

	Plate parallel to				
	{100}	{110}	{111}	{210}	{311}
HCl	2.51	11.18	6.67	12.59	6.85
Na$_2$CO$_3$ soln.	8.00	3.5	6.0	7.5	12.5

In this respect the studies of BECKE in 1885 by treatment of differently oriented plates of fluorite with hot hydrochloric acid and soda solutions are very instructive. Some of his results are tabulated in Table 31.

2. Structural Considerations

Depositional Energy of Ionic Crystals. Thus far we have considered crystal growth strictly geometrically, assuming that the growth velocities of different faces of a crystal are different. Before the development of structural crystallography, attempts were made to relate these differences to the surface tensions of crystal faces. We now know, however, that this is significant only in the case of extremely small crystallites.

The calculations of depositional energies of individual lattice particles by W. KOSSEL since 1927 and I. N. STRANSKI since 1928 led to an important breakthrough in clarifying this phenomenon. We shall consider first the growth of a crystal of the NaCl-type, and only as a first approximation calculate energies based solely on electrostatic (Coulombic) forces involved in the deposition of individual

Fig. 268. Deposition of an ion in a chain of ions

steps. We shall consider first a one-dimensional lattice, that is, an ion chain consisting of alternating positive and negative ions (Fig. 268). The work which must be expended in order to separate an ion with the charge $+e$ to a distance r from an ion with a charge $-e$, is e^2/r. Conversely this work is released if the ion with charge $+e$ is brought from infinity to a distance r from the ion $-e$. The deposited ion which we assumed had the $+e$ charge is attracted by the neighboring negative ion with charge $-e$ situated at distance r, is repelled by a second (positive) ion at distance $2r$, is attracted by the next (negative) ion at distance $3r$, etc. Through summation the depositional energy is given as follows:

$$A'_e = \Phi' \frac{e^2}{r} = \frac{e^2}{r}\left(1 - \frac{1}{2} + \frac{1}{3} - \frac{1}{4} \pm \cdots\right) = \frac{e^2}{r} \cdot \ln 2 = 0.6932 \frac{e^2}{r}.$$

For deposition in a planar lattice (Fig. 269) we obtain the expression:

$$A''_e = \Phi'' \frac{e^2}{r} = \frac{e^2}{r}\left[\left(1 - \frac{2}{\sqrt{2}} + \frac{2}{\sqrt{5}} - \frac{2}{\sqrt{10}} \pm \cdots\right) - \frac{1}{2} + \frac{2}{\sqrt{5}} - \frac{2}{\sqrt{8}} \pm \cdots\right]$$

$$= 0.1144 \frac{e^2}{r}.$$

Exact mathematical consideration of the summation shows that it is necessary to take into account only very few ion chains running parallel to the [100] boundary. The additional inner lying chains contribute insignificantly to the depositional energy.

An additional important source of depositional energy is that which is released when an ion far distant from the edge of a cube face takes up a site which is to become an extension of the structure (Fig. 270, 1). This increment of energy can be calculated in a manner analogous to the two previous cases:

$$A'''_e = \Phi''' \frac{e^2}{r} = 0.0662 \frac{e^2}{r}.$$

For the total depositional energy for site 3 in Fig. 270, we arrive at the following relationship, because of the additive character of electrostatic forces:

$$A_e = \frac{e^2}{r}(0.6932 + 0.1144 + 0.0662) = 0.8738 \frac{e^2}{r}.$$

Lattice Energy of Ionic Crystals. From the previous expression it is possible to calculate the lattice energy A_Φ of NaCl. This is the energy which is released when one mol of the crystal is formed. A cube of NaCl consisting of one mol of

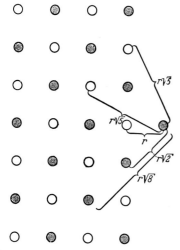

Fig. 269. Deposition of ion at the edge [100] of a planar lattice

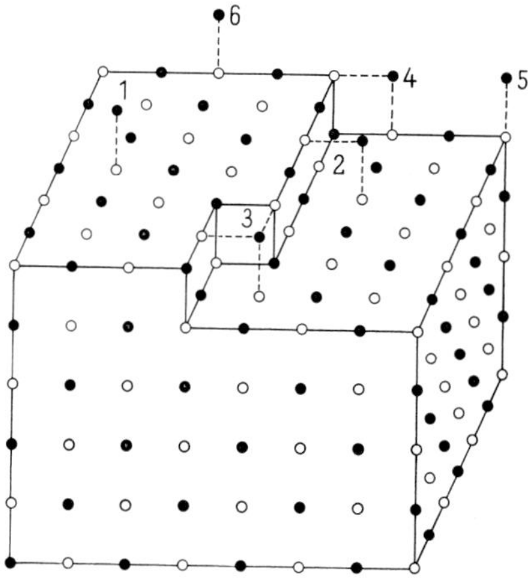

Fig. 270. Deposition of ions onto a NaCl lattice. Numbers correspond to those in Table 33

NaCl has an edge length of 3.0 cm or about 10^8 Na-Cl interionic distances. Therefore, during formation the number of depositions of type 3 as shown in Fig. 270 so greatly predominates over all the others, that the energy released during formation can be considered as follows:

$$A_\Phi = 2 \cdot N_L \cdot A_e = N_L \cdot 1.7476 \, \frac{e^2}{r} \, .$$

N_L is the Avogadro's number ($6.02 \cdot 10^{23}$) and the factor 2 is introduced, because during deposition of a formula unit of NaCl, the energy $2 \cdot A_e$ is released, since both one Na$^+$ ion and one Cl$^-$ ion are involved. The constant 1.7476 is called the Madelung constant after the man who first made this calculation. It applies to all crystals of the NaCl-type. For a lattice with higher valence ions the valence z must likewise be taken into account. In general then the following expression applies:

$$A_\Phi = N_L \cdot \alpha \cdot \frac{z^2 \, e^2}{r} \, .$$

α is the Madelung constant. Some values for the Madelung constant for different structure types are given in Table 32.

Table 32. *Madelung constants for different structure types*

Structure type	α
CsCl	1.7627
NaCl	1.7476
Sphalerite	1.6381
Wurzite	1.6413
Fluorite	5.0388
Rutile	4.82
Anatase	4.80
Cuprite	4.4425

This calculation of electrostatic lattice energy, as noted earlier, is only a first approximation. It can be substantially improved by taking into account also the van der Waal's attractive and repulsive forces between ions. The van der Waal's attraction of the two oppositely charged ions does not extend significantly to any large distance. On the contrary it becomes insignificant at the same distances used for the sums of ionic radii in crystal chemistry. Accordingly this attractive force can be ignored. However, a significant repulsion term must be introduced into the equation which is exponential in form. Thus it follows:

$$A_{\Phi_g} = A_{\Phi} + A_{\text{v.d.w.}} - N_L \frac{b}{r^m}.$$

Compressibility data are used in evaluating the value of m. The necessary calculations for determination of m and $A_{\text{v.d.w.}}$ are beyond the scope of this introduction.

Growth of NaCl Crystals. In order to use these relationships in considerations bearing on crystal growth, it is sufficient to use the approximate expressions for deposition energies, since we are only interested in the orders of preference for face development. It is evident that in the growing crystal, ions enter those sites which result in the greatest possible release of energy. Since, in the expression for depositional energy, the factor e^2/r is common for all deposition possibilities, we shall concern ourselves here with only the variable term, which is designated

Table 33. Φ values of the deposition energies for ions in NaCl type structure on a crystal with $\{100\}$ as only form

Site	Form of summation of Φ values	Resulting Φ value	
1	Φ'''	0.0662	
2	$\Phi'' + \Phi'''$	0.1806	
3	$\Phi' + \Phi'' + \Phi'''$	0.8738	Deposition Fig. 270
4	$\frac{1}{2}\Phi' + \Phi'' + \frac{1}{2}\Phi'''$	0.4941	
5	$\frac{1}{4}\Phi' + \frac{1}{2}\Phi'' + \frac{1}{4}\Phi'''$	0.2470	
6	$\frac{1}{2}\Phi'' + \frac{1}{2}\Phi'''$	0.0903	
7	$\frac{3}{2}\Phi' + \Phi'' + \frac{1}{2}\Phi'''$	1.1872	
8	$\frac{7}{4}\Phi' + \Phi'' + \frac{1}{4}\Phi'''$	1.3440	Dissolution Fig. 272
9	$2\Phi' + \Phi'' + \Phi'''$	1.5669	
10	$2\Phi' + \frac{3}{2}\Phi'' + \frac{1}{2}\Phi'''$	1.5910	
11	$2\Phi' + 2\Phi'' + \Phi'''$	1.6814	

as Φ. In the upper portion of Table 33 some Φ values are given for the six crystal sites corresponding to those in Fig. 270.

From these values it follows that deposition at site 3 is energetically most favorable. The crystal will continue to form those chains which have already been started. If the chain continues to develop out to the boundary of the crystal, the next most favorable stage is site 4 and a new chain is initiated from the edge. Thus growth of those cubic lattice planes already started is completed before new layers are added. Only when the construction of a lattice plane is completed, can a new lattice plane be begun. The energetically most favorable site for the beginning of a new lattice plane is at the corner at site 5. Deposition at sites 1 and 6 is improbable.

This theory thus explains the formation of the primary growth form $\{100\}$ for NaCl. What is the situation, however, with the other forms such as $\{110\}$ and $\{111\}$? In the dodecahedral lattice plane there are also chains of Na$^+$ and Cl$^-$ ions. These chains are so situated with respect to each other that one Na of one chain always has two Na ions of adjacent chains as neighbors. Therefore Na$^+$ and Cl$^-$ chains occur perpendicular to the NaCl chains. The deposition energy for the free NaCl chain parallel to [100], Φ'_{110} is again 0.6932, but that for the edge [001] of a lattice plane (110) is negative: $\Phi''_{110} = -0.0270$. For deposition on a completed $\{110\}$ plane of the crystal $\Phi'''_{110} = 0.2077$ is obtained. This is due, as

Fig. 271 shows, to an ion occurring in this plane being brought into juxtaposition to two attracting neighbors instead of one in the case of the {100} plane. Thus chains initiated on the dodecahedral surface will continue to grow at a more rapid rate than it would on a cube surface, since $\Phi'_{110} + \Phi'''_{110}$ is 0.9009. Also deposition of an ion on a (110) surface is energetically more favorable than on a cube surface. But lateral completion of the layer becomes difficult. The chains thus form at some distance from one another. The dodecahedral face, therefore, has a greater growth velocity than the cube face. It slopes, however, in step formation in the direction coinciding with the cube edges. In fact, the dodecahedral faces formed by growth from spherical crystals show striations in these directions.

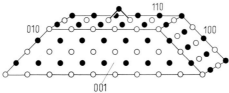

Fig. 271. Deposition of an ion on a smooth atomic dodecahedral plane of NaCl

The octahedral lattice planes, which in the case of the NaCl type structure would contain like ions only if they were formed smooth on an atomic scale, consist for similar reasons of stepped growth forms. The octahedral face growth velocity is very great. Although it has been possible to rationalize the cubic crystallization morphology of NaCl, the development of the most important forms for CsCl and CaF_2 cannot be satisfactorily explained in a similar manner.

The above theory enables us to explain some extremely important facts, however. Let us consider the growth sphere. We saw on the basis of geometrical considerations, how certain individual faces gradually predominate. We know now that of the infinite number of face orientations which the NaCl sphere offers during growth, the cube faces expand laterally, since all zones of the cube edge continue to grow rapidly. They offer the maximum energy gain upon deposition. The faces which occur, however, increase very slowly in thickness. The dodecahedral and octahedral faces grow rapidly as stepped faces. Intermediate regions are rough because on them irregular growth takes place.

The growth of crystals with other than ionic bonding affords nothing essentially new. Naturally the deposition energies are different from those involving ionic bonding. A crystal of formula type AB with the NaCl structure can assume other values than NaCl for the absolute deposition energy as well the relationships for different positions. As a result other forms can be energetically more favorable. Since the calculation of deposition energies for metallic and covalent crystals is less well documented than for ionic bonding, we shall not go into further details here.

Dissolution of NaCl Crystals. Upon dissolution of a crystal those ions are abstracted whose removal requires the least amount of energy. We shall consider a cubic crystal with a partially formed (001) lattice plane (Fig. 272). As dissolution occurs it will begin (corresponding to the deposition energies 3 and 7—11 in Table 33) at site 3. As soon as the ion chain parallel to [100] is completely dissolved away, further dissolution of the (001) lattice plane is initiated at site 7. As the lattice plane is completely destroyed, removal of the ion at site 8 requires the least expenditure of energy. A cubic NaCl crystal without cracks and fissures is so dissolved that it is first decomposed parallel to the cube face, an ion is released at site 8 at a corner, etc. If cracks are present, the chains so exposed are dissolved.

Upon dissolution of a solid sphere, again those chains are decomposed that are parallel to the zone of the cube edges. Therefore it is by no means necessary that faces with simple indices should be produced. Instead curved faces with curvature parallel to the three cube zones occur. The curvature results from the formation of small partial faces with increasing or decreasing inclination with respect to one another. During growth the {100} faces spread laterally by growth of chains and become morphologically important as a result of their low growth velocity. Upon dissolution, curved faces are produced by the chain decomposition in the zone direction. In the case of NaCl these are described as pyramidal cube faces. These are faces which have been built up from chains in the zone directions of the cube. This importance of zonal relations is not confined to the NaCl crystal. This is generally true, as numerous studies of form development have shown. The importance of directions in relation to the faces may not be disregarded.

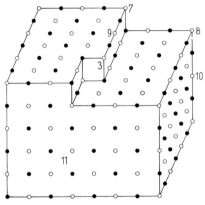

Fig. 272. Removal of ions from the NaCl lattice. Numbers correspond to those in Table 33

Our previous treatment of crystal growth was in at least two respects greatly oversimplified. We first of all assumed that the crystal is an ideal one, secondly we assumed that the material being accreted occurs in the form of isolated ions on the surfaces of the forming crystal. We shall deal in turn with the significance of these deviations from reality.

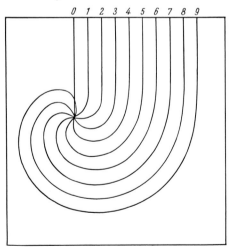

Fig. 273. Origin of a growth spiral in several stages of development (0—9). At the start the left side of the step is higher than to the right of it. The spiral, seen from above, winds upward clockwise

Growth of a Real Crystal. In the example of the (100) face of NaCl, the deposition energy is considerably less on a completed face than that required for completion of an atomic layer already started. Another way of expressing this is to say that for lateral expansion of a partially formed layer on the surface, a considerably lower supersaturation is necessary than for initiating a new layer. Therefore, one should expect macroscopic growth to take place only above a certain supersaturation (according to theoretical considerations of crystallization from the vapor phase, this should be of the order of 50%). This is in considerable contradiction to actual observation. A way out of this paradox is found in that we do not observe the growth of ideal crystals, but instead real crystals containing imperfections.

Especially important in this respect are the screw dislocations observed on the faces of many crystals (see Fig. 185). This was first noted by BURTON, CABRERA, and FRANK in 1949. We assume first of all that a straight step must

a   b

Fig. 274. (a) Circular and (b) polygonal growth spirals on (0001) of SiC (after VERMA). Magnification (a) × 175, (b) × 60

run from the point of emergence of the dislocation to the boundary of the crystal (for example, in the [100] direction in NaCl). Through the deposition of material on this edge, the step gradually takes on the form of a spiral (Fig. 273). Such growth spirals have been noted repeatedly on crystallographic surfaces. If the step height measures only a few Ångstroms, its detection requires special methods of study which we cannot go into here. We want to note, however, that on the prism faces of beryl, growth spirals with a step height of only 8.5 ± 1.0 Å have been described. This amount corresponds well with the corresponding interplanar spacing in the structure. Step heights of growth spirals can be considerably greater than the corresponding lattice spacing, reaching sometimes several hundred Ångstroms. Fig. 274 shows two examples of growth spirals on the (0001) faces of silicon carbide, SiC. Fig. 275 shows a growth spiral on (111) of sphalerite. If a crystal grows by accretion of material in growth spirals, the face can be displaced any distance parallel to itself without the necessity of accretion taking place on completed faces. Instead of a completely planar layer, spreading out to the border of the crystal, followed by the accretion of the next layer, etc., spiral staircase-like bent layers, rather than completely planar layers, are formed. The axis of the spiral is the screw dislocation.

Deposition of Foreign Matter. Up to now in our treatment of crystal growth we have assumed that individual ions impinge on the crystal. This is only strictly true for crystal growth from the vapor phase. Much more important are the variations resulting from solution. This process is more important in the case of mineral formation. During growth from aqueous solutions, for example, ions are always to a greater or lesser extent hydrated. For crystallization of an anhydrous salt the ions must be freed of their hydration envelopes. In addition, water molecules are adsorbed to a great extent on the external surfaces of crystals. Moreover, certain impurities in the solution can be adsorbed on crystal surfaces.

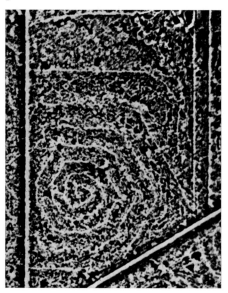

Fig. 275. Polygonal growth spiral on the tetrahedral face of sphalerite (after VERMA). Magnification × 350

If we consider NaCl again as a distinct example (Fig. 270, Table 33), we find that foreign ions are preferentially adsorbed at the sites of greatest deposition energy, and are thus fixed at sites 2, 3, 4, and 5. These are the active sites in ionic crystals. Then follows deposition at the edges of a completed crystal, and finally on its faces.

By incorporation of radioactive ions, adsorption and introduction of ions into a crystal can be followed experimentally (O. HAHN). These crystals are "self-photographing" because of their radio-activity and indicate that the foreign ions are situated at the corners and edges of crystals.

Dipoles are likewise bound to an ionic lattice. In this case the corners and edges play a less important role than in ionic adsorption. Since the electrostatic attraction of a neutral face of an ionic crystal, as for example the {100} on NaCl, falls off very quickly with distance, adsorption occurs especially by small dipole-molecules such as water and ammonia. Cleavage surfaces of crystals are covered very quickly with a water layer. Large organic molecules are selectively adsorbed if they contain a group such as the hydroxyl group with a dipole moment.

The adsorbed ions are not necessarily so strongly adsorbed that they are incorporated into the structure. If for a certain face they have a greater retention time than for others, a change in the growth velocity of that face and with it a

modification in form of the crystal may be effected. Thus we can understand the
effect of solution constituents discussed previously on page 164.

Growth Accessories. In our discussion of growth spirals, we have seen that
a crystal face need not be planar. It is important that the various phenomena of this
kind are often so large that they can be observed by means of a hand lens or

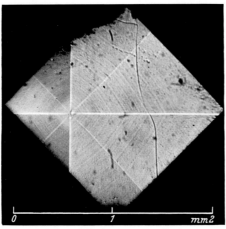

Fig. 276. {hkl} vicinal faces on a cube face of analcite. The apex of the vicinal pyramid lies
to the left of the center of the cube face. (After KALB)

even by the unaided eye. Probably growth spirals only occur on a scale necessitat-
ing high magnification to observe them. The prism faces {$10\bar{1}0$} of quartz, for
example, are frequently horizontally striated. On its rhombohedral faces on the
other hand, very flat irregularities with rounded surfaces are often observed.

In a theoretical classification of variations of a crystal face from the ideal,
two cases should be distinctly differentiated:

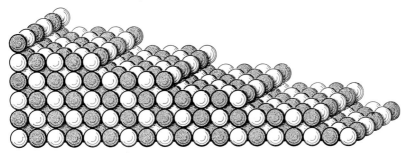

Fig. 277. Model of vicinal plane formed from widely spaced steps; and with very small angle
of inclination

1. There is first of all the essentially ideally formed crystal. In this case, however,
faces can be formed which seem to contradict the law of small rational indices.
These faces, however, usually almost coincide with a low index face and are thus
called *vicinal* faces (vicinus, lat., neighbor). Fig. 276 shows an example of vicinal
faces and illustrates a cube face of the mineral analcite modified by a very flat
eight-sided pyramid {hkl}. Fig. 277 illustrates a similar situation for NaCl showing the construction from cubic planes of a very slightly inclined $0kl$-face. If
the indices of vicinal faces vary over small distances, rounded faces are produced.

Frequently, as shown in Fig. 276, striations can be seen which correspond most certainly to considerably greater step-heights than a single interplanar spacing.

2. Variation from planar faces can also originate when the crystal under consideration is really not a single crystal in the strictest sense, but is formed from blocks tilted somewhat with respect to each other. This gives rise to parketted surfaces about which we have already spoken in our discussion of crystal imperfections (p. 94) and for which Fig. 183 illustrates a typical example. We should include growth spirals also in this tabulation of growth accessories.

Crystal Growth Not Leading to Convex Polyhedra. If we proceed from crystal growth as we have already treated it to that involving much greater supersaturation or supercooling, considerably different types of relationships occur.

Fig. 278. Snow flake as an example of dendritic growth ($\times$ 30). (After NAKAYA)

In this case the lateral spreading velocities of faces as compared to material deposition on the faces themselves no longer plays as great a role. As a result, by means of rapid accretion of material at the sites of high growth velocities, different forms occur which deviate radically from the usual aspect of a crystal. A well-known example of this is the crystallization product of water in the form of snow flakes. Fig. 278 gives one example from a great collection of possibilities. Such growth forms, in which a branching skeleton of crystallographically oriented needles has replaced the usual complete crystal, are called *dendrites* (dendron, gr., tree).

It is certainly by no means possible by varying the conditions of crystallization to produce at will from all substances either polyhedral crystals or dendrites. In addition to ice, ammonium chloride, which has the CsCl structure, and many metals have a strong tendency to produce dendritic forms.

The individual branches of dendrites appear on careful examination to have rounded boundaries (Fig. 279). After the initial extremely rapid growth dies out, planar faces are gradually produced. The dendrites can slowly grow out into an ordinary crystal. Since the fine needles are very easily deformed, completion of the dendrites in forming crystals with parketted surfaces can occur. However, it should not be inferred that every parketted crystal must have been formed by this mechanism.

Dendritic formation is also known in the formation of negative crystals (see p. 165). Their production can be well demonstrated with large ice crystals. These can be produced artificially in the laboratory or are produced in nature when large water surfaces are gently frozen. Nuclei are produced first at the

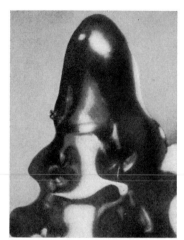

Fig. 279. Point of a copper dendrite (×350). (After GRAF)

Fig. 280. Tyndall figures in ice. Picture taken parallel to hexagonal axis of the crystal. (After BASS and MAGUN)

coldest place, therefore at the surface, with most (0001) planes parallel to the water-air interface. This growth continues with depth so that ice crystals broken from a pond or lake are oriented parallel to the base. If the light from an arc lamp is concentrated by means of a lens on a small area of the ice crystal, cavities filled with water are formed within the crystal plate outward from small inclusions, water bubbles, etc. As shown by TYNDALL, these have (Fig. 280) the form of snow flakes and "ice flowers". They represent dendritic growth forms of ice.

Related to the dendrites we should mention here "capillary" crystals and crystal "whiskers". These include a variety of different phenomena of which some have been known by mineralogists for a long time. In the last decade a great deal of experimental and theoretical work has been carried out in this area.

These growth phenomena, in common with dendrites, exhibit long-fibrous form. In contrast to dendrites, however, they are in typical cases non-branched. Usually they are straight with a major lattice direction as fiber direction. Sometimes they possess bends or are bent. Sometimes they exhibit corkscrew shaped forms. Their thickness may vary from a few hundredths to about 50 microns. They can reach several centimeters in length. It is interesting that the strengths of whiskers can approach theoretical strength values. Thus we must conclude that they contain no imperfections or so few (say a single screw dislocation), that this theoretical strength is not appreciably affected. Characteristically the highest strength values are obtained from the thinnest fibers (see p. 110).

Fibrous growth can occur under the most variable conditions, from solution, from the vapor phase, and in the solid state. Also it is possible by the ordinary slow crystallization of NaCl or KCl for thin straight fibers to grow out occasionally from the cube faces (Fig. 281). Especially widespread among the minerals are fibrous formed crystals which result from the recrystallization of salt hydrates upon exposure to the atmosphere or by crystallization from a porous substrate (salt efflorescence). Sometimes fibrous forms are the common natural crystallization product. Silver commonly crystallizes as "hair silver" and amphiboles are often fibrous. The most fibrous of the latter are known from Alpine fissures (byssolite) or as amphibole asbestos, which can even be woven into coarse fabric.

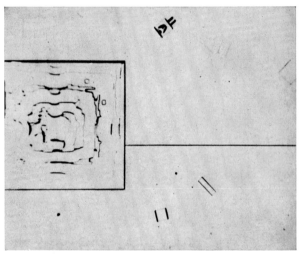

Fig. 281. NaCl whisker growing out from a NaCl crystal in aqueous solution ($\times$ 50). (After Evans)

Among the amphiboles one finds all gradations from extreme needle-like crystal fibers to approximately equidimensional crystals. We designate as whiskers in the special sense fibrous crystals which have grown out of a solid substrate, for example, from the tin plating on sheet metal, without the need for a fluid phase. They grow from their base outward and are therefore related to diffusion processes in the substrate. It is quite likely that screw dislocations play an important role in their development.

The type of fibrous growth resulting from nuclei selection described previously on page 164, should not be confused with the phenomena described here.

Destruction of a Real Crystal. Dissolution, or more generally destruction of a real crystal is also basically different from the relationships for ideal crystals. Accordingly to our previous notions (p. 169), the dissolution of a NaCl cube should lead to the development of planar {100} surfaces and then, beginning at the corners, to rounded forms. Especially unfavorable, according to our previous ideas, is the removal of an ion from the interior of a smooth cube face (site 11 in Fig. 271 and Table 33). Therefore, it should not be expected that dissolution should begin at such sites.

However, just the opposite situation is observed. If the surface of a crystal is dissolved, and thereby etched, and observed under the microscope, it is observed that the dissolution begins from individual points on the surface, and forms there small pits, called *etch figures*. Their appearance depends on the conditions of etching, specifically on the etching reagent. Their symmetry, however, always corresponds to the face symmetry, if we neglect certain special cases using optically active etch reagents. Two examples of etch figures are given in Fig. 282. These are etch figures developed on the rhombohedral faces of calcite. It can be noted that in both cases the symmetry plane of the face runs vertically in the figure. Therefore, etch figures provide a means for ascertaining crystal class, as already indicated previously (p. 30).

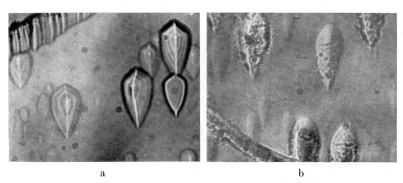

a   b

Fig. 282a and b. Etch figures on the rhombohedral cleavage surface of calcite. (a) with citric acid and (b) sodium hydroxide as etch agents (× 200). (After PATEL and GOSWAMI)

It remains to question why such etch pits form. This is related again to the real structure of the crystal. A crystal face is never ideally planar over thousands of identity periods, but in fact contains a multitude of imperfections. Long ago the formation of etch figures was explained as resulting from solution along cracks (Fig. 283). However, there are additional variations from ideality such as foreign inclusions and dislocations, which are important here.

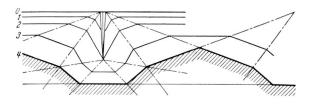

Fig. 283. Origin of etch figures (after R. GROSS). *0—4* dissolution stages

If, for example, a crystal of LiF is deformed, it shows as does NaCl, translations along {110} planes (see p. 104). In the plane of movement the number of dislocations is markedly increased. Accordingly the etch figures are arranged on {100} cleavage faces of mechanically strained LiF crystals in straight lines which correspond to the intersections of the cube face with dodecahedral planes (Fig. 284).

Through lateral growth neighboring etch pits can overlap and finally give rise to etch knobs. Fig. 283 serves to illustrate this.

Future Prospects. The theories of crystal growth proposed by KOSSEL and STRANSKI, as we have seen, clarify a series of phenomena and for others at least point toward their solution. There are various reasons why these theories are not completely satisfactory. Chemical forces, which we cannot yet accurately calculate, except for the limiting case of ionic bonding, influence the deposition energies. In addition, these relationships are appropriate only for deposition of individual isolated atoms, which is a radical simplification of what really occurs in nature. Very crucial, too, is the fact that these relationships are concerned with the growth of ideal crystals, and we know that imperfections play a very crucial role. Thus it is no wonder that in assessments of fundamental values these relationships alone are not capable of solving all the problems of crystal morphology.

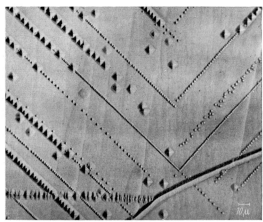

Fig. 284. Etch figures on (100) of LiF ($\times$ 350). Note the linear arrangement of the intersections of the shear planes {110} and the cube face. (After Gillman and Johnston)

The morphology of a crystal depends on its structure and on its conditions of formation. The influence of structure is asserted in the Kossel-Stranski theory in the deposition energies. Other investigators have attempted to solve the relationships between structure and morphology from the standpoint of lattice geometry (Bravais; Donnay and Harker) or with more formal bonding principles (Hartman and Perdok). The fulfillment of the mineralogist's dream, namely, to be able to relate the morphology of a mineral to its conditions of formation unfortunately still lies in the distant future, because of the multitude of form-influencing factors.

Intensive experimental and theoretical work in the last century leads us to expect that in the area of mineralogy a great deal of progress is also to be expected in the future. Consider that today very large quartz crystals and even diamonds can be produced industrially. A great and exciting, if also difficult, area of research still lies wide open before us.

PART TWO

Petrology

V. Some Physical-Chemical Fundamentals

1. Nucleation and Growth of Nuclei

Melting Point Determination. In the last chapter the matter of crystal growth was discussed from a geometrical and structural viewpoint. It is now necessary to examine the question, "When does a crystal crystallize from a melt?". The obvious answer is that it occurs when a fluid is cooled a bit below the melting temperature (melting point) which prevails at some definite pressure. In order to determine the exact melting point in those cases where it is not possible to directly observe the melting process, it is possible to take advantage of the fact that heat is liberated during crystallization, the so-called heat of melting or crystallization. If a melt, for example, of a simple metal, is allowed to cool slowly, and the temperature measured as a function of time, it is observed that in spite of the cooling, a definite temperature is reached and the melt remains at this temperature for a short period of time. This is the precise melting point. For this short period of time the drop in temperature is compensated for by the liberated *heat of melting*, or crystallization. Only when the melt has completely crystallized does the temperature decrease further. Conversely, it can be observed upon heating crystals that at the melting point, because of absorption of the heat of melting, a temperature increase is delayed until everything is fluid. In a like manner boiling points can be determined through similar effects of the heat of vaporization. Changes in structural modification can be noted likewise by similar effects due to liberation of the heat of transformation. A different method involves heating a melt to varying temperatures in the vicinity of the melting point and then cooling it rapidly (quenching). The solid product is then studied optically or by X-ray methods to ascertain whether crystals have formed. This static method is used widely for complex systems.

Supercooling. In the case of natural silicates, as well as with silicates synthesized in the laboratory, the liquid to solid transformation often takes place by solidification of the melt to a glass, rather than with the formation of crystals. Such a glass does not have a definite melting point. One observes a temperature range over which softening of the glass occurs, the softening interval. Such supercooled melts have no regular crystal structure, but only a minor degree of molecular order. The supercooling of a melt can occur only in the absence of a seed crystal of the same composition. Often structurally similar foreign crystals will induce crystallization. A good example of the effect of a seed crystal is the melt of sodium acetate, $NaC_2H_3O_2 \cdot 3H_2O$, which can be cooled readily from its melting point at $58.2°$ C to room temperature without crystallization. Supercooling is aided by adding a little water to the normal salt. If a tiny crystal of the salt is then thrown into the supercooled melt, the crystallization can be observed and evolution of the heat of crystallization can be detected, for example, by means of a thermocouple.

Centers of Nucleation. If crystallization of a melt takes place in the absence of seed crystals, it is observed that at first individual centers of crystallization (nuclei) spontaneously form, from which crystallization proceeds. The rate of formation of these nuclei immediately below the melting point is very low. Very small crystals have a lower melting point than larger megoscopic ones, because of their much greater surface energy. They are stable, therefore, only at temperatures below the melting point. Such micro-crystals have also a greater solubility. They are soluble, for example, in an aqueous solution which is already saturated with respect to larger crystals of the same substance. This situation plays an important role in the metamorphism of rocks, to be discussed later. Thus, from a melt crystal nuclei first form following some supercooling, even though no

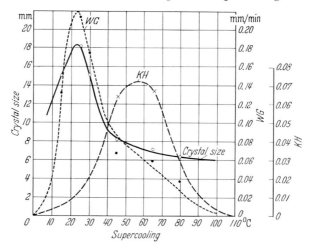

Fig. 285. *KH*, number of nucleation centers; *WG* growth rate of the prism faces of nepheline with increasing supercooling in a melt. (After H. G. F. Winkler)

nuclei were previously present. Upon further supercooling the number of centers of nucleation then increases. It can be rationalized that thermal motion at first allows only ocassional aggregation of atoms or groups of atoms to form crystals. With decreasing temperature the probability of crystallization becomes greater, as shown in Fig. 285, where the curve *KH* forms a maximum. The number of centers of nucleation, *KH*, decreases to zero with greater supercooling, because now the viscosity of the melt has become so great, that the ions or molecules can no longer aggregate to form nuclei.

The rate of growth (Fig. 285, *WG*) of individual nuclei is very low at temperatures just below the melting point. This increases, as does the number of nuclei, with further supercooling because, accompanying the decrease in thermal motion, there is an increase in the rate of deposition. Only when with decreasing temperature there is a significant increase in viscosity, does the rate of growth diminish.

As we have already seen in discussing the geometrical aspects of crystal growth, it is improper to refer so simply to the rate of growth, and strictly speaking we should consider growth velocities of individual crystal faces. These must be investigated individually. From the number of nucleation centers and the rate of growth, the crystal size as related to supercooling can be calculated. H. G. Winkler has been able to correlate the cooling relations with the size of included crystals in dike rocks (see Fig. 285).

In order for a glass to form during cooling, the temperature interval in which nucleation power and growth rate are high must be passed through rapidly.

2. Single Component Systems

Phases. We can also consider a crystal and its melt from another viewpoint. A crystal and its melt both consist of the same matter and are said to constitute a single component system. Crystal and melt are distinguished by means of the structural arrangement of their constituent atoms. In the solid state these, as we know, are for the most part quite regularly arranged. In the fluid state the degree of order is much lower, extending over very small regions or domains. Frequently the expression "phase" is used in this connection. Regions of homogeneous character which are separated by interfaces, are denoted as separate phases, as for example, the gaseous, fluid, and solid phases. Several phases exist in the solid state, when chemically different crystals occur together, or if one component occurs in different structural arrangements (polymorphism).

Equilibrium. A crystal and its melt at the melting point are said to be in equilibrium. This concept can be related to a balance. A small temperature increase causes the components to become completely molten; a decrease completely solid. Equilibrium is sometimes not attained in natural processes, as we have just seen in discussing the supercooling of a melt. Equilibrium is

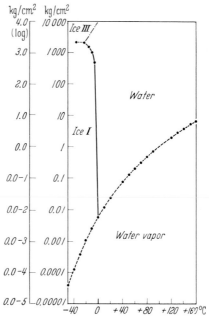

Fig. 286. Complete pressure-temperature diagram for H_2O

defined, moreover, in terms of a definite pressure and, strictly speaking, only for crystals above a certain size. We are referring here to homogeneous (hydrostatic) pressure. When a melting point is indicated without further qualification, one atmosphere of pressure and a crystal size above $^1/_{1000}$ mm or $1\ \mu$ is implied.

The System H_2O. In Fig. 286 are shown the phase relations of water at different temperatures and pressures. We can see three curves passing through a common point, the triple point. The two dashed curves define the gaseous region. To the left is the stability field for ice and between the fields for ice and water vapor, is the stability field for liquid water. The boundary curve between ice and water vapor is called the sublimation curve. At temperatures and pressures lying along this curve, ice and the vapor phase are in equilibrium. At $P-T$ conditions lying along the boundary curve separating liquid water and water vapor, water boils. This boiling curve terminates at 374° C and 225 kg/cm² pressure, the so-called critical point (see page 226). The solid curve indicates equilibrium between ice and liquid water and represents the melting curve.

Generally the melting point of a substance is increased as a result of an increase in pressure. Ice is an unusual exception in this respect, a fact which is important for certain geological processes. Its melting point is lowered by the application of pressure. If we plot the experimentally determined melting temperature of ice as a function of pressure, we obtain the curve shown in Fig. 287. Ice and water are in equilibrium, therefore, at —4.1° C at 500 kg/cm² pressure and at —8.7° C at 1,000 kg/cm². Ice has a lower specific gravity than water and thus floats in water. When water freezes it expands and will burst its container if its walls cannot contain the pressure corresponding to the prevailing equilibrium temperature. If the container is rigid, the water is not able to freeze. Expansion of ice plays a very important role in rock weathering. As Fig. 286 shows, at a prevailing pressure of 2,200 kg/cm², the melting point of ice is —22° C. If the temperature decreases further, and the pressure increases, the structure of ice changes — a different "modification" of ice is formed. Ice I transforms to ice III; a new solid phase or modification forms in place of the original.

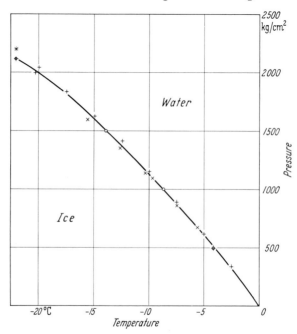

Fig. 287. Melting diagram for ice

Polymorphism. Changes in structural modification are exceptionally frequent. This phenomenon is called polymorphism. It was first correctly understood in 1821 by EILHARD MITSCHERLICH in Berlin. As early as 1788 the Berliner mineral-chemist KLAPROTH had observed that calcite has the same chemical composition — CaCO₃ — as aragonite, although the former crystallized with ditrigonal-scalenohedral morphology, the latter orthorhombic-dipyramidal. The findings of KLAPROTH were in conflict with the generally accepted definition of HAÜY of a "mineral species", according to which every chemical substance could occur with only one basic morphology. As a result of very detailed analysis, a variety of impurities, such as MgO, FeO, and MnO were found in calcite, and were suspected to be the cause of the anomalous morphology. In 1813 STROH-MEYER in Göttingen consistently found in his aragonites strontium which had been discovered by KLAPROTH in 1793. This had been overlooked by other analysts. Additional analysts confirmed most of his results, which suggested the small amount of strontium impurity to be the cause of the anomalous calcite crystal form. This interpretation brought to a close the old concept of mineral form, when eight years later MITSCHERLICH proved by experiment that $Na_2HPO_4 \cdot H_2O$ and sulfur have duplicate morphologies. A profusion of discoveries followed and today the number of similar observations is too numerous to mention.

The dependence of polymorphic transformations on structural arrangement has already been elaborated in detail in the chapter on Crystal Chemistry (p. 55—65). There we have seen that in the case of the carbonates, nitrates, and borates, the structure with small cations in trigonal array is stable; with large cations, in orthorhombic array. In $CaCO_3$ and KNO_3 the cation size is such that at one atmosphere pressure at low temperatures, the orthorhombic, and at high temperatures the trigonal forms are stable. On the other hand, at high pressures the trigonal calcite can be converted to orthorhombic aragonite. Examples of other kinds of polymorphism will be referred to in specific places later.

From the standpoint of the concept of equilibrium, two structural modifications of the same substance can, as with a crystal and a melt, at a given pressure, be in equilibrium with one another at a definite temperature (for example at 2,200 kg/cm² and $-22°$ C in the case of ice I and III). Their stability fields are separated by a boundary curve, analogous to a melting curve in a pressure-temperature diagram. In the one field one modification crystallizes and is stable; in the neighboring field the other is stable. Like supercooled melts, differing structural modifications can form under temperature-pressure conditions for which they are not stable. Such *metastable* modifications can be extremely persistent; even more so than a supercooled melt or glass.

Let us summarize once more by means of the diagram for the system H_2O (Fig. 286). Using pressure and temperature as coordinates, the lines of the diagram represent the boundaries between two phases. We have in the upper left of the diagram the stability field of ice III, below it the field of ice I. From it, by means of the melting curve, the field for water lies to the right, and below this the field for water vapor. This is bounded from the field of ice I above by the sublimation curve, and from water by the boiling curve. Points at which three boundary curves converge, here the melting, boiling, and sublimation curves, are designated as *triple points*. We have, therefore, the four stability fields of the phases water, water vapor, ice I and ice III. We shall say no more about the other modifications of ice which have been produced artificially.

The System SiO_2. We shall refer now to another single component system — the system SiO_2, shown schematically in Fig. 288. At earth surface temperature and pressure, low quartz is stable. At 575° C it transforms to high quartz and at 870° C tridymite appears. Above 1,470 °C cristobalite is the stable phase. It is to be noted, moreover, that the transformation low-high quartz takes place without delay upon heating. It can be rationalized that only minor structural changes are necessary during this transformation (see p. 62). During the transformation of high quartz to tridymite, the structure must be significantly reconstructed. This transformation is promoted in melts of LiCl or Na_2WO_4. In this case some alkali is included in the tridymite structure. Melts of silica can be supercooled easily, producing a glass that is technically useful in laboratory ware, because of its insensitivity to temperature changes and to acids. In addition silica glass is used in ultraviolet lamps, because it transmits light in this wave length region. Tridymite and cristobalite can be supercooled also. The low temperature modifications of tridymite and cristobalite can exist also at low temperatures. There exist all gradations from amorphous silica gel to the poorly crystallized α-cristobalite in opals to β-cristobalite. An additional SiO_2 modification has been produced in the laboratory. At very high pressures coesite and at higher ones, stishovite form (Table 34). Both phases are also found naturally

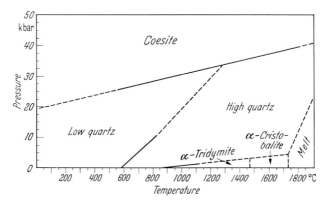

Fig. 288. Pressure-temperature diagram for the anhydrous system, SiO_2. (After Boyd and England)

Table 34. *The natural modifications of SiO_2 and their properties*

Modification		Crystal class	Specific gravity	Indices of refraction in sodium light
Stable	Unstable			
At 1 atmosphere pressure		32	2.651	ω 1.5442
Quartz				ε 1.5533
↓ 575°				
	High quartz	622	2.518 at 600° C	ω 1.5328 ε 1.5404 at 580° C
↓ 870°				
High tridymite		6/mmm	2.3	
	↓			
	(Low) tridymite	mmm	2.26	n_α 1.469 n_β 1.469 n_γ 1.473
↓ 1470°				
High cristobalite		$m3m$		
	↓ 270—280°			
	(Low) cristobalite	422	2.32	ω 1.487 ε 1.484
1713°				
↓ Melt				
	Silica glass		2.203	1.4558
High pressure modifications				
Coesite		2/m	3.01	n_α 1.593 n_γ 1.597
Stishovite		4mmm	4.28	ε 1.826 ω 1.799

where very high temperatures and pressures developed from the impact of meteorites on quartz bearing rocks, as for example in the Meteor Crater in Arizona and in the Nördlinger Ries.

Quartz which crystallizes above 575° C converts upon cooling to low-quartz. Since high quartz has a higher hexagonal symmetry than trigonal low-quartz, the former converts upon cooling into twins of low quartz. The twinning takes place according to the Dauphineé law (p. 98), in which the 3-fold axis takes on additional 2-fold symmetry and becomes a 6-fold axis. From the orientation of the twin planes relative to the crystal faces, it is possible under favorable circumstances, as O. MÜGGE showed in 1907, to determine whether the twinning is a growth phenomenon taking place below 575° C, or whether it is a matter involving conversion from high-quartz. If one first etches the crystal, making the twin planes visible, and then notes that they are intersected by the trapezohedral and dipyramidal faces, crystallization above 575° C is confirmed. In the case of growth twins, however, the twin planes and crystal faces coincide. Untwinned crystals must have formed below 575° C. In this way quartz can be used as a *geologic thermometer*, giving information on the temperature of formation of a rock. The temperature of the low-high quartz inversion changes with pressure, as Fig. 288 shows. If this is not taken into account, the "thermometer" indicates temperatures which are too low.

The System Carbon. As a third example of a single component system, we will consider the carbon system. It is generally known that there are two modifications of carbon, graphite and diamond. For a number of years it has been possible to treat this system not only theoretically but also experimentally. It is now possible to synthesize diamond in its stability field with the help of catalysts. In Fig. 289 the cross-hatched area indicates the $P-T$ conditions under which diamond has been synthesized. The graphite—diamond transformation curve is slightly inclined to the left in the diagram. The graphite—melt curve is very steep. The diagram shows that at earth surface temperatures and pressures diamond is unstable. Diamonds have been found in meteorites (Arizona crater), therefore forming under conditions of temperature and pressure that can be shown in Fig. 289. It is more difficult to explain, with the help of this diagram, the occurrence of diamonds in volcanic pipes.

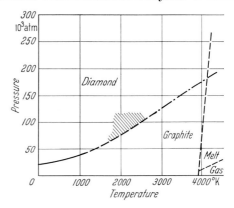

Fig. 289. Phase diagram for carbon (after BOWENKERK et al., 1959)
———— thermodynamically calc.;
- - - - experimentally determined;
-·—·—·- extrapolated;
〰〰 region in which diamond is experimentally synthesized

3. Two Component Systems

The System KNO$_3$—H$_2$O. Until now we have considered only single component systems. How do the crystallization relations change, when we have two components, for example, when KNO$_3$ crystallizes from an aqueous solution? Based on the usual growth process, it would appear that there is nothing fundamental to change in our thinking. The deposition of ions should take place just as from a melt. It is likely, however, that differences will occur, since in addition to the individual ions of the one component, water molecules are present. Very likely these could have an influence on the kind of face development, and influence the crystal habit.

In the case of KNO_3, the orthorhombic modification is stable below 127.8° C. This should precipitate from aqueous solution at room temperature. However, if we allow a drop of concentrated KNO_3 solution to evaporate under the microscope, the formation of trigonal rhombohedral crystals is first observed. These

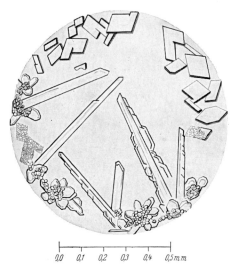

Fig. 290. KNO_3 crystallization by evaporation under the microscope. The first-formed rhombohedral crystals are transformed upon contact with the later forming orthorhombic needles (middle right). In their vicinity the rhombohedra are dissolved (left above)

should be stable only above 127.8° C. Thus an unstable structural type appears first, a phenomenon which has been observed among other substances, and is still not adequately explained, although it is referred to as the "Ostwald step rule". Following the rhombohedral crystals, orthorhombic needles precipitate, mostly from the border of the drop (Fig. 290). When these needles, during their growth, extend into the vicinity of a rhombohedron, the latter is dissolved (upper left of Fig. 290). If a needle comes in contact with a rhombohedron, the latter changes into an aggregate of orthorhombic crystals (center right of Fig. 290). In this way the instability at room temperature of the trigonal modification can be observed directly.

The System Diopside—Anorthite. In considering equilibrium in two component systems, we must keep in mind that we are dealing with three variables, temperature, pressure, and the concentration of the two constituents. Strictly speaking we must represent the phase diagram in three dimensions. Usually a two-dimensional diagram is used, in which the pressure is assumed to be constant. The influence of pressure can be important for rock forming processes, so we shall give it consideration later on. We shall first consider situations in which the pressure is held constant. Usually we let the abscissa represent the variation in concentration (Fig. 291). The left corner of the diagram, labelled diopside, represents 100% pure $CaMg[SiO_3]_2$; at the right, 100% anorthite, $Ca[Al_2Si_2O_8]$.

The ordinate represents the temperature. If we assume that our diagram is to represent a pressure of one atmosphere, we can plot on the temperature axis the melting point of diopside at 1,390°C and of anorthite at 1,550°C. Impurities or admixtures lower the melting or freezing temperatures of each end member, the temperature decrease at low concentrations being proportional to the number of moles added. (Raoult-van t'Hoff law). The two melting curves decrease toward the center and meet at a common point. A normal to the abscissa from this point gives the composition of the lowest melting mixture, in this case 1,270°C

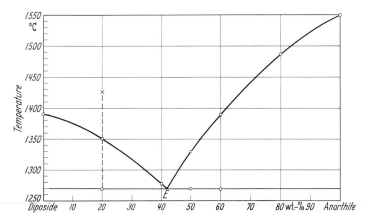

Fig. 291. The binary system, diopside—anorthite (after BOWEN) circles represent experimental points

at 42% anorthite. This point is called the *eutectic point* (from Gr. eu, good; tectein, to melt). In hydrous systems this point is called the cryohydratic point (Gr. kryos, frost). In such a diagram the region above the melting curve is the stability field of the melt. Points on the curve represent melt and crystal in equilibrium-diopside crystals on the left and anorthite on the right. If we start with a melt of composition X (Fig. 291) and temperature 1,439°C, nothing happens upon cooling until the melting curve is reached at 1,350°C. At this point diopside crystals precipitate out, the residual melt becoming richer in anorthite. The melt remains in equilibrium with diopside crystals and changes its composition along the melting curve until, at 1,270°C, the eutectic composition is reached. At this point both diopside and anorthite precipitate out until no melt remains. The composition of the total mass of diopside and anorthite corresponds to that of the original melt. We would experience analogous behavior if we had started out with an anorthite-rich melt. Then anorthite would precipitate out first until, at the eutectic point, diopside and anorthite would co-precipitate.

In such two component systems, determination of the melting curves is carried out with the aid of the crystallization curves of different compositions, as shown in Fig. 292.

Eutectic Structures. The structures which result from the crystallization of such two component systems are very informative. These simple relationships can serve as a model for the more complex magmatic rocks. If a melt does not have exactly the eutectic composition, the first crystals to precipitate out depend on which side of the eutectic point the composition lies. Following crystallization, we would find relatively large crystals of one kind in a finer grained groundmass of the two components. These structures are analogous to those of many magmatic rocks. In addition, this simple model shows that the crystallization sequence has nothing to do with the melting temperature of the two end members. A mineral with high melting point like anorthite can be precipitated at lower temperature and later than a low melting companion, such as diopside. The temperature of formation of a mineral depends, therefore, also on the composition of the melt.

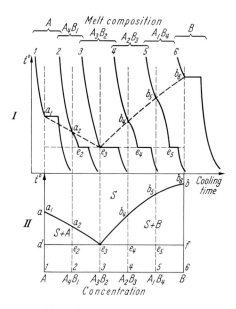

Fig. 292. Determination of melting diagrams from cooling curves (after VOGEL). $a_1, a_2 \ldots$ "Haltepunkte" of the A-rich melt; $b_1, b_2 \ldots$ of the B-rich melt; $e_1, e_2 \ldots$ of the eutectic

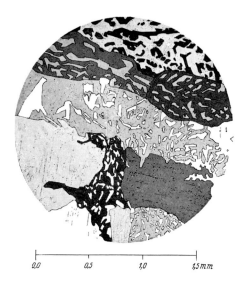

Fig. 293. Graphic granite, from a boulder in the Kulm, Schloss Waldeck, Edertalsperre, between crossed nicols. Angular cross sections of quartz in orthoclase

At the eutectic composition one frequently observes with metals structures which have a certain similarity to those of the so-called *graphic granites*. The latter exhibit cross-sections of quartz in potassium feldspar which resemble Hebraic characters (Fig. 293). It is disputed, however, whether the components are crystallized as eutectic systems. All of these kinds of structure are by no means to be explained in this way.

Influence of Pressure. We want now to bring pressure into the picture, by calculating from the Clausius-Clapeyron equation the increase in melting point with pressure. This is necessary because direct observation of the influence of pressure on such silicate systems cannot be made rapidly. The equation is:

$$\frac{dT}{dP} = \frac{T\,(V_{cr} - V_{fl})}{Q}.$$

P is the pressure, T the absolute temperature of the melting point ($^\circ$C $+ 273^\circ$), V_{fl} the specific volume of the melt, and V_{cr} of the crystal, and Q the heat of melting. We find a 19° melting point increase for every 1,000 kg/cm^2 pressure

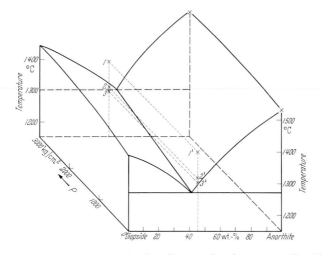

Fig. 294. Pressure, temperature, concentration diagram for the system, diopside—anorthite

increase for diopside, and only a 4° increase for anorthite. The experimental investigations by YODER in 1952 gave a value for diopside of 13°C for 1,000 kg/cm^2 over the range of pressure shown in Fig. 294. In this figure the eutectic point becomes a line, ascending with increasing pressure and shifting laterally at the same time (somewhat exaggerated in the figure). However, the shift in eutectic composition is more pronounced than the rise in eutectic temperature. The melting curve of Fig. 294 has become a slightly curved surface. Let us now consider two melts of the same composition and at the same temperature. Point 1 (behind the plane of the diagram) is at high pressure, point 1′ (in the plane of the diagram) at low pressure. If the melt is near to the eutectic composition, it may happen, because of the slope of the eutectic line, that upon cooling at constant pressure (isobar) the same melt will at high pressure (point 1) crystallize out diopside, but at low pressure (point 1′) anorthite. A rock solidified under pressure at depth can produce different crystallization products than one crystallized at the earth's surface. If we cool a melt under high pressure until crystals are precipitated (point 2), and then reduce the pressure (point 2′) the previously precipitated crystals are again melted. This is analogous to a sudden outpouring of lava in connection with a volcanic eruption. If we then continue to cool the melt at the lower pressure (point 2′), it can happen that we are now on the opposite side of the eutectic point (point 3), as shown in Fig. 294, and that now the other kind of crystals precipitate out.

Also, a solidified rock can, by pressure reduction, become fluid again. (Compare points 3 and 3′ in Fig. 294.) This might happen if pressure is relieved by formation of a crack or fissure. Since the melt would be lighter than the solid rock, it could ascend into the fissure. In this way basaltic magmas can make their way from depth to the surface.

Early formed crystal inclusions may in both cases not always be completely remelted. They can remain as corroded residues.

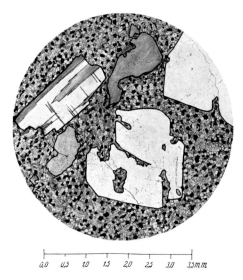

Fig. 295. Rhyolite, Colmitz, Saxony; between crossed nicols. Large corroded quartz and a feldspar with twin lamellae in a fine-grained groundmass of quartz, feldspar and mica

In many eruptive rocks we can observe quartz inclusions which exhibit signs of solution. Fig. 295 shows this phenomenon in a rhyolite. Such corroded olivine inclusions have also been observed. Our simple model indicates clearly how such phenomena can take place. However, we must be aware that other possible explanations may be equally appropriate (p. 194, 205).

Gibbs' Phase Rule. Our previous knowledge of the equilibrium relations and fields of stability of individual phases can be summarized in the GIBBS' Phase Rule (1876). The individual phases of the single component system $-H_2O$, water, water vapor, ice I and III, have been illustrated figuratively in a two-dimensional diagram. We could freely vary pressure and temperature within these two dimensions. We can say that we have two degrees of freedom. The phase relationships between two phases in equilibrium, such as water with water vapor or ice I or ice III, are represented by a curve. If we arbitrarily select the pressure, the temperature is likewise fixed. We have in this case only one degree of freedom. If finally we wish to have three phases together in equilibrium, such as water, water vapor, and ice I or water, ice I and ice III, the equilibrium is represented by a triple point. Pressure as well as temperature is fixed. We have accordingly no degrees of freedom. If several components, for example, diopside and anorthite, occur together, an additional variable, or degree of freedom is introduced, the concentration. So for a melt at temperatures above the melting surface (Fig. 294), we have three degrees of freedom. If a melt is to be in equilibrium with one kind of crystal, we would be allowed 2 degrees of freedom, temperature and pressure varying along the melting surface; to be in equilibrium simultaneously with two kinds of crystals, two degrees of freedom permiting variation along the eutectic line. Thus in a single component system, there are two degrees of freedom for one phase, one degree for equilibrium between two phases, and no degrees of freedom for three phase equilibrium. This can be formulated as follows:

No. of phases + no. of degrees of freedom = no. of components + 2 .

While we are already familiar with the use of the terms phase (p. 183) and degree of freedom, it is necessary to define more precisely the term "component". Perhaps it would be better to say "independent constituent". In usage one must be careful to count only those constituents which can transform from one phase to another independently of other constituents. A shorthand expression for the GIBB's phase rule is:

$$P + F = C + 2 .$$

In rocks often we shall be able to consider the concentrations and, therefore, the number of independent constituents, as fixed. At the same time pressure and temperature can be varied over a wide range. Thus we have two degrees of freedom and $P = C$. The number of phases (kinds of minerals) equal the number of components present. This is the mineralogical phase rule emphasized first by V. M. GOLDSCHMIDT.

All of this and the following considerations apply only to equilibrium reactions. In petrology we must be aware that equilibrium will not always be obtained. We shall be able, however, to recognize this disequilibrium, only if we understand equilibrium.

The System Leucite—SiO₂. We return to our simple eutectic system, which we have described in Fig. 291, and ask the question, "What happens if the two components A and B react with one another and form a third compound A_2B?". In such a case we would have two two-component systems, $A-A_2B$ and A_2B-B. Diagramatically the two systems would be drawn side by side.

The situation becomes somewhat complicated if the compound A_2B undergoes decomposition, as is often the case, before reaching the melting point. We shall select as an example the system leucite, $K(AlSi_2O_6)-SiO_2$, in which the intermediate compound K-feldspar, $K(AlSi_3O_8)$ forms. As the phase diagram (Fig. 296) shows, the K-feldspar melts with decomposition (incongruently) at $1,170°$ C. If a melt of the K-feldspar composition is cooled, leucite crystals precipitate out below the temperature corresponding to the intersection of the melting curve (about $1,550°$ C). Leucite crystallazition continues until $1,170°$ C. At lower temperature the previously formed leucite crystals are dissolved in reacting with the melt to form K-feldspar crystals, if enough time is provided so that equilibrium can be maintained. With further cooling, the composition of the melt arrives at the eutectic point and then K-feldspar and tridymite crystallize out together. The latter converts to quartz upon further cooling. Melts whose compositions lie between $K(AlSi_2O_6)$ and $K(AlSi_3O_8)$ do not crystallize out tridymite, because the available SiO_2 is used up first. The early formed leucite does not completely disappear, but only to the extent that it corresponds to the leucite: K-feldspar ratio in the melt. Only the first formed leucite crystals are lost through reaction with SiO_2. In general, in systems with an incongruent melting point, dissolution effects on crystals can occur without pressure changes, as described in p. 192. We note in addition from Fig. 296, that quartz and leucite cannot occur together, at least if equilibrium is to be attained.

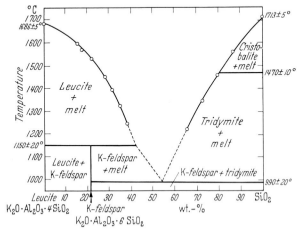

Fig. 296. The system $K(AlSi_2O_6)—SiO_2$

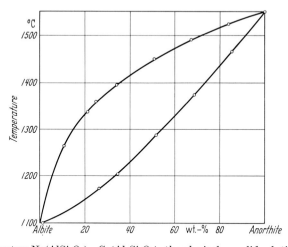

Fig. 297. The system $Na(AlSi_3O_8)—Ca(Al_2Si_2O_8)$; the plagioclase solid solution. (After BOWEN)

This incongruent melting can be demonstrated very beautifully with the salt hydrohalite, $NaCl—H_2O$, according to BRAITSCH. Monoclinic (pseudohexagonal) crystals up to 2 mm in size crystallize out of a solution of NaCl, saturated at 30° C, when cooled to about —10° C. At room temperature the birefringent hydrohalite crystals can be recognized in a microprojector as they are decomposed with the precipitation of NaCl crystals.

Mixed Crystal Systems (Solid Solution). A further complication arises if the two components form mixed crystals with one another, as in the system anorthite, $Ca(Al_2Si_2O_8)$—albite, $Na(AlSi_3O_8)$. These particular mixed crystals are called plagioclase. The two components are considered as completely miscible for this discussion (see, however, p. 76). Their phase diagram is illustrated in Fig. 297. We note that two curves connect the melting points of the two end members. The upper one serves as the lower boundary of the stability field of the melt (liquidus); the other as the upper boundary of the solid phase field (solidus). We shall trace again the fate of a melt, for example, of composition An_{50}, upon cooling. When the liquidus curve is reached, a solid phase begins to crystallize out. The composition of the precipitated mixed crystal is obtained by drawing a line parallel to the abcissa from the point of intersection on the liquidus. The point of intersection with the solidus gives the composition of the mixed crystals in equilibrium with the melt at this temperature. The melt changes its composition along the liquidus with further cooling. The mixed crystals change composition along the solidus until the point is reached at which they have the composition of the original melt. Then the melt is completely crystallized. If we had undertaken the cooling so slowly that equilibrium could be continually maintained, the plagioclase crystals would have continuously reacted with the melt and possessed finally the exact composition of the original melt. If, however, cooling had proceeded so rapidly that the first formed crystals could not react with the melt, the resulting crystals would have cores consisting of the first formed anorthite-rich plagioclase and outer layers poorer in anorthite than the final melt.

The continuous plagioclase solid-solution series can be subdivided into members to which special names are given. Different authors do not agree on the exact subdivision into members. We shall use the following divisions (see appendix p. 422).

Albite	0— 10%	Anorthite
Oligoclase	10— 30%	Anorthite
Andesine	30— 50%	Anorthite
Labradorite	50— 70%	Anorthite
Bytownite	70— 90%	Anorthite
Anorthite	90—100%	Anorthite

In systems in which the melting behavior is similar to the plagioclase system, it is common for the centers of crystals to be richer in the higher melting component. The olivine system, Mg_2SiO_4—Fe_2SiO_4, is analogous. In this case Mg_2SiO_4 is the higher melting component, and natural olivine crystals show repeated zoning, becoming more iron-rich toward the outside of the crystal.

If we heat a crystal, the processes involved in cooling a melt are reversed. That is, first an albite-rich melt is formed, which becomes more and more anorthite-rich along the liquidus with further heating, until the melt has the composition of the original plagioclase crystal. Again the crystals in equilibrium with the melt being produced change their composition along the solidus. If equilibrium is not maintained, crystals with albitic cores and anorthitic shells result, the zoning being reversed from that produced by crystallization.

In general in multicomponent systems, the curve representing complete crystallization upon cooling and initiation of melting upon heating is called the solidus; the boundary curve between the melt and the onset of crystallization, the liquidus.

Ionic Capture. The phenomenon, illustrated by plagioclase, that in mixed crystals higher valence ions are preferentially "captured", plays an important role in geochemistry. By capture we refer to the fact that a higher proportion of the highest valence ion enters into the crystalline phase than is retained by the melt. Such capture is associated with two conditions. First the melting curve must decrease continuously from the melting point of the higher melting compound to the lower. Also, as with plagioclase, the high melting end member must also contain the higher valence ion. In addition, it is necessary that equilibrium be interrupted, either by incomplete reaction of the first-formed crystals by rapid cooling, or by isolation from their original environment by settling in a large magma chamber. Finally, the inclusion of the higher valence ions must result in a charge balance in the crystal. In plagioclase, if the divalent Ca^{++} ion replaces monovalent Na^+ ions, the charge is compensated by the coupled substitution of a trivalent Al^{+++} ion for a tetravalent Si^{++++} ion. The balance can be attained also by creation of lattice vacancies, as in the case of $LiCl—MgCl_2$ solid solution (p. 91).

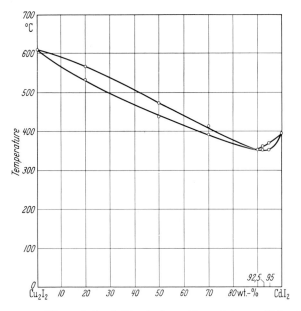

Fig. 298. The system $CdI_2 — Cu_2I_2$. Solid solution with a minimum. (After HERZ and BULLA)

If one plots diagramatically the foreign ion content in the crystalline phase against that in the melt or solution, at low concentrations of foreign ions in mixed crystals, an essentially linear plot results. The absorption of the foreign ions follows the Nernst distribution law, that is, at low concentrations the number of foreign ions in the crystalline phase is proportional to the concentration in the solution or melt.

In solid solution systems the liquidus and solidus can exhibit also a minimum, as illustrated in Fig. 298 for the system $CuI—CdI_2$. In this case, on the CdI_2 side, Cd is captured in the solid phase, on the Cu_2I_2 side, the lower valence ion Cu. This latter form of ion substitution is referred to as admission.

The inclusion of foreign ions into a lattice in addition is very dependent upon the magnitudes of the ionic radii as we have already seen (p. 64). Only atoms or groups of atoms which are of the proper size to fit into the assemblage can be accepted into a crystal. The "fit" is a relative term. It depends on the lattice type and especially on temperature. The higher the temperature, the more easily can a structure accommodate a constituent which is somewhat too large or small. It is further evident that ions of less suitable size are admitted into a crystal in more restricted numbers. This leads to restricted or limited miscibility between the two end members. An informative phase diagram in this respect is that for the system NaCl—KCl (Fig. 299). Upon cooling from a melt, mixed crystals of all compositions between the two end members can be obtained. In this system both the liquidus and solidus form a minimum at 663°C. From KCl-rich melts, KCl-rich crystals precipitate first; from NaCl-rich melts come NaCl-rich crystals. Again, if equilibrium is maintained, the final mixed crystals will have a composition corresponding to that of the initial melt. Upon further cooling of the mixed crystals of intermediate composition, it can be observed that they unmix, undergoing a rearrangement in the solid state. Lamellae of NaCl appear in KCl crystals, or vice-versa, depending on the composition of the initial melt and crystals. The lower curve in Fig. 299 indicates the temperatures at which this unmixing or exsolution takes place. The system of

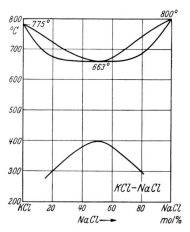

Fig. 299. The system NaCl—KCl.
(From D'Ans-Lax)

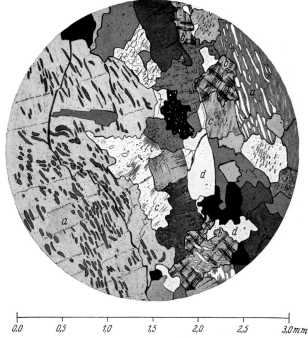

Fig. 300. Hypersthene granite, Stalheim, Norway; between crossed nicols. *a* Perthite intergrowth of orthoclase and albite; *b* Microcline with clearly crossed twin lamellae, in part with interlayered albite; *c* orthoclase with albite and twin lamellae; *d* quartz, clear, bright, and dark

lamellae produced is similar to that which can be observed in many feldspars, which are called perthites (Fig. 300). In this case also the exsolution involves K- and Na-compounds, namely $K(AlSi_3O_8)$, orthoclase, and $Na(AlSi_3O_8)$, albite. K^+ has an ionic radius of 1.33 Å, Na^+ 0.98 Å. Apparently at low temperatures the one ion does not fit into the structure of the other compound.

This is confirmed further in the system KNO_3—$NaNO_3$ (Fig. 301). If we compare the two systems (Fig. 299 and 301), we observe in the NaCl-KCl system a wide temperature gap between the solidus and exsolution curves. In the system KNO_3—$NaNO_3$ the exsolution curve intersects the liquidus and solidus curves and becomes, in fact, a part of the latter. The maximum extent of solid solution in the system KNO_3—$NaNO_3$ is indicated in Fig. 301 by the dashed lines. One sees also that a melt of eutectic composition crystallizes as a mixture of crystals exhibiting the maximum amount of solid solution in each phase. With decreasing temperature the mixed crystals revert in composition to that of the two pure end-members.

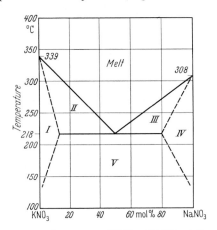

Fig. 301. The system KNO_3—$NaNO_3$ (after D'Ans-Lax). I Completely crystallized homogeneous K-rich mixed crystals; II K-rich mixed crystals and melt; III Na-rich mixed crystals and melt; IV Completely crystallized homogeneous Na-rich mixed crystals; V Completely crystallized heterogeneous mixture of K- and Na-rich mixed crystals

The expression liquidus is frequently used more generally for the melting curve in systems in which no solid-solution is involved. Thus in the system diopside-anorthite (Fig. 291), the horizontal line is the solidus, the melting curve the liquidus. In systems having immiscibility gaps, as in Fig. 301, the pair of lines separating the field of the melt and fields II and III represent the liquidus. Those lines along the boundary between fields I and II, II and V, III and V, and III and IV represent a solidus.

4. Three Component Systems

The Concentration Triangle. We want to turn now to the three component systems. Therefore, we must now consider three constituents, in addition to pressure and temperature. We can represent variations in composition in one planar diagram, if we represent the sum of the three as equal to 100% and utilize the percentages to represent each constituent. For representation we use an equilateral triangle (Fig. 302). At any corner the concentration of one component is 100%, the other two 0%. The geometrical locus representing 33% A is a line drawn parallel to BC at a distance 33 from BC. Likewise 16% B is represented by a line parallel to AC at a distance 16 from AC. From the intersection of these two lines, the composition of the three component system is uniquely determined. The line parallel to AB, representing 51% C must pass through the intersection of the other two lines. Thus a point at the intersection of the three lines represents a composition 33% A, 16% B, 51% C. The sides of the composition triangle correspond to two-component systems. We need now only to construct the concentration-temperature diagrams for the two-component systems, to derive a three-dimensional model of our three component system, within a trigonal prism. We cannot, of course, consider the pressure simultaneously. What is the configuration of the surface of the three-dimensional prismatic model? That depends completely on the kind of system. When we join three simple eutectic two-component or binary systems of the sort shown in Fig. 291 (p. 189), we get within the triangle a *ternary eutectic point*, connected to each of the binary eutectic points by eutectic lines.

The System Anorthite-Albite-Diopside. We shall consider only the system albite-anorthite-diopside, illustrated in Fig. 303. We have already dealt individually with two of the binary systems. The third system, albite-diopside, has an eutectic point very close to the pure albite end and exhibits no solid solution. In the resulting three component (ternary) system, there is no ternary eutectic point, only an eutectic line or trough. In order to represent this three-dimensional figure simply, accurately, and quantitatively in two dimensions, (a plane), we treat the situation just as a cartographer deals with topography. Contour lines of the temperature gradients, so-called isotherms, are projected onto the concentration triangle, as is indicated in Fig. 303. The system is in this way represented to scale in Fig. 304. Therefore, within the triangle, we have represented two kinds of information at the same time: concentration and the configuration of the crystallization planes and lines. We shall consider first a melt with the composition 50% diopside, 25% albite, and 25% anorthite. If the temperature of this melt sinks to 1,275°C, only crystals of diopside begin to crystallize out. The residual melt becomes depleted in diopside, and its concentration is changed upon further cooling along a line connecting the composition of the melt and the diopside corner of the triangle. This is called the *crystallization path*. This path

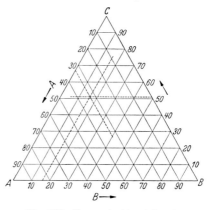

Fig. 302. Concentration triangle

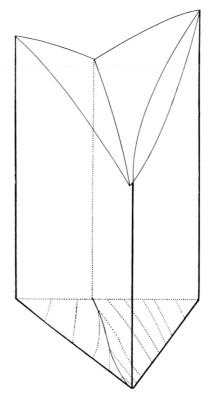

Fig. 303. The system albite-diopside-anorthite (in three dimensions)

is followed to the eutectic line which it intersects at 1,235°C. At this point plagioclase now crystallizes out also, and as mixed crystals which, as in the binary system, are more anorthite-rich than is the melt. We can determine their composition from Fig. 297. Crystallization on the solidus is not altered by the presence of diopside. Upon further cooling, the melt changes its composition along the eutectic line. In order to determine the composition of the crystalline phase in equilibrium at any point on the eutectic line, we must extend, until it cuts the plagioclase side of the triangle, a line connecting the point with the diopside corner. From Fig. 297 we ascertain the solidus composition in equilibrium with the point of intersection on the plagioclase liquidus. So, in the case of our starting composition, we find that crystallization on the eutectic line ceases at about 1,200° C, because at this temperature the plagioclase crystals have the composition

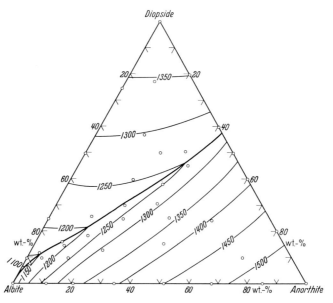

Fig. 304. The system albite-diopside-anorthite projected on the concentration triangle (after BOWEN). Circles denote experimental points

An$_{50}$, the same albite:anorthite ratio as the initial melt. It is assumed that equilibrium was maintained. This would be the case for very slow cooling. If the cooling takes place more rapidly so that equilibrium is not achieved, or if the first formed plagioclase crystals are removed, then the crystallization of diopside and plagioclase must continue past 1,200° C. The melt becomes richer in albite than when equilibrium prevails, since no anorthite is available from the dissolution of the first formed plagioclase. Finally the fluid phase attains a composition at which plagioclase, richer in albite than before, is crystallized out along with diopside.

We want to discuss the method for constructing crystallization paths for a somewhat more complicated case, referring to Fig. 305. If we cool down a melt, represented by point 1 in the plagioclase field, we determine the composition of the plagioclase which precipitates out by cooling to the liquidus surface, similarly as above. We draw a line through point 1 and the diopside corner. Its intersection, L_1, with the plagioclase side of the triangle gives us, purely geometrically, the albite:anorthite ratio of the melt. We ascertain from Fig. 297 the corresponding ratio on the solidus and plot this point S_1 on the plagioclase side of the triangle. In order to construct the crystallization path to the eutectic line, we take now a point S_2 on the plagioclase side and determine from Fig. 297 the corresponding composition of the melt L_2. The line connecting the diopside corner with L_2 and the line connecting 1 and S_2, intersect at the corresponding point 2 in the crystallization path. Through repetition of this process with S_3, L_3, S_4, L_4, etc., the crystallization path can be constructed with desirable accuracy. After the eutectic line is reached, crystallization proceeds along the eutectic line until point 6 is reached, where crystallization ceases. Point L_6 gives the albite:anorthite ratio of the melt at point 6, and L_1 the corresponding composition of the plagioclase crystals in equilibrium with it. L_1 gives also the ratio in the original melt. These

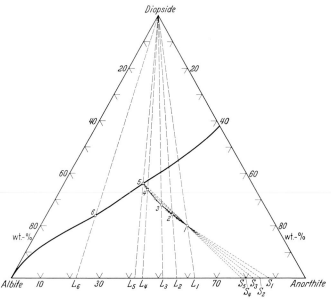

Fig. 305. Construction of crystallization paths in the system albite-diopside-anorthite

constructions are appropriate only under the assumption that equilibrium is maintained always. If this is not the case, if anorthite is removed from the system, it behaves as a system richer in albite. This disequilibrium is especially important in rock formation, as we shall see.

These few examples must be sufficient to show what great importance the theory of heterogeneous equilibrium, as this branch of physical chemistry is called, has for mineralogy. A deep understanding of this field is strongly recommended for every prospective mineralogist. Phase diagrams are only clear summaries of observational data, but the nature of the summary, and conversely the meaning of the phase diagrams require a certain familiarity with the diversity of phenomena.

5. Hydrous Melts

Until now we have considered only dry systems. In the last decade a number of hydrous systems have been investigated at high temperatures and pressures. We have many reasons to assume that water has played an important role in the occurrence of magmatic rocks (see p. 223). Therefore, four important examples of the influence of water on the crystallization of rock forming minerals will be considered.

The Binary System SiO$_2$—H$_2$O. Fig. 306 shows how the melting curve is depressed with increasing water vapor pressure. The cristobalite field disappears at about 450 kg/cm², the tridymite field at 1,400 kg/cm².

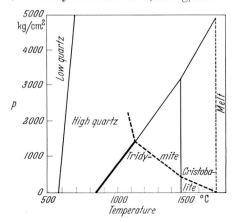

Fig. 306. Schematic pressure-temperature diagram for the system SiO$_2$—H$_2$O (after TUTTLE and BOWEN, 1958). ----- Melting curve for the anhydrous system; ---- Melting curve dependent on water vapor pressure

The System Diopside—Anorthite—H$_2$O. A lowering of melting temperature is always observed in hydrous systems. It is observable in the system diopside-anorthite. Since this is a three-component system, in the two-dimensional diagram (Fig. 307) only one specific water vapor pressure of 5,000 kg/cm² has been illustrated. The melting curves at lower water vapor pressures would lie between those for 5,000 and 0 kg/cm². This diagram, in combination with Fig. 294, shows that in a system involving only two minerals, the temperature of formation

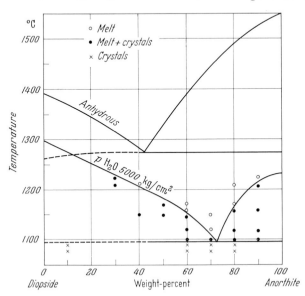

Fig. 307. Comparison of melting curves for the system diopside-anorthite under anhydrous conditions and at a water vapor pressure of 5,000 bars. (After YODER in ROY and TUTTLE, 1956)

depends first on the concentration of diopside and anorthite components, second on the total pressure, and third on the water vapor pressure.

The System Albite—Anorthite—H$_2$O. As an additional example, Fig. 308 shows the dependence of the plagioclase phase diagram on water vapor pressure. From it we see that albite under 5,000 kg/cm^2 water vapor pressure melts at about 750°C.

The Alkali Feldspar System. We had seen on p. 194 that in the dry system K-Feldspar melts incongruently at 1,170°C. Fig. 309 shows the dry system at the left. It differs from the simple anhydrous system NaCl—KCl of Fig. 299 (p. 197) in that, in addition to the feldspar mixed crystals, the leucite phase occurs also. At 1,000 kg/cm^2 H$_2$O pressure (center diagram) the leucite field becomes smaller and at a water pressure of 5,000 kg/cm^2 (right diagram) it has disappeared. This phase diagram corresponds in form to the anhydrous KNO$_3$-NaNO$_3$ system (Fig. 301). Therefore, at high water vapor pressures, K-feldspar can be formed directly from the melt.

It is to be noted that with increasing water vapor pressure one phase, leucite, disappears (is unstable), although no water or OH ions are incorporated into the minerals.

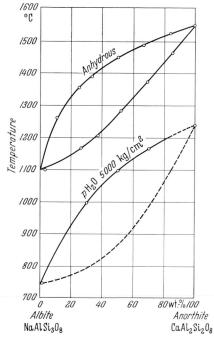

Fig. 308. Comparison of the melting curves for the system albite-anorthite under anhydrous conditions and at 5,000 bars water vapor pressure. (After YODER, STEWART and SMITH, 1956)

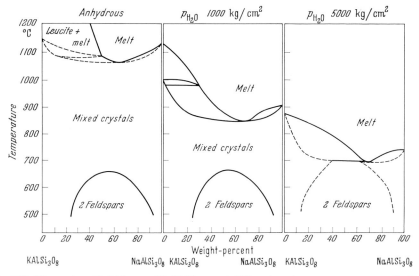

Fig. 309. The system K-feldspar—Na-Feldspar at different water vapor pressures. (Left and center after BOWEN and TUTTLE, 1950; right after YODER, STEWART and SMITH, 1956)

VI. Formation of Magmatic (Igneous) Rocks

1. Differentiation

The Reaction Principle. The rocks of the earth's crust are divided usually into three groups: magmatic rocks which crystallize from a fluid melt, sedimentary rocks which are mechanically or chemical-biologically formed from weathering products, and metamorphic rocks which form by transformation processes from the two previously mentioned groups. The transition between magmatic and metamorphic rocks is gradational and subdivision somewhat arbitrary.

In the following we shall consider as magmatic all rocks which are produced from a melt, regardless of the manner in which the melt originated. There remains, however, in many instances, doubt as to whether a rock has crystallized from a true melt, that is, one which was at one time completely fluid, or whether it is related to partial melting or to transformation products under the influence of gases and fluids. These processes will be considered in part IX on metamorphism.

Probably the most striking aspect to consider concerning magmatic rocks formed from a melt, is the observation that all graduations exist between light colored, quartz-rich, low density rocks and low silica, dark, high density ones. Again and again attempts have been made to explain the diversity of rock types by modifications of one primary magma. In fact, a series of processes can be advanced which, depending on the circumstances, lead to variable end products upon cooling of a melt. One possibility is based on the mixed crystal formation in the plagioclase system, arising from incomplete attainment of equilibrium as referred to above (p. 195). Let us assume that anorthite-rich plagioclase crystallizes out of a magma first. These crystals are heavier than the melt, sink down into the magma chamber, and are removed from reaction with the surrounding melt. Thus the melt becomes enriched in albite. A *continuous crystallization series* results, perhaps with bytownite resulting in the lower part of the magma chamber and oligoclase or albite in the upper part.

Another but *discontinuous series* occurs in systems with incongruent melting points. As an example, let us consider the two component system, $MgO - SiO_2$, illustrated in Fig. 310. Between SiO_2 (which occurs as cristobalite at the temperatures illustrated) and Mg_2SiO_4 (forsterite, an end member of the olivine series), there occurs the compound $MgSiO_3$, enstatite[1]. In effect, enstatite is a diopside in which Ca has been replaced by Mg. It can serve as a representative of the large family of pyroxenes. Enstatite melts incongruently with decomposition into forsterite and SiO_2 at 1,557°C. From a melt containing 60% SiO_2, forsterite crystallizes out first upon cooling to the melting curve. If the temperature is lowered still further, point D may be reached, at which temperature forsterite and melt are no longer in equilibrium. The previously formed forsterite crystals react with the melt to form enstatite crystals. The forsterite crystals are resorbed, therefore. Some of the solution features which are observed with magmatic olivines may be referred to such processes. If the early formed forsterite

---

[1] In experimental melts a monoclinic modification, clinoenstatite, forms. For simplicity, in the following discussion we shall always refer to the natural mineral enstatite.

crystals were removed from the melt, for example by settling, enstatite crystallization would occur directly, until, at point E, enstatite and cristobalite would crystallize out together.

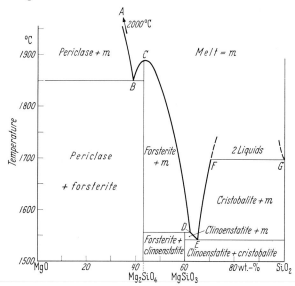

Fig. 310. The two-component system $MgO-SiO_2$. (After ANDERSON, BOWEN and GREIG)

Such mineral reactions upon cooling give rise to the discontinuous series, forsterite-enstatite. If we refer more generally to olivine and pyroxene, and enlarge the series to include hornblende and biotite, and connect this and the continuous plagioclase series with quartz, K-feldspar, and hydrothermal solutions (see p. 223), as natural observations indicate, we obtain a scheme for the crystallization sequence of a magma. It corresponds to the crystallization sequence observed in individual rocks.

The continuous plagioclase series involves framework silicates. In the discontinuous olivine-biotite series crystal structures change progressively from inosilicates with discrete $[SiO_4]$ tetrahedra, into chain and ribbon silicates, to sheet structures. Bonding energies increase in this sequence. The two series indicate for us the mineral composition of the most important eruptive rocks, as the following scheme shows:

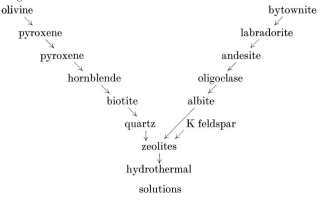

If we rearrange the two series so that the heavy minerals of the lefthand series are arranged in a horizontal row, with the light minerals above them, and then insert the corresponding magmas in between, we obtain the schematic listing shown below.

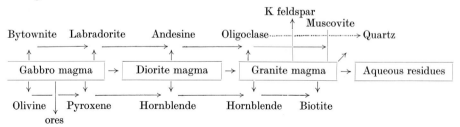

This shows how, by means of differential setting of minerals in the melt, acid (siliceous) rocks can originate from a basic magma. From a magma of the composition of a mixture of anorthite and olivine, bytownite and olivine crystallize out first. If these crystals were isolated from reaction, labradorite and pyroxene would follow, forming a rock that corresponds to a gabbro. If these minerals were also removed from the system, hornblende and andesine would crystallize, forming a diorite, etc. It is to be noted that the basic (silica-poor) rocks also have a low water content. During the course of this differentiation process, we proceed from essentially anhydrous to hydrous melts and finally to hydrous residual solutions (hydrothermal solutions). However, natural rocks are often observed which do not fit this simple scheme. Many basalts carry olivine, pyroxene, and andesine, for example.

As we have discussed above, reactions between early crystallized minerals and the melt take place in the two two-component systems we have used as models. The concepts employed here to account for chemical differentiation were emphasized by N. L. BOWEN, and are referred to as the *reaction principle*. It provides a far-reaching explanation of the variability of igneous rock magmas. The subsidence or rise of minerals in a melt in conjunction with reaction is one of the likely explanations for the variability of igneous rocks. A classic example is afforded by the Palisades diabase (basalt) sill occurring in the vicinity of New York City. This is an intrusive sill about 300 meters thick, in which a concentration of about 20% olivine occurs in a narrow zone 15—20 meters above the lower contact. It is important that the typical columnar structure of the basalt extends undistorted through the olivine-rich zone.

These differentiation processes do not depend on the mode of origin of the melt, and apply equally well to those originating through metamorphic processes.

Filter Pressing. Progressive separation of early formed crystals from a melt need not result only from gravitational settling of the heavy constituents. This can be brought about also by a filter pressing process in which the melt is squeezed out from the early formed crystals. This can happen when a partially crystallized melt is subjected to differential pressures. The process is similar to the action of a fruit press, in which the juice is separated from the pulp. Such a process can be initiated by mountain building orogenic movements. This process has been employed to explain the occurrence of some anorthosites, an almost monomineralic rock consisting of calcium-sodium feldspar. The process may play an even more general role in folded mountain regions.

Assimilation. An additional concept, developed especially by DALY, to explain magmatic differentiation, is assimilation. This involves inclusion of foreign rocks into a magma as it makes its way from depth toward the surface of the earth. In fact, inclusions of other igneous rocks and sediments which clearly show signs of alteration or partial solution are often found in magmatic rocks.

We can again formulate a model to describe this process in simple cases by choosing again the simple two-component systems albite-anorthite and forsterite—SiO_2.

Let us consider a plagioclase melt (Fig. 297) with the composition 50% albite, which has just reached the liquidus curve at 1,450°C. To this melt is added a plagioclase crystal of composition 10% albite, which is at the same temperature. We assume no higher temperature, because a magma that ascends into the earth's crust in general will be only slightly superheated, that is, its temperature will lie only slightly above that at which the first crystals begin to crystallize out. We know in fact, from natural observations, that at times formation of crystals in magmas has already begun before intrusion of the magma upwards. Thus the melting curve was reached previously. Therefore, we are justified in assuming in our model system that the melt had just attained the temperature of 1,450°C. At this temperature a plagioclase with 20% albite is in equilibrium with the melt. The added crystal with 10% albite is analogous to a crystal formed at an earlier stage from the melt. It must react therefore with the melt to approach 20% albite, if equilibrium is to be maintained. As the inclusion reacts, the melt maintains its position on the melting curve or surface and the further course of crystallization is not influenced. Some heat of reaction is evolved. The reaction is exothermal, because it is an equilibrium reaction which takes place with decreasing temperature. If this heat is not dissipated, the temperature of the melt increases somewhat.

If we had added a cold crystal to the melt, at first the melt would cool somewhat with a corresponding lowering of the starting point for further crystallization. The subsequent course of crystallization is not affected. In each case the course of crystallization proceeds, in spite of the addition, as it would without the addition of foreign crystals. However, an end point would be reached with a higher anorthite content, due to the introduction of this component by the inclusion. The reaction of the inclusion corresponds completely to analogous reactions with crystals first formed directly from a melt, if it remains in equilibrium with the melt.

If, on the other hand, we add a plagioclase crystal with 80% albite to the melt it cannot generally exist at 1,450°C in the solid state, and so melts. If it is colder than the melt when added, the melt is first cooled and the corresponding feldspar containing 20% albite crystallizes out, that is, if the melt is not superheated. In either case, the inclusion is melted and incorporated in the fluid state into the melt. The melt as a result becomes richer in albite and takes longer to crystallize, and then with phases richer in albite. The course of crystallization proceeds further to the right in the scheme illustrated above (p. 206). Such melting of inclusions takes place only when they are richer in albite than the melt.

We can observe the same relationships in the system forsterite—SiO_2. If we add forsterite to a melt from which enstatite has been crystallized, the forsterite reacts with the melt in part or completely, depending upon the amount, changing to enstatite. If we were to add enstatite to a melt from which forsterite had crystallized, the enstatite would melt.

We can quite generally conclude, therefore, that the reaction principle provides us with information on the behavior of inclusions in magmas. Inclusions of rocks corresponding in composition to early crystallization stages react with the evolution of the heat of reaction, having no effect on subsequent crystallization. They are dissolved by the melt. Inclusions, corresponding in composition to later stages of crystallization, are melted although the melt is cooled by them. The course of crystallization is displaced in the direction of mineral compositions of later crystallization stages. These considerations are strictly applicable to igneous rock inclusions. They can, however, be appropriately adapted to sedimentary rock inclusions also. Thus sandstone or quartzite inclusions in basalts frequently show reaction rims of pyroxene and glass (Fig. 311). By the introduction of quartz the course of crystallization, olivine to pyroxene, is displaced in the direction of pyroxene. Glass is formed as a result of localized cooling. For

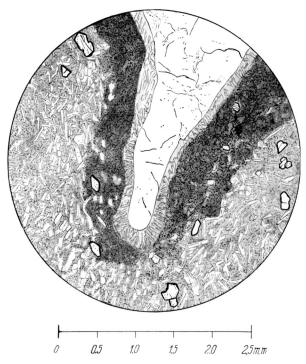

Fig. 311. Quartzite inclusion in basalt, (Steinberg by Meensen, southwest of Goettingen). Around the inclusion is a glassy reaction rim with pyroxene needles, grading into a normal basalt, with feldspar laths and augite inclusions (strongly outlined in a finely crystalline groundmass

such melting to take place, it is necessary that the heat content of the melt be sufficiently large to prevent cooling of the total melt. Because the heat contents of magmas near the earth's surface are low, inclusions from crustal rocks exhibit usually only slight reaction (as in Fig. 311). Geochemical investigations have shown in addition that Ca and Mg rich rocks, such as melilites, could not have been formed by assimilation of limestones or dolomites. They have higher Ni and Cr contents than could have originated from sediments (WEDEPOHL, 1963). On this basis we must conclude that the assimilation of sediments by magmas near the earth's surface plays a much lesser role in altering the Ca, Mg, SiO_2, and Al_2O_3 content of igneous rocks than was earlier assumed. The uptake by a melt of water from argillaceous sediments appears to be a much more important phenomenon.

Fluid Immiscibility. Additional modes of differentiation have been suggested. One of these involves liquid immiscibility of silicate magmas. An example of such immiscibility is illustrated in the right-hand portion of the diagram for the system $MgO-SiO_2$ (Fig. 310). A melt containing SiO_2 and minor MgO occurs in the field bounded by the SiO_2 ordinate and the dashed line. If we progress horizontally to the left (increasing MgO concentration), at a composition corresponding to the intersection with this dashed line, immiscibility occurs. Beyond this line two melts coexist. The composition of the two melts corresponds at any fixed temperature to the intersections of a horizontal line and the two dashed ones projected on the abscissa. The relative proportions of the two melts depend on the composition of the initial melt from which they formed. Such immiscibility in the fluid state provides another possible explanation for the diversity of magmatic rocks. However, experimental investigations have failed to substantiate an important role for immiscibility in natural silicate systems. Moreover, the influence of water in a melt appears, based on recent experiment, to render liquid immiscibility unlikely.

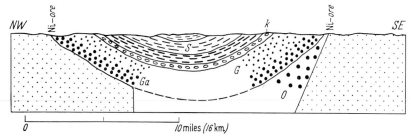

Fig. 312. Schematic cross section of the intrusive deposit at Sudbury, Canada (after COLEMAN [see DALEY]). *S* younger sediments; *k* conglomerate; *G* granite; *Ga* gabbro (norite); *O* older gabbro (norite)

In *sulfide-silicate systems* liquid immiscibility does play a role in mineral formation. The sulfide which occurs frequently in natural melts is pyrrhotite, $Fe_{1-x}S$. Its melt is heavier than silicate melts and would sink in them. In this case we can use as a model for this process, the system methyl alcohol-hexane. We can color 4 ml of methyl alcohol with methyl orange and add 6 ml of hexane. At room temperature the two fluids do not mix and the hexane remains colorless. At about 50°C complete miscibility occurs, the resulting fluid becoming homogenously orange colored. Upon cooling again fine droplets of methyl alcohol separate out in the hexane, and sink because of their higher specific gravity (methyl alcohol 0.79, hexane 0.66). Finally the orange colored methyl alcohol segregates as a separate layer. If we were to freeze the system during the stage of immiscible droplet formation, we would have an analog to the occurrence of pyrrhotite droplets and schlieren in many gabbros. Complete unmixing of this kind on a very large scale has been suggested to account for the formation of the famous Sudbury mineral deposits in Canada (Fig. 312). There is considerable opposition to this interpretation of origin, however. This mineral deposit, as a result of the crystallization of pentlandite, (Fe, Ni) S, is the most important nickel deposit in the world. Sudbury ore contains 2.5—3% nickel and had an annual production in 1938 of about 100,000 T Ni. Similar, but much smaller mineral deposits occur in Sohland on the Spree, Horbach in the Black Forest and at Petsamo in northern Finland. In Sudbury platinum is also produced

(1954: 10 T), admixed to the extent of only 0.2 g per ton of ore. This serves as a good example to stress the economic importance of minor impurities in ores. The average platinum content of igneous rocks is 0.005 g/T; in ultrabasic rocks, 0.02 g/T. Thus in the Sudbury ore natural processes have already brought about an enrichment of Pt. Immiscibility has been suggested also as an important factor in silicate-iron oxide melts. The occurrence of magnetite in drop-like form has been cited as evidence of liquid immiscibility, even though it is observed rarely in this form. It is possible that the great magnetite-hematite deposits in northern Sweden originated by such unmixing of fluid magmas. The origin of carbonate magmas, as observed in the volcanic eruptions in Tanganyika, could have originated by immiscibility in the fluid state, as has been established experimentally in the system albite$-Na_2CO_3$.

2. Survey of Igneous Rocks

Methods of Classification. The changes which a melt can experience, either by unmixing in the fluid state, assimilation of foreign rocks, or by crystal settling and filter pressing, suffice to some extent to demonstrate how the diversity of eruptive rocks originates. The processes themselves are not yet sufficiently understood to permit formulation of a general genetic classification. Therefore, other criteria must be utilized for systematic classification. Three approaches have been attempted for classification, based on chemical composition or mineral content, or on geological relationships. Also the geological age has been utilized with some success.

Chemical history and mineralogical composition must be closely related, but the examples of two- and three-component systems have just shown us that even in such simple cases, different mineral assemblages can form from the same kind of melt, depending upon the conditions of crystallization. May we be reminded of only one example, the system diopside-anorthite (Fig. 291). For an understanding of rock genesis, conditions of crystallization are extremely important. A pure chemical classification would simply obscure the genetically important criteria.

The determination of mineral composition is carried out primarily by microscopic studies of *thin sections*. These are rock slices which have been cut to about 0.03 mm thickness and cemented with Canada balsam ($n = 1.537 \pm 0.003$) or kollolith ($n = 1.533 \pm 0.003$) onto a glass microscope slide. Such thin sections were first produced in 1851 by Sorby in England and in 1852 by Oschatz in Germany. Mineral identification in thin section requires the application of crystal optics (III. 5). Crystal optics has always been fostered by mineralogists in practice. Good petrographic work is not possible without mastery of the methods of crystal optics. In the case of fine-grained rocks and in other special cases, X-ray methods are used for mineral identification, especially powder methods. Studying minerals in rocks, utilizing a variety of methods, constitutes one of the most important jobs of the mineralogist.

Structures. Genetically as important as the mineral composition is the arrangement of the mineral constituents, that is their articulation. This is always carefully studied and described by petrographers. In Germany, as elsewhere, a distinction is made between rock structure and rock texture. By *structure* we mean the manner of construction from the individual constituents, the building blocks. By texture we mean a higher order articulation, a spatial arrangement of equivalent structural groups. For example, a masonry wall built of bricks or of field stone would be said to have a brick — or fieldstone structure, but a gothic or romantic texture. Unfortunately, outside of Germany these expressions are used in a different sense. For the most part, in the English speaking countries, the term "texture" is used to mean structure, and the term "fabric" to mean texture. "Structure" corresponds to a still greater order of arrangement, referred to as Absonderung in Germany, and illustrated by columnar structures in basalts, jointing in rocks, etc. Because of these differences in usage, it is often useful to use the more general expression "Gefüge" (in German).

The structure expresses the manner in which the mineral constituents fit together and contact each other, and indicate, therefore something of the crystallization processes of the magma. It indicates the crystallization sequence, dissolution processes, and other things as well. The structure of a glassy rock, for example, is informative, because this structure is related especially to the cooling rate (see p. 182), but is also dependent upon chemical composition. Rocks containing little silica, solidify less often as a glass than silica rich rocks. All gradations exist between glassy (hyaline) and fully crystalline (holo crystalline) rocks. In predominantly glassy rocks crystallization at times takes place in radial aggregates or "spherolites". Often incipient crystallization takes place forming hair-like crystals, or trichytes.

Another important structural manifestation is the crystal morphology. Crystals which grow without interference in the melt take on their characteristic morphologies; the crystals are said to be *euhedral* and the rock *idiomorphic*. Earlier formed crystals hinder the growth of crystals formed later, interfering with their development. Thus they show only partial morphological development and are said to be *sub-hedral*, and the rock containing them, *hypidiomorphic*. If morphology is completely undeveloped, the crystals are *anhedral* and the rock *allotriomorphic* or *xenomorphic*. If the crystals are anhedral as a result of simultaneous crystallization of all the constituents, the rock is said to be *panidiomorphic*. A special case of this is the graphic granitic structure, also referred to as micropegmatic, granophyritic, pegmatophyritic, or micrographic structure. When dealing with K-feldspar-quartz assemblages, DRESCHER-KADEN suggested the term Schriftgranite (graphic-granite) if the quartz is partially bounded by planar surfaces; if not he suggests the term *granophyre*. He suggests the term myrmekite for analogous plagioclase-K feldspar-quartz assemblages. We had noted earlier (p. 191) the similarity between these and eutectic structures. Similar structures can also form by means of replacement phenomena, as we shall note later when we discuss metamorphism.

Finally, of special genetic significance is the *relative grain size* of the mineral constituents of a rock. As a result of uniform, very slow cooling, as occurs with magmas crystallizing at great depth, the individual crystals all grow to about the same size. Under these conditions diffusion transfers sufficient matter, in the time available, to permit formation of an equigranular structure. An example is illustrated in Fig. 313.

It is possible to study directly the crystallization of other types of rock structures, as we observe lava flows from volcanoes. Melts such as these, which are suddenly transported to the earth's surface and are thereby suddenly cooled, crystallize with glassy or fine grained crystalline structures. These structures are, therefore, diagnostic for extrusive or surface rocks. If the melt is cooled slowly, the first formed crystals can continue first to grow until a stage is reached in which the entire melt crystallizes. In the model two component system (Fig. 291, p. 189), this is when the eutectic is reached. It may also happen that such a magma may be cooling slowly at depth, and then be rapidly extruded to the surface and cooled. In both cases inclusions or *phenocrysts* may occur embedded in a fine grained groundmass. This is called a *porphyritic structure* (Fig. 295, p. 192). The word porphyr (greek: purpur) originally meant a red rock which happened to exhibit this structure. Its meaning has changed in the course of time from a color to a structural connotation. Porphyritic structures are found especially in dike rocks, formed by the extrusion of a magma into cold country rock; they are found as well in many extrusive rocks. As we mentioned earlier

Fig. 313. Equigranular structure. Granite (La Ginnea, Genoa), between crossed nicols. *a* orthoclase, large somewhat cloudy crystals showing twinning; *b* plagioclase, large crystals with narrow twin lamellae and one zoned crystal; *c* quartz, clear, "pincher" shaped between feldspars; *d* mica, small crystals showing cleavage; one crystal intergrowth in zoned plagioclase

(p. 192) the inclusions or phenocrysts can show evidence of dissolution or partial remelting. An additional kind of structure forms, in which at first relatively small crystals of one mineral crystallize, and these are included in larger later formed crystals of another mineral. This is called a *poikilitic* structure (gr. poikilos, mottled). In metamorphic rocks, analogous structures are called *poikiloblastic*. A special case of this is the *ophitic* structure (gr. ophis, snake) common to silica-poor rocks, in which tabular crystals of plagioclase appear in thin sections as laths lying within large augite crystals. If the space between feldspar laths is formed of continuous individual mineral grains (of augite or olivine), it is referred to as *intergranular* structure. The structure is referred to as *intersertal* if a fine grained or glassy groundmass fills in between the laths. Usually one observes something intermediate between intersertal and ophitic structures, as illustrated in Fig. 314.

   Textures. While structures express the physical and chemical conditions of crystallization, textures give us insight into the mechanical relations of the melt. Textures which do not show directional orientation indicate that the melt was subjected to substantially no movement during and after crystallization. Flow textures indicate movement (Fig. 315) and in certain cases even permit detailed analysis of the fluid movement, for example, by measurement of laminar crystals (sanidine) arranged parallel to the flow direction. These directions, however, cannot be interpreted to indicate in which of the two opposite directions movement took place.

Other directed textures form under the influence of external forces, which act after the solidification of the rock. They will be mentioned later when we discuss rock metamorphism.

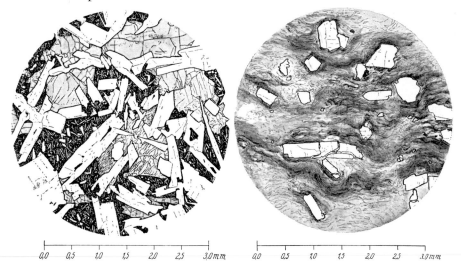

Fig. 314. Pyroxene andesite (Sababurg, Reinhardtswald, north of Kassel). Plagioclase (white) partly lath-shaped in orthorhombic pyroxene (gray with fractures), both in fine-grained groundmass

Fig. 315. Flow texture in rhyolite (Grantola by Luino, Lake Maggiore). Phenocrysts of sanidine in a glassy groundmass

Geological Classifications. If we now attempt a classification of igneous rocks based on our prevailing knowledge, we encounter numerous difficulties. For sometime the distinct differences in structures have been used generally to denote the site of crystallization. Rocks formed at great abyssal depths in the earth are designated as *plutonic*. Melts solidified between other rocks at intermediate (hypabyssal) depth form dike rocks, and if poured out onto the surface, *effusive* or *extrusive* rocks. These distinctions are therefore geological ones, and cannot always be made with certainty. This is particularly so because all gradations must exist from abyssal to hypabyssal to extrusive rocks. The hypabyssal group itself is, in fact, a transitional group which is often omitted in classification schemes. However, this designation has become so much a part of our nomenclature that we shall retain it here.

An additional geological distinction, used almost exclusively in Germany, involves subdivision of extrusive rock into "old" and "young" varieties. This distinction is confined generally to the Paleozoic. Older Paleozoic basaltic rocks are called *diabases*, basalts occuring in the upper Paleozoic (Permian) are still given the special name, *melaphyres*. These names should be discontinued. In the English-speaking countries, generally speaking, the term diabase is used for coarse grained basalts which occur as dike rocks, and are synonymous with dolerite. The old extrusive rocks have in many places during the course of earth history undergone changes and are weakly metamorphosed or "anchimetamorphic". It is recommended that in Germany, as elsewhere, the previous terms for "old" extrusive rocks be confined to these anchimetamorphic rocks. An unaltered

Paleozoic basalt, such as occurs in Scandinavia, if not in Germany, should simply be called a basalt.

Two types of dike rocks are customarily distinguished. One group consists of rocks which have the same composition as an observed or assumed parent rock, but which differs from it in its structure. These rocks are called porphyries, if they contain dominantly K-feldspar, and porphyrites, with plagioclase. The name of the parent rock is included, giving rise to terms like granite porphyry, diorite porphyrite, etc. The word porphyry, as indicated earlier (p. 212) is a structural term. The name porphyril is applied customarily to anchimetamorphic extrusive rocks. It would be more satisfactory to use the appropriate rock name, for example, rhyolite. An additional group of dike rocks contains mineral constituents different from the presumed parent rock. If the light mineral fraction is enriched relatively, the rock is called an *aplite*. If the dark minerals predominate, the rock is called a *lamprophyre*. These rocks are also referred to as diaschistic, segregated dikes, as opposed to unsegregated aschistic rocks, the first group. Today the segregation theory, from which this terminology is derived, is no longer accepted and aplites and lamprophyres appear to be rocks of different origin.

Mineralogical Classification. The further subdivision of rock types can be carried out, based on mineral content as proposed by JOHANNSEN, NIGGLI, and TRÖGER. For plutonic rocks the ratios of the light constituents, quartz, feldspars, and feldspathoids, are used. The feldspathoids (shortened "foids") include leucite ($K[AlSi_2O_6]$), nepheline ($Na_3K[AlSiO_4]_4$), as well as the rarer minerals analcite ($Na[AlSi_2O_6] \cdot H_2O$), nosean, sodalite, hauynite, and cancrinite. The formulae for the last four minerals can be easily compared as follows:

For every 6 moles of nepheline ($NaAlSiO_4$) there occurs 1 Na_2SO_4 in nosean, 2 $NaCl$ in sodalite, 1 $CaSO_4$ in hauynite, and 1 $CaCO_3$ in cancrinite. In these minerals numerous additional substitutions occur. Their exact formulae are tabulated in the mineral tables appended on p. 422 and p. 424. All of these tectosilicates contain less SiO_2 than the feldspars, and thus cannot occur simultaneously in equilibrium with quartz. This was indicated earlier in discussing the phase diagram for leucite (Fig. 296, p. 194). From these considerations it is possible to represent rock compositions utilizing two contiguous concentration triangles (Fig. 316). The apex of the upper triangle represents 100% quartz and its base gives ratios of alkali to anorthite plagioclase feldspar. This also serves as the base for the second lower triangle, with 100% "foids" represented by its apex. The resulting diagram permits a quantitation subdivision of rocks according to their light mineral content. The compositional boundaries of some typical rock types are indicated in Fig. 316. Corresponding data are compiled in the Appendix C 1. The dark mineral constituents, including biotite, hornblende, pyroxene, and olivine are omitted from the diagram. They are included and summarized in Table 35. In this table the names of alkali rocks are enclosed in frames. The size of type gives an indication of the abundance of reach rock type. (See also p. 220, Table 41.)

It is necessary to say a little more about nomenclature. Rocks which contain predominantly light minerals are said to be *leucocratic* (gr. leucos, white); those with predominantly dark minerals, *melanocratic* (gr. melas, black). Sometimes a color index is also used, which indicates the percentage of dark-colored minerals (including olivine) present in the rock. Frequently one distinguishes between "acid", that is, silica-rich rocks which are usually light colored, and dark-colored "basic" rocks. In Table 35 individual typical rocks are indicated and their SiO_2 contents are given following the compilation of analyses by TRÖGER. In the

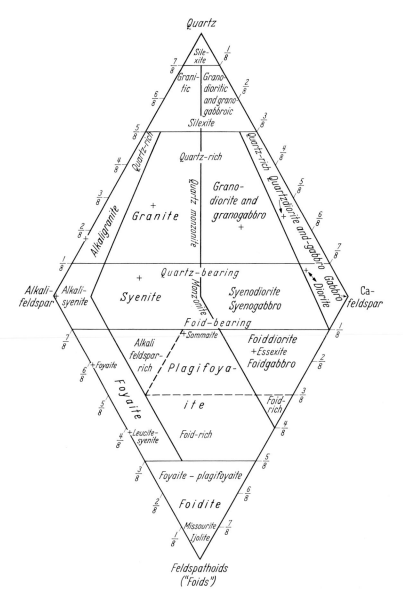

Fig. 316. Classification of plutonic rocks with more than 25% light minerals. (After NIGGLI)

appendix the corresponding chemical and mineral compositions for these typical rocks are given.

The world wide distribution of rock types is not homogeneous. HARKER (1896) and BECKE (1903) made the observation that alkaline rocks occur around the Atlantic Ocean, and calcalkaline rocks around the Pacific. Later NIGGLI subdivided the alkaline rocks into rocks with a preponderence of sodium, which correspond to BECKE's Atlantic suite. Alkaline rocks with predominant potassium, such as occur in the area of the Mediterranean Sea, especially in central Italy,

Table 35. *Summary of the common igneous rock types*

	SiO₂ in excess Quartz bearing			SiO₂ saturated; most without quartz						Undersaturated in SiO₂					
% SiO₂ on average	75 — 69 — 67	60	62 — 58	56	50 — 46		55	44 — 41		53	40 — 30
light minerals	Quartz and dominantly K-feldspar / Plagioclase			dominantly alkali feldspars / Feldspars dominantly plagioclase ab < 50 / an < 50						Feldspathoids with feldspar / without feldspar			predominantly monomineralic constituents		
dark minerals				biotite, hornblende, pyroxene				in part olivine		partly olivine			light	dark	
Plutonic rocks	**Granite** Alkali granite	**Granodiorite** / Quartzdiorite Tonalite / Adamellite		Syenite / Sodium-Syenite / Monzonite	Diorite	Gabbro Norite		Nepheline-Syenite / Essexite			Anorthosite (plagioclase)	Peridotite (olivine pyroxene) / Dunite (olivine)	
(Plutonites)													
Extrusive rocks (Vulcanites)	Rhyolite / Rhyodacite Dacite			Trachyte with sanadine / Latite Trachyandesite	Andesite	**Basalt** Alkali olivine-basalt and Tholeiitic basalt		Phonolite / Nepheline-tephrite[a] / Nepheline-basanite[a] / Limburgite with glass	Nephelnite / Leucitite / Melilithite				
anchimetamorphic	Quartz porphyry	Quartz porphyrite / Quartz Keratophyre		Keratophyre with albite	Porphyrite	Diabase						Kimberlite Picrite (olivine, augite, transition to basalt)	
Glasses	Obsidian Pitchstone (>3% H₂O)					Sideromelane Palagonite with H₂O						Monchiquite (Na)	
Dikes	Aplite and lamprophyre			Kersanite (K)		Camptonite (Na)							

[a] Notes corresponding leucite rock.

he called the Mediterranean suite. The nomenclature for alkali and calcalkali rocks used by various authors has varied somewhat and is indicated in Table 36 (after BARTH).

Table 36. *Terminology for geographic rock clans*

HARKER, BECKE	Various German and English authors		TYRRELL	PEACOCK	NIGGLI
Pacific	subalkalic	calc-alkalic	calcic	calcic / calc-alkalic	calc-alkali series = Pacific
Atlantic	alkalic	alkalic	alkalic	alkalic-calcic / alkalic	soda series = Atlantic
					potash series = Mediterranean

Today we usually make distinctions between so-called tholeiitic and olivine-alkali basalt clans. YODER and TILLEY give the following classification, based on the normative mineral content. (Calculation of mineral norms is explained on p. 219.)

Tholeiite, supersaturated with SiO_2: quartz + hypersthene.

Tholeiite, saturated with SiO_2: hypersthene.

Olivine-tholeiite, undersaturated with SiO_2: hypersthene + olivine.

Olivine basalt: olivine.

Alkali basalt: olivine + nepheline.

On the basis of modal (see p. 219) mineral composition, the olivine-alkali basalt types generally contain diopsidic pyroxene (augite) while the tholeiitic types contain additional pigeonitic and possibly orthopyroxene.

Chemical Classifications. The subdivision of the alkali and calcalkali rocks into Atlantic, Mediterranean, and Pacific suites is a chemical classification. Arrangement into such "petrologic provinces" follows from the chemical analyses of rocks. If one compares rock analyses, it is difficult to make direct comparisons from weight percentages of the constituent oxides. Therefore, molecular quotients are calculated from the weight percentages of the analyses. The weight percentages are divided by the molecular weights and multiplied by 1,000. These molecular quotients or molecular numbers are compiled in various ways so that mutual chemical relationships can be shown graphically. In Germany the representation of NIGGLI is generally used, as is the case in the following example. The molecular numbers for Al_2O_3, $FeO + MgO + MnO$ (including Fe_2O_3 calculated as FeO), $CaO + BaO + SrO$, and $K_2O + Na_2O + Li_2O$ are recalculated to 100%. We obtain the four groups $al + fm + c + alk = 100$. SiO_2 and, where appropriate, TiO_2, P_2O_5, etc. numbers are calculated proportionately. Molecular number Al_2O_3: molecular number $SiO_2 = al:si$. Finally the proportions of K_2O and MgO are calculated from molecular numbers:

$$k = \frac{K_2O}{K_2O + Na_2O + Li_2O}; \quad mg = \frac{MgO}{FeO + MnO + MgO}.$$

As an example of this type of calculation, the granite of Wurmberg from Braunlage investigated by H. NIEMANN, can be used (Table 37).

If one has a large number of analyses to compare, we usually utilize diagrams in which the al, fm, c, alk, k, and mg values are plotted against si-values. As an example, values calculated from the analyses of the plutonic rocks of Table 35 (excluding syenite) are plotted in Fig. 317. One can see very clearly the decrease in fm and c and the increase in al and alk, with increasing si. This form of chemical

Table 37. *Calculation of Niggli values for granite from Wurmberg at Braunlage, Harz.* (From H. NIEMANN, 1958)

	Weight %	Molecular number × 1000		Relative Numbers	
SiO_2	73.34		1221	si	= 413
TiO_2	0.13		1.6	ti	= 0.5
P_2O_5	0.12		0.85	p	= 0.3
			130.7	al	= 44.2
Al_2O_3	13.32				
Fe_2O_3	1.11	as FeO 13.9 ⎫			
FeO	1.14	15.9 ⎪			
MnO	0.017	0.2 ⎬ 36.2		fm	= 12.2
MgO	0.25	6.2 ⎭			
CaO	1.24		22.1	c	= 7.5
Na_2O	3.05	49.2 ⎫ 106.7		alk	= 36.1
K_2O	5.42	57.5 ⎭			
			295.7		100.0
S	0.1				
H_2O^+	0.82			k	= 0.54
H_2O^-	0.16			mg	= 0.17
	100.21			c/fm	= 0.61
Corrected for S/O	−0.03				
	100.18				
Density	2.62				

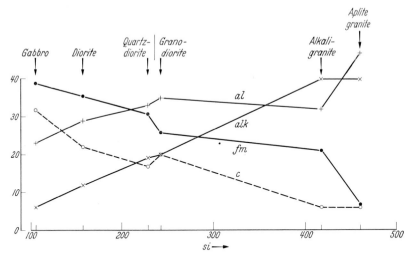

Fig. 317. Differentiation diagram of the plutonic rocks of Table 35

expression has its limitations, however. We must be cautious about reading too much into the relationships revealed. It is easy to denote variations by calculation which do not represent the natural conditions, especially since too much weight may be given to insignificant variations of local origin or even due to errors in analytical techniques.

Another method of recasting chemical analyses is used primarily in the United States. Standard or normative minerals are calculated with the help of molecular numbers. This method usually is called the CIPW norm, after its originators, CROSS, IDDINGS, PIRSSON, and WASHINGTON. The normative minerals are listed in Table 38. The calculation is simple, when SiO_2 is in excess. Table 39 indicates how the calculations are made. The detailed procedure is described by A. HOLMES.

Table 38. *Norm minerals (CIPW) and symbols*

Quartz	q	Wollastonite	Diopside	wo	Magnetite	mt
Corundum	c	Enstatite	di	en	Hematite	hm
K-feldspar	or	Ferrosilite		fs	Ilmenite	il
Albite	ab	Forsterite	Olivine	fo	Apatite	ap
Anorthite	an	Fayalite	ol	fa	Pyrite	pr
Leucite	le	Acmite		ac	Calcite	cc
Nepheline	ne					
Kaliophilite	kp					

Table 39. *Calculation of CIPW-norm for Wurmberg granite*

	SiO₂ 1221	TiO₂ 1.6	P₂O₅ 0.85	Al₂O₃ 130.7	Fe₂O₃ 6.9	FeO 15.9	MnO 0.2	MgO 6.2	CaO 22.1	Na₂O 49.2	K₂O 57.2	S 3.1	Molecular Number	Weight %
Quartz	530												530	31.8
Orthoclase	345			57.5							57.5		57.2	31.9
Albite	295.2			49.2						49.2			49.2	25.8
Anorthite	38.6			19.3					19.3				19.3	5.4
Corundum				4.7									4.7	0.5
Hypersthene {	6.2							6.2					6.2 }	1.2
	6.0					5.8	0.2						6.0 }	
Magnetite					6.9	6.9							6.9	1.6
Ilmenite		1.6				1.6							1.6	0.2
Apatite			0.85						2.8				0.85	0.3
Pyrite						1.6						3.1	3.1	0.4
														99.1
										H₂O⁺ }				1.0
										H₂O⁻ }				
														100.1

For the Wurmberg granite, as Table 40 shows, the agreement between normative and optically determined feldspars and quartz is quite good. We can notice at the same time a serious disadvantage of norm calculations, namely that mica is not taken into consideration in the calculation. Thus the norm is only a representation of the analysis, at best expressing that which could have crystallized from the magma. Instead of this *normative* mineral content, the *modal* content is usually given now, determined by quantitative optical studies. Whenever possible, modal analyses so determined should be given.

Abundance of Igneous Rock Types. Table 41 gives a summary of the distribution of the most common igneous rocks. According to all estimates, granites, granodiorites, and quartz-diorites are most common. These plutonic rocks make up about 80% of the volume of the Earth's upper crust. The extrusive rocks have not been included in Table 41 because, according to WEDEPOHL, even when we include the extensive plateau deposits, they collectively make up only 1—2% of the total volume of the Earth's crust. Among the extrusive rocks, DALY estimated the volume ratios of basalt:andesite:rhyolite at 50:10:1.

The predominance of granitic rocks has led to the idea that they originate in the crust by means of processes which take place in the zone of metamorphism, by complete or partial melting of sediments. However, having made this assumption, it is not apparent why so little of its extrusive equivalent, rhyolite, is found in the crust, and why so much (50 times) basalt occurs relatively.

Table 40. *Mineral composition of Wurmberg granite; comparison of modal analyses and norms based on chemical analyses* (after H. NIEMANN, 1958) *with CIPW-norm*

	Modal volume %	Calculated volume %	Calc. after CIPW-norm weight %
K-feldspar	33.6	33.2	32.0
Plagioclase (15% An)	31.5	31.4	31.2
Quartz	30.4	32.0	31.8
Biotite and chlorite	3.6	2.5	—[a]
Ores	0.7	0.5	1.8
Residue	0.3	0.4	0.4

[a] 1.2% hypersthene.

Table 41. *Abundance of igneous rocks in the upper crust in volume %.* (After K. H. WEDEPOHL)

	North American Cordilleran and Appalachian (DALY, 1933)	North American Cordilleran (MOORE, 1959)	Canadian Shield (GROUT, 1936)	Average based on geochem. considerations (after WEDEPOHL)
Granite	55	35	(< 50)	45
Granodiorite	29	19	(< 25)	} 35
Quartz diorite	} 5	34		
Diorite		2		5
Gabbro, etc.	7	11	11	15
Ultrabasic	0.5			0.5

In order for partial melting of sediments to take place, we must expect a relatively high content of volatile constituents, especially water and carbon dioxide. In a later chapter on volatile components it will be shown that granitic melts, because of their water content, can rarely find their way to the Earth's surface. It is generally accepted today that basalts do not originate in the Earth's crust, but from deeper layers, in the mantle (see p. 333).

3. Abundance of the Chemical Elements

Summary. Thus far we have considered only a few of the commonest elements and a small number of minerals composed of them. We must now take a look at the occurrence of the other elements in igneous rocks. The determination of the abundance of the elements (including their isotopes) and their manner of distribution in the Earth's crust represents the field of geochemistry, in its narowest sense. In the broader sense, geochemistry involves the entire study of the origin and destruction and alteration of minerals and rocks.

The elements considered thus far are actually the most abundant constituents of igneous rocks. They are listed in the first column of Table 42 and constitute about 99% of the chemical components of rocks.

The eight elements form a limited number of igneous rock-forming minerals. From LARSEN'S data on the abundance of minerals in different rock types, and from the estimated abundance of rock types (Table 41), WEDEPOHL has calculated the average mineral composition of igneous rocks, as shown in Table 43.

Table 42. *Abundance of elements in upper crust in ppm = g/t.* (After WEDEPOHL)

> 10,000 weight %	10,000—100	100—10	10—1	1—0.1	0.1—0.001
O 47.25	Ti 4700	V 95	B 9	I 0.5	Se 0.09
Si 30.54	P 810	Ce 75	Gd 8.8	Tm 0.3	Hg 0.08
Al 7.83	F 720	Cr 70	Sm 8.6	Bi 0.2	In 0.07
Fe 3.54	H 700	Zn 60	Pr 7.6	Sb 0.2	Ag 0.06
Ca 2.87	Mn 690	Ni 44	Dy 6.1	Cd 0,1	(Ar 0.04)
K 2.82	Ba 590	La 44	U 3.5	———	Pd 0.01
Na 2.45	C 320	Y 34	Ta 3.4	1.3	(Pt 0.005)
Mg 1.39	Cl 320	Cu 30	Yb 3.4		Au 0.004
———	S 310	Nd 30	Er 3.4		(He 0.003)
98.69	Sr 290	Li 30	Hf 3		(Te 0.002)
	Zr 160	N 20	Sn 3		(Re 0.001)
	Rb 120	Nb 20	Br 2.9		(Ir 0.001)
	———	Ga 17	Cs 2.7		(Rh 0.001)
	9730	Pb 15	Be 2		(Os 0.001)
		Sc 14	Ho 1.8		(Ru 0.001)
		Co 12	As 1.7		———
		Th 11	Eu 1.4		0.369
		———	Tb 1.4		
		621	W 1.3		
			Tl 1.3		
			Ge 1.3		
			Lu 1.1		
			Mo 1		
			———		
			79.7		

98.69 % Column 1
1.043% Columns 2—6

99.733%

Table 43. *Average mineral composition of igneous rocks.* (After WEDEPOHL)

	%		%		%
Plagioclase	42	Pyroxene	4	Olivine	1.5
K-feldspar	22	Biotite	4	Titanium	1
Quartz	18	Magnetite	4	minerals	
Amphibole	5			Apatite	0.5

The elements listed in columns 2—6 of Table 42 occur either in separate accessory minerals, or substituting in the structures of the more common mineral constituents. For the most abundant rock forming minerals WEDEPOHL has given (Table 44) the estimated average composition of those elements which substitute in the structure, omitting those elements which are essential in the formulation of a particular mineral. For example, the abundance of Ca, Na, Si, and Al is not indicated for plagioclase.

Table 44. *Estimated average concentration of elements in the most important rock forming minerals.* (From WEDEPOHL)

	X%	0.X%	0.0X%	0.00X%	0.000X%
Plagioclase	K	Sr	Ba, Rb, Ti, Mn	Ga, V, Zn, Ni	Pb, Cu, Li, Cr, Co, B
K-feldspar	Na	Ca, Ba, Sr	Rb, Ti	Pb, Li, Ga, Mn	B, Zn, V, Cr, Ni, Co
Quartz				Al, Ti, Fe, Mg, Ca	Na, Ga, Li, Ni, B, Zn, Ge, Mn
Amphibole		Ti, F, K, Mn, Cl, Rb	Zn, Cr, V, Sr, Ni	Ba, Cu, Co, Ga, Pb	Li, B
Pyroxene	Al	Ti, Na, Mn, K	Cr, V, Ni, Cl, Sr	Cu, Co, Zn, Li, Rb	Ba, Pb, Ga, B
Biotite	Ti, F	Ca, Na, Ba, Mn, Rb	Cl, Zn, V, Cr, Li, Ni	Cu, Sr, Co, Pb, Ga	B
Magnetite	Ti, Al	Mg, Mn, V, Ni, Cr, Ti, Ca	Cr, Zn, Cu	Ni, Co	Pb, Mo
Olivine			Mn, Co	Zn, V, Cu, Sc	Rb, B, Ge, Sr, As, Ga, Pb

We conclude from Tables 42 and 44 that many elements, such as Cu, Zn, and Pb, which are essential to our everyday needs, occur in very small amounts in the average rock. Elements such as silver and gold occur in amounts of less than 1 ppm ($<0.0001\%$). These rare or trace elements occur only in certain parts of

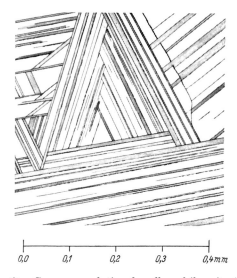

Fig. 318. Titanomagnetite. Coarse exosolution lamellae of ilmenite (dark gray) after {111} in magnetite (light gray). (After SCHNEIDERHÖHN-RAMDOHR)

the earth's crust where they have formed mineral deposits. Here they have become concentrated by processes which we still do not fully understand by and large. On the other hand there are elements like titanium which are relatively abundant, but of which the layman is rarely cognizant.

Titanium. Titanium can serve as an example to illustrate the different ways in which the elements occur in igneous rocks. The most ubiquitous titanium mineral is *ilmenite*, $FeTiO_3$, occurring particularly in basic igneous rocks. Sometimes, in a manner similar to *magnetite*, it is segregated from a magma as an independent rock. Magnetite itself also frequently contains titanium. Magnetite is very widespread as an accessory mineral and is lacking only in many acid granites and glass-rich extrusive rocks. At high temperatures magnetite can take up considerable amounts of titanium in solid solution, forming mixed crystals with ulvospinel, Fe_2TiO_4. Upon cooling exosolution occurs. Oxidation takes place simultaneously, precipitating lamellae of ilmenite parallel to $\{111\}$ of magnetite (Fig. 318). The titanium oxide, rutile, occurs in biotites and pyroxenes in the form of small laths. Exosolution phenomenon are probably involved here also. They can survive the weathering of these minerals and become incorporated into sediments. Quartz also occasionally contains rutile inclusions. It is uncertain to what extent exosolution is involved here. In many cases they are certainly foreign inclusions.

In acid and weakly basic rocks, especially syenites, the mineral *titanite* occurs. This is an inselsilicate with the composition $CaTi[O]SiO_4$. In very basic rocks titanium occurs in *perovskite*, $CaTiO_3$. In nepheline and leucite bearing extrusive rocks *melanite* occurs. This is a calcium-iron garnet, $Ca_3Fe_2(SiO_4)_3$, which contains up to 25% TiO_2. The titanium probably replaces the iron. In addition to these high-Ti accessory minerals, titanium is often found substituting in structures for major constituents in pyroxene, biotite, hornblende, and olivine (see Table 44). Many augites, contain up to 5% TiO_2, and are called titanoaugite.

Phosphorus. Another important element is phosphorus. It occurs almost exclusively in the accessory mineral *apatite*, $Ca_5(F, Cl, OH)(PO_4)_3$. In igneous rocks apatite contains F, and in much lesser amounts Cl, especially in basic rocks. Hydroxy-apatite is confined to sediments. Apatite is the primary natural source of phosphorus. The phosphorus content of an igneous rock, like that of titanium, increases with decreasing SiO_2-content (especially in alkali rocks). Apatite originates as a magmatic segregation in large amounts in only one locality, the Chibina Tundra on the Kola Peninsula. Monazite, $CePO_4$ (containing Th and rare earths) is found ocassionally in granites, and more rarely the mineral *xenotime*, YPO_4.

Zirconium. Zircon, an inselsilicate, is distributed widely in granites, syenites, quartz porphyries, and trachytes. It is by far the most important zirconium mineral.

Sulfur. Sulfur is distributed in all igneous rocks as pyrite, FeS_2. Next in importance is *pyrrhotite*, FeS, which occurs in basic rocks, particularly those of the gabbro family. *Chalcopyrite*, $FeCuS_2$ is not rare. The copper content of an igneous rock is due to its chalcopyrite content. In addition to the sulfides, sulfur is sometimes present in the sulfate-bearing silicates, *nosean*, $6(Na[AlSiO_4]) \cdot Na_2SO_4$, and *hauynite*, $6(Na[AlSiO_4]) \cdot CaSO_4$, which occur almost exclusively in young nepheline- and leucite-bearing extrusive rocks. Hauynite is especially abundant in the Mühlstein lavas of Niedermendig (Germany). In other rocks, sulfate ions indicated in analyses occur in fluid inclusions (see p. 224).

4. The Role of Volatile Constituents

It was shown earlier that water affects crystallization in SiO_2 and silicate systems, especially by lowering the melting temperature. From observations of volcanoes and their emanations, it has been known for a long time that magmas contain water and other volatile constituents. The predominant constituent of volcanic gases is water vapor, making up generally 90 volume percent. CO_2 is next most abundant, and then N_2. H_2, H_2S, and SO_2 have been observed also. It has become clear that the content of these latter gases is dependent on the temperature of the volcanic gas.

It has been possible to obtain information on the amount of gases released by degassing of magmas, from figures determined in 1919 in the region of Katmai volcano in Alaska. There, in the "Valley of 10,000 Smokes", ZIES estimated that over an area of only 77 km², the following quantities of gases were being evolved annually from a magmatic source of rhyolitic composition at shallow depth:

$$480 \cdot 10^6 \text{ tons } H_2O$$
$$1.25 \cdot 10^6 \text{ tons } HCl$$
$$0.2 \cdot 10^6 \text{ tons } HF$$
$$0.3 \cdot 10^6 \text{ tons } H_2S.$$

In the laboratory gases have been produced by experimental degassing of rocks. The greater portion of these gases occur in fluid inclusions. GOGUEL reported the following range of values for H_2O in minerals from seven granites (in mm³/g at 0°C and 760 torr):

$$\begin{array}{ll} \text{quartz} & 10-1{,}400 \ H_2O \\ \text{feldspar} & 10-6{,}100 \ H_2O \\ \text{biotite} & 600-4{,}300 \ H_2O. \end{array}$$

The water content of the biotite was represented by free H_2O, and does not include OH water released by dehydroxylation.

The System Salt—Water. Ever since consideration has been given to volcanic phenomena, these volatile constituents have been repeatedly assigned an important role in mineral formation. However, it was only through the development of physical chemistry that a deeper understanding of their importance has become possible. By 1920 P. NIGGLI had investigated and clarified extensively their relationships. However, only in the last 25 years has it become possible to investigate these processes experimentally. We shall begin the discussion of these somewhat complex relationships, utilizing a simple example, the system salt-water. Here we will be considering a simple eutectic system. Such a two-component system cannot, of course, substitute for a multicomponent system, but it can serve as a model in many fundamental respects. The molten salt and water must exhibit unlimited miscibility. We consider first an isobaric section of a system in which both components have very similar boiling points. The boiling curve is the phase boundary between fluid-vapor and is quite analogous to the solid-fluid boundary in a completely miscible system in the solid state (Fig. 297, p. 194). There are two vapor pressure curves, of which the one defines the beginning, the other, completion of condensation from the vapor state. The first, the condensation curve, is analogous to the "liquidus" in solid-liquid systems; the second, the boiling curve corresponds to the "solidus". By vapor, we mean a gas that is in equilibrium with a condensed and, therefore, fluid or solid phase. The visible mixture of condensed water droplets and air, existing between the two vapor pressure curves, is usually called steam. Strictly speaking this mixture is saturated steam, and the real gas is superheated steam.

Let us turn now to a generalized salt-water system in which the boiling point of the salt is about 1,000° higher than that of water. The pressure is established at one atmosphere. The vapor pressure curve of the mixture rises from the lower to higher boiling temperature, just as does the melting curve in the solid-liquid system, albite-anorthite (Fig. 297). When the boiling points are so dissimilar, it is possible for the boiling curve to intersect twice that portion of the melting curve which rises from the eutectic point to the melting point of the higher melting component. Such is the case in Fig. 319. Here $e - s_1 - s_2 - sm_s$ is the solubility curve of the salt in water, and can just as well be considered a melting curve. At s_1 it is cut by the boiling curve and at higher temperature only vapor and salt coexist in equilibrium. Only at higher temperature, corresponding to s_2, does condensation of water vapor take place again, at salt concentrations greater than s_2. Conversely, upon cooling from a higher temperature to point s_2, boiling occurs. This boiling which takes place upon cooling is called *retrograde boiling*.

If we now consider a melt of very low water content at point x, upon cooling it takes a path along the melting curve from sm_s to s_2 and crystals of salt precipitate. Likewise in a multicomponent system the non-volatile constituents can crystallize just as if no water were present. With continued cooling the melt is enriched in water, or more generally in all volatile constituents. This is very important in numerous respects. The more water or other volatile constituents present, the more can they be incorporated into mineral phases which are forming. In addition the viscosity, which increases upon cooling in dry melts, decreases in the presence of volatile constituents. They make the melt more mobile.

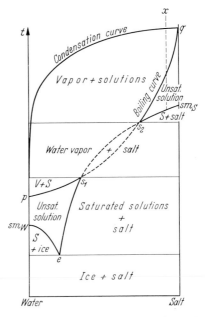

Fig. 319. The system salt-water, schematic, at atmospheric pressure

If the pressure at the second boiling point is not sufficient to hold the water in solution, boiling occurs. This retrograde boiling at atmospheric pressure can be demonstrated easily, if water vapor is introduced into a KNO_3 melt and then the melt is cooled, for the system $KNO_3 - H_2O$ corresponds at one atmosphere pressure to the phase diagram in Fig. 319. In silicate systems, for example, albite-anorthite, retrograde boiling takes place only at substantially higher pressures.

Supercritical Phenomena. Until now in our salt-water system the pressure has not been considered. We have seen already the PT diagram for the single component system H_2O (p. 183). It is important also to consider the supercritical region, which is illustrated in Fig. 320. In this three dimensional diagram the surface separating various states of water is depicted, so that the specific volume can be ascertained as related to temperature and pressure. The values for pressure and specific volume (cm^3/g) are plotted logarithmetically. On the left, ice occurs at temperatures below $0°$. To the right is the stability field of fluid water, and then that of the gaseous state. The unshaded area is bound by the two-phase boundary. On the two-phase boundary two values for specific volume are plotted for each pair of T and P values, one for water and one for gas saturated vapor. For example, if we start at low pressure on the $200°$ isotherm and raise the pressure until the isotherm intersects the two phase boundary, at this pressure (about 30 kg/cm²) the liquid and gaseous phases are in equilibrium. The same is true at the intersection of the $300°$ isotherm. However, the $400°$ isotherm no longer cuts the two-phase boundary because it is above the critical point, defined by the critical temperature of $374°C$ (t_{kv}) and the corresponding critical pressure of 225 kg/cm². Above the critical temperature there is no difference between gas and liquid, and one can refer only to a fluid state. An important question now is whether H_2O in the supercritical state can transport dissolved substances. It appears that solubility in the fluid state depends on density, and thus the logarithm of the solubility, L, is proportional to the log of the total density, ϱ. If we plot $\log L$ against $\log \varrho$ we obtain a straight line. The proportionality constant varies with the substance and for a given substance with the association number. For example, for SiO_2 it would be different from $Si(OH)_4$, $Si_2O(OH)_6$ and $SiO(OH)_3$ (GLEMSER). Table 45 gives some values for solubilities of some oxides, sulfates, $CaCO_3$ and ZnS at $500°C$ and $1,000$ kg/cm² pressure, as reported by MOREY.

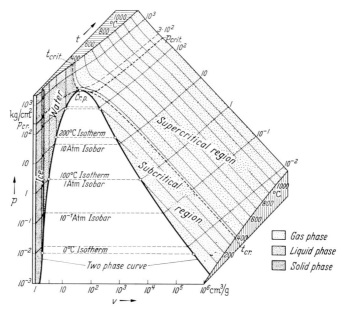

Fig. 320. Surface separating various phases of the one component system — H_2O. (Drawn after data from KENNEDY, by K. JASMUND, 1952)

Table 45. *Solubilities of some oxides, and sulfides as well as $CaCO_3$ and ZnS in g/T.*
(After MOREY, 1957)

At 500° C and 1,000 kg/cm² H₂O pressure				With 7% CO₂ in addition
CaSO₄	20	UO₂	0.2	
BaSO₄	40	Al₂O₃	1.8	
PbSO₄	110	SnO₂	3.0	50
Na₂SO₄	4,300	NiO	20	43
CaCO₃	120	Fe₂O₃	90	230
ZnS	204	BeO	120	
		SiO₂	2,600	19,000

The Complete Diagram. In order now to refer back to two-component systems we want to use a three-dimensional diagram. Fig. 321 illustrates a hypothetica diagram for two components A and B, which have the same melting and boiling points to a first approximation. In the right foreground we see the $P—T$ plane of component B, representing a one component system with three two-phase curves extending from the triple point O_B: the sublimation curve $b—O_B$ (solid-vapor), the melting curve $r—O_B$ (solid-liquid), and the vapor pressure surve $O_B—K_B$ (liquid-vapor) terminating at the critical point K_B. In the left background we see the one-component system A, with corresponding points a, O_A, and K_A. In between, the relations for mixtures of A and B can be depicted. We see in the isothermal section which bounds the diagram on the left, the pressure

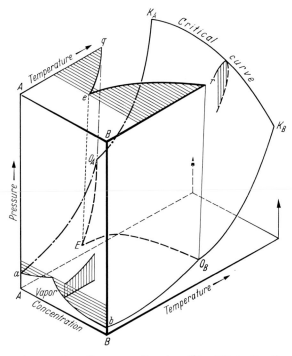

Fig. 321. Pressure-temperature diagram, salt-water. (Simplified after ROOZEBOOM)

dependence of the system at constant and very low temperature (without petrologic significance). At the top of the diagram, at high pressure, is an arbitrarily selected isobaric section, showing the familiar two-component system with a simple eutectic, bounded by $A—B—r—e—q$. From the eutectic point e, the dotted eutectic line extends to E, where the solid, liquid, and vapor phases are in equilibrium. To the right rear lies the critical curve, $K_A—K_B$. $K_A—K_B—O_B—O_A$ is not a surface, but a three dimensional pillow-shaped volume, as shown by the perpendicular, partially cross-hatched section. The upper (in the diagram) but lower temperature surface of the "pillow" is the boiling surface, the lower the condensation surface. In the diagram several sections through regions where two phases coexist are shown by means of cross-hatching. Especially important is the three-phase boundary, $O_B—E—O_A$, along which solid, liquid, and gas are in equilibrium. It bounds the melt surfaces $E—O_B—r—e$ and $E—O_A—q—e$. The two-phase surfaces which occur within the diagram are not indicated in full, so as not to confuse the diagram.

15*

If we cut an isobaric section somewhere through the middle of the diagram, we obtain a view of a two-component system with eutectic and boiling and condensation curves, such as we had described initially (p. 225). If the boiling points of the two components are very different, the boiling curve will cut the melting curve in two places, and we obtain an isobaric section analogous to Fig. 319, with first and second boiling points.

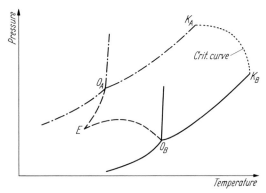

Fig. 322. Projection of a two-component system $A-B$, on the $P-T$ plane of the system-B. Melting point of $A \sim B$

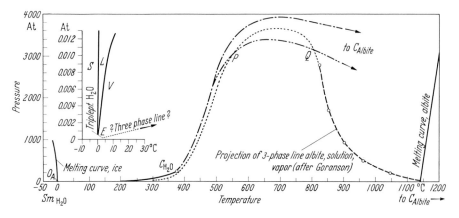

Fig. 323. Projection of the system albite-water on the $P-T$ plane of albite. (After the investigation of GORANSON)

We can project the entire system on a plane, for example the $P-T$ plane of one of the components. Fig. 322 corresponds to the projection of Fig. 321. In order to represent in this way a system with greatly differing boiling points, the observations of GORANSON for the system albite-water are plotted in Fig. 323 as indicated by various dotted lines. Solid lines represent the pure systems. The remaining lines indicate possible projected relationships.

Such a diagram raises the question as to whether the critical curve always remains above the three-phase boundary, as is the case in systems with approximately equal vapor pressures, or whether, due to the presence of volatile constituents, especially water, the two curves intersect, as the bottom curve of Fig. 323 indicates. In alkali silicate$-H_2O$ systems the critical curve is not intersected, but in the system SiO_2-H_2O it is. Thus we can assume this to be the case in numerous silicate$-H_2O$ systems. This means then that between the points of intersection (analogous to P and Q in Fig. 323), crystallization from the super-critical state can occur.

Volatile Constituents and Intrusion of Magmas. We have already noted (p. 202 and 203) the influence of H_2O on different one- and two-component systems. In all of these instances, the pressure imposed on the system is equal to the partial pressure of H_2O. An important consequence of these experiments is that the melting temperatures are lowered due to the water. This has been established in the case of granites also. A dry granite begins to melt at the earth's surface at about 960°C. At 15 km depth, corresponding to a pressure of about 4,000 kg/cm^2 and an equivalent water vapor pressure, melting begins at 650°C. Under these conditions it can contain about 9% water in solution. Below 650°C it is solidified. At 6 km depth, at a pressure of 1,600 kg/cm^2, it would be fully solidified at 700°C. A granitic melt, rising upward in the earth's crust, would be solidified at relatively shallow depths and would not succeed in reaching the surface, if it were not heated above 960° from the beginning. Basalts on the other hand have a very low water content and their crystallization temperatures are much higher, at about 1,090°C, and increase only a little with increasing pressure. By means of these relations, H. G. F. WINKLER has explained the rarity of granitic extrusive rocks, that is, rhyolites, relative to the great abundance of their plutonic equivalents, granites. The water content of granitic magmas thus depends on their having been derived at least for the most part by the meta-morphism of sediments. We shall say more about this later (see p. 292). Basalts on the other hand are derived from deeper layers of the earth, originating at high temperatures in the earth's mantle, rather than the crust (see p. 333).

We want to consider now the relations of H_2O in a silicate magma, completely enclosed in a magma chamber. We must distinguish first between the water content of a melt and the partial pressure of water. By partial pressure we mean the water vapor pressure which we would measure if we were able to introduce an appropriate apparatus in various places in the melt. From without, the homo-geneous pressure is exerted on the magma reservoir from the overlying rock mass. This is called the rock pressure. Fig. 324 reproduces the conditions in such a melt at a constant temperature of 1,000°C as a function of external pressure. The data were taken by KENNEDY (1955) from the work of GORANSON on albite-water melts, which behave very much like a granite melt. The curve descending to the right indicates the water content of the melt when the H_2O pressure is equal to the external pressure. It indicates the maximum water content in the melt at different pressures. Such a system cannot remain stable. The H_2O vapor pressure, when it equals the external pressure, rises very quickly with increasing depth. Water would diffuse against the pressure gradient, and the H_2O pressure would become greater than the external pressure, causing the chamber to explode. The curves descending to the left indicate the amount of water dissolved in the melt, when the partial pressure of H_2O ranges from $500-3,500$ kg/cm^2. They terminate at the saturation curve. Let us consider a large magma chamber extending from 7.2 km to a depth of 10.6 km. The external pressure at 7.2 km is 2,000 kg/cm^2. If the magma at this depth is saturated, it contains 7.5% water. At the bottom of the magma chamber at 10.6 km depth the external pressure is 3,000 kg/cm^2. At this pressure the same melt would contain in solution only 3.3% water. The water migrates, therefore, against the external pressure. It is concentrated in the upper part of the magma chamber. The water is squeezed out, so to speak, as would be expected from its large molecular volume.

Such a magma reservoir would certainly not have the same temperature throughout. Along its borders and especially at the top it would be cooled down. The cooler a melt is, the more water it can take up. At constant external pressure, the water content increases about 0.5 weight percent for each 100°C decrease in temperature. Water migrates, therefore, to the cooler areas on the borders of the chamber. This means, first of all, that the roof and border portions have a lower crystallization temperature than the core, and secondly, that the volatile constituents are enriched on the outer margins of the chamber. In very large granite bodies it can frequently be observed that the margins of the body are coarser grained, in part porphyritic, and richer in mineral-bearing cavities. This is described as miarolitic development.

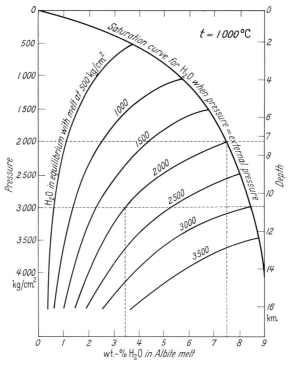

Fig. 324. Equilibrium distribution of water in an albite melt in the earth's gravity field.
(After GORANSON and KENNEDY, 1955)

The concentration of H_2O in those portions of a magma reservoir lying close to the earth's surface can lead to eruptions, if the water vapor pressure becomes greater than the external pressure confining the melt. This would be the case if more water is present than the melt can dissolve, or it could result from a decrease in water solubility with falling temperature, corresponding to retrograde boiling (Fig. 319, p. 225). GORANSON has computed that an albite melt, containing 4.2% water, is in equilibrium at 1,100°C at a pressure of 606 kg/cm², corresponding to a depth of $2^1/_4$ km external rock pressure. This pressure is sufficient, therefore, to hold the water in solution. After cooling to 819°, albite crystals make up 56% of the system and the residual melt contains 9.5% water. The pressure has climbed now to 3,000 kg/cm². It would be necessary now to have an overburden of 13 km of rock to hold the water in the melt. The existing rock pressure is insufficient, and a volcanic eruption or explosion would take place.

We know from the Krakatau Volcano in the Dutch East Indies, that during the eruption in 1883, 18 km³ of rock were ejected. The dust cloud reached 27 − 30 km

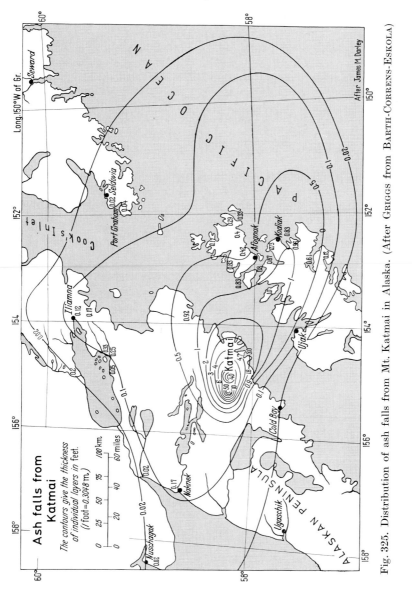

Fig. 325. Distribution of ash falls from Mt. Katmai in Alaska. (After GRIGGS from BARTH-CORRENS-ESKOLA)

in height and the ash falls covered 827,000 km². During the Katmai eruption in Alaska in 1912, 21 km³ of rock were ejected. The ash distribution is mapped in Fig. 325. We can see that volcanic ash deposits can extend to great distances from the explosion crater. The outermost contour of Fig. 325 corresponds to an ash bed of 6 mm thickness. Volcanic ash can be sedimented in small amounts over the entire earth. It contributes significantly to ocean deposits in regions far

removed from land, such as in the Pacific, where rates of sedimentation of de-
tritus from the continents are very slow. Ash deposits consist either of material
from the ejected fluid magma that is exploded into more or less fine angular
fragments, or of fragmented country rock. Glass tuffs form, if droplets of melt
solidify in the air. Glassy fragments, from which gases have been expelled, form
pumice deposits. Often the magma may exist below the liquidus temperature
before eruption and contain crystals which have already precipitated. Eruption of
such material forms crystal tuffs. At the present time all loose or friable volcanic
products are grouped together as *tephra*. Ash, containing glass and crystals, and
ejected along with hot gases, forms *ignimbrites* or welded tuffs, in which the hot
and still deformable glass particles fuse upon deposition. Such rocks are often
difficult to distinguish from lavas.

At Katmai, rhyolitic magma was ejected, at Krakatau, dacitic magma.
Basaltic magmas contain initially very small amounts of water at most, but
these small amounts can be concentrated in the roof of a magma chamber and
lead to eruption.

If an eruption occurs the magma can flow out. During the course of eruption
it becomes more and more gas-deficient and more viscous. This is especially true
of magmas enriched in H_2O and SiO_2, which when degased are much more
viscous than basaltic magmas. The values for viscosities of some melts in poises
$(g \cdot cm^{-1} \cdot sec^{-1})$ at $1,150°C$ and atmospheric pressure are:

$$olivine\ basalt\quad \sim 9 \cdot 10^2$$
$$andesine\ basalt \sim 8 \cdot 10^4$$
$$albite\qquad\qquad 1 \cdot 10^8.$$

BURNHAM (1963) investigated the influence of water on the viscosity of a melt
of granitic composition containing 8.8% H_2O, between $700°$ and $900°C$ at $4,800$ to
$7,400$ bars. He reported the following values, independent of pressure, in poises:

$$at\ 900°C\quad 2.8 \cdot 10^4$$
$$800°C\quad 1.3 \cdot 10^5$$
$$700°C\quad 1.3 \cdot 10^6.$$

The viscosities at $800-900°C$ correspond in order of magnitude to the viscosities
of commercial glasses at these temperatures. The water content causes a reduction
of several tens of percent compared to dry melts.

The hot, water-deficient and relatively fluid basalts can give rise to extensive
sheet eruptions flowing from far extending fissures. Basalt sheets cover $750,000\,km^2$
in the Parana Basin in Brazil, $650,000\ km^2$ in the Deccan Plateau in India, and
$50,000\ km^2$ in the Karroo area of South Africa. Present day production of lavas
is estimated at between 0.3 and $1\ km^3$ $(1-3 \cdot 10^9\ t)$ annually. In these estimates
the submarine eruptions, about which we know very little, are not included.
According to the experimental investigations of YODER and TILLEY, their course
of crystallization is the same as that of terrestrial basalts. They form no hydrous
or sodium-enriched minerals. Only at the rapidly cooled surface of a submarine
flow, do we find a hydrous glass, palagonite, as was observed by the author in
1930 in a basalt collected from 2,000 meters in the ocean. Zeolites can occur also
in the palagonite.

Volcanic emanations and their products will be considered later (p. 240).

Differentiation by Volatile Constituents. Until now we have considered only
the effects of water. It does not migrate alone, but contains dissolved constituents.
Morey has shown for the system $H_2O-Na_2O-SiO_2$, that fluid H_2O at $4,000°C$ and

2,250 kg/cm² pressure contains 8.1% Na_2O and 11.3% SiO_2. In contrast, the solubility of alkali aluminum silicates is very much less. We can assume, however, as did G. KENNEDY, that alkali silicates can be transported along with the water migrating in a magma chamber. This transport can take place only by diffusion and must, therefore, happen very slowly.

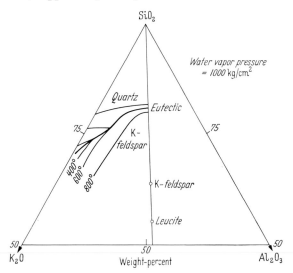

Fig. 326. The system $K_2O-SiO_2-Al_2O_3-H_2O$. (After TUTTLE and BOWEN from KRAUSKOPF)

If the alkali silicates during the course of time are concentrated at the top of the magma chamber, the melting point of a granitic melt is significantly decreased, as Fig. 326 shows. This represents the three-component system $SiO_2-K_2O-Al_2O_3$ in the same manner as illustrated in Fig. 302, p. 199, at an external pressure of 1,000 kg/cm², equal to the water vapor pressure. Only a few isotherms are indicated which accompany the eutectic. It can be seen that the eutectic is lowered from over 800° to below 400°C, as the K_2O content increases. Melts exist which are rich in alkali and volatile constituents, especially water. Rocks, which probably were formed from such melts, are called pegmatites. They will be discussed later (p. 235).

In addition to alkali silicates, other substances can be dissolved in supercritical water, as we have seen earlier (p. 226, Table 45). If these solutions are released during crystallization of the melt, they can penetrate into porous country rock or rise along faults to the surface and thereby revert from the fluid state to hot aqueous solutions. We can imagine, therefore, continuous development of pegmatites and hydrothermal solutions from one magma. This does not infer, of course, that all the constituents of the hot, hydrothermal solutions come from the magmatic source. As they penetrate the overlying rocks, water and other matter is incorporated from the surroundings. Today it is possible to study such processes, using isotope analysis as a tool. Thus, the investigations of waters from hot springs in areas of recent volcanism in North America, based on the ratios of H^1 to H^2 and of O^{16} to O^{18}, have made it probable that primary or juvenile water is present in amount $\leq 5\%$ (the limit of error of the analytical methods). That is to say, magmas contribute only a very small amount of water to hot springs.

The question as to how sulfides have been transported has indeed not yet been satisfactorily solved. The solubility of the sulfides in water is extraordinarily low. Values in Table 46 have been calculated by ELLIS from thermodynamic data (for more detail see KRAUSKOPF, 1961). At a pH of 3, the solubility of Ag_2S and Cu_2S is increased by a factor of 100, the other sulfides by 1,000. However, with the exception of MnS, this is still much too low to account for transport in such solutions. A temperature increase to 300°C likewise does not produce sufficient solubility. While the solubilities of Ag_2S, Cu_2S, PbS, and ZnS increase with temperature, they decrease for FeS and MnS.

Table 46. *Calculated solubilities of heavy metal sulfides in water in g/T.*
(From KRAUSKOPF after ELLIS)

	25° C	100° C	200° C	300° C
Ag_2S	$1.4 \cdot 10^{-9}$	$5.7 \cdot 10^{-7}$	$9.9 \cdot 10^{-5}$	$2.5 \cdot 10^{-3}$
Cu_2S	$2.1 \cdot 10^{-9}$	$1.7 \cdot 10^{-7}$	$8.0 \cdot 10^{-6}$	$1.6 \cdot 10^{-4}$
PbS	$7.9 \cdot 10^{-6}$	$1.1 \cdot 10^{-4}$	$1.7 \cdot 10^{-3}$	$2.4 \cdot 10^{-2}$
ZnS	$8.8 \cdot 10^{-5}$	$2.3 \cdot 10^{-4}$	$7.8 \cdot 10^{-4}$	$9.7 \cdot 10^{-4}$
FeS	$1.9 \cdot 10^{-1}$	$1 \cdot 10^{-1}$	$8.8 \cdot 10^{-2}$	$8.8 \cdot 10^{-2}$
MnS	$1 \cdot 10^{-2}$	$1.7 \cdot 10^{1}$	5.2	$8.7 \cdot 10^{-1}$

One possibility for raising solubility is by the formation of complexes. Thus BARNES could show that in the system $ZnS-H_2O-NaOH$ at an ionic strength of 10.3 molar, and a pH of 8.2, at 25°C and 6 kg/cm² pressure, 2.7 g/L ZnS is dissolved as $ZnHS_2^-$-ions. This is more than ten times the value found by MOREY (Table 45) for pure water. Similar complex formation was observed also to increase the solubility of sulfides of Hg and Ag. However, in all of these cases the pH must be more or less strongly alkaline to obtain sufficiently high solubilities. It is very questionable, whether the necessarily high H_2S partial pressures are attained naturally. The question as to how the sulfide ores are transported in aqueous solutions, requires, therefore, still additional experimental effort.

Summary of Magmatic Mineral Formation. Volatile constituents, especially water, play a double role in igneous rock genesis. They influence first of all the intrusion of a magma into the earth's crust and can cause explosive eruptions. Secondly, mineral deposits can form from them, which are rich in minerals absent from igneous rocks.

On the basis of previous discussion we shall organize the processes of igneous rock formation as follows:

1. Processes in the silicate melt: differentiation, formation of plutonic rocks at high and of extrusive rocks at low pressures.

2. Processes in residual solutions: Pneumato-hydrothermal mineral formation. Pegmatites at high pressure, hydrothermal mineral deposits and exhalative mineral formation at low pressures.

In the classification of mineral deposits a pneumatolytic stage is included usually between the pegmatitic and hydrothermal stages. The word pneumatolytic was coined in 1851 by R. BUNSEN (gr., pneumo, gas; lyein, dissolve). He used the term to describe solution and reaction processes in fumaroles on the earth's surface. Today the term is applied to the action of gases at depth under supercritical conditions and to the minerals formed as a result.

These stages are bound together transitionally. If one attempts a classification based on depth of the magma source, we can as we approach the earth's surface distinguish deep plutonic, plutonic, subvolcanic, and volcanic sources. The pegmatitic and pneumatolytic stages are limited generally to a plutonic source.

However, the degassing of subvolcanic and volcanic magmas is fundamentally different only in that the pressures are lower and the paths shorter. The distance from the magmatic source has been used also in classification, with terminology such as intramagmatic, perimagmatic, apomagmatic, and telemagmatic being applicable. Mineral deposits whose affiliation with a magma cannot be proven, are called cryptomagmatic. In addition the site of formation of a mineral deposit, rather than the depth of its magmatic source has been described, leading to abyssal, hypabyssal, epicrustal, subaquatic, aerial, and sub-aerial designations. Finally the temperature of formation has been used for classification, utilizing the terms hypothermal, mesothermal, and epithermal. These five principles of classification are not equivalent and their coordinated usage must be established from case to case, when knowledge permits.

5. Pneumato-hydrothermal Mineral Formation

Pegmatites. We shall adopt the classification based on depth of originating solutions and begin with pegmatitic mineral deposits. These are precipitated from silicate-rich aqueous solutions at high temperatures and pressures. The most magmatic-like members of this mineral group include feldspar, quartz, and mica. Feldspar and mica decrease in abundance with decreasing temperature, which corresponds in general to an increase in distance from the magmatic source. Quartz on the other hand increases in amount until it may become the main mineral in hydrothermal veins, into which the pegmatite may grade at lower temperatures. The temperature of formation of pegmatites may be accepted as the temperature span lying between $350°$ C and the higher crystallization temperature of the magma.

Pegmatites (gr. pegma, framework) fill fissures which are opened either in the magmatic parent rock itself, or in the neighboring country rock. Such fissure fillings are generally called veins. Frequently pegmatites are characterized by very large crystals. Mica and feldspar crystals often occur with diameters of 1 meter, and beryl crystals several meters in length have been observed. The development of giant crystals indicates direct crystallization from a supercritical state because, in supercritical fluids, ions have the mobility approaching that of a gas, due to the high temperature, and on the other hand the spatial packing which approaches the density of a liquid. These conditions prevail, as we have seen (p. 227), within only a limited part of the p-v-t system.

In addition to the elements that are abundant in magmas, in different pegmatites the elements lithium, beryllium, boron, zirconium, hafnium, molybdenum, tantalum, thorium, uranium, and the rare earths are enriched often relative to granites. Fluorine, tin, tungsten, copper and gold occur as well in pegmatites as in pneumatolytic and hydrothermal deposits. We cannot consider here in full the mineral associations which occur in pegmatites, only a few specific types will be singled out.

Feldspar pegmatites are probably the most widespread. The feldspar is predominantly K-feldspar, less often albite, and occurs in association with much quartz. These pegmatites, in a fresh state or altered to kaolinite, serve as raw materials for the ceramic industry. If mica is present in abundance, it is usually muscovite or phlogopite, which are in demand by the electroindustries as condenser materials. Biotite pegmatites are rare. The gem stone beryl, as the blue or blue-green variety called aquamarine, as well as topaz and tourmaline, usually occur in association with feldspar and quartz.

Zircon-, titanite-, and phosphate pegmatites are much rarer and serve as a source of supply for mineral collectors. Many unusual minerals have been noted in them. They occur usually in association with syenites. Noteworthy rare minerals which they contain include monazite, $CePO_4$, which contains $ThSiO_4$ as well as rare earths in solid solution, euxenite, a rare earth niobate, and tantalite, an iron tantalate-niobate.

Cassiterite-wolframite pegmatites represent a transition into pneumatolytic veins. Cassiterite and wolframite are the most important ores of tin and tungsten. Tungsten is a very important alloying constituent of steel, and is used also as filaments for incandescent lights. The hard metal widia is tungsten carbide. In the Middle Ages tungsten was much less esteemed. The superstitious miners believed that it devoured the valuable tin ore. This was the origin of the German name for tungsten, wolfram. These pegmatites carry the lithium micas lepidolite and zinnwaldite, from which the element lithium is obtained.

In addition to many cassiterite-wolframite veins, the molybdenite veins are also included under pneumatolytic deposits. In addition to molybdenite, MoS_2, these usually carry quartz and occasionally bismuth ores. Ninety-three percent of the world's production of steel-alloying molybdenum is produced from the pneumatolytic dikes of the Climax mine in Colorado, U.S.A.

Hydrothermal Mineral Deposits, Ore Veins. Mineral deposits derived from hydrothermal solutions can occur in different forms. Such hot solutions can rise into fissures and form deposits which are called veins. They can impregnate fissures in the country rock, reacting with it, and replacing it. Such mineral deposits, in which the ore formation takes place subsequent to formation of the country rock are called *epigenetic*. Mineral deposits in which the ore deposition takes place simultaneously with the rest of the rock constituents are called *syngenetic*. Sedimentary iron ore deposits (p. 274), are examples of the latter.

In the following paragraphs we shall consider primarily the vein deposits. Gold-tourmaline-quartz and tourmaline-copper-quartz veins form the connecting link between pneumatolytic and hydrothermal deposits. These are historically the real mineral deposits of the mining profession. Only in recent times have pegmatites been exploited for their mineral content. In hydrothermal veins gold, silver, copper, lead and tin are found. These were the real metals, as important in earlier times as they are today. The minerals from which they were won, especially the sulfides, were called ores, or in German Erz, a name of distinction. Even today among some miners this term is not considered suitable for the iron minerals. These ore veins have been of great importance to the history of mineralogy and geology. Freiberg in Saxony, where these vein deposits were exhaustively studied long ago, was one of the cradles of this science, especially since the time of ABRAHAM GOTTLOB WERNER (1749—1817). Here systematic and descriptive mineralogy was developed, which is fundamental to modern mineralogy, and was necessary and useful at that time. It is interesting that in Freiburg the beginnings of genetics found a patron in BREITHAUPT. His paragenesis of minerals was in the year 1849 a great achievement, because here the whole mineral assemblage, not the individual mineral, was emphasized. The careful description of the mineralization sequence in a vein is an important basis for interpreting their origin. In the vein represented in Fig. 327 a fissure is filled from both walls. Quartz, sphalerite and arsenopyrite crystallized first, followed by the other minerals as the quartz continued to grow.

An astonishing amount has been written about vein mineral assemblages, and there has been much speculation, but little has been contributed toward adequate understanding through quantitative experimental and theoretical investigations. Consequently it is necessary to propose a purely descriptive classification based on mineral content. Following SCHNEIDERHÖHN, we distinguish the following mineral assemblages, which are designated with the old expression "formation":

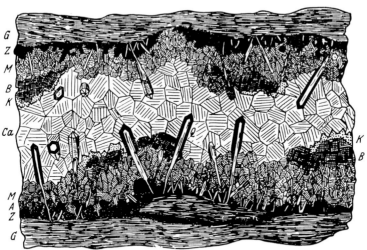

Fig. 327. Order of crystallization in a symmetrical vein of the Himmelsfürst-Fundgrube at Brand by Freiberg in Saxony. *G* country rock, sericitized gneiss; on prismatic quartz *Q*, and silver rich sphalerite *Z*, with arsenopyrite *A*, follow rhodochrosite ($MnCO_3$) *M*, and the main mass of quartz, galena *B*, chalcopyrite *K*, and calcite *Ca*. (From W. MAUCHER)

    I. Gold- and gold-silver-formation.
    II. Copper- and sulfide-formation.
    III. Lead-silver-zinc formation.
    IV. Silver-cobalt-nickel-bismuth-uranium formation.
    V. Tin-silver-bismuth-tungsten formation.
    VI. Antimony-mercury-arsenic-selenium formation.
    VII. Oxide iron-manganese-magnesium formation.
    VIII. Ore barren formation.

In I and II gold, silver, and copper occur in the native state. In the remainder, until group VI, sulfides predominate. The mineral assemblages of the different formations are summarized in Table 47. Plutonic ore deposits of group I type occur in Germany in the Fichtelgebirge and in Austria in the Hohen Tauern. The latter was very important during the Middle Ages. To the sub-volcanic deposits of type I belong the gold ores of Siebenbürgen. As type II deposits we should mention the immense pyrite deposits in southern Spain and Portugal (Huelva) and smaller occurrences in the Rheinish Schiefergebirge, especially around the Siegerland and at Kupferberg in Schlesien. To group III belong the veins at Freiberg in Saxony, smaller occurances in the Schwarzwald (Black Forest), in the Rheinish Schiefergebirge on the lower Lahn, and the long-famous occurances in the Harz at Clausthal, Lauterberg and in the Ostharz. Examples of formation IV worthy of noting are the silver occurrences at Kongsberg in Sweden, and the veins at St. Andreasberg in the Harz, at Wittichen in the Schwarzwald (Black Forest), and at Schneeberg and St. Joachimstal in the Erzgebirge. Group V deposits are especially important in Bolivia (Potosi) and group VI type deposits are represented by the large mercury ore deposits of Idria (Carniola) and Almaden (Spain) and the smaller ones of Landsberg at Obermoschel in the Pfalz. As group VII represent-

Table 47. *Abundance of important minerals in hydrothermal veins.* (After SCHNEIDERHÖHN)

		Formation						
Mineral		Gold-silver		Copper and pyrite	Lead-silver-zinc	Silver-cobalt-nickel-bismuth-uranium	Tin-silver-tungsten-bismuth	Antimony-mercury-arsenic-selenium	Oxidized and barren
		plutonic	sub-volcanic						
Elements	Arsenic								
	Bismuth								
	Copper								
	Silver								
	Gold								
Sulfides	Argentite	Ag_2S							
	Chalcocite	Cu_2S							
	Sphalerite	ZnS							
	Chalcopyrite	$CuFeS_2$							
	Stannite	Cu_2FeSnS_4							
	Tetrahedrite	$(Cu, Ag, Fe, Zn, Hg)_3 (Sb, As) S_{3-4}$							
	Enargite	Cu_3AsS_4							
	Galena	PbS							
	Cinnobar	HgS							
	Stibnite	Sb_2S_3							
	Bismuthite	Bi_2S_3							
	Pyrite	FeS_2							

Sulfides
- Gold-silver telluride
- Lead-silver-copper sellenide
- Cobalt-nickel arsenide
- Silver-antimony and arsenic sulfide

Oxides
- Cassiterite SnO_2
- Uraninite UO_2
- Hematite Fe_2O_3
- Wolframite $(Fe, Mn) WO_4$
- Scheelite $CaWO_4$
- Quartz SiO_2

Silicates
- Adularia $K[AlSi_3O_8]$
- Sericite (muscovite) and chlorite
- Fluorite CaF_2
- Calcite $CaCO_3$
- Dolomite $MgCa[CO_3]_2$
- Siderite $FeCO_3$
- Rhodochrosite $MnCO_3$
- Barite $BaSO_4$
- Zeolites

In most deposits and in large amount.

In most deposits, but in small amounts, or in a few deposits in large amount.

Rare and in small amounts.

atives, the siderite veins of the Siegerland and smaller hematite veins in the Schwarzwald and Thüringer Wald are noteworthy. Finally, among the examples of the ore barren formations, the fluorspar veins of the Harz, the Thüringer Wald, Vogtland, and in the Oberpfalz are important, especially for the production of hydrofluoric acid. Barite veins are mined in the Harz and Bad Lauterberg, on the Werra at Albungen, in the Thüringer Wald, on the Dill, and in the Schwarzwald and Spessart. Barite is used in the manufacture of white paint, for the weighting of textiles and paper, and as materials for protection against radiation. Intermediate between the ore barren and ore bearing veins there are transitional types of veins. The types of ore, if any, which precipitate, evidently depend considerably on the conditions of crystallization.

Mineralization of hydrothermal veins takes place generally at depth, although they grade sometimes into surficial hot spring deposits. Formerly distinctions were made between *juvenile springs* and *vadose springs*. The former were derived from magmatic waters, the latter from surface waters which, after circulating within the crust, rise to the surface again. A lively controversy took place, especially in the 1880's as to whether ore deposits derive their mineral content from magmas or from the leaching of the rock by *lateral secretion*. The controversy ended with such a complete defeat of the lateral secretionists, that today the influence of the country rock is almost completely ignored, certainly without justification. In this situation also, several roads probably "lead to Rome", and many minerals, especially the gangue minerals (other than ore minerals) may be derived from constituents in the country rock. Thus in the case of alpine mineral veins, the influence of the country rock has been demonstrated. On the other hand, the upwelling gases and solutions of magmatic origin affect the country rock. Deposits constituting valuable ores can be precipitated in the pores of the country rock, giving rise to mineralization in so-called *impregnation ore deposits*. Some of the greatest copper deposits, such as those at Bingham (U.S.A.), were formed in this way. Also by reaction between the country rock and gases and solutions rising along a fissure, new mineral formation can occur by partial or complete replacement of the original rock, giving rise to *replacement deposits*. This replacement of country rock is associated with the later stages of rock-forming processes, in the region of metamorphism.

Exhalative Mineral Formation. Exhalative mineral deposits, forming as sublimation products from volcanoes, represent the last stage of the magmatic sequence, grading gradationally into hydrothermal mineralization. A characteristic suite of minerals forms from the emitted gases upon cooling and by reaction with the atmosphere. Some of the minerals, represented by their chemical formulae are:

$NaCl$, KCl, NH_4Cl, $CaCl_2$, $PbCl_2$, $2KCl \cdot PbCl_2$, $MnCl_2$, $FeCl_2$, NaF, MgF_2, Fe_5N_2, S, Se_xS_y, AsS, As_2S_3, PbS, CuS, HgS, ZnS, FeS, NiS, FeS_2, MgO, PbO, CuO, Fe_2O_3 and $B(OH)_3$.

Also, in the vicinity of extinct volcanoes, hot springs and gaseous emanations occur. These are listed below in order of decreasing associated temperature:

Hot fumaroles with H_2O, HCl, SO_2, CO_2, H_2, N_2.
Solfataras with H_2S.
Steam springs, with only H_2O.
Moffettas with CO_2 and H_2O.
Geysers.
Thermal springs, medicinal springs, mineral springs and sulfur springs with H_2S.

There is a very extensive literature concerning these post-volcanic phenomena. This is especially true of the thermal springs, because of their medicinal use. An example is the description according to RITTMANN of the solfataras in the region of Lardarello in Tuscany. Here over an area of about 200 km², from more than a hundred bored wells, $26 \cdot 10^6$ t of steam with temperatures up to 250°C, and pressures to 25 kg/cm², are produced annually. This amounts to about $2 \cdot 10^9$ kilowatts of energy. The average composition of the steam is:

$$
\begin{array}{ll}
H_2O & 955.52\ ^0/_{00} \\
CO_2 & 42.65\ ^0/_{00} \\
H_2S & 0.88\ ^0/_{00} \\
H_3BO_3 & 0.30\ ^0/_{00} \\
NH_3 & 0.30\ ^0/_{00} \\
CH_4 & 0.15\ ^0/_{00} \\
H_2 & 0.04\ ^0/_{00}.
\end{array}
$$

The high boron content is geochemically important. Earlier boron was produced from this source.

Vesicles, or bubbles formed by expanding gases, form within volcanic rocks themselves. These are often mineralized, for example, with calcite, the fibrous variety of quartz called chalcedony, or with zeolites. These zeolites are hydrous tectosilicates with porous structures in which the water is so loosely held that it can be driven off easily upon heating with essentially no change in the silicate structure. The structure will rehydrate upon further exposure to an atmosphere saturated in water vapor. The zeolitic water can be replaced also by other gases such as H_2S, CS_2 and CCl_4. Some typical zeolites are chabasite (Ca, Na_2, K_2) $[Al_2Si_4O_{12}] \cdot 6H_2O$, heulandite $Ca[Al_2Si_6O_{16}] \cdot 5H_2O$, stilbite $Ca[Al_2Si_7O_{18}] \cdot 7H_2O$, natrolite $Na_2[Al_2Si_3O_{10}] \cdot 2H_2O$ and scolecite $Ca[Al_2Si_3O_{10}] \cdot 2H_2O$. The last two zeolites form mixed crystals, the Na-rich members natrolite, intermediate members mesolite, and the Ca-rich, scolecite.

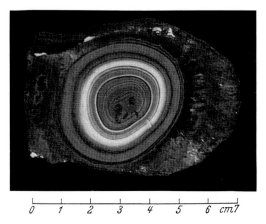

Fig. 328. Festungasgate

We can obtain information about the temperature of formation of these cavity fillings from *agates* which they frequently contain. Agate consists of colored, usually fibrous or finely crystalline quartz with some opal, and frequently contains larger quartz crystals within it. They occur in the vesicles of basaltic rocks such as the so-called melaphyres of Idar-Oberstein and in south Brazil and Uruguay. A very common type, Festungsagate, exhibits concentric banding (Fig. 328). From this NACKEN deduced that the silica is homogeneously deposited concentrically above the critical temperature of water, and thus from the fluid phase. This type of agate, therefore, should have been formed somewhat above

375°C, since the critical temperature of water is insignificantly increased by the small addition of silica. Since the quartz enclosed within the agate is the low temperature variety, the agate formation must have taken place likewise below 575°C. Another type, Uruguay agate (Fig. 329), contains in addition to the

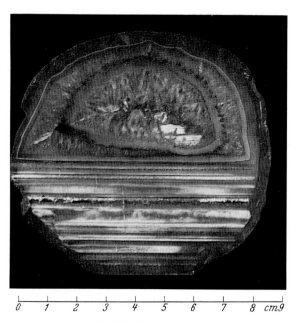

Fig. 329. Uruguay agate

concentric banding around the border, planar layers within. This indicates that the latter had deposited from aqueous solution under the influence of gravity, and that during the formation of the agate, the temperature had decreased below 375°C.

Banding in agates is usually explained in terms of rhythmic deposition from solutions diffusing through the silicious mass, analogous to the formation of Liesegang rings. However, many observations indicate that the banding can just as well indicate rhythmic periodic degassing.

VII. Weathering and Soil Mineral Formation

1. Mechanical Weathering

The petrogenetic processes which produce new mineral assemblages, either by alteration of previously formed rocks, or by recombination of alteration products, are quite different from those which produce igneous rocks. Those alteration processes which take place at the surface of the earth, at the earth-atmosphere interface, are called weathering processes. Weathering products formed in situ without transport form soils; following transport they form sediments. Alteration of previously formed rocks which takes place at depth or at the surface as a result of magmatic influence is considered a part of the metamorphic process.

Weathering processes are usually classified as mechanical or chemical in nature. Mechanical destruction of rocks is accomplished mainly by three processes, insolation (thermal weathering), frost wedging, and salt expansion.

Thermal Weathering. *Insolation* occurs when a rock at the surface is repeatedly heated and cooled. The exposed rock surface expands upon heating to a greater extent than its interior and upon cooling contracts again. As a result of the stresses which develop, the outer rock surface is broken up partly into granular particles and partly into large and small shards. The extent to which these two kinds of products are produced depends on the characteristics of the rock and on the severity of the weathering action.

For crystals of most minerals, exact data is available on the magnitude of expansion due to heating; on the other hand only old, probably less reliable data are available for rocks. The pressures which result from expansion can be calculated from the coefficients of expansion and compressibility. For quartz, a 40° temperature increase produces a pressure of 545 kg/cm². For rocks unfortunately values of the two coefficients have not been determined for comparable specimens so that calculations have no significance. Completely conclusive experimental investigations of this type of weathering are still lacking.

Frost Wedging. Frost action is somewhat better known. It depends on the fact that water is an extraordinarily unusual substance which expands upon changing from the fluid to the solid state, that is, upon freezing. Thus a vessel which encloses water can burst upon freezing. The pressure which develops upon freezing can be obtained directly from the pressure-temperature diagram for the single component system H_2O and the melting curve of ice (Fig. 286, p. 183, 184). The pressure can attain a value up to 2,200 kg/cm² at −22°C. At higher pressures or lower temperatures, we enter the stability field of a different ice modification, which has a lower specific volume than water. Thus 2,200 kg/cm² is the maximum pressure at which ice wedging can generally occur. In order for frost action to be effective, it is also necessary that the pores containing the water be so constructed that the crystallizing ice is restricted and is not free to crystallize unhindered. Thus, entrances to the pores must be constricted. In addition the pore volume must be more than 90% filled, because the specific volume of water is

90% that of ice. The influence of the rate of cooling, which is frequently mentioned, could depend on initial cooling of the pore constrictions, resulting first in sealing off the pore from the remaining fluid. With a rapid drop in temperature these outer openings of the pores would be cooled first, forming ice crystals, which could serve as nuclei for the supercooled water within the pore. Even in cylindrical pores ice action can take place if a plug whose adherence to the pore walls is stronger than the wall itself develops from the surface inward.

Salt Expansion. Similar conditions characterize two of the three different processes which collectively are implied by the term salt expansion. One kind of salt expansion is based on the fact that a supersaturated solution has a volume that is less than the combined volumes of a saturated solution in equilibrium with precipitated crystals. Upon crystallization, a pore pressure develops if crystals, growing inward, block the entrances to the pores. In the case of alum solutions, it is possible to calculate, taking into account the compressibility of water, that a pressure of 130 kg/cm² would develop.

Another kind of salt expansion is related to the ability of many anhydrous salts to take up structural water. As a result of hydration, the change $CaSO_4 \rightarrow CaSO_4 \cdot 2H_2O$ results in a calculated pressure increase of about 1,100 kg/cm², the change $NaSO_4 \rightarrow NaSO_4 \cdot 10H_2O$ about 250 kg/cm², and $Na_2CO_3 \rightarrow Na_2CO_3 \cdot 10H_2O$ about 300 kg/cm². A pore pressure can only develop under conditions such that permeability permits access of water to the salt, but at the same time prevents migration of the salt crystals, as, for example, by access through layers of very fine porosity.

A third kind of salt expansion results from the pressure exerted on its surroundings by a growing crystal. The maximum pressure developed is in this case related to supersaturation. A crystal possesses a greater solubility under pressure. The greater the supersaturation, the greater the pressure with which the crystal can be in equilibrium. The following formula applies:

$$P = \frac{R \cdot T}{v} \ \ln \ \frac{C}{C_s}.$$

P is the excess pressure in atmospheres, R the gas constant (0.08203 l atm./degree), T the absolute temperature, v the mole volume of the crystalline substance, C_s the saturation concentration without influence of pressure (that is, the equilibrium concentration between crystal and solution), C the concentration at which the solution and crystal are in equilibrium at pressure P. From a 175 percent supersaturated alum solution, alum octahedra develop a 40 kg/cm² growth pressure against glass. A crystal can only exert pressure if the surface tensions between crystal, solid neighbor, and crystallizing solution are such that the solution can penetrate between the crystal and its surroundings. Thus, alum cubes (as contrasted with octahedra) develop no growth pressure with respect to glass or mica plates substituted for glass. The pressure exerted by growing crystals, however, has often been greatly exaggerated. For example, it is frequently implied erroneously that rock fissures containing hydrothermal mineral veins have been formed as a result of growth pressure.

All three types of salt expansion are manifest by cooling. The effect of supersaturation is assisted, in addition by removal of water, therefore, by aridity; hydration expansion is assisted by alternating aridity and humidity. Since increases in moisture occur frequently even in arid regions as a result of fog, salt expansion is considered as an important weathering agent in arid regions. Frost weathering, on the other hand, is related to frequent alternations of freezing and thawing. The greater the number of cycles, the more intensive the frost action. Insolation has frequently been described as an important weathering agent in desert regions, but is certainly not confined there.

2. Chemical Weathering

Solution. Mechanical weathering greatly assists chemical weathering, because it results in rock disintegration and very substantially aids chemical attack. When mechanical weathering is hindered, for example, by polishing a rock surface, chemical weathering proceeds very slowly. Thus in Scandinavia, where much of the terrane was smoothly polished by Pleistocene glaciers, chemical weathering has been exceedingly slow since the retreat of the ice, even though the surface has become populated with moss and moorland.

In nature only a few rocks and minerals are subject to the simplest form of chemical attack, solution in water. NaCl, KCl, and other easily soluble salts can exist for substantial times only in very arid regions. In humid regions the simple solution of only gypsum and anhydrite can be observed.

The process of carbonate dissolution is quite complex. Carbon dioxide dissolved in water plays the crucial role, as we shall see later when we discuss the origin of carbonate rocks. It is sufficient here to point out that the solubility of $CaCO_3$ rises strongly with the CO_2 content of water. Since the solubility of CO_2 in water decreases with increasing temperature, the solubility of $CaCO_3$ is likewise reduced.

Silicate Weathering. The central problem of weathering is the weathering of silicates, since these make up more than three-fourths of the earth's crust. The crust is 66 weight percent feldspar (22% K-feldspar and 42% plagioclase; see Table 43, p. 221). Thus we can consider the breakdown of feldspar as a model for silicate weathering. It has been known for a long time that the alkalis potassium and sodium, in feldspar, go into solution very easily. This can be demonstrated very easily by putting some powdered K-feldspar in water. If an appropriate indicator, such as bromthymol blue is added, in a short time the solution shows an alkaline reaction. The behavior of aluminium and silicon during weathering has been much less clear until recently. For a long time two differing views were held. The older view advocated breakdown of feldspars by hydrolysis, as a result of which colloidal silicic acid and aluminum hydroxide were formed. Later these could react, leading to the formation of aluminium silicates. After the lattice structure of crystals was demonstrated with the help of X-rays, a second hypothesis was suggested. According to this, after the removal of alkalis and a part of the SiO_2, the feldspar structure collapses into the structure of kaolinite ($Al_2[(OH)_4Si_2O_5]$). More recent experimental studies have shown, however, that both views are incorrect, and that the feldspar goes into ionic solution. Therefore the silica and alumina are, at least at first, removed in true solution. Thus, under normal conditions the feldspar is gradually but completely dissolved and its constituents remain at first in solution. As a result of this dissolution a very thin rind forms on the feldspar which consists essentially of Al_2O_3 and SiO_2, always in the ratio of more than $5 SiO_2$ to $1 Al_2O_3$. The dissolution of the core takes place through this layer, and simultaneously the layer is broken down, so that its thickness does not increase during the destruction of the feldspar. The thickness of the layer was determined to be about 0.00003 mm. Experiments have shown that leucite, another framework silicate, weathers in the same manner.

In the case of muscovite, the rate of dissolution of different components is so different, that residual skeletal layers can be produced. As a characteristic of the layer structure, the diffusion rate of the K ions is relatively much greater than in feldspar. For the inselsilicate olivine, the dissolution rates of all the components are approximately the same, so that it is dissolved in water some-what like NaCl. It must be emphasized that this experimentally established behavior of silicates applies only to very dilute aqueous solutions at temperatures between 20° and 40°C and in open systems. Reactions involving concentrated salt solutions and completely or approximately closed systems, as well as higher temperatures, can lead to the formation of kaolinite pseudomorphs after feldspar. The mechanism of pseudomorph formation will be commented on later (p. 309).

3. The Behavior of Si, Al, and Fe in Soils

What happens now to those ions which have gone into solution? Different ions behave in different ways. We shall first consider their fate immediately after weathering, because primarily at this stage they play an important role in the soil.

	Particle diameter		
	10^{-3} 10^{-4} 10^{-5} 10^{-6} 10^{-7} 10^{-8} cm		
Name	Suspensions Emulsions	Sols	Molecular or ionic solutions
Retained by	Coarse filter	Dialysis membranes Ultra filter	Semipermeable septa
Sedimented	By self	Flocculates	Are stable

Fig. 330. The colloidal region

Alkali ions are the most stable in solution, the alkaline earths somewhat less so. These ions are transported essentially completely away in solution. Alkali chlorides and sulfates may remain in the soil or migrate in it in arid regions, as do the calcium salts, gypsum, $CaSO_4 \cdot 2\,H_2O$ and calcite, $CaCO_3$. Silicon, aluminum, and iron on the other hand precipitate out again for the most part, usually right in the soil. During weathering, new minerals form from these components by processes which are very important in soil formation.

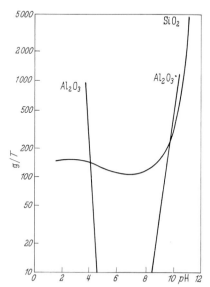

Fig. 331. Solubility of silica gel and aluminum hydroxide as a function of hydrogen ion concentration

Colloids. These weathering products are mostly very fine-grained. They are colloids and thus their study is an important aspect of that branch of physical chemistry called colloid chemistry. Colloids constitute a transitional size grade between coarse grained sediment and matter of ionic and molecular dimensions (Fig. 330), that is to say, they comprise particles of 10^{-5} to 10^{-7} cm diameter.

Colloidal particles can be solid, liquid or gaseous. The solid colloids, as far as inorganic origins are concerned, may be crystalline or amorphous. Thus the colloidal state has today only a size connotation. This needs to be emphasized, because it was believed early in the study of colloids that all of them were amorphous, as in glue (gr., kollos) from which the name was derived. Even today the terms colloidal and amorphous are interchanged in the mineralogical literature, leading to much confusion. As long ago as 1917 SCHERRER showed by X-ray studies that the particles in colloidal gold sols are crystalline. Likewise in mineralogy we shall be dealing mostly with solid crystalline colloids.

One of the few exceptions occurs in the system SiO_2-H_2O. During weathering, silica occurs first as a true silicic acid. When the solubility is exceeded, this silicic acid changes to a sol, a colloidal suspension. In Fig. 331 solubilities in the systems silica gel-water and aluminum hydroxide-water are given in relation to the hydrogen ion concentration expressed as pH. pH is the exponent of the reciprocal of the hydrogen ion concentration. In pure water the ion product calculated in gram ions per liter is:

$$[H^+] \cdot [OH^-] = 10^{-14}.$$

If in solution the two ions are present in equal amounts, the H^+ ion concentration is 10^{-7}, the pH is 7. If an excess of H^+ ions is present, the solution is acid and the pH less than 7. For example, if $[H^+] = 10^{-3}$ and $[OH^-] = 10^{-11}$, the pH is 3. On the other hand, pH is greater than 7 in alkaline solutions. If $[H^+] = 10^{-12}$ and $[OH^-] = 10^{-2}$, the pH is 12. It is to be noted that since the pH values are exponents, a unit change in pH, say from 3 to 4, represents a ten-fold change in hydrogen ion concentration.

A saturated solution of silica may become charged with excess silica if water is lost from the system, or as a result of a decrease in pH. The excess SiO_2 no longer remains as ions in solution, but as submicroscopic particles of hydrous SiO_2. Colloidal sols which contain such swollen hydrated particles are called hydrosols, or more generally lyophilic sols (gr., attracted to water or solutions). The solubility data given in Fig. 331 refer to the solubility of this sort of gelatinous hydrous silica. The solubility of quartz is only about 10 percent that of this form of SiO_2.

In contrast to the hydrophilic silica sols, are the hydrophobic or lyophobic sols, which consist of essentially crystalline particles. In the systems $Al_2O_3-H_2O$ and $Fe_2O_3-H_2O$, sols intermediate in character are encountered. In these cases sols or gels form which X-ray examination may show to be either crystalline or amorphous.

Hydrophobic sols are significantly less stable in solution than hydrophilic ones. They can be made to settle out or coagulate by the addition of ions to the suspension. Sol particles are electrically charged and, since the charge on each particle is the same, they tend to repel one another and stay suspended. The added ions neutralize these charges, permitting individual particles to come together into floccs. The process is called flocculation. The product is called a coagel. Hydrophilic sols also transform from a state of fine particle distribution in a fluid to one of greater aggregation, into what is called a gel. In this case, however, the influence of added ions is not as great as with hydrophobic sols. The tendency to flocculate depends in this case on the degree of hydration. That, is, the less hydrated the particles, the more nearly they approach the character of hydrophobic particles. In the system SiO_2-H_2O, the swelling due to hydration is at a minimum in weakly alkaline solutions. Such a SiO_2 sol can be flocculated if the salt concentration exceeds 10 millimoles/liter [equivalent to 0.164 g $Ca(NO_3)_2$ per liter].

The Behavior of Silicon. In soils dissolved silica can be abstracted again from solution in several ways. Certain plants, for example, diatoms, grasses, and equiseta (scouring rushes) can extract silica from solution. Silica can also be precipitated by evaporation or by acidifying an alkaline solution (pH > 8.5), the latter by means of carbonic acid, which originates from the decomposition of organic substances. Alkali silicate solutions are destroyed by carbonic acid, with the formation of a hydrous SiO_2 or gel. From this, more or less well-ordered low cristobalite first crystallizes and later fibrous (chalcedony) or granular quartz. The initial amorphous $SiO_2 \cdot H_2O$ particles in the gel are less stable than cristobalite, and this less than quartz. A substance consisting of amphorous SiO_2 or this type of cristobalite is called *opal*. That variety called precious opal, which is prized as a gem stone, owes its desirable play of colors to its unique microscopic structure. It is composed of tiny globules of SiO_2 arranged in a close-packed array. The diameter of the globules varies in different opals, but lies in the range of the wave lengths of visible light. Therefore, light interference occurs between submicroscopic layers in a manner which can be predicted by the Bragg equation (p. 149). Crystallization of SiO_2 gels also results in the formation of mammillary or reniform structures. Many other minerals, in particular hydroxides, form similar structures. It must be stressed, however, that it is not valid to draw the conclusion from such structures that pervious colloidal phenomena were involved. For example, calcium carbonate incrustations often exhibit very similar structures, even though they were most certainly deposited from true solution.

Extensive deposition of SiO_2 is noted in desert regions where water, rising in the soil by capillarity, deposits siliceous crusts at the surface or results in silicification between sand grains in sub-surficial deposits.

Dissolved silica can react also with other minerals, such as calcium carbonate, depositing quartz. Silicification can take place which can be similar to the effect of metamorphic processes (see p. 306).

The Behavior of Aluminum. Behavior in the system Al_2O_3—H_2O (Fig. 331) is significantly different. Aluminum remains dissolved in acid (pH < 4) as well as in alkaline solutions (pH > 9; under certain conditions > 10). It precipitates out as aluminum hydroxide near neutrality. This precipitation can be caused by evaporation, or when an alkaline solution is acidified, and when an acid solution is made alkaline. Again carbonic acid is important, although other acids probably are occasionally active. An acid solution can become alkaline or neutral by loss of its acid constituent (in the case of carbonic acid by heating) or by the effect of neutralizing reactions, such as reaction with calcium carbonate. In this way rather pure deposits of technically important aluminum ores have formed. These are called *bauxites* after the region of Les Beaux in South France where they were first found.

Formation of Aluminum Silicates. Silica and aluminum hydroxides do not only precipitate from solution as separate phases. They combine to form compounds, aluminum silicates, whose structures we have considered earlier (p. 73). Examples are *kaolinite* [$Al_2(OH)_4Si_2O_5$], and *halloysite* [$Al_2(OH)_4Si_2O_5$] $\cdot$ $2H_2O$. Another is *montmorillonite*, [$Al_2(OH)_2Si_4O_{10}$] $\cdot$ n H_2O which occurs in greater amounts in association with altered volcanic tuffs. Rocks composed primarily of montmorillonite are called bentonites; those of kaolinite, kaolins. Mica like minerals, similar to muscovite [$KAl_2(OH, F)_2AlSi_3O_{10}$], perhaps form also at earth surface temperatures. How these reactions take place is not known in detail. Laboratory syntheses have been carried out at temperatures above $100°C$ from silica and aluminum hydroxide gels. Halloysite has not been synthesized.

It is very likely that the natural synthesis of crystalline minerals in soils takes place directly from very dilute true solutions. This would require in any case a much lesser expenditure of energy, than if the starting material existed already in the colloidal state. Based on our knowledge of crystal growth, it is extremely unlikely that colloidal particles can combine directly to form a crystalline structure. The formation of aluminium silicates depends, of course, on their individual solubilities but also on the solubilities of their components. Where relatively much Al and little Si occur in solution, kaolinitic silicates ($Al_2O_3 : SiO_2 = 1 : 2$) will form. This condition would prevail in soils with pH values < 4, in conformity with Fig. 331. Under alkaline conditions, where the pH > 8.5, much more Si is in solution, and conditions would be more favorable for montmorillonitic silicates ($Al_2O_3 : SiO_2 = 1 : 3$ to $1 : 4$). These relationships have been confirmed independently by the hydrothermal syntheses of NOLL and by appropriate studies of soils.

The ultimate behavior of the two elements silicon and aluminium will vary depending on reaction conditions and on climatic and local conditions.

The Behavior of Iron. The iron ion is different from aluminum in that it can occur in two oxidation states, as Fe^{2+} and Fe^{3+}. Later, when we deal with sedimentary iron ores (p. 273), we will discuss the solubility of iron as it relates to the oxygen content of the solution, to its redox potential. It is sufficient to establish here that in the presence of oxygen iron is practically insoluble. It can be transported only in colloidal form as a ferric hydroxide sol.

In the absence of oxygen, iron is stable and soluble as a divalent ion in equilibrium with carbonic acid, much like the calcium ion (see Fig. 350, p. 273). Also like Ca, it precipitates out, forming ferrous carbonate ($FeCO_3$) upon loss of CO_2. Ferrous iron is often transported in conjunction with humic acids. Their presence, however, probably only indicates that the redox potential is low and that transport as the carbonate is possible. As soon as oxygen centers the system, the hydroxide, $FeOOH$, precipitates out.

In the case of iron hydroxides, a particular property of hydrophobic sols is important. Before flocculation occurs they may be protected by a coating of a hydrophilic sol. Colloids which provide such protective action are called *protective colloids*. An error which appears over and over in the mineralogical literature needs to be mentioned. Protective colloids are only effective against flocculation, not against dissolution, since solution would be possible through the hydrophilic coating or hull. A large amount of iron may be transported as such protected colloids and be distributed widely in the sea before the protective hull is destroyed or rendered ineffective. When this happens, the iron hydroxide flocculates.

We distinguish between two iron hydroxide minerals, goethite or α-FeOOH, which is the most common, and lepidochrosite or γ-FeOOH. The latter has a platy morphology, the former usually a fibrous one. The name goethite was used originally for the γ-FeOOH, but now for α-FeOOH. Upon dehydroxylation, iron hydroxides transform into Fe_2O_3, either an α-form called *hematite*, or a γ-form called *maghemite*. Maghemite forms more often, however, as a result of the oxidation of Fe_3O_4, *magnetite*. Under certain conditions the hydroxides can change directly to magnetite.

Soil Profiles. When we investigate soils and their development, we must take into account numerous factors. Those minerals which go into solution and those which form anew, depend on the source material, on the climate, on the topographic situation, on the organisms living in and on the soil, and on the interval of time during which these factors have been active. Thus it is to be borne in mind that the succession of climatic changes throughout the past can be superimposed upon the soil. The science of agronomy is devoted to studying these processes. We shall consider here only one example, summarized in Fig. 332, of soil development on the basaltic rocks in Hawaii. Here the climate is warm and constantly humid, but rainfall fluctuates greatly. In regions of low rainfall, the clay mineral montmorillonite forms in the soils; with increasing rainfall, kaolinite, and finally Al and Fe hydroxides. Montmorillonite formation parallels development of alkalinity in the more concentrated soil solutions. With increasing dilution, the influence of carbonic acid is noted, the soil solutions become neutral or slightly acid, and kaolinite forms. Upon further leaching, kaolinite is also dissolved and Al-hydroxides remain behind.

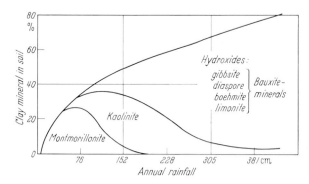

Fig. 332. Development of clay minerals in Hawaiian soils in a constantly humid climate. (After SHERMAN, 1952)

In climates where intervals of repeated rainfall and aridity prevail, the soils are not only leached downward from the surface, but water migrates upward in the soil during times of aridity and can give rise to mineral formation.

Weathering products can exhibit all gradations between X-ray amorphous and more or less well crystallized minerals. Weathering products in the soil are predominantly those with layer lattices, such as the Al and Fe-hydroxides, montmorillonite, and kaolinite. Soils which are rich in hydroxides are frequently called *laterites*. There is some disagreement, however, over the exact definition for laterite.

Bauxites, composed primarily of aluminum hydroxides, are weathering products. Tertiary and younger bauxites consist primarily of gibbsite (hydrargillite), γ-Al(OH)$_3$, Mesozoic bauxites of boehmite, γ-AlOOH, and those of Paleozoic age of diaspore, α-AlOOH. There are, however, many exceptions to these generalizations. Bauxites are our chief source of aluminum.

Occasionally, in depressions and joints in limestone, pisolitic iron ores occur, probably as remanents from lateritic weathering. A typical ore might consist of about two-thirds goethite and one-third kaolinite.

Thus, as the inorganic constituents of soils, we find the unaltered residues of weathering, minerals formed as weathering products, and finally true and colloidal solutions which still circulate within the soil. In addition, the soil contains organic components, which consist partly of organisms, and partly of humus derived from their remains. Layer silicates play an important role in the soils, both as residual minerals and as weathering products. As a result of their high surface areas they can adsorb ions, which can be exchanged reversibly with other ions in solution. Especially important in this respect are micas, kaolinite, and montmorillonite. The mica in soils is probably mostly residual from weathering.

Montmorillonite has the capacity to adsorb ions between its layers as well as on its external surfaces, so that it has an effectively greater specific surface.

4. Weathering of Ore Deposits

Iron-bearing Ores. In the previous discussion we were concerning ourselves with weathering of normal, or the widely distributed common rock types. Different conditions are prevalent in other special cases. Because of their economic importance, we need to consider the effects of weathering on ore deposits. These generally contain for the most part iron sulfides which, upon weathering, form iron hydroxides.

Miners have for a long time been familiar with the "iron caps" or gossans which frequently overlie mineral deposits. As an example of hydroxide formation, we can consider the breakdown of FeS_2. Although the pyrite form is rather stable, the marcasite modification decomposes easily in moist air according to the following series of reactions:

$$4\,FeS_2 + 4\,H_2O + 14\,O_2 = 4\,FeSO_4 + 4\,H_2SO_4$$
$$4\,FeSO_4 + 2\,H_2SO_4 + O_2 = 2\,Fe_2(SO_4)_3 + 2\,H_2O$$
$$2\,Fe_2(SO_4)_3 + 8\,H_2O = 4\,FeOOH + 6\,H_2SO_4$$

Summary equation:
$$4\,FeS_2 + 10\,H_2O + 15\,O_2 = 4\,FeOOH + 8\,H_2SO_4.$$

Thus both ferrous and ferric sulfates are formed as intermediate products. This is important because gold, which commonly occurs as an impurity in pyrite, is somewhat soluble in the presence of ferric sulfate and so can be carried away. According to the above reactions, from each mole of FeS_2 two moles of H_2SO_4 are produced. This sulfuric acid can react with other minerals producing, for example, gypsum, through reaction with limestone. Especially important is the utilization of oxygen; all in all, 15 moles of O_2 for every 4 moles of FeS_2. Thus we are dealing with an oxidation phenomenon. Mineral deposits so produced by the weathering of sulfides under the influence of oxygen in the air are referred to as *oxidized mineral deposits*.

Magnetite also oxidizes readily to Fe_2O_3, usually forming α-Fe_2O_3, hematite. The external morphology of magnetite crystals may be preserved, with the formation of so-called pseudomorphs (pseudos, gr. false) of hematite after magnetite. Such a pseudomorph is sometimes called *martite*. Sometimes this oxidation takes place with preservation of the gross aspects of the crystal structure. In this case γ-Fe_2O_3, *maghemite*, is formed, which is strongly magnetic like magnetite. As we had noted earlier (p. 91) the magnetite structure is built from a cubic close packed array of oxygen atoms. When oxidized to maghemite this packing is not affected, but Fe ions migrate into the outer layers formed as a result of addition of oxygen, according to the equation,

$$4\,Fe_3O_4 + O_2 = 6\,Fe_2O_3.$$

Thus Fe vacancies develop in the original Fe lattice. This process results in the formation of fine grained aggregates, rather than pseudomorphs.

Lead and Copper Ores. Whereas iron sulfides form hydroxides, because their sulfates are unstable, lead sulfides alter to the very insoluble sulfate, anglesite ($PbSO_4$). By reaction with carbonic acid this may give rise to the carbonate, cerrusite ($PbCO_3$). Copper sulfides alter to basic carbonates such as the green variety, malachite $[Cu_2(OH)_2CO_3]$ and the blue azurite $[Cu_3(OH)_2(CO_3)_2]$.

Cementation Zone. During the weathering of sulfide deposits, the solutions produced can react at greater depth, where no oxygen is present, with fresh primary sulfides present there. In this way at the expense of the sulfides of base metals (Fe), sulfides of precious metals, such as copper and silver, are formed. Thus there is an enrichment due to the formation, for example, of chalcocite, Cu_2S, bornite, Cu_5FeS_4, and argentite, Ag_2S. This enriched zone is called the zone of cementation or of supergene enrichment.

VIII. Sedimentary Rocks

1. Clastic Sediments

Introduction. The mechanical and chemical weathering products of rocks, after they have been transported and redeposited, are called sediments. The transporting agents are water, wind, and ice, and in rare instances organisms.

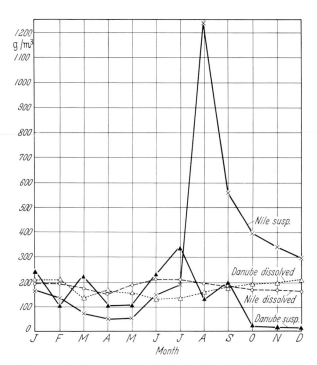

Fig. 333. Annual transport of suspended and dissolved load in the Danube and Nile Rivers. (According to PENCK)

Deposition takes place under the influence of gravity, as a result of settling, flocculation, and chemical precipitation, the latter either directly or through the action of organisms. Likewise evaporite deposits are sediments because they are redistributed products of weathering. On the other hand tuffs, even though sedimented after transport, are not sediments because they are not products of weathering.

We have seen that as a result of chemical weathering new minerals are formed, of which the hydroxides and aluminum silicates are the most important. In addition some minerals escape weathering, either because like quartz they are very insoluble or because erosion sets in before chemical weathering has come to an end. These residual minerals, as well as weathering products and ions in solution, constitute the raw materials for sediment formation. The resistant

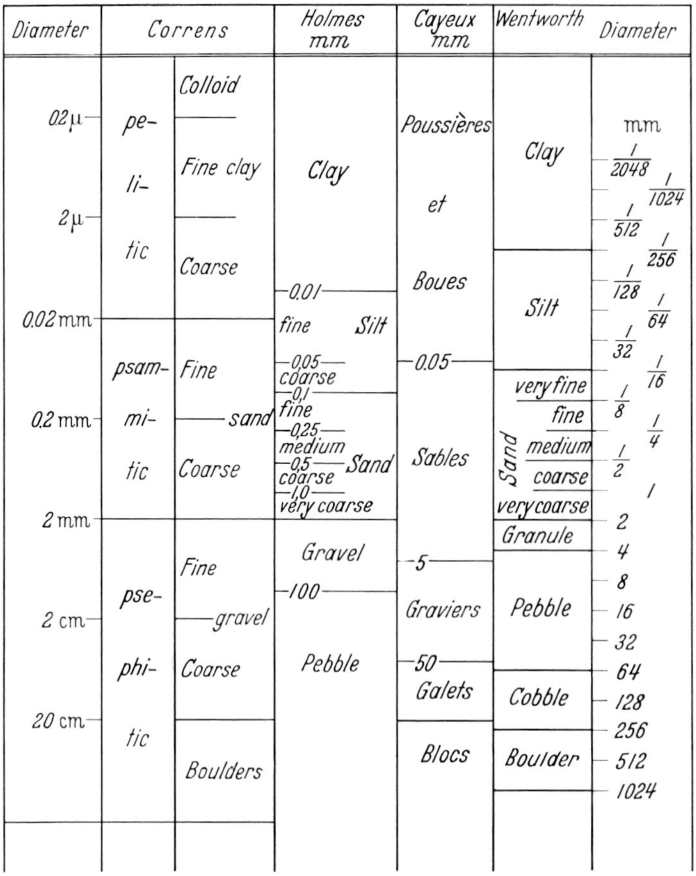

Diameter	Correns		Holmes mm	Cayeux mm	Wentworth	Diameter
0.2 μ	pe-	Colloid	Clay	Poussières	Clay	mm
		Fine clay				$\frac{1}{2048}$
	li-			et		$\frac{1}{1024}$
2 μ						$\frac{1}{512}$
	tic	Coarse				$\frac{1}{256}$
			−0.01−	Boues	Silt	$\frac{1}{128}$
0.02 mm			fine Silt			$\frac{1}{64}$
	psam-	Fine	−0.05− coarse	−0.05−		$\frac{1}{32}$
			−0.1− fine		very fine	$\frac{1}{16}$
0.2 mm	mi-	──sand	−0.25− medium		fine	$\frac{1}{8}$
			−0.5──Sand	Sables	medium	$\frac{1}{4}$
	tic	Coarse	coarse −1.0−		coarse	$\frac{1}{2}$
			very coarse		very coarse	1
2 mm					Granule	2
		Fine	Gravel	−5−		4
	pse-		−100−		Pebble	8
2 cm		──gravel		Graviers		16
						32
	phi-	Coarse	Pebble	−50−		64
				Galets	Cobble	128
20 cm						256
	tic			Blocs	Boulder	512
		Boulders				1024

Fig. 334. Summary of different grain size classification of clastic sediments

minerals comprise mainly the sandstones. The aluminum silicate weathering products accumulate, along with the finest grained resistates, to form clays. These two groups, along with deposits of gravel, pebbles, and boulders, constitute the clastic (gr. klazein, to crush) sediments. Limestones, phosphates, siliceous rocks, and evaporites form from solution.

Rivers and streams are the most important transport agents. Fig. 333 shows two examples of the variations in transport capability of large rivers. Although the suspended load can vary considerably during the course of a year, the dissolved load remains noticeably constant, as shown here for both the Danube at Vienna and the Nile at Cairo.

Clastic sediments are classified according to their grain size. Rocks whose constituents have diameters greater than 2 mm are called *psephites* (psephos, gr., stone); between 2 and 0.02 mm *psammites* (psammos, gr., sand), and less than 0.02 mm *pelites* (gr. pelos, clay). In Fig. 334 is given the classification used here

(Germany), as well as the English (HOLMES), American (WENTWORTH) and French (CAYEUX) equivalents.

Grain-size Distribution. Conditions of transport and sedimentation are generally such that a sediment is produced whose particles exhibit a variety of grain size classes. The grain-size distribution is determined by sieving and in the case of smaller particles, by screening the sediment. It is convenient to subdivide size distribution arithmetically into groups of equal size range. From a sieve analysis of a well-graded gravel, one can adopt the usual numerical progression, grouping grains which are $1-2$, $2-3$, $3-4$ mm, etc. Usually, however, the size distribution covers such a wide range, that it is useful to adopt a logarithmic classification. In the United States a logarithmic scale to the base 2 is used, involving the grouping $\frac{1}{16}-\frac{1}{8}$, $\frac{1}{8}-\frac{1}{4}$, $\frac{1}{4}-\frac{1}{2}$, $\frac{1}{2}-1$, $1-2$, $2-4$, $4-8$, $8-16$ mm, etc. In Germany sub-division to the base 10 is used giving groupings such as $0.002-0.02$, $0.02-0.2$, $0.2-2$; $2-20$, $20-200$ mm, etc. If we want to sub-divide these further, it is sensible and convenient also to make the sub-divisions decadal-logarithmically, so that equal intervals result, such as $0.02-0.063$, $0.063-0.2$, $0.2-0.63$, $0.63-2$ mm, etc., based on grain diameters. The detailed size distribution should be determined accurately by sieving and screening. Sands, gravels, and boulders can of course be fairly accurately differentiated visually or with a hand lens. The nomenclature based on grain size for clastic sediments is given in Table 48.

Table 48. *Grain sized classification.* (After v. ENGELHARDT et al.)

Clay		Sand				Gravel				
	silt	medium sand		fine gravel		medium gravel				boulders
fine clay	coarse clay (silt)	fine sand		coarse sand		fine gravel		coarse gravel		
		very fine sand	fine-med-ium sand	coarse-med-ium sand	gravely sand	fine gravel	fine-med-ium gravel	coarse-med-ium gravel	boul-der-gravel	boulders
0.002	0.02	0.063	0.2	0.63	2.0	6.3	20	63	200 mm diameter	
(after DIN 4022:)	fine	med-ium	coarse	fine	med-ium	coarse	fine	med-ium	coarse	
clay	silt			sand			gravel			stones

Graphical Representation of Size Distribution. Two methods are customarily used for graphical representation of sieve and screen analysis. The first is the *distribution curve*, based on construction of bar graphs or histograms. Along the abscissa the chosen size-grades are plotted. The amount of each size grade, as weight percent, is plotted along the ordinate. The areas of each bar of the histogram must be proportional to the percentage of each constituent size grade. Then the curve which outlines the histogram is the distribution curve (Fig. 335). We can see readily the advantage offered when equal spacings are used for equal changes in size grade. If unequal spacings are used, changes must be made in the ordinate plot for each grade, if the area is to represent the amount of each size grade present.

While the distribution curve gives us a rather graphic picture of the grain size distribution, is it not as easily visualized directly from the second type of presentation used, the *cumulative curve*. This type of graphical representation

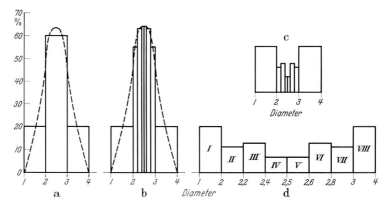

Fig. 335 a—d. Correct and incorrect representation of distribution curves (from BARTH-CORRENS-ESKOLA).

(a) Three equally spaced grain size groups:

1—2 =	20%
2—3 =	60%
3—4 =	20%
	100%

(b) The middle grain size group subdivided. The grain size groups recalculated for true area representation

Fraction	Base $\times$	Height = %	Amount
I 1—2	1.0 × 20	20	
II 2—2.2	0.2 × 55	11	
III 2.2—2.4	0.2 × 63	12.6	
IV 2.4—2.5	0.1 × 64	6.4	60
V 2.5—2.6	0.1 × 64	6.4	
VI 2.6—2.8	0.2 × 63	12.6	
VII 2.8—3	0.2 × 55	11	
VIII 3 —4	1.0 × 20	20	
		100	

(c) With incorrect height and correct base
(d) With incorrect base and incorrect height

has the advantage of being more useful for statistical analysis. In Fig. 336, six different schematic cumulative curves are illustrated, and qualitatively interpreted.

The grain size distribution of a clastic sediment is the result of a combination of transport and depositional variables. Their interrelationships are usually so complex, that it is not possible to draw definite conclusions from grain size distributions, concerning transport and depositional processes. One might be able to conclude, for example, that sands deposited by wave action on beaches, would be particularly well-sorted. That is, they would have a very narrow range of particle sizes. However, river sands and wind blown dune sands can exhibit similar grain size distributions (Fig. 337). Glacial tills, deposited by ice, have generally a very broad grain size distribution; they are especially poorly sorted (Fig. 338). Other criteria, related to transport and sedimentation history, include grain shape and *degree of rounding*.

The median diameter (md), obtained from a cumulative curve, can be used as one means of characterizing clastic sediments. This indicates that grain size for which 50 percent of the grains are smaller and 50 percent are larger. Another parameter frequently used to characterize sediments is the *sorting coefficient*, given as $So = \sqrt{Q_3/Q_1} \cdot Q_1$ and Q_3 are the first and third quartiles. Q_1, represents that diameter which has 25% of the distribution smaller than itself. The third quartile, Q_3, is that diameter which has 75% of the distribution smaller than itself. The better sorted a sediment, the smaller the difference between Q_1 and Q_3, and, therefore, the closer the sorting coefficient, So, will approach the value 1. Values up to 1.5 represent well sorted and beyond 2, poorly sorted sediments.

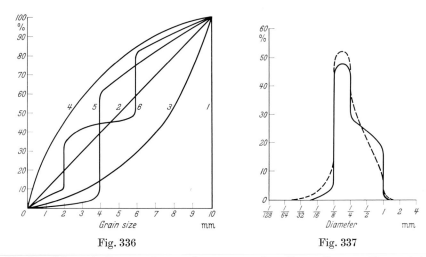

Fig. 336   Fig. 337

Fig. 336. Schematic diagram of cummulative curves (from BARTH-CORRENS-ESKOLA.) *1* grain size of only 10 mm; *2* all grain sizes equally distributed; *3* little fine, much coarse material; *4* much fine, little coarse material; *5* maximum at grain-size of 4 mm; *6* maximum at 2 and 6 mm; minimum at 4 mm

Fig. 337. Grain size distribution of a river sand ———— and a dune sand – – – –.
(From BARTH-CORRENS-ESKOLA)

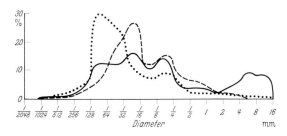

Fig. 338. Grain size distribution of glacial tills. (From BARTH-CORRENS-ESKOLA)

Psephites. In the case of psephitic rocks, the degree of rounding of grains is used as a parameter in classification. Loose sediment composed of rounded pebbles is called gravel, of angular blocks, rubble. The corresponding consolidated rocks are called *conglomerates* and *breccias*.

Psammites. In the case of the finer sediments, sands and sandstones, classification is not based so much on grain shape, but rather mineralogical composition of constituent grains and interstitial materials. Feldspar and chlorite rich sandstones, also containing rock fragments, are called *graywackes* (Fig. 339); sandstones containing much feldspar are *arkoses*; and those containing abundant carbonate, *calcarenites*. Calcium carbonate can also occur as a cement between detrital grains in *calcareous sandstones*. Detrital grains are cemented by silica in *siliceous sandstones*. If the original quartz grains are cemented by quartz, the result is a *quartzite*. When clay occurs interstitially, we have an *argillaceous sandstone*.

Residual rock fragments in sandstones are usually coarser than 2 mm, as long as they do not themselves consist of very fine-grained material. Quartz and feldspar predominate between 0.02—2 mm, and the clay minerals below

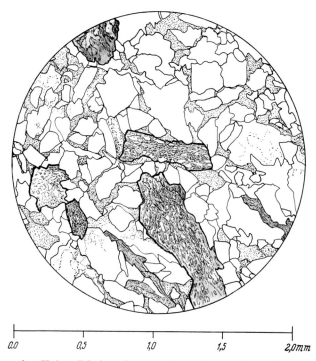

0,0	0,5	1,0	1,5	2,0mm

Fig. 339. Graywacke, Kulm, Ederbringhausen, Eder. Quartz: drawn lightly; mica: drawn lightly, showing cleavage; micaceous ground mass: stippled; rock fragments, composed of quartz and mica: drawn heavily

0.02 mm, as Figs. 340 and 341 show. Contrasted in these figures are the grain size distributions and mineral compositions of a coarse coastal sand from North America and a fine-grained sand from 150 meters depth, off the mouth of the Amazon River, which grades into a clay.

The average chemical analysis of pelitic and psammitic rocks in Table 49 indicates that chemical differentiation takes place during the sedimentation of clastic sediments. The psammites are on the average richer in SiO_2 than pelites. In individual instances, this differentiation can lead to essentially pure quartz sandstones. In graywackes usually $K_2O < Na_2O$, whereas in sandstones $K_2O > Na_2O$.

Guide Minerals. In addition to the major mineral constituents mentioned, sandstones also contain still other minerals in much smaller amounts. The investigation of these minor constituents has become important in the last decade. It is possible with the help of these accessory minerals in many cases to identify and correlate sedimentary layers, especially in borings, where so little sample is recovered that the characteristic guide fossils are often lacking. In practice the investigation of such minerals is usually confined to those "heavy" minerals which have a specific gravity greater than 2.9. They are usually separated in the laboratory from the lighter constituents by means of heavy liquids, such as bromoform. It should be emphasized that proper identification of heavy minerals requires careful mineralogical crystal optic work, without which quite serious errors in identification can occur. Very often identification is restricted to easily recognized heavy minerals such as rutile, zircon, garnet, and tourmaline, and with the help of statistics interpretations are attempted. It is frequently more profitable to place more value on observation of individual mineral species. For example, distinction between yellow and red garnets, and rounded and non-rounded zircons in different size fractions, have proven very useful in investigations in the north German Rhaet.

Table 49. *Average chemical composition of clays and sands*

	Clays and shales (average of 277 samples, after WEDEPOHL)	Sands and sandstones (average of 253 samples, after CLARKE)
SiO_2	58.9	78.7
TiO_2	0.77	0.25
Al_2O_3	16.7	4.8
Fe_2O_3	2.8	1.1
FeO	3.7	0.3
MnO	0.1	0.01
MgO	2.6	1.2
CaO	2.2	5.5
Na_2O	1.6	0.5
K_2O	3.6	1.3
H_2O^+	5.0	1.3
H_2O^-		0.3
P_2O_5	0.16	0.04
CO_2	1.3	5.0

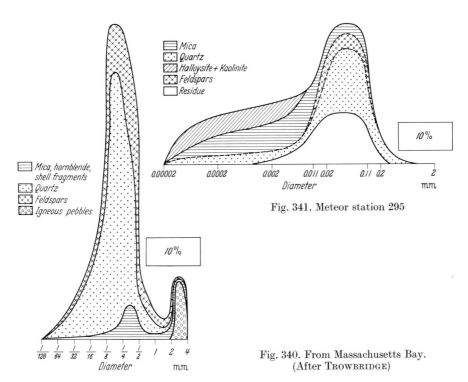

Mica
Quartz
Halloysite + Kaolinite
Feldspars
Residue

Mica, hornblende, shell fragments
Quartz
Feldspars
Igneous pebbles

0.00002   0.0002   0.002   0.011 0.02   0.11 0.2   2
Diameter   mm

10%

Fig. 341. Meteor station 295

10%

1/128 1/64 1/32 1/16 1/8 1/4 1/2 1 2 4
Diameter   mm

Fig. 340. From Massachusetts Bay. (After TROWBRIDGE)

Fig. 340 and 341. Grain size distribution and mineral composition of two coastal sands

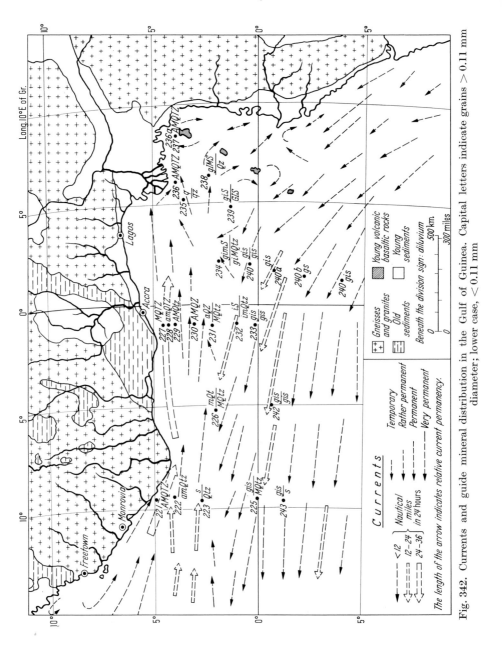

Fig. 342. Currents and guide mineral distribution in the Gulf of Guinea. Capital letters indicate grains > 0.11 mm diameter; lower case, < 0.11 mm

The mineral assemblages occuring in ancient sediments need not always be the original ones. The numerous diagenetic processes which are at play in a sediment after sedimentation and prior to metamorphism can dissolve minerals or form new ones. The extent to which a mineral is "stable", depends on the nature of these diagenetic processes.

It is questionable though, whether heavy minerals alone are sufficient to unravel the source of the sediment. We must always be seeking additional guide minerals. By noting the presence of "desert quartz", characterized by its round-ing and iron oxide coating, in the Cape Verde Basin, it became clear that desert dust was blown there during the last ice age. Sediments collected in the Gulf of Guinea during the Meteor expedition, and studied mineralogically, primarily by V. LEINZ, serve as a particularly fine example of the effect on guide mineral distribution by ocean currents. Since only the sources of the mineral assemblages are to be illustrated, it is not important that the sediments lie in part in the deep sea. As Fig. 342 shows, the strong Guinea Current, flowing from the west at more than 0.5 m/sec, carries a characteristic assemblage of splintery augite (A), microcline (M), tourmaline (T), zircon (Z), and rounded quartz grains (Q). These

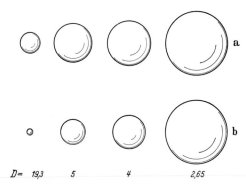

Fig. 343a and b. Relative size of spheres of differing density and equivalent (a) settling and (b) rolling velocities

minerals are derived from the adjacent mainland and distributed by the current flowing parallel to the coast. From the south the South Equatorial Current transports young volcanic material, glass (G) and a characteristic augite (I), derived from the predominantly basaltic rocks of the island chain Fernando Po, Principé, São Thomé, Anno Bom, and St. Helena. It also carries splintery quartz (S) along with it, which comes from the mainland coast to the south. It is still noted as the most abundant mineral the farther removed from the source. The other larger grains have been left behind during the course of transport. As is shown here in the case of augite and quartz, crystal morphology is a diagnostic property worth noting. It is to be noted further, that from the effect of the Guinea Current, two sands collected from the northeast point of Fernando Po Island contain only heavy minerals from the 100 km distant north coast, but none from the island itself.

This study shows also that one must be very cautious in correlating beds on the basis of similar trace mineral content. In Fig. 342 at sample locations where two sets of mineral notations are given, the lower one indicates sediments which are known to have been deposited during the last glaciation. In attempting to correlate these in a manner analogous to correlation procedures for borings, one would conclude that the diluvial sample at station 225 was of the same age as the recent marine sediment at station 222. The same error might be made relative to the diluvial sediment at station 232.

Placer Deposition. A natural enrichment of heavy minerals can occur in deposits formed by the running water of streams and rivers, as well as by wave action along the shores of the ocean. Along the shore incoming waves carry sediment in suspension. This quickly settles out and individual grains are caused to roll along the bottoms. Fig. 343 depicts the relative sizes of grains of gold $(d = 19.3)$, magnetite $(d = 5)$, garnet $(d = 4)$ and quartz $(d = 2.65)$ which have (a) the same settling velocities in water and (b) the same rolling velocity. The rolling velocity is that water velocity just sufficient to set a grain in motion. If the water velocity is just sufficient to put a quartz grain in motion, only heavier materials proportionally smaller than those shown will roll away with it. The greater the difference in specific gravity between mineral grains, the smaller the grains left behind. The relationship between grain size and specific gravity of particles of equal settling velocity is expressed by the formula of STOKES,

$$\frac{r_1}{r_2} = \frac{\sqrt{d_2 - 1}}{\sqrt{d_1 - 1}}$$

where r_1 and r_2 are the radii and d_1 and d_2 the specific gravities of the equivalent spheres (for exact calculations involving grains > 0.05 mm in diameter, the more complex formula of OSÉEN must be used). The rolling or traction velocity is governed by the following formula of NEWTON

$$\frac{r_1}{r_2} = \frac{d_2 - 1}{d_1 - 1} .$$

In the flowing water of streams it is probably a combination of settling and removal by traction, resulting from turbulence, that leads to enrichment of heavy minerals in sediments. As a result of this winnowing process, placer deposits have formed in which gold and platinum, precious stones, such as diamond or topaz, and ores like cassiterite have become concentrated. These deposits represent a geochemically important concentration, also observed in ancient sediments.

Pelites. While psammites are composed essentially of coarse grained resistant minerals, pelites or clays consist of the very fine grained weathering products. To the chemist or ceramist the term clay has quite a different connotation than as used by the petrographer. The raw material for fine ceramic products is the rock material called kaolin, which consists predominantly of the clay mineral kaolinite. Kaolins occur as metamorphic-hydrothermal deposits, or as residual weathering deposits, sometimes sedimented following relatively short transport. This concept of a clay would thus embrace numerous true sediments. The term clay is used in this way in the heavy ceramic, in particular the brick industry. These argillaceous sediments represent the depositions of the finest grained materials from running or standing bodies of water. Deposition of coarse-grained sediment gives rise to psammites, fined grained sediment to pelites. There is general lack of agreement on the dividing line between the two types of sediments. Since the properties of rocks vary continuously with grain-size, the boundary is wholly arbitrary. We shall consider as clays those rocks whose constituents are predominantly within the $2-20\,\mu$ range. We shall consider $20\,\mu$ as the upper limit of clay-size material.

As deposits of the finest sediments, clays consist first of all of residual weathering products which remain for a long time in suspension, either by virtue of their fine grain-size or their platy morphology. In addition they consist of newly formed minerals which are also fine-grained and platy in habit. In addition clays often contain appreciable amounts of organic remains, calcareous and siliceous tests, as well as partially decomposed organic matter. A fourth group of constituents form subsequently in the sediment by diagenesis, and include FeS_2, glauconite, and some carbonates.

When the different clay minerals are transported into the ocean, their sedimentation behaviors may vary. Illites and kaolinites may settle out much more rapidly than montmorillonite, which may remain in suspension for a much longer time.

Although it was formerly believed that all clays consisted primarily of kaolinite, we know today that the most common constituents of sedimentary clays are imperfect, poorly crystallized micas, which are deficient in potassium, perhaps as a result of replacement by H_3O^+ ions. This chemical and structural deficiency may be so extensive that it results in mixed layering, in which mica and montmorillonite layers are intimately intergrown. The entire group of deficient micas is frequently called the illite group. These micas are probably for the most part detrital residual weathering products. By means of K-A age determination methods, it has been shown in some instances in young sediments, that these micas are older than the age of the sediment containing them. They were derived from older sediments which blanketed the greater part of the earth's surface. In ancient sediments micas are also found which are younger than the sediment containing them, having formed by diagenesis or by growth of smaller mica particles. Diagenetic chlorite occurs especially in those clays which have been deposited from highly saline waters, produced by evaporation of sea waters. Thus clay mineral formation is not restricted to development in soils with subsequent incorporation into sediments. They can form also directly in the sediment.

Depending on their degree of consolidation and fissility, clays may be designated as *clay-stones* or *shales* (bedded). Some claystones owe their hardness to cementing agents, especially carbonates. Because of their very fine particle size, characterization of the mineral composition of clays by microscopic studies is very limited. X-ray diffraction studies are most useful in this respect. Characterization of clays, based on chemical analysis or particle size distribution alone, is not likely to be very successful.

Sedimentary Structures and Textures. Having become familiar with the constituents of clastic sediments, we want to look now at their characteristic structures. We have already considered their textural characteristics in dealing with grain-size distributions. The most important and diagnostic structural characteristic of sediments is their layering or *bedding*. This is so characteristic that we frequently refer to sedimentary rocks as layered rocks. The bedding or stratification is an expression of variations in material supply during deposition, which has changed in some way between deposition of contiguous layers. Fig. 333 (p. 253) illustrates the annual variations in suspended load characteristic of different rivers. The sedimentary column provides evidence of the effects of climatic variations on sediment supply. We can frequently observe quite thin clay films deposited between two identical beds of limestone. This is interpreted as indicating transport of clay sediment during a brief interval of high rainfall during a period of otherwise high aridity. In lakes, which are fed by glacial streams, the influx of sediment is greatest in summer, and relatively coarse particles sediment out. During the course of winter the fine particles are deposited, when sediment supply and water movement have ceased. In this way laminated deposits of clays are formed. Such stratified Pleistocene glacial lake deposits are also called *varves*. These have been used to count the number of years which have lapsed since the retreat of glaciers. Volcanic ash eruptions, changes in climate and sea-level, and changes in the productivity of organisms can give rise to stratification. Thus problems of stratification are important in petrology in reconstructing earth history.

In sediments deposited from flowing media such as wind, water, and ice, often there is preserved evidence of the *direction of flow*. In glacial deposits, linear

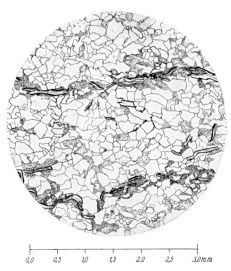

Fig. 344. Buntsandstein, Karlshafen (Weser). Quartz and some feldspar: thin lines; mica: heavy lines; fine grain ground mass of mica and some quartz: stippled

deposits of glacial drift are oriented with their long axes in the direction of flow. This direction is preserved in the ground moraine after the ice melts. In rapidly flowing water, flat pebbles are arranged like shingles, tilted in the direction of stream flow. In slowly flowing water certain objects, like shreds of seaweed and animal remains such as graptolites or pteropod shells, can be easily lined up parallel to the direction of flow. In moving, as well as in calm water, platy objects such as mica flakes (Fig. 344) and pelecypod and other shells, are deposited parallel of the bottom. Such mica plates can give rise to fissility parallel to the platelet surface. This phenomenon has been given the misleading name, primary cleavage. It would be better to reserve the expression cleavage for structures formed by later changes.

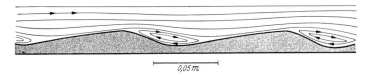

Fig. 345. Current circulation about current ripples. (After TWENHOFEL from BARTH-CORRENS-ESKOLA)

If a fine mud is caused to move down a slope and becomes mixed with overlying water, suspension or *turbidity currents* are formed. The suspension will have a higher density than pure water. Values up to 1.2 have been observed. Therefore, they have the ability to transport coarse material within them over long distances. Sediment finally deposited from such turbidity currents will show *graded bedding*, with coarser material at the bottom, grading upward into finer material.

Both as a result of flow of water and wind as well as wave motion, wavy sediment surfaces can be formed. From the geometry of these so-called *ripple marks*, which may have wave lengths from centimeters to hundreds of meters (dunes), the mode of occurrence can be deduced. Current ripples are asymmetrical (Fig. 345) whereas, as a result of the back and forth motion of waves, oscillation or wave ripples are symmetrical (Fig. 346). If the current direction changes, superimposed

Fig. 346. Oscillation ripples. (After TWENHOFEL, from BARTH-CORRENS-ESKOLA)

ripple marks are formed in response to the changing currents. In cross section the sediment then shows *crossed bedding*. This can happen also as a result of a change in current velocity, for example, in the formation of delta deposits.

Additional kinds of irregular surfaces can form as a result of slumping of clumps of sediment on a sloping surface. Such subaquatic *slump structures* are a form of folding which may be quite similar in appearance to folds formed by tectonic processes.

2. Limestone and Dolomite

Solubility of Calcium Carbonate. Bedding is not restricted to clastic sediments. It is a characteristic property also of sediments of chemical or biogenic origin, such as calcareous muds.

Next to clastic sediments, limestones are the most widely distributed. In order to understand their mode of origin it is necessary that we first clarify the solubility relationships of calcium carbonate. Usually one finds the statement that calcium carbonate is soluble as the bicarbonate. Since this can lead to some misunderstanding, we shall prefer to consider the interrelationships of ions in solution. The solubility of calcium carbonate in pure water is expressed by the solubility product,

$$[Ca^{++}] \cdot [CO_3^=] = L(\sim 10^{-8}). \qquad (1)$$

In natural environments carbonic acid is almost always present and it dissociates according to the relationship:

$$\frac{[H^+][HCO_3^-]}{[H_2CO_3]} = K_1(\sim 10^{-6}). \qquad (2)$$

This equation is designated as the first dissociation constant of carbonic acid. The HCO_3^- ions can dissociate further, according to the expression:

$$\frac{[H^+][CO_3^=]}{[HCO_3^-]} = K_2(\sim 10^{-10}). \qquad (3)$$

This second dissociation constant is very small, indicating that HCO_3^- dissociates only very slightly. If H^+ and CO_3^- ions were to be found in solution they would strive to combine according to equation (3). Limestone in aqueous solution produces Ca^{++} and $CO_3^=$ ions, although very few in number. If H^+ ions are added to the solution, $CO_3^=$ ions are utilized to form HCO_3^-, the equilibrium of equation (1) is distrubed, and additional Ca^{++} goes into solution in order to establish equilibrium of the three reactions. On the other hand, if we remove H^+ ions from solution, $CaCO_3$ must precipitate, because of the resulting excess of $CO_3^=$ ions in solution. We find, therefore, that by adding carbonic acid, or acids in general, dissolution of calcium carbonate takes place; reduction of acidity results in carbonate precipitation. Since in nature only carbonic acid plays an important role, the concentration of carbon dioxide in solution is the most important factor affecting carbonate formation. The solubility of carbon dioxide is very dependent upon temperature. It is reduced by half over the temperature interval from $0°$ to $20°$ C. Therefore, the temperature influence is extremely important. Of course, it only

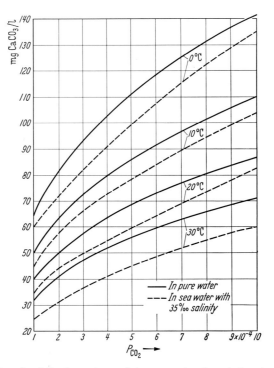

Fig. 347. Solubility of calcite in water and in sea water in relation to CO_2-pressure and temperature. (After WATTENBERG)

plays a role in cases where a gaseous phase is present and in contact with the solution. The solubility of carbon dioxide, like all gases, is increased with pressure. This effect perhaps may be important in the case of many springs, in which case a pressure decrease would occur, except on the ocean bottom where elevated pressure prevails. However, a voluminous supply of carbon dioxide, sufficient to exceed the saturation limit, has not been demonstrated up to now.

At a fixed carbon dioxide concentration the equilibrium changes with temperature, the solubility of calcium carbonate [Eq. (1)] decreasing with rising temperature. In addition the equilibrium constants of Eq. (2) and (3) are changed, K_2 growing more rapidly than K_1. The temperature rise is effective here also in diminishing the solubility of calcium carbonate. The pressure also affects the dissociation of carbonic acid, increasing the solubility of calcium carbonate in water (at fixed CO_2-content).

Finally the effect of salinity is to be considered. If we add Ca^{++} or $CO_3^=$ ions to an equilibrium solution of $CaCO_3$ in pure water, without varying external conditions, $CaCO_3$ must precipitate, since the solubility product constant, L, is indeed constant. The solubility is reduced. Foreign ions will increase the solubility, changing the constant, L. In addition, complex formation probably plays a role. As the ultimate result the solubility of calcium carbonate in sea water does not differ appreciably from that in pure water, as Fig. 347 shows. Aragonite instead of calcite as a precipitate possesses a greater solubility. The solubility product of calcite in sea water at $25°C$ and one atmosphere pressure is 4.5×10^{-9}; for aragonite, 7.1×10^{-9} (BERNER, 1965).

Terrestrial Limestone Formation. In fresh water the influence of foreign ions can play only a subordinate role. Calcareous surface deposits, as have been described especially from South Africa, form where water rises in the soil by capillarity and evaporates at the surface. In areas of high precipitation, carbonic acid charged water dissolves limestone within the mountains at low temperatures and this, when it flows to the warmer surface, precipitates out as travertine. Plants can also play an important role in that they remove carbon dioxide from water. In inland lakes we sometimes find limestone deposits which are called lake marls. In this case the decrease in $CaCO_3$ solubility can be attributed to evolution of carbon dioxide due to a rise in temperature, as well as its removal by assimilation by green plants. It has been calculated that a lake bottom covered with the plant species *Potamogeton lucens* can form annually approximately 5 g/cm^2 of calcium carbonate.

Marine, Inorganic Carbonate Formation and Dissolution. Marine carbonate precipitation is far more important and widespread. We know today, primarily as a result of the investigations of H. WATTENBERG, that the surface water of the ocean is at least saturated and, in the tropics, always supersaturated with calcium carbonate. This supersaturation can be relieved only with difficulty and then only by means of $CaCO_3$ nuclei. Quartz and calcareous shells of animals are ineffective as seeds for precipitation. Only when shells are pulverized by the surf and freed of their organic coatings, are they effective as seeds. We should expect inorganic carbonate precipitation, therefore, primarily only in shallow seas. There, as a result of complete reduction of supersaturation, as much as 80 g of calcium carbonate could precipitate out of a cubic meter of sea water. Since a continual supply of new supersaturated sea water can be brought in by ocean currents, limestone deposits of considerable thickness could form in this manner.

The deeper portions of the ocean are to a considerable degree undersaturated with $CaCO_3$, because at the lower temperature, the higher pressure, and a supply of CO_2 from decomposing organic substances, the supersaturation of water sinking from higher levels is decreased. Thus, in many places in the deep sea, dissolution of calcium carbonate can take place.

Marine Biochemical Carbonate Formation. In addition to inorganic processes, limestone can originate also from biochemical processes. A great many organisms form their shells and tests from calcium carbonate. We can formulate the following classification, in which organisms are grouped according to their form of habitat into benthonic (sessile), planktonic (floating) and nektonic (free swimming) forms.

1. *Plants*:
a) Benthonic calcareous algae: Lithothamnien, Halimeda, etc.
b) Planktonic calcareous algae: Coccolithophoridae.
2. *Animals*:
a) Benthonic: corals, calcareous sponges, foraminifera, bryozoa, brachiopods, echinoderms, molluscs, worms, crustaceans.
b) Planktonic: foraminifera, pteropods.
c) Nektonic: crustaceans (trilobites, ostracods).

In addition, green marine plants can contribute to carbonate deposits by assimilation of CO_2 from marine waters. Finally, we can mention the effect of bacteria, whose activity indirectly leads to carbonate deposition by removal of H^+-ions in the production of NH_3. We cannot elaborate further here on these effects.

Table 50. *Distribution of marine sediments.* (After the results of the "Challenger" expedition, after T. W. VAUGHAN, 1924, from WATTENBERG, 1933)

Name of sediment	Area covered in km²	Per cent covered	
		Earth's surface	Sea bottom
Globigerina ooze	128,000,000	25.2	37.4
Pteropod ooze	1,040,000	0.2	0.3
Diatomaceous ooze	28,200,000	5.5	8.2
Radiolarian ooze	5,930,000	1.1	1.6
Red clay	133,000,000	26.2	38.8
Calcareous sand	6,620,000	1.3	1.9
Volcanic sand	1,550,000	0.3	0.43
Green sand and silt	2,200,000	0.4	0.6
Red silt	259,000	0.05	0.07
Blue silt	37,500,000	7.3	10.8
Total	—	67.55	100.0

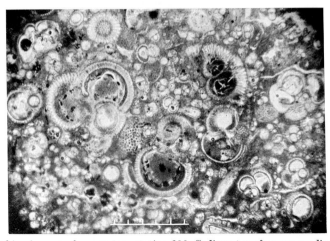

Fig. 348. Globigerina ooze from meteor station 286. Sediment surface perpendicular to scale. Magnification: two scale divisions, 0.1 mm. (From BARTH-CORRENS-ESKOLA)

Table 50 summarizes data available today on the world-wide distribution of calcareous deposits in recent marine sediments. In particular we should note that *globigerina ooze* is composed primarily of foraminifera. It need not, however, be composed predominantly of globigerina. Fig. 348 represents a section cut through a specimen of globigerina ooze. If all of the calcareous shells were dissolved, only an argillaceous component, *red clay* would remain. This consists of argillaceous weathering products of terrestrial origin, of volcanic material transported in part by winds, and of newly formed diagenetic minerals. Its usual brown color arises from the oxygen content of the deep water which serves as oxidation agent of iron-rich colloids.

In shallow marine sediments also foraminifera can contribute significantly, as Table 51 shows. Calcareous algae, which play an essential role here, contribute greatly to the formation of so-called coral reefs, as indicated in Table 52. It is likely that the calcareous algae fraction has been overestimated, because they are usually more fragile than corals and contribute an abundance of fragments to the sediment.

Table 51. *Contribution of different lime-forming organisms to the composition of some shallow sea sediments*

Grain size class	Depth in m	81	70	64	94	66
Diameter in mm	Carbonate content %	88	80	87	65	86
20—2	% of grain size class in total sediment	9.3	21.5	55.1	5.6	14.4
	Calcareous algae %	75	76.2	++	47.4	++
	Corals %	—	7.1	+	10.5	++
2—0.2	% of grain size class in total sediment	89.2	62.7	19.0	71.6	83.8
	Foraminifera %	11.3	5	25	41.8	18.8
	Calcareous algae%	51.3	} 64	} 75	14.9	} 87
	Other biogen. Material %	29.6			11.4	
	Mineral grains %	7.8[a]	31[b]	—	2.9[c]	1.2
Location		2° 34.9′S 39° 17.7′W	8° 5.3′S 34° 34.9′W	South point Sal Island Cape Verde	4° 54.8′N 9° 28.1′W	4° 30′N 1° 0.4′W

++ abundant; + little.
[a] Includes: 59% quartz, 19% plagioclase, 10% orthoclase.
[b] Predominately quartz.
[c] Includes 52.5% Glauconite.

Table 52. *Composition of the uplifted Mailupe reef, east of Honolulu, Hawaii.* (After POLLOCK, from CORRENS)

		Totals:	
Attached branching coral colonies	22%		
Lithothamnian crusts (on coral)	30%		
Lithothamnian nodules	14%	Corals	24%
Sand between nodules	17%	Lithothamnia alone	44%
Reworked coral fragments	2%	Sand coral and lithothamnian	
Uncharacterized materials	15%	fragments, etc.	32%
	100%		100%

At many places over the earth carbonate sedimentation occurs in quite shallow water, in conjunction with prolific development of carbonate forming organisms. Fig. 349 presents a schematic cross section through a platform of the Bahama Islands. In quite shallow water calcareous mud is deposited, which

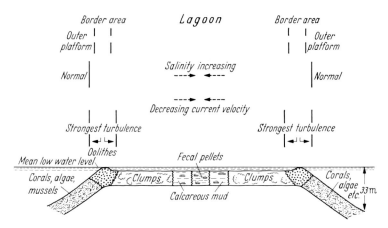

Fig. 349. Schematic cross section through a platform of the Bahamas. (After PURDY)

can be admixed with up to 40% of fecal pellets produced by the indigenous living fauna. At the reef-like borders of the platform strong turbulence prevails. At this point spherical *oolites* form from the supersaturated sea water as a result of precipitation of calcium carbonate around calcium carbonate nuclei. An oolite particle, called an ooid, will remain in suspension, until it has grown too large for the turbulence to sustain it in suspension. Oolites here make up about 70% of the sediment. The origin of strange calcereous clumps, called grapestones, is as yet unexplained. In the area noted they may make up as much as 35% of the sediment. At the outer edges of the platform algae, corals, and pelecypods are found. The fine calcareous mud in many places consists of aragonite needles. Whether these represent inorganic precipitates or are pulverized remains of the abundant calcareous algae Halimeda, is still disputed. Primarily as a result of reworking of reef material, a poorly crystallized Mg-rich calcite is formed. Table 53 gives the aragonite and Mg-content of the hard parts of some marine organisms. Calcite, containing very little magnesium in its structure, is found in deeper water.

Because of its distorted structure, Mg-rich calcite is more soluble than aragonite, which in turn is more soluble than low Mg calcite. If sea water retreats, exposing such a calcareous mud, rainwater preferentially dissolves the high magnesium calcite and aragonite, with the deposition of low Mg-calcite as a cement. Aragonite oolites may be coated by this secondary calcite, forming hollow spheroids by subsequent dissolution of the aragonite. They may be filled later by calcite. If this rapidly hardened limestone is covered again by sea water, it can be reworked by wave action and incorporated as pebbles into newly formed sediment.

In the case of sediments permanently covered by sea water, diagenetic transformation can occur only after burial by additional sediment (see p. 293). Under these conditions pseudomorphs of low Mg-calcite form after high Mg-calcite.

In contrast to earlier views, we know today that in addition to dolomite, mixed crystals of calcite with little Mg and of magnesite with little Ca can form. A little ordered Mg-rich calcite has been found also in shells of organisms (Table 53), although aragonite can accept only very little Mg into its structure. Strontium is accepted into both structures; up to $\sim$2,000 g/T in calcite and $\sim$3,000 g/T in aragonite.

Table 53. *Magnesium carbonate content of marine organisms in relation to aragonite content.*
(After Chave)

		Aragonite content	MgCO$_3$ content
Algae	Coccoliths	0	?
	Lithothamnians, etc.	0	7.7—28.7
	Halimeda	100	∼1
Protozoa	Plankt. Foraminifera	0	2—15.9
	Ceratobuliminids	100	?
Coelenterates	Calcareous sponges	0	5.5—14.1
	Madreporasians	100	0.1—0.8
	Alcyonarians	0	6.1—13.9
Annelids	Serpula	0—99	6.4—16.5[a]
Echinoderms	Echinoids	0	4.5—12
	Star fish	0	8.6—16.2
	Brittle stars	0	9.2—15.8
	Sea lilies	0	7.9—15.9
Bryozoa	Schizaporella	58—78	>4[a]
Brachiopods		0	<4 ?
Pelecypods	Ostrea, Pectin, Anomyo	0	1.3—2.8
	Chama, Arca	100	0.1
	Spondylus	25—100	0.2[a]
	Lima	80	0.3
Gastropods	Crepidula, Strombus ⎱	100	0.1—0.3
	Patella, Terebra ⎰		
	Nerita	15—70	0.71—1.55[a]
Cephalopods	Argonauta	0	7
	Nautilus, Spirula	100	0.05, 0.35
Arthropods	Decapoda	0	5.2—10.8
	Ostracoda	0	2—10.2
	Barnacles[a]	0	1.35—4.6

[a] In the calcite portion.

Dolomite Formation. The old puzzle relating to the formation of dolomite is nearer solution today than ever before. We know from natural observations that dolomite can be formed shortly after or even contemporaneously with carbonate deposition from sea waters, especially in lagoons in which high salt concentration prevails. Very high local salt concentrations may result when carbonate sediments are exposed as described above. In this case it results from the evaporation of pore water. Under these conditions dolomite can form.

In addition, progress has been made in the experimental synthesis of dolomite. Table 54 gives the solubility relationships of calcite and dolomite at room temperature and at various salinities. Both minerals exhibit maximum solubility at intermediate salinities. Additional investigations in the polycomponent system Na—Ca—Mg—Cl—SO$_4$—CO$_3$—H$_2$O lend further support to these observations.

In addition to contemporaneous dolomitization, later secondary dolomitization can occur. *Dedolomitization* has been observed, involving reversal of equilibrium and the solution of dolomite leading to deposition of calcite.

Table 54. *Solubility of calcite and dolomite in sea water at 25° C.* [Based on data from
I. R. KRAMER (1959) calculated by E. USDOWSKI (1964)]

Salinity °/₀₀	Calcite mg CaCO₃ / 1,000 g H₂O	Dolomite		
		mg CaCO₃ / 1,000 g H₂O	mg MgCO₃ / 1,000 g H₂O	mg CaMg(CO₃)₂ / 1,000 g H₂O
60	10.3	3.7	3.1	6.8
45	10.5	4.5	3.8	8.3
35	6.6	3.1	2.6	5.1

Nomenclature. All gradations exist between limestones and clays. The following scheme can serve for classifying such rocks and for indicating their technical use.

95	85	75	65	% Kalk	35	25	15	5
Hochprozentiger Kalkstein	Merge- liger Kalk	Mergel- kalk	Kalk- mergel	Mergel	Ton- mergel	Mergel- ton	Merge- liger Ton	Hochprozentiger Ton (Kaolin)

| 5 | 15 | 25 | 35 | % „Ton" (= Nichtcarbonat) | 65 | 75 | 85 | 95 |

	10		25	30	40		75		90
Weiß- kalk	Wasserkalk	Zementkalk	Roman- kalk	Portlandzement	Ziegelton	Feuer- fester Ton

| 90 | 75 | 70 | 60 | % CaCO₃ | 25 | 10 |

Kalk means chalk, calcareous, or limestone; *Mergel* means marl; *Ton*, clay.

This terminology with some modification was adapted from LUFTSCHITZ.

3. Sedimentary Iron and Manganese Deposits

Terrestrial Iron Ore Formation. In contrast to calcium and magnesium, iron can be transported as a carbonate only under very special conditions. Important in this respect is the complete absence of oxygen in solution. Ferrous carbonate is less soluble than calcium carbonate, as Fig. 350 shows, but nevertheless considerable amounts of iron can be transported in this way. Springs and streams carrying such dissolved ferrous carbonate are found especially in marshy regions. The iron can be precipitated out as iron carbonate in much the same way as calcium carbonate, that is, by loss of CO_2 from solution, for example, as a result of a temperature increase. Such mineral deposits are known in marshy regions and are often called white iron ores. Similar fossil iron deposits also occur in conjunction with coal beds, and are then designated in a misleading manner as clay ironstones.

Frequently it will happen that the iron carbonate charged water will dissolve oxygen. When this happens iron hydroxide precipitates. In addition, bacteria may initiate precipitation. They are able to use the 58 Kcal liberated in the breakdown of 4 moles of $FeCO_3$ to $Fe(OH)_3$. Iron ore formation of this kind in

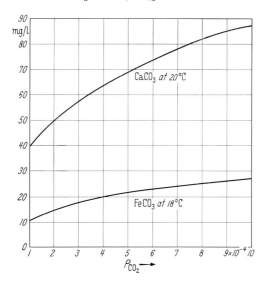

Fig. 350. Solubility of $FeCO_3$ and $CaCO_3$ in relation to CO_2 pressure

inland lakes gives rise to so-called *lake ores* or, when later filled in, to *limonitic iron ore*. Occasionally the iron phosphate, vivianite, $Fe_3^{2+}[PO_4]_2 \cdot 8H_2O$, forms first as the most insoluble compound. Then the carbonate ore, white iron ore, and finally, limonitic hydroxide ore forms, giving rise to layered deposits (Fig. 351).

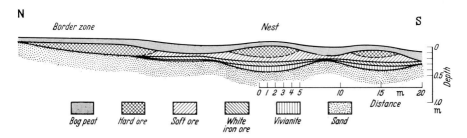

Fig. 351. Cross section through a limonitic iron ore deposit. (After BANDEL from BARTH-CORRENS-ESKOLA)

Redox Potential. A reducing environment may be found whenever excess organic matter is present, so that all oxygen is utilized in the oxidation of the organic matter. Today we consider oxidation and reduction in a more general sense than simple loss or gain of oxygen. Oxidation involves increasing the positive or decreasing the negative valence of an atom and thus the loss of electrons. In like fashion reduction involves a gain in electrons. We utilize the redox potential, Eh, to measure quantitatively the oxidation or reduction capabilities of a medium. The Eh represents in volts the number of electrons necessary to reduce the medium.

If a platinum electrode is immersed in a solution containing equal concentrations of Fe^{+2} and Fe^{+3} ions, it can be demonstrated that the Fe^{+2} ions give up electrons to the platinum, giving it a negative charge. The Fe^{+3} ions tend to take on electrons, giving the electrode a positive charge. The actual net charge on the platinum electrode indicates which of the two reactions dominate. The more negative the redox potential, the greater the reducing power of the less

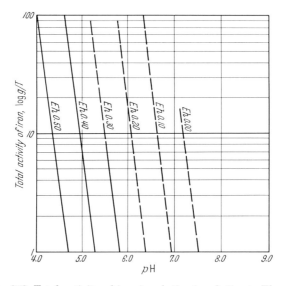

Fig. 352. Total activity of iron in solution in relation to Eh and pH

oxidized substance. In aqueous solutions, with which we are always dealing in sediments, it is always necessary to take into consideration the pH, that is, the prevailing H^+ and OH^- ion concentrations. Thus the calculated equilibrium is shifted between the Fe^{+2} and Fe^{+3} hydroxides:

$$Fe(OH)_2 + H_2O = Fe(OH)_3 + H^+ + e$$

according to the following equation:

$$Eh = 0.271 - 0.059 \times pH.$$

Thus equilibrium lies in the acid region at positive Eh and in the alkaline region at negative Eh.

In nature observed pH values lie for the most part between 4 and 9, the Eh values between $+0.6$ and -0.5 volt. Fig. 352 indicates the total dissolved iron in relation to pH and Eh. Activity is the thermodynamic means of representing concentrations of real solutions, which differ from those of ideal solutions. For very dilute solutions, as in the case of Fig. 352, activity is practically equivalent to the ideal solubility.

Marine Iron Ore Formation. While terrestrial iron ore formation basically is readily understood, the explanation of marine deposits presents important difficulties. The iron content of present ocean water is extremely low. About

6—7 mg are present per ton of sea water. About 1,000 times more iron is present in colloidal solution. This is still far less than the 50 g/ton for the purest quartz sand. On the other hand we know that in the geologic past, great amounts of marine iron ores have been deposited. Prime examples are the minette ores in Lothringen and the Dogger oolitic ores in southern Germany. As long as oxygen is present in sea water, practically no iron can be present in true solution. The ore deposits mentioned contain numerous remains of organisms, indicating that the ores were deposited in an oxygen bearing medium in sufficient amounts to support animal life. One can only conclude that the iron was transported as hydroxide sols, which were flocculated in the marine environment. The floccs often became attached to mineral particles suspended in the water. Continued

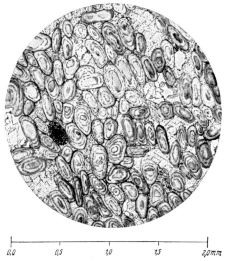

Fig. 353. Iron oolite (Minette) Fentschtal, Lothringen. The black object is rolled up fragment of mineralized echinoid plate. In the ground mass, calcite, stippled with cleavage, and quartz

build up gave rise to concentric layering. When the spheroids became so heavy that they could no longer remain in suspension, they sank to the sea floor where growth ceased. The resulting forms are called ooides and the accumulated rocks oolite (Fig. 353). It is essentially irrelevant how large the original nuclei were. In turbulent sea water, other materials such as clay minerals can be transported away, resulting in a concentration of iron minerals on the sea bottom locally. Since present rivers carry only very small amounts of iron ($\sim$1 mg/liter), very special weathering conditions must have prevailed in the source area on land. They must have existed on a grand scale which we have not observed on earth anywhere in recent times.

It has also been suggested that in marine zones with negative redox potential and abundant CO_2, the iron could be leached out of normal sediments, transported as ferrous iron, and reprecipitated, depending on pH and Eh, either as carbonate, sulfide, or ferric hydroxide. Such processes are certainly possible. The formation of extensive iron ore deposits, however, would necessitate conditions which could be made to conform only with great difficulty to the ocean circulation, which is invoked by density differences, the earth's rotation, and wind patterns. Such processes would also imply that very extensive regions of normal sediments would have to be leached. Clays and shales contain on the average (Table 49) 6.5% and sands and sandstones 1.4% $Fe_2O_3 + FeO$.

The formation of extensive sedimentary iron ore deposits has not taken place throughout geologic time, but is restricted to certain periods. The formation of iron coatings on mineral grains, which appear similar to oolites, can probably also form concretions (see p. 311) on or in muddy sediment after deposition. One must be extremely careful in trying to interpret the history of sedimentary iron ores, because after deposition numerous changes, chemical reactions, and migration of material can be expected. During the course of time colloidal iron hydroxides recrystallize to goethite, at the same time incorporating co-precipitated aluminum hydroxide into its structure. Upon further alteration the hydroxide loses its water, forming Fe_2O_3 or Fe_3O_4, or it reacts with silica gel that was transported and precipitated with it as a sol, forming silicates. A part of these may be micas, similar to glauconite, and another part chlorites $(Mg, Fe, Al)_3(OH)_2$ $[(Si, Al)_4O_{10}]$, transitional to cronstedite $(Fe^{+3}, Fe^{+2})_6(OH)_8[Si, Fe^{+3})_4O_{10}]$, which has the kaolinite structure. Consideration of the origin of these minerals belongs in the chapter on rock transformation.

Glauconite Formation. In coastal regions, lagoons, and similar basins, primary carbonate ore deposition can probably sometimes occur, although more frequently

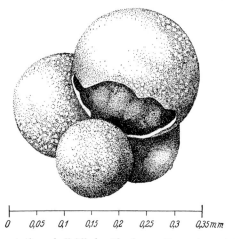

$$\vdash\quad\quad\quad\quad\quad\quad\quad\quad\quad\quad\dashv$$
$$0\quad\ 0{,}05\quad 0{,}1\quad 0{,}15\quad 0{,}2\quad 0{,}25\quad 0{,}3\quad 0{,}35\,mm$$

Fig. 354. Foraminifera shell filled with glauconite, meteor station 276

the $FeCO_3$ results from diagenesis in the sediment. The existence of iron silicates in solution in sea water is not possible, however. In spite of this the iron silicate glauconite, with average composition $(K, Na, Ca_{0.5})_{0.84}(Fe_{0.19}^{II}, Mg_{0.4})(Al_{0.47}, Fe_{0.97}^{III})_2(OH)_2[(Al_{0.35}, Si_{3.65})O_{10}]$, is found on the sea bottom. Forming on the sea floor, it must be a very early diagenetic mineral. Not infrequently foraminifera shells are found filled with glauconite (Fig. 354). It is difficult to recast the many analyses of glauconite into a simple generalized formula. This may be related to the fact that alteration takes place readily on the sea bottom, but more likely to the collection of most samples from surface outcrops. YODER and EUGSTER have attempted to interpret glauconites as mixed crystals of celadonite, KFe^{+3}-$MgSi_4O_{10}(OH)_2$, muscovite $KAl_2Si_4O_{10}(OH)_2$, and pyrophyllite, $Al_2Si_4O_{10}(OH)_2$. Divalent iron is almost always present in glauconite, presumably substituting for magnesium. It is also likely that glauconites include different minerals, which fall only in part in YODER and EUGSTER'S system, and may be in part derived from biotite. Glauconite could be formed also from montmorillonite. Glauconites with divalent iron must have been formed at the appropriate Eh. A portion of the ferrous iron can have been oxidized in exposed outcrops.

Since sea water is essentially a NaCl solution it is really surprising that a potassium silicate crystallizes from it. Many observations indicate that the site of origin of glauconite is often not free sea water, but perhaps in the intestinal tracts of marine organisms. This would provide a source of potassium from ingested plants and a reducing medium necessary for incorporation of ferrous iron.

Sulfide Formation. Reducing environments can occur in sea water as well as in sediments. Reducing conditions may exist in those portions of the sea separated from the general ocean, so that they are not affected by deep ocean currents. Here hydrogen sulfide can form at the deeper water levels. At the surface of such ocean segments a prolific fauna and flora are found. Remains of organisms undergo decomposition as they settle to the sea bottom and in the deeper levels oxygen is consumed by bacteria, which oxidize the organic matter to CO_2. If no oxygen from surface waters in equilibrium with oxygen in the air is supplied by sinking currents, decomposition of organic substances is continued by anaerobic bacteria. They form hydrogen sulfide either by breaking down proteins or by utilizing oxygen from sulfate ions in sea water for oxidation of carbonaceous substances, whose presence is prerequisite for the activity of these bacteria. Table 55 summarizes data indicative of reducing conditions for a characteristic section in the Black Sea, in whose upper water levels the oxygen gradually decreases and is present to about 150 meters depth. At this depth H_2S appears and increases downward.

Table 55. *Redox potentials, oxygen and hydrogen sulfide concentrations and $SO_4^=/Cl^-$ ratios in the Black Sea.* [After RICHARDS (1965), SKOPINTSEV (1957) and SKOPINTSEV *et al.* (1958)]

Sea depth in m	Redox potential Eh millivolts	Oxygen concentration ml/liter	H_2S concentration ml/liter	$SO_4^=/Cl^-$
0	395	5.60		0.1408
25	408	7.06		—
50	404	6.35		0.1418
100	340	1.08		0.1408
150	− 26	0.25	0.02	0.1402
200	− 88	0.08	0.67	0.1400
300	−139	0	1.74	0.1394
500	−170	0	3.60	0.1387
750	−152	0	5.29	0.1377
1,000	−144	0	6.15	0.1380
1,500	−129	0	7.34	0.1378
1,750				0.1378
2,000				0.1361

The prerequisite for H_2S charged water, therefore, is a well oxygenated surface water layer, populated with abundant organisms. Any iron in this surface water, which would be present as iron hydroxides rather than in solution, forms sulfides from hydrogen sulfide, directly as FeS_2. Pyrrhotite also occurs in sediments, but only as a rarity. Such muds formed by the influence of decomposing organic substances are called sapropels (gr. sapros, rotting). In the Black Sea sediments contain up to 2.5% FeS_2. POMPECKJ compared the Black Sea with the sea of the Posidonia shales in the Lias Epsilon of Germany; later also the sea from which the lower Zechstein (Permian) Kupferschiefer was deposited. It contains in places up to 3.6% copper, 4.1% zinc, 2.6% lead, and 0.9% silver. These elements are combined in sulfides. According to recent investigations of WEDEPOHL these same sulfides must be precipitating out by bacterial H_2S production in normal sea water today (see Table 63, p. 290), but in such small amounts, that even a current mechanism which would supply fresh water from time to time is insufficient to explain the high contents in sediments. A supplementary supply from the continents must be considered. It could be shown that in the Rotliegenden (lower Permian) terrestrial sediments surrounding the Kupferschiefer Sea, enrichment of these metals had already taken place under high Eh conditions. Upon changing to a lower Eh they could be mobilized. These sediments contain also up to 0.5% V, 0.03% Cr, 0.12% Ni, 0.04% Co, and 0.15% Mo all of which can be correlated with the carbon content. This suggests that these metals are bound to the organic constituents of the sediment.

Sulfide muds always contain, in addition to clay constituents, such an amount of organic matter as to suggest that an excess is present over that necessary to produce hydrogen sulfide. It is very difficult to advance a mechanism to produce in an ocean basin the pure sulfide deposits such as those illustrated in the Rammelsberg ore deposits at Goslar in the Harz Mountains. It is necessary to propose direct outpouring over a very restricted area of heavy metal bearing waters of relatively high concentration, for example, from volcanic exhalations. Then one would have a sort of mixed volcanic-sedimentary deposit. Measurements of the stable sulfur isotopes make it likely that, in addition to the H_2S supply, anaerobic bacteria were also active.

Sulfide bearing sediments can form also beneath oxygenated bottom waters if the hydrogen sulfide forms within the sediment. In contrast to water, this H_2S is virtually fixed. Oxygen can be introduced only very slowly either by flowing into the pores in the sediment or by diffusion. If within a sediment the rate of burial is greater than the rate of oxidation of the organic constituents, oxygen consumption and H_2S production occur. Thus in the blue muds distributed widely over the present ocean bottoms, the upper centimeter is usually oxidized and colored brown, the layers beneath containing FeS_2 and colored dark gray by organic matter. Argillaceous, organic rich sediments are probably the source rocks for petroleum. The organic constituents change as the sediment undergoes an increase in temperature and pressure and organic phases migrate into adjacent porous rocks (reservoir rocks).

Sedimentary Manganese Deposits. Considerably less is known about the origin of manganese than about sedimentary iron ore deposits. Manganese, like iron, forms divalent and higher valence ions. Divalent manganese occurs in sediments as the carbonate, and as a minor component in solid solution in calcite and dolomite. Trivalent manganese occurs occasionally as *manganite*, $MnO(OH)$. It has a lower symmetry than goethite, $FeO(OH)$, but has similar lattice constants. *Hausmannite*, Mn_3O_4, is a rarer manganese mineral with a spinel-like structure.

The tetravalent manganese oxide, MnO_2, occurs in a variety of forms. A well crystallized form, which possesses a tetragonal lattice similar to rutile, is called polianite. Pyrolusite, βMnO_2, forms as very fine grained, pseudomorphs after $MnO(OH)$. Structurally defective pyrolusite with composition ranging from $MnO_{1.7}MnO_2$ is used commercially in batteries. Psilomelane is a collective mineralogical term for manganese ores of the general composition (Ba, H_2O) Mn_5O_{10} Cryptomelane, $K_{\leq 2}Mn_8O_{16}$ has the α-MnO_2 structure and usually contains potassium. The silicate braunite, $Mn^{2+}Mn_6^{3+}|O_8|[SiO_4]$, occurs also in sedimentary rocks.

Manganese compounds are more readily soluble than the corresponding iron compounds. Under natural Eh and pH conditions, Fe^{2+} is more easily oxidized than Mn^{2+}. Thus, during sedimentation manganese and iron can be separated quite effectively. This situation is an important factor in ore deposition in the sea, as well as in terrestrial deposits. Thus manganese concentrations, always containing some iron, are found in deep sea sediments in the form of irregular nodules, locally in such great concentration that consideration is being given to their exploitation as ore. The manganese is derived perhaps in part from dissolved foraminifera shells, which can contain up to 0.02% MnO, but probably primarily from the submarine weathering of volcanic material.

Manganese is biologically an important element, being necessary for photosynthesis. Plants can contain manganese of the order of 0.1 g/kg of dried material.

4. Phosphate Deposits

Phosphorus is an element of especially great biologic importance. Along with nitrogen, it is one of those elements which regulate the productivity of organisms on the land and in the sea. Accordingly the phosphorus content of sea water varies between 1 and 60 mg P per ton, depending on the population of organisms. The source of phosphorus is the weathering of apatite in igneous rock, which brings it into solution, making it available to plants. The average value for the phosphorus content of organic substances can be taken as about 0.6% P in dried material. Animals pick up phosphorus by ingesting plants and, as is well-known, vertebrates concentrate it in their skeletons. Here the phosphorus content may vary up to about 14.7% P. It is present usually as a phosphate with the apatite structure, in which (OH) has replaced the fluorine or chlorine (hydroxy apatite). Human beings ingest about 2.6 g P per day. The concentration and accumulation of phosphorus in the bones of animals is an important source of phosphorus. Fossil fecal deposits (*coprolites*) occasionally accumulate in sediments. *Guano* forms as a result of reaction between limestone and fluid bird excrement. The phosphorus content of sedimentary iron deposits is due in part to the precipitation of phosphate with iron hydroxide, and partly to the incorporation of organic substances, especially skeletal remains. Invertebrates can also contain significant amounts of phosphorus, as Table 56 indicates.

Table 56. *Phosphorous content in skeletal parts of invertebrates; in %*

Foraminifera	0—trace	Annelids	
Siliceous sponges	0	Serpula	trace
Calcareous sponges	0.34	Hyalinoecia	9.05
Corals		Onuphis	9.43
Madreporida	0.0—trace	Bryozoa	trace—0.26
Alcyonaria	trace—1.30	Brachiopods	
Echinoderms		with calc. shells	trace—0.11
Crinoids	trace—0.19	with chitinous shells,	
Echinoids	trace—0.28	lingula	14.94—18.34
Star fish	trace—0.11	Pelecypods	trace—0.07
Brittle stars	trace—0.14	Gastropods	trace—0.17
Holothuria	trace—1.38	Cephalopods	trace
		Crustaceans	
		Balanids	0.0—0.15
		Crabs	0.82—3.39
		Calcareous algae	0.0—0.08

Reworking and redeposition of sedimentary phosphate gives rise to deposits which have been given numerous names. Usually they are grouped together as *phosphorites*. The phosphate component has the apatite structure, with substituted F, Cl, OH, and $CO_3^=$ ions. According to the available solubility data, this phosphate should precipitate directly from sea water at a pH < 8.

5. Siliceous Rocks

Silica also has a geochemical cycle dependent to a considerable extent on organic processes. Rivers flowing into the sea today carry SiO_2 in true solution. Their SiO_2 content (see Table 58, p. 282) is appreciably less than the solubility of amorphous SiO_2 (see Fig. 331). Sea water is undersaturated therefore in SiO_2. As a result no direct precipitation or crystallization can take place. Some silica can find its way into a sediment by adsorption, but by far the greater portion is abstracted from sea water by organisms which use it to form shells or skeletal material. In this form it is precipitated as opal. The most important of such organisms are the siliceous algae, the diatoms. In fresh water environments diatoms also extract silica from waters and soil solutions to form shells. Fresh water lake deposits of diatom shells are called *Kieselgur* or diatomaceous earth. In the ocean their development is restricted mainly to the nutrient rich waters of the higher latitudes. Here diatomaceous muds are widely distributed as deep sea sediments. In the lower, warmer latitudes *radiolaria* and *silico flagellates* take over as siliceous organisms. All three groups are planktonic, settling to the sea floor after death.

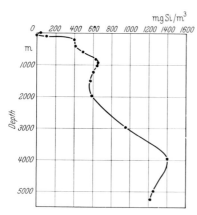

Fig. 355. Vertical distribution of dissolved silica in the west African coastal region. (After WATTENBERG from BARTH-CORRENS-ESKOLA)

Enroute to the sea bottom some silica is dissolved. This is evident in Fig. 355 which shows the distribution of dissolved silica in sea water. We must presume also that in sediments, especially those rich in organic matter and with high pH, the siliceous shells are dissolved further. It is no surprise, therefore, that in the geologic record, the delicate diatom shells are preserved only rarely, whereas the more robust and coarser radiolaria often are preserved beautifully in Silurian and Kulm (Carboniferous) sediments. An example is the *radiolarite* shown in Fig. 356. It is erroneous to deduce that such sediments must be deep sea deposits, simply because they consist only of robust shells. This indicates only that the more delicate shells have been dissolved and implies nothing about whether the solution resulted during settling to depth or occurred subsequently in the sediment. The silica content of sediments frequently can stem from diatom and other siliceous shells, even when they are no longer in evidence, as a result of subsequent redistribution of silica within the sediment. In Table 57 some data for bottom samples of the Meteor expedition are given. These indicate that in still unaltered calcareous as well as argillaceous sediments, considerable amounts of organogenic silica can be admixed. During the course of diagenesis segregation of carbonate and silica may take place. It is common to find nodules of SiO_2 in limestone. These are usually referred to as chert nodules. SiO_2 can migrate in clays also, forming siliceous nodules.

Fig. 356. Etched radiolarite, Kulm. (From SCHWARZ, Naturmuseum Senckenberg-Archive No. 2033, from BARTH-CORRENS-ESKOLA)

Table 57. *Composition of siliceous organism-rich deep sea sediments from the Meteor expedition*

Station No.	Ocean depth in m	Depth in core in cm	Siliceous organisms %	$CaCO_3$ %	Clay and remainder %	Age
242 u	5,156	68.5—70	61.4	4.1	34.5	glacial
238 u	2,787	78.5—80	31.4	17.7	50.9	glacial
247 o	5,171	0—2.5	29.3	20.5	50.2	recent
228 o	2,822	0—1.5	24.0	5.4	70.6	recent
225 u	5,164	44—45	17.2	57.2	25.6	glacial
230 o	5,024	0—2	16.1	1.1	82.8	recent
241 u	4,075	89.5—91	14.9	74.4	10.7	?
233 o	5,010	52.5—54	13.7	14.6	69.7	glacial
247 u	5,171	30.5—32	13.3	46.3	40.4	glacial ?

On the sea floor, sessile or attached animals, such as *siliceous sponges*, can supply considerable amounts of silica to the sediment. Siliceous sponges are undoubtedly the source of supply of silica of the flints so widely distributed in the upper Kreide (Cretaceous). Thus we can keep in mind that not only could the sponges have been dissolved on the sea floor, but the silica must have migrated in fresh sediment and, in addition, migration and reprecipitation occurred later, for example, after the formation of fissures in the chalk.

Bedded siliceous rocks are sometimes called *lydian stone*; the individual bands *chert*. *Nodular* siliceous accumulations, essentially of diagenetic origin (p. 306), are called *hornstones*, or when found in chalk, *flint*.

6. Evaporite Deposits

The Source of Ions. We will consider now those chemical constituents which go into solution during weathering and are carried ultimately in solution into the ocean. We are concerned first of all with the alkali cations, which form no insoluble compounds at the earth's surface, and with the alkaline earths' whose salts, including carbonates, are fairly insoluble. As we have already seen, in the presence of carbon dioxide, they can be transported easily in solution. The important anions are carbonate (CO_3^-) and bicarbonate (HCO_3^-), sulfate (SO_4^-) and chloride (Cl^-). Table 58 permits a comparison of the composition of river

Table 58. *Comparison of river and sea water compositions in g/T water. The corr. values obtained by substracting salts washed in by rain.* (Essentially after CONWAY, 1942)

	River water from igneous terrain		River water from sediment terrain		Aver. comp. river water		Sea water
	ob-served	corr.	ob-served	corr.	ob-served	corr.	
Ca	6.8	5.8	37.5	37.5	29.8	29.6	410
Na	4.9	2.8	9.6	4.1	8.4	3.8	10,470
Mg	1.2	0.9	6.3	5.6	5.0	4.4	1,280
K	1.9	1.6	3.5	3.3	3.1	2.9	380
CO_3	15.5	15.5	63.1	63.1	51.2	51.2	138
SO_4	4.8	0.5	22.0	22.0	17.7	16.6	2,650
Cl	3.2	0.2	10.1	0.0	8.3	0.0	18,970
SiO_2	10.3	10.3	19.4	19.4	17.1	17.1	6
other constituents	1.4	1.4	7.1	7.1	5.7	5.7	92
total salinity	50	39	179	162	146	131	34,396

water with the composition of igneous rocks given in Table 42. Such a comparison indicates that the cations, but not the anions, are derived from the igneous rocks. The table shows very clearly that SiO_2, Al_2O_3 and Fe_2O_3 are transported in very small amounts as ions. These oxides combine to form weathering products and contribute very little as ions in river water. The alkali and alkaline earth content of river water varies considerably, especially in the case of Ca. This is the consequence of the fact that about 75% of the earth's surface is covered with sedimentary and only 25% by igneous rocks. If limestone is quantitatively a more important member of the sedimentary cover in a particular area, because of its relatively high solubility it is reflected in the local composition of river water. Such factors are not adequate, however, to account for the observed variations in anion contents. The anion excess in river water is due to their having been derived from volatile constituents from magmas. A significant part of the Cl^- in river water stems from sea water. Fine droplets produced by ocean waves are distributed by wind over the continents and washed by rain into the streams. These "cyclic salts" have been subtracted from the values for river water as reflected in the corrected values in Table 58 (after the calculations of Conway). CO_2 is produced also by the respiration processes of animals and plants, and is utilized further by green plants. NO_3^- is of organic origin.

Terrestrial Evaporite Formation. If a river flows into a collecting basin on land which has no outlets to the sea, and evaporation takes place, dissolved salts precipitate out. Depending on the drainage basin, carbonate, sulfate, and chloride deposits may form. Table 59 gives a few analyses from some of the quite varied continental evaporite deposits. In addition to *soda* ($Na_2CO_3 \cdot 10H_2O$), the mineral *trona* ($Na_2CO_3 \cdot NaHCO_3 \cdot 2H_2O$) occurs as an important carbonate. *Glauber salts* ($Na_2SO_4 \cdot 10H_2O$) and *thenardite* (Na_2SO_4) are found as common sulfates. As borates are the minerals *borax* ($Na_2B_4O_7 \cdot 10H_2O$) (the most important commercial source of boron) and *kernite* ($Na_2B_4O_7 \cdot 4H_2O$). In addition to differences due to source area, climatic differences can lead to varied salt deposition in continental deposits. Carbonates can be precipitated out at lower temperatures, sulfates only at higher temperature, and the deposition of the very soluble chlorides takes place at the highest temperature.

Table 59. *Some continental evaporite deposits* (After CLARKE)

	1	2	3	4	5	6
Na	39.15	31.16	15.27	31.03	34.71	36.26
K	0.62	12.98				0.73
Mg			9.75	0.07	1.50	
Ca			1.31	0.16		
CO_3	41.15	38.08		0.16		5.13
SO_4	11.83	11.98	72.96	64.84	4.66	18.29
Cl	2.10	6.41	0.45	0.17	54.47	36.65
B_4O_7	3.2					0.77
SiO_2	1.96					2.18
Fe_2O_3				0.11		
H_2O					4.66	
residue				3.46		

1 North arm, Old Walker Lake, Nevada.
2 Alkali crust, Westminster, Orange, California.
3 Perth Lake, Nevada.
4 From bottom of Altai Lake, Siberia.
5 Salt Lake, 7 miles east of Zandia Mtns., New Mexico.
6 5 miles west of Black Rock, Nevada.

Salt Content of Sea Water. While the composition of continental evaporites is very strongly dependent on local conditions, ocean water has a very uniform composition. The total salinity varies somewhat; surface waters in the tropics have salinity of 3.8%, in the Arctic 3.4%, and in the western Baltic, 1.5%. Nevertheless the individual ion ratios remain very constant. The main constituents of sea water are summarized in Table 60.

Table 60. *Main constituents of sea water at $35^0/_{00}$ salinity*

Cations	g/kg	Anions	g/kg
Sodium	10.75	Chlorine	19.345
Potassium	0.39	Bromine	0.065
Magnesium	1.295	SO_4	2.701
Calcium	0.416	HCO_3	0.145
Strontium	0.008	BO_3	0.027

Mineralogy of Marine Evaporites. If an arm of the ocean is cut off and isolated, evaporation leads to the formation of salt deposits. The German deposits of Zechstein (Permian) age have been thoroughly and well-studied. As a result of evaporation, calcium carbonate is first to crystallize out of sea water. We have mentioned that the warm surface water of the tropics is even supersaturated with calcium carbonate. It is still uncertain to what extent primary dolomite precipitation takes place. Quantitatively the inorganic precipitation of carbonates does not amount to much. From a body of sea water 3,000 m deep, a layer of calcite only 16 cm thick would form. Following the carbonates is the precipitation of sulfate and chloride salts. Some of the salts precipitated from sea water are indicated in Table 61, the most common salts being emphasized in italics.

The System CaSO$_4$—H$_2$O. In order to understand the conditions of formation of these salts, we shall recall first the processes by which crystallization of a salt from its solution takes place. We will illustrate again the two component system CaSO$_4$—H$_2$O, concerning ourselves only with very low concentrations of CaSO$_4$,

Table 61. *Some evaporite minerals*

Name	Formula	Symbol
Chlorides		
Halite	NaCl	n
Sylvite	KCl	sy
Bischofite	MgCl$_2$ · 6 H$_2$O	bi
Carnallite	KMgCl$_3$ · 6 H$_2$O	c
Sulfates		
Anhydrite	CaSO$_4$	
Gypsum	CaSO$_4$ · 2 H$_2$O	
Kieserite	MgSO$_4$ · H$_2$O	ks
Leonhardtite	MgSO$_4$ · 4 H$_2$O	lh
Pentahydrite	MgSO$_4$ · 5 H$_2$O	5h
Hexahydrite	MgSO$_4$ · 6 H$_2$O	hx
Epsomite	MgSO$_4$ · 7 H$_2$O	e
Polyhalite	Ca$_2$K$_2$Mg(SO$_4$)$_4$ · 2 H$_2$O	
Bloedite	Na$_2$Mg(SO$_4$)$_2$ · 4 H$_2$O	bl
Loewite	3[Na$_{12}$Mg$_7$(SO$_4$)$_{13}$] · 15 H$_2$O	lö
Vanthoffite	Na$_6$Mg(SO$_4$)$_4$	vh
Leonite	K$_2$Mg(SO$_4$)$_2$ · 4 H$_2$O	le
Langbeinite	K$_2$Mg$_2$(SO$_4$)$_3$	lg
Chloride-sulfate		
Kainite	K$_4$Mg$_4$Cl$_4$(SO$_4$)$_4$ · 11 H$_2$O	k

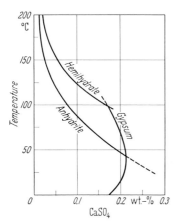

Fig. 357. System CaSO$_4$—H$_2$O. (After Posnjak)

since behavior at high temperature is of no concern to us here. Likewise we are not interested in behavior below 0°C. The system CaSO$_4$—H$_2$O is important to us because these sulfates precipitate out of sea water following the alkaline earth carbonates. In Fig. 357 the solubility relations are illustrated. Along the abscissa the equilibrium concentration of CaSO$_4$ in water is plotted; along the ordinate, temperature. At low temperatures we have *gypsum*, CaSO$_4$ · 2 H$_2$O, as a precipitate. The solubility curves for anhydrite and gypsum intersect at 42°C. Above this temperature *anhydrite* is the stable precipitate. However, no anhydrite is precipitated above 42° from aqueous solution. Instead gypsum forms metastably up to 97°C. Above this temperature it then transforms to the hemi-hydrate, CaSO$_4$ · $^1/_2$ H$_2$O, which is called *bassanite* when it occurs naturally. The hemi-hydrate is called also plaster of Paris, when gypsum is carefully dehydrated by heating to 120—130°C. Plaster of Paris very easily takes up water again to form gypsum during the setting process. Likewise when sea water is artifically evaporated in salt pans, gypsum always forms.

In the German evaporite deposits thick anhydrite beds are found overlying the carbonates. Probably these formed from gypsum after deposition under the influence of high temperatures, higher pressures and circulating salt solutions. In support of this supposition are the textural relationships and the occurrence of pseudomorphs of anhydrite after gypsum. In outcrops at the surface the anhydrite is completely or partially changed to gypsum again by the influence of surface water.

Two Salts in Aqueous Solution. If we now consider two salts in aqueous solution, we can conceive of three types of situations. If the two salts have a common ion, the solubilities are mutually diminished, if no intermediate compound can form. Fig. 358 illustrates, by means of a three dimensional diagram,

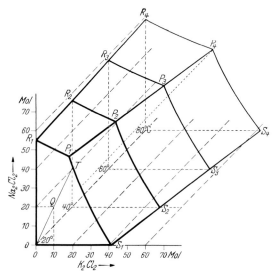

Fig. 358. Saturation diagram NaCl—KCl in water from 20° to 80°C; moles salt in 1,000 moles water. (After D'Ans from Barth-Correns-Eskola)

the dependence of the mutual solubility of KCl and NaCl on temperature. Moles of K_2Cl_2 in 1,000 moles of H_2O are plotted from left to right, moles of Na_2Cl_2 from bottom to top, and the temperature range 20°—80°C from front to back in the diagram. The basal surface gives by means of curve S_1—S_4 the solubility of KCl in water, curve R_1—R_4 gives that of NaCl. As we can see, the solubility of NaCl is changed very little with temperature, that of KCl much more significantly. Surface S_1P_1—S_4P_4 indicates how much KCl and NaCl can be in solution with KCl as precipitate; surface R_1P_1—R_4P_4 represents the same for NaCl as precipitate. A solution is in equilibrium with precipitated NaCl as well as KCl along the line of intersection of both planes, corresponding to line P_1—P_4. If a solution of composition Q (10 moles K_2Cl_2, 20 moles Na_2Cl_2 in 1,000 moles H_2O at 20°C) is evaporated it will cut the curve P_1S_1 at point T. Concentration beyond this point, as a result of evaporation, will precipitate out KCl, the solution will become less concentrated in KCl until concentration P_1 is reached, and then NaCl will precipitate out as well. A KCl and NaCl saturated solution (P_4) will precipitate out KCl alone, by cooling along the indicated dotted line. In this way the two salts can be separated from each other.

The second type of situation involves two salts with common ions and which form a compound. An example is $MgCl_2$ and KCl which form *carnallite*,

$MgCl_2 \cdot KCl \cdot 6H_2O$ (named after a mining superintendent, v. CARNALL). Fig. 359 illustrates a schematic section at 25°C through a three dimensional diagram for $MgCl_2$—KCl analogous to Fig. 358. Again we shall consider an unsaturated solution (point Q) and allow it to evaporate. At point T, KCl precipitates out and continues until at point C the double salt precipitates. Now KCl and carnallite are in equilibrium. In the solution there is, however, still too much $MgCl_2$, which reacts with the precipitated KCl to form carnallite, until the solution has the composition of point B. Now $MgCl_2 \cdot 6H_2O$ (*bischofite*) and carnallite are in equilibrium and coprecipitate.

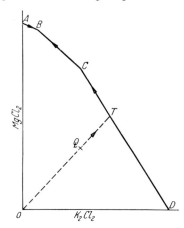

Fig. 359. Saturation in system $MgCl_2$—KCl, schematic. (From BARTH-CORRENS-ESKOLA)

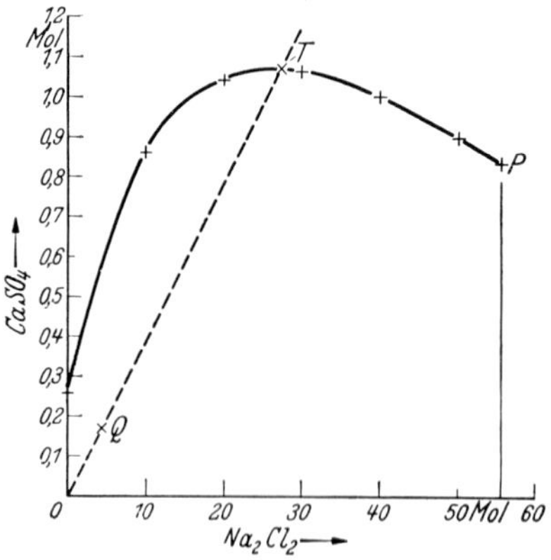

Fig. 360. Saturation diagram, NaCl—CaSO$_4$ at 25°C; Moles salt in 1,000 moles water. (After D'ANS from BARTH-CORRENS-ESKOLA)

The third case is one in which the two salts have no common ions. Then the solubilities are mutually increased. The solubility of $CaSO_4$ in water is greatly increased by the addition of NaCl (Fig. 360); the solubility of NaCl is less affected by $CaSO_4$. By evaporating a solution with a composition Q, gypsum precipitates first until point P is reached, and only then does NaCl begin to precipitate. This increase in solubility can be utilized in effecting the solution of gypsum and anhydrite rocks.

The Order of Crystallization from Sea Water. When sea water evaporates, calcium carbonate and perhaps also dolomite precipitate first as the most insoluble components. Only when 70% of the sea water has evaporated, does gypsum begin to precipitate; by 89.1% halite, and only when 99.2% evaporated, does carnallite come out. Here we cannot consider in detail the many possibilities of evaporite deposition. It is the great contribution of the physical chemist VAN'T HOFF to have clarified considerably the solubility relations of these salts. In the following we shall look briefly at the formation of potassium salts and assume that calcium carbonate, gypsum, halite, and also polyhalite have already precipitated. This precipitation does not result in well-developed separate layers. More often layers containing predominately anhydrite are interstratified with layers rich in rock salt.

Table 62 from O. BRAITSCH summarizes the theoretical crystallization sequence, under different conditions and based on 100 m of rock salt, that would result in the previously not detailed precipitation sequence A. The small numerals specify the salts listed in Table 61. After A, follows the series B, during which epsomite (e) and bloedite (bl) are precipitated in addition to halite. During series C we meet, depending on the conditions, sylvite (sy), kainite (k), and leonite (le), along with halite and epsonite, etc. In deriving this table it is assumed in the three left hand columns, that stable equilibrium prevailed at 15°, 25°, and 35°C. The two right hand columns indicate crystallization with metastable equilibrium at 15° and 25°C.

Table 62. *Theoretical primary crystallization from normal sea water by static evaporation without reaction at the transformation points (from* BRAITSCH). *Thickness based on a 100 m rock salt layer A. Composition in weight %. Mineral notation taken from Table 61*

Layer	Stable equilibrium			Metastable equilibrium	
	15° C	25° C	35° C	15° C	25° C
B_1	20 m	6.3 m 33 n 67 e 72 n 28 bl	8.7 m 74 n 26 bl	20 m 33 n 67 e	6.3 m 72 n 28 bl
B_2		4.5 m 20 n 80 e			5.8 m 24 n 76 e
C_1	3.4 m 32 n 52 e 16 sy	6.3 m 29 n 30 e 41 k	8.5 m 11 n 89 k	8.2 m 30 n 53 e 17 sy	4.5 m 33 n 47 e 20 le
C_2	5 m 33 n 67 k	5.7 m 21 n 3 hx 76 k	3.2 m 14 n 1 k 85 ks		3.0 m 22 n 58 e 20 sy
C_3		1.7 m 11 n 4 ks 85 k			
D_1	2.9 m 21 n 79 c	3.6 m 12 n 40 ks 48 c	4.5 m 12 n 29 ks 59 c	10.3 m 17 n 23 e 60 c	0.65 m 7 n 38 e 55 c
D_2	3.3 m 10 n 29 e 61 c			0.5 m 18 n 39 hx 43 c	14.5 m 7 n 35 hx 58 c
D_3	3.1 m 18 n 30 ks 52 c			0.8 m 17 n 37 5H 46 c	1.95 m 9 n 53.5 h 38 c
D_4				0.4 m 24 n 32 lh 44 c	1.3 m 9 n 62 lh 29 c
E	33.5 m 0.5 n 1 ks 2.5 c 96 bi	38 m 0.5 n 1 ks 0.5 c 98 bi	39 m 0.5 n 0.25 ks 0.25 c 99 bi	34.2 m 0.5 n 4.5 lh 3 c 92 bi	34 m 0.5 n 5 lh 0.5 c 94 bi

How does a typical salt sequence appear in nature? In Fig. 361 an example is illustrated. The profile begins on the right at 0 meters. A comparison with Table 62 shows that the correspondence between theory and observation is quite poor, even when we quite ignore the sequence left of 150 m, where a fault occurs. The evaporite sequence was calculated also for higher temperatures up to 83°C and somewhat better correspondence was achieved, but we cannot accept such high temperatures. The highest marine water temperature recorded was 36°C in the Persian Gulf. From the kieserite-carnallite relations one can conclude that temperatures around 40°C prevailed in the case described.

How do we account for the discrepancy between the laboratory experiment and nature? The composition of sea water could have been different. It appears

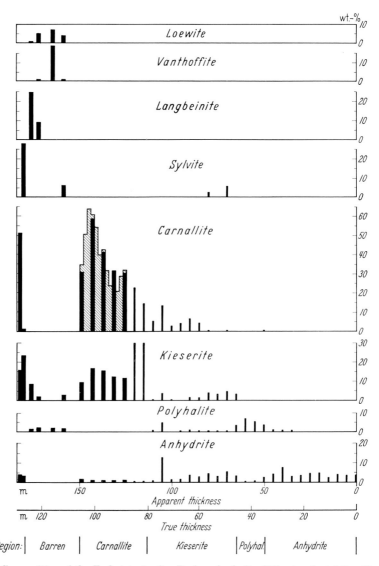

Fig. 361. Composition of the Zechstein 2 salts, Berlepsch shaft of Neustassfurt (after RIEDEL, 1912). Cross hatched carnallite content after BOEKE (1908). NaCl = remainder to 100%, not shown, nor are impurities. A fault occurs at 150 m. Rocks to the right of it are primary, to the left altered by solution metamorphism. (From BRAITSCH)

certain that in a portion of the Zechstein Sea a depletion of $MgSO_4$ occurred. It is possible to calculate also the crystallization sequence from such sea water. When this is done somewhat better agreement results between observed and theoretical evaporite crystallization. Another important reason for the observed discrepencies is metamorphism. The crystallized salts react at only moderate temperatures, as will be shown later.

Even after the effects of metamorphism are taken into account and all the observed salts explained with qualitative agreement, there always remain very significant quantitative discrepancies. For example, much more anhydrite has been formed proportionally than sea water should yield. On the other hand kieserite and carnallite are less abundant than predicted and bishofite is completely absent. This is the last salt to precipitate out and evidently is not often formed in evaporites. The great thickness of anhydrite indicates that during the initial evaporation fresh sea water was introduced repeatedly, and so this dilution must be taken into account. The effect is to lead to anomalously thin deposits of salts precipitating from the later concentrated solutions.

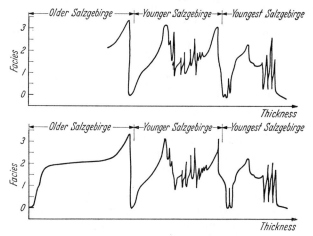

Fig. 362. Schematic picture of the salt seams in Hansa-Silberberg (above) and Bergmanns-segen (below) (after Lotze from Barth-Correns-Eskola). On the horizontal axis the sequence of deposition is indicated, on the vertical, the kind of deposition: *0* signifies non-saline sediment; *1* anhydrite; *2* halite; *3* potassium salts

In support of this is the cyclic nature of the evaporite sequence. This can only happen through the influx of new sea water. This rhythmic salt deposition is very beautifully displayed in the two profiles shown in Fig. 362.

7. Rare Elements in Biogenic and Chemical Sediments

We have followed until now in sedimentation only a few especially common elements. We want now to take note of the rarer elements. Their abundance in sea water is indicated in Table 63.

Similar to what we had observed in igneous rocks, we find here also relatively high values for some elements usually considered rare, and very low values for some more familiar ones. We can comment on only a few of these.

Bromine is enriched so strongly in sea water (Table 60) that it is produced from it in the United States. During the formation of evaporites, Br is isomorphously incorporated into the chloride phases. Its behavior during crystallization of salt solutions was studied by Boeke before 1908, and in the last 25 years has become a much used indicator for genetic and stratigraphic purposes. In other sediments the bromine content depends on the origin and fate of organic matter. Algae contain up to 0.12% and the coral genus *Gorgonidae* up to 0.26% Br in the dried state.

Iodine is enriched in organisms. Laminaria algae can contain up to 1.7% I based on dry weight. At one time iodine was extracted from such algae. In eva-

Table 63. *Content of minor constituents in sea water in milligrams/ton*

Sr	8,000	Mn	3—5	La	0.3
B	4,800	Zr	4	Ag	0.3
Si	3,000	U	3	Ne	0.3
F	1,300	As	3	Sn	0.18
N	300	V	2	Cd	0.11
Li	180	Cu	1—2	W	0.1
Rb	120	Al	1	Se	0.1
P	70	Ti	1	Ge	<0.1
I	30	Th	0.7	Cr	0.05
Mo	13	Cs	0.6	He	0.05
Ba	13	Co	0.5—0.04	Sc	0.04
Zn	10	Sb	0.5	Hg	0.03
Fe	6—7	Ce	0.4	Tl	<0.01
Ni	5	Y	0.3	Au	0.009

porites it occurs in anhydrite and polyhalite in *liniensalz*, an interstratification of anhydrite and halite, and is present in salt clays (up to 20 mg/t). The circulation of iodine at the earth's surface has been studied especially well because of its medical importance. It is enriched in the upper layers of the soil (600 to 8,000 g/t). Rain water contains 0.2—5 mg/t, river water about the same amount. Through rain water, iodine is introduced into the saltpeter deposits on the coast of Chile, where it is oxidized to iodate and removed from atmospheric circulation.

Fluorine occurs in sediments combined either in micas or in phosphates.

Boron like bromine is enriched in sea water (Table 60), and associated with the micas in argillaceous rocks. The boron silicate tourmaline plays only a very minor role. Several boron minerals occur in evaporite deposits. The most common of these is boracite, $(Mg, Fe, Mn)_3 ClB_7O_{13}$.

Among the rare cations, *strontium* is by far the most abundant. In spite of this, separate strontium minerals are rare in marine sediments. This is because it is camouflaged by incorporation into calcium compounds. It has been determined that aragonite contains up to 4.7% SrO, calcite 0.14%, anhydrite 0.69%, and primary gypsum 0.33%. Recrystallization of carbonates and sulfates can liberate Sr and in the presence of $SO_4^=$ ions celestite can form.

Rubidium is incorporated into carnallite and to a lesser extent in sylvite evaporite deposits.

Of the remaining elements, *nitrogen* is of special interest. It is the main constituent of the atmosphere, comprising 78.08% of its volume. It probably evolved as a gaseous emanation very early in the history of the earth. As a result of bacterial activity and to a lesser extent of electrical discharges in the atmosphere, it is combined into nitrates and nitrites. Organisms utilize nitrogen primarily in the synthesis of protein. After death this protein decomposes. In the sea this breakdown proceeds approximately as follows: protein→amino acids→urea→ammonia→nitrite→nitrate. The nitrogen content of surface waters varies considerably, depending on biological conditions. In evaporites only ammonium ions are noted, comprising up to 16.9% g/t in carnallite. Evidently in the concentrated brine, oxygen is insufficient to oxidize the ammonia further.

On land nitrate occurs in many places in small amounts as *saltpeter*, $NaNO_3$. This is formed during the bacterial decomposition of organic matter. In the case of the very extensive Chilean nitrate deposits, numerous origins have been suggested, including derivation from volcanic exhalations, wind-blown sea water droplets, decomposition of nitrogenous organic matter, and even electrical discharges in the atmosphere. A fully satisfactory explanation has not been offered as yet.

8. Structures and Textures of Biogenic and Chemical Sediments

These chemically and chemical-biogenically deposited rocks are usually bedded like the clastic rocks. Here also the bedding is due to changes in sedimentation conditions. In evaporite deposits "annual rings", thin anhydrite laminae interspersed in rock salt, occur which result probably from periodic influx of and deposition from sea water. In a similar manner inorganic limestone laminae can form in shale beds. In the case of biological sediments, variations can result from changes in the living conditions of organisms, for example, climatic changes. Thus clastic and calcereous or siliceous deposits can follow one another. Organogenic depositional structures can form from encrustations of lime-forming organisms, especially algae. We have already mentioned the formation of calcareous and iron hydroxide ooids. Macroscopically the true ooids are very similar in appearance and origin to the pseudo-ooids. The latter are recognizable by revealing small rock fragments, usually coated with thin crusts. In addition to calcite, aragonite, dolomite, siderite, barite, phosphorite, opal, and chalcedony have been described as forming ooids. Ooid-like forms certainly can form also in muds as concretions, subsequent to sedimentation. This brings us finally to the oft-mentioned transformation of rocks, that is, to metamorphism (gr. meta, over again; morphe, form).

IX. Metamorphic Petrogenesis

1. Types of Metamorphism

We include under metamorphism all those changes which affect a rock through reactions which preserve solid phases at least partially. We exclude weathering processes on the one hand and complete remelting on the other. Such transformations can occur through changes in temperature and pressure alone. Load pressure, resulting from the superposition of later-formed rocks, is sufficient to accomplish metamorphism. Under normal conditions in the upper layers of the earth a geothermal gradient of about 3° per 100 meters exists along with a hydrostatic ("lithostatic") pressure of about 27 kg/cm². Rock transformations under such $P-T$ conditions result in *load metamorphism* or *subsidence metamorphism*.

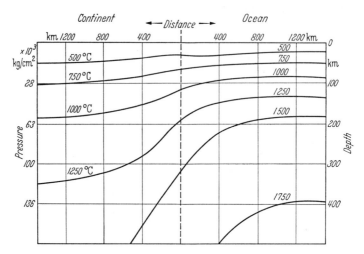

Fig. 363. Temperature and pressure distribution in the earth to a depth of 500 km. (After MacDonald, 1964)

The geothermal gradient varies from place to place and in addition decreases in general with increasing depth. It is steeper beneath the continents than beneath the ocean basins. Thus, theoretically it is possible to propose different geothermal gradients, depending on assumptions relative to the earth's thermal history and internal composition. Fig. 363 shows the temperature distribution proposed by MacDonald (1964), which was calculated, based on a uranium content (heat producing element) of $3.3 \cdot 10^{-6}\%$ for the earth's mantle. Pressure distribution beneath the continents, according to Bullen, is given on the left of Fig. 363.

Locally in the vicinity of magma bodies, the temperature gradient rises significantly. If this results in localized temperature effects on rocks, we speak of *contact metamorphism*. Under these conditions, therefore, we have a steep temperature gradient and relatively low load pressure. Extensive rock transformations over wide areas give rise to *regional metamorphism*. In this case low temperature gradients and high load pressures are characteristic. Subsidence to great depths is frequently coupled with mountain building (tectonic) processes. During tectonism characteristic rock fabrics develop and the rocks may be plastically deformed. Therefore, deformed rocks, earlier called *crystalline schists* (Schiefer), usually result during regional metamorphism.

In order to describe the processes which produce metamorphism, we shall distinguish between changes which are linked with gross movements of solid material and those which are not. We begin with transformation processes devoid of rock movement, which are static and involve only *recrystallization*. If the original mineral phases persist, we speak of *isophase* recrystallization. If the original phases react to form new phases, this is *allophase* recrystallization. In both cases the chemical constituents remain the same. The change is *isochemical*. If material is introduced the change is called *allochemical*. We shall discuss first the processes of recrystallization, then *mechanical deformation* and finally their combined roles.

2. Chemical Processes in Metamorphism

a) Isochemical Metamorphism

Fundamentals

Diagenesis. The transformation of rocks begins in the case of sediments immediately after deposition. The consolidation of a loose calcareous mud into a solid limestone is one of those processes which does not differ basically from a metamorphic process. However, such a rock is not referred to in general usage as a metamorphic, but rather as a sedimentary rock. The processes involved, for example, in the consolidation of sediments or the formation of concretions, and for that matter all processes which do not require high temperature or pressure, are usually separated from metamorphic processes under the term *diagenesis*. It is difficult to draw a sharp boundary between diagenetic and metamorphic processes, because those minerals which might be diagnostic are exceptionally difficult to discover (see zeolite facies, p. 303). There is not much to be gained, however, by coining a new term, such as anchimetamorphism, which is sometimes used to define an intermediate stage. Rock transformations depend in addition not only on pressure and temperature, but also on the nature of the rock. For example, evaporites undergo significant change at very low temperatures. Since what matters to us here is to establish the determining factors in metamorphism, we shall deal with diagenesis and metamorphism together, in order to avoid repetition.

Isophase Recrystallization. We shall discuss in the following section those processes which lead to crystallization of rocks, and consider first a loose calcareous mud which is saturated with water. In such a mixture, first of all, the solubility is different for different constituents. Aragonite and Mg-rich calcite have a higher solubility than calcite. In addition there is a noticeable effect of grain size on solubility. If the pore solution is saturated with respect to very small particles, it is supersaturated for large ones. The large particles thus grow at the expense of the smaller ones.

When the small particles are used up, during recrystallization, further precipitation of calcium carbonate can take place with further filling in of the pore space. This can occur if the pore solution undergoes concentration changes. We have seen (p. 266) that a temperature increase or lowering of pressure leads to precipitation of calcium carbonate. Temperature decreases and pressure increases lead to its dissolution. Such changes can be induced by geologic factors such as elevation above the water level, subsidence to greater depth, and the opening up of joints and cracks, to mention only a few. As a result of dissolution, small carbonate particles disappear faster than large ones for purely geometric reasons. This process along with the greater solubility of very small particles leads to a general increase in grain size. This can be confirmed by observation, by noting that even in strongly recrystallized limestones, large fossil shells are preserved, whereas the smaller ones or smaller fragments have been dissolved.

As a result of these processes the loose sedimentary particles are compacted together. However, the amount of carbonate in solution is probably insufficient to change, for example, a calcareous mud with 50% pore volume into a dense limestone. This requires the influence of a third factor in recrystallization, *differential pressure*. A porous rock is compressed as a result of the superimposition of later deposited sediments. Numerous crystals or crystal aggregates are formed which support the fabric and the imposed load and thus are subjected to differential pressure from above. Other crystals will be surrounded hydrostatically by pore water and, therefore, subjected only to hydrostatic pressure. A crystal under differential excess pressure, that is to say, under *stress*, is more soluble. Therefore, those crystals not under stress must grow at the expense of the stressed ones. The same principle applies in the precipitation of minerals in cavities or vugs, where material is dissolved from the enclosing rock. This principle bears the name of the Göttingen physicist, RIEKE. The same formula applies here as to growth under differential pressure (see p. 244).

In the case of recrystallization of calcium carbonate, an example of isophase metamorphism, a solid rock forms gradually at low temperature and pressure from a loose material. With a further increase in temperature, as in the vicinity of a magmatic body, the grain size increase continues, with the formation of *marble* as a contact product. Marble owes its translucent warm tone to its coarse grained calcite texture.

Calcareous sandstones behave in similar fashion to pure carbonate chalk. In the case of pure quartz sandstone, secondary quartz will precipitate out forming oriented overgrowths around original sand grains. The resulting rock is a *quartzite*. In the case of the so-called Tertiary quartzites, the cementing silica has been supplied from external sources. If the silica, as in this case, precipitates out only as a groundmass or matrix, the process is called *silicification*. In other cases the SiO_2 can be derived by pressure solution. The argillaceous matrix of other sandstones is mostly not diagenetic in origin, but occurs as fine-grained material introduced mechanically during sedimentation. Under pressure of the overlying rocks, such sands can also develop a certain compactness, in much the same way as a pharmacist formulates pills by compaction.

In the organic siliceous sediments, colloidal chemical processes augment the dissolution and reprecipitation phenomena. The silica not only goes into true solution, but the water-deficient gel which constitutes the organic siliceous skeletons can be peptized, that is, converted to a sol. This happens especially in weakly alkaline solutions such as form by NH_3 formation during the breakdown of organic compounds in the absence of oxygen.

Allophase Recrystallization. We have until now considered only precipitation and dissolution processes. Increases in temperature and pressure can induce sedimentary precipitated minerals to react with one another also. Such allophase metamorphism is observed following very slight temperature rises in evaporite deposits.

As a model, which is suitable for lecture demonstrations, we shall use the reaction:

$$NaClO_3 + KCl \rightarrow NaCl + KClO_3.$$

In aqueous solution at room temperature (20°C) this reaction always proceeds to the right. It is clear that it proceeds in the direction of products of least solubility. The product of the solubility product constants on the left side is greater than on the right. This reaction can readily be followed microscopically by adding water to some small crystals of KCl and $NaClO_3$. The newly formed rhombohedron-like monoclinic crystals of $KClO_3$ can be recognized immediately by their birefringence.

Solubility relationships, and thus the reaction direction, are dependent upon temperature. Thus, such a reaction may proceed in one direction below a certain temperature and in the opposite direction above it. Thus, in the case of the following reaction,

2 kainite   +   carnallite $\xrightarrow{\;>76°\;}$ 2 kieserite   + 3 sylvite + solution
$$2(KCl \cdot MgSO_4) \cdot 2.75\,H_2O + KCl \cdot MgCl_2 \cdot 6\,H_2O \rightarrow 2(MgSO_4 \cdot H_2O) + 3\,KCl + MgCl_2 + 9.5\,H_2O$$

it proceeds to the right above 76°, to the left below this temperature. For a long time it has been assumed that in experimental work we can substitute a higher temperature to compensate for the long times involved in natural chemical reactions. Reactions such as those described above demonstrate that this notion is false.

The Wollastonite Phase Diagram. Silicates also can form at low temperatures. As examples we can cite the small albite and K-feldspar crystals found in limestones and marls, such as those of the Muschelkalk of central Germany. These two minerals can be distinguished from their higher temperature equivalents by their optical properties (optic angle). Usually, however, neoformation of silicates is brought about at much higher temperatures.

A series of reactions, of great importance in clarifying isochemical recrystallization of silicates, has been investigated experimentally in the last 20 years. This has been made possible by the production of apparatus capable of maintaining high temperatures and pressures. We shall consider an example, based on calculations by V. M. GOLDSCHMIDT in 1912, utilizing an approximate form of the Nernst heat law. This is the reaction:

calcite + quartz $\rightleftharpoons$ wollastonite + carbon dioxide
$$CaCO_3 + SiO_2 \;\rightleftharpoons\; CaSiO_3 \quad + CO_2$$

In spite of the apparent simplicity of this particular reaction, it serves to illustrate many things about such reactions.

Curve 1 of Fig. 364 is the equilibrium curve calculated by GOLDSCHMIDT in 1912. Curve 2 was determined experimentally by HARKER and TUTTLE in 1952. Curve 3, calculated from new thermodynamic data by DANIELSSON in 1956, lies about as far to the left of the experimental curve as GOLDSCHMIDT's curve is to the right. The three curves give a distinct impression of the extent of deviation between calculation and experiment.

What does such a curve (2) indicate to us? We remember from the phase rule that $P + F = B + 2$. In this system we have four phases. Three are solid, quartz, calcite and wollastonite; one is a gas, CO_2. We have three independent components: CaO, SiO_2 and CO_2, and, therefore, one degree of freedom. If we choose a temperature at which all four phases are in equilibrium, this fixes the pressure, and vice versa. The curve represents these fixed temperatures and pressures. Therefore, it is called a univariant curve. For all temperatures and pressures which are not dependent on one another, and which, therefore, do not lie on the curve, we have two degrees of freedom. The univariant curve thus separates two *divariant* fields, in which three phases are stable. On the left, at low temperatures and pressures, we always have quartz and calcite and in addition one of the other phases, wollastonite or CO_2. On the right we always have wollastonite and CO_2 and either quartz or calcite. Therefore, if we find quartz and calcite in a rock, $P-T$ conditions to the left of the univariant curve have prevailed. When we find wollastonite with quartz, or with calcite, the rock must have formed at temperatures and pressures to the right of the curve.

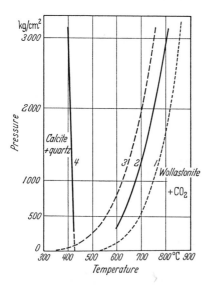

Fig. 364. Temperature-pressure curves for the wollastonite reaction

Our considerations up to now have assumed that the CO_2-pressure is equal to the total pressure in the system. This is also true of many other reactions investigated experimentally. Thus, curves $1-3$ of Fig. 364 apply only to closed systems. If, in an open system, all CO_2 can escape, conditions are then defined by curve 4, which was calculated by BARTH after the expanded *Clausius-Clapeyron* equation (see p. 191). Natural conditions are certainly intermediate between these two extremes. BARTH suggests that wollastonite formation takes place usually in a region somewhat to the right of curve 4. In addition, we must in many cases keep in mind that water is also present in the system. In these cases the $H_2O:CO_2$ ratio plays a role. In such a case the equilibrium curve would also fall between curves 2 and 4 (GREENWOOD, 1962). It is to be noted in addition that impurities, for example, Mg- or Fe-content, would cause the system no longer to be univariant. That is to say, it would possess more than one degree of freedom.

Our diagram does establish that if, at constant temperature, we move in the direction of higher pressure, the reaction proceeds so that the volume of the system becomes smaller, in this case at the expense of CO_2. On the other hand, when the pressure decreases, a volume increase is favored. This regular relationship is called the *volume rule*. If we hold the pressure constant, those phases form which upon a temperature increase take up heat upon reacting. With a temperature decrease those phases form which liberate heat. If we change both the temperature and pressure, we must rely on the *Nernst temperature rule* to predict the reaction direction. In order to illustrate the chemical relationships, we utilize an equilateral composition triangle such as that shown in Fig. 365, in which the mole percent of constituents is indicated. On the vertical dashed line the compositions of some starting materials are indicated (points a, b, c). If an assemblage with the composition a is heated under pressure, the composition is driven toward a', forming wollastonite + quartz + CO_2. A mixture with the composition b, upon reaction intersects the join wollastonite-calcite, forming wollastonite $+$ calcite $+ CO_2$. Composition c leads to the formation of only wollastonite $+ CO_2$. Such diagrams permit us to recognize by means of the appropriate compositional join those minerals which can occur together as a result of metamorphic processes.

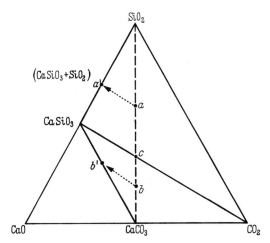

Fig. 365. Triangular diagram of the system $CaO-SiO_2-CO_2$

Reactions in the Solid State. We generally imagine such transformations as being accompanied by the formation of a melt or assisted by interstitial fluids, water or water vapor present in the rock. We imagine that transformations take place in the presence of a fluid or gaseous phase until gradually the entire rock is transformed. Thus, at any instant, only a small segment of the rock is undergoing reaction. This action on the part of fluids is not at all necessary. We know today that crystals can react with one another in the solid state in the absence of fluids. Such reactions are exemplified, for example, by unmixing upon cooling as mentioned earlier on page 197. The rate of these solid state transformations depends, in addition to temperature, on the perfection of a crystal structure. The more defective a lattice (see p. 94), the more rapidly the solid state reaction proceeds. Lattice defects can be induced also by mechanical stress. Thus, in deformed rocks the components react more easily than in unstressed ones. The

Table 64. *Maximum thickness of diffusion layer in the solid state. ($Na_2CO_3 +$ metakaolin, after* JAGITSCH, *1949)*

Temperature in ° C	Layer thickness after 10^8 years
700	1,000 cm
600	60 cm
500	1.8 cm

significance of solid state reactions must, however, not be overemphasized. Diffusion occurs only above a certain threshold temperature and then the reaction rate is still very low. As an example, Table 64 gives some data from JAGITSCH (1949), who investigated the reaction of soda with metakaolinite. It is very improbable that extensive rock complexes can be diffused by reaction in the solid state.

Pore Films and Pore Melts. In unconsolidated sediments a large pore volume is characteristic. It diminishes with increasing consolidation, but even in rocks which appear dry, a very thin pore film of fluid can be present in which ions can migrate by diffusion. With rising temperature, more and more dissolved material can be taken up in the film. This can lead to the formation of partial melts which can themselves migrate under certain conditions.

Facies Classification

The Zonal Concept. Transformations in an isochemical system depend on the temperature and pressure to which the system has been subjected. Thus, BECKE in 1903 distinguished between rocks near the earth's surface, subjected to mild metamorphism and those at depth which were strongly transformed. He suggested as characteristic *typomorphic minerals* of the deeper zone, the minerals pyroxene, garnet, biotite, Ca-rich plagioclase, orthoclase, sillimanite, cordierite, and olivine; for the upper zone, zoisite-epidote, muscovite, chlorite, albite, antigorite, and chloritoid. Later GRUBENMANN inserted an intermediate stage, distinguishing three zones of increasing temperature and pressure, which he called the *epizone, mesozone,* and *katazone.* This terminology is still used in Germany today.

BARROW (1893), and later TILLEY in Scotland, introduced another type of zonation indicator. They utilized a concept of *index minerals* to characterize the metamorphism of pelitic sediments. Their progression begins with a chlorite zone, with the index mineral chlorite representing the lowest grade of metamorphism. With progressively increasing metamorphism, the biotite-, almandine-, staurolite-, and kyanite-zones follow. Metamorphism reaches its highest intensity or grade with the sillimanite zone. One can thus characterize mineral associations of like conditions of formation.

Definition of Mineral Facies. A further kind of classification of metamorphic rocks was suggested by ESKOLA (1915). He started from the premise that rocks having the same bulk chemical composition when in equilibrium, as indicated by the Phase Rule (see p. 193), must under like conditions form the same mineral associations. If the chemical composition changes, so must the mineral content in accordance with theoretical principles. Such mineral-assemblages ESKOLA called *facies*, an expression which had common usage for a long time in geology (GRESSLY, 1838) for classification of rock and fossil associations. His definition of mineral facies (1939) is as follows: "A particular facies comprises all rocks which, by virtue of identical bulk composition, exhibit identical mineralogical composition. The mineral composition will vary with bulk chemical composition according to systematic rules. The significance of this principle is based on the observation that the mineral paragenesis of metamorphic rocks conforms in many cases to the laws of chemical equilibrium. This definition of facies, however, carries with it no assumption that chemical equilibrium prevails."

Since its introduction, the facies concept has been discussed by many workers and expounded in different ways. The most recent redefinition has been given by FYFE and TURNER (1966) as follows: "A metamorphic facies is one of a succession of metamorphic mineral associations, which are linked together repeatedly in space and time, so that a constant and predictable correspondence exists between the mineral composition of each rock and its bulk chemical composition." There have been in addition further commentaries on metamorphic facies. Following the precedent of ESKOLA, the various facies are named after the characteristic rocks which form them, for example, the greenschist facies. However, different rocks are grouped together under one facies according to the nature of the parent rock. If we want to use the facies classification for classifying metamorphic rocks, we must make an exceptionally large number of subdivisions. For the

classification of metamorphic rocks, mineral composition and fabric should be
considered as well as chemistry. The gross chemical composition of a metamorphic rock, which we can determine, does not necessarily represent the exact
composition of the parent rock. Therefore, the facies concept asserts nothing
about the original parent material and does not take into account subsequent
metasomatism. These must be inferred from the chemistry, the fabric, and field

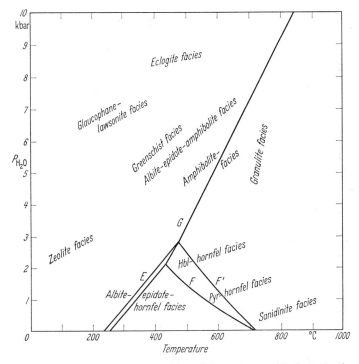

Fig. 366. Summary of the approximate position of the metamorphic facies in the $P-T$ diagram (from TURNER and FYFE, 1966). The lines shown represent the phase boundaries calculated by FYFE for kyanite-andalusite (E) andalusite-sillimanite (with range of error)
(F, F'), kyanite-sillimanite (G)

observations. Nor does the facies concept presume that a mineral association is
always in equilibrium. It only implies that under certain geologic conditions the
same mineral transformations occur in response to the same chemical factors.
Thus, it is noteworthy that metastable phases frequently form outside of their
stability fields in nature. Examples are aragonite and gypsum (among the carbonates and sulfates) and diamond. It is generally assumed that this is not the case
with silicate formation. Metastability of silicates is encountered, however, as a
result of retrograde metamorphism (see p. 305). In addition, one must keep in
mind that in experimental studies of metamorphism only a limited number of
components can be considered simultaneously. The equilibrium situation can be
altered (see p. 296) as a result of additional components. It also follows from these
limitations that there exists a continuous gradation between facies. Experimentally determined univariant equilibrium curves can be used only with caution.
Therefore, in Fig. 366, which gives a summary of the entire metamorphic domain,
facies boundaries are not drawn in. The curves indicated in Fig. 366 indicate the

calculated stability fields for kyanite (left) and andalusite (below) and sillimanite (right), with the latitude of error for each curve indicated (double curves). On the same $P-T$ scale, the same and some additional important equilibria are indicated in Figs. 367. It is opportune again to emphasize (see p. 296) that the partial pressures of the appropriate gases, such as H_2O and CO_2, must be considered. In Fig. 366 and 367 these are always considered to be equivalent to the total rock pressure.

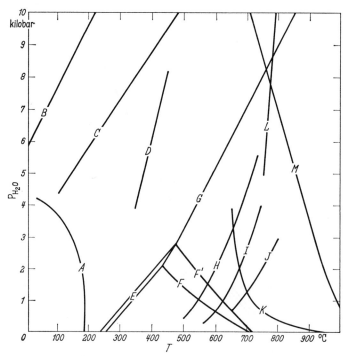

Fig. 367. Phase boundaries for some metamorphic reactions. Increasing entropy from left to right (from TURNER and FYFE, 1966). A analcite + quartz → albite + water (CAMPBELL and FYFE, 1965); B jadeite + quartz → albite (CRAWFORD and FYFE, 1965); C aragonite → calcite (CRAWFORD and FYFE, 1965); D lawsonite → anorthite + H_2O (CRAWFORD and FYFE, 1965); $E-G$ see Fig. 366; H muscovite + quartz → sillimanite (or andalusite) + K-feldspar + H_2O (EVANS, 1965); I muscovite → K-feldspar + corundum + H_2O (EVANS, 1965); J calcite + quartz → wollastonite + CO_2 ($P = P_{CO_2}$) (HARKER and TUTTLE, 1956); K melting curve for granite (TUTTLE and BOWEN, 1958); L melting curve for muscovite ($P = P_{total}$) (SEGNIT and KENNEDY, 1961); M melting curve for basalt (YODER and TILLEY, 1962)

Construction of ACF and $A'KF$ Diagrams. In order to represent diagrammatically the mineral associations of different facies, triangular diagrams of the kind illustrated in Fig. 365 are usually used. Since only three components can be represented, it is necessary to greatly simplify compositional representations of most naturally occurring rocks. A representation called the ACF diagram, suggested by ESKOLA, is usually used to represent rock composition. SiO_2 is not represented graphically because it is present in excess in many rocks and thus has no influence on the mineral assemblages. In addition the accessory components H_2O and CO_2 are ignored. One corner of the triangle, A, represents the molecular proportions (see p. 217) of $Al_2O_3 + Fe_2O_3$ not combined with Na or K ($Al_2O_3 + Fe_2O_3 - [Na_2O + K_2O] = A$). C represents the molecular proportion of CaO, not including that bound in apatite. F represents $MgO + MnO + FeO$, excluding the amounts of these tied up in biotite if present. These values are recalculated so that $A + C + F = 100\%$ and are thus expressed as molecular percentages.

In addition, a so-called $A'KF$ diagram can be used to represent the K_2O content of a metamorphic rock. In this case K_2O takes the place of CaO in the

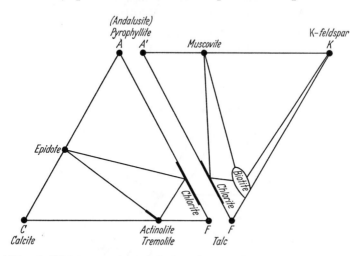

Fig. 368. ACF and $A'KF$ diagram for the albite-epidote-hornfels facies. (From WINKLER, 1965)

ACF diagram. A' used in this representation need not be identical to A in the ACF diagram. One can, of course, carry out these calculations only if the percentage mineral composition is known. If muscovite ($Al_2O_3 : K_2O = 3 : 1$) is present, as is often the case, one substracts from A in constructing an ACF diagram three times as much Al_2O_3 as there is K_2O in muscovite. In the case of $A'KF$ diagrams on the other hand, only $1\,K_2O$ is omitted in addition to CaO. Also in the case of CaO, only that amount of CaO should be substracted which corresponds to the normal or actual Ca-minerals present. This would correspond to all of the CaO in anorthite ($CaO : Al_2O_3 = 1$), to $^1/_3$ CaO in grossularite, etc. Thus, we must know the quantitative mineral content in order to construct these diagrams and cannot work with the bulk chemical analysis alone. For detailed discussion of all aspects of these calculations, we must refer to special references such as that by WINKLER (1965).

The facies classification of metamorphic rocks has been expanded significantly and refined during the course of the last two decades. This has been the result of extensive field and petrographic work, as well as experimental work in the laboratory. To bring the two approaches into agreement is an important research objective. Here it is possible only to introduce the subject of facies investigations.

Contact Metamorphic Facies. As mentioned earlier, the confining pressure is low during contact metamorphism. With progressively rising temperature, we encounter the albite-epidote-hornfels-, the hornblende-hornfels-, and the pyroxene-hornfels-facies. The expression "hornfels" comes from the horny translucent appearance frequently exhibited on thin edges of unaltered rock.

The mineral combinations of the *albite-epidote-hornfels facies* are illustrated in Fig. 368. In this diagram the extent of solid solution is indicated by the heavy lines and by a circular field in the case of biotite.

Characteristic mineral assemblages are epidote + calcite, tremolite + calcite, epidote + albite (not indicated in Fig. 368) + chlorite and muscovite. Pyrophyllite has not been found in contact metamorphic rocks. It could be expected according to the reaction:

$$\text{kaolinite} + 2\,\text{quartz} \rightleftharpoons \text{pyrophyllite} \qquad + H_2O$$
$$Al_2(OH)_4[Si_2O_5] + 2\,SiO_2 \quad \rightleftharpoons Al_2(OH)_2[Si_4O_{10}] + H_2O$$

Its absence may be explained by the fact that many sedimentary clays have sufficient potassium present to form muscovite instead.

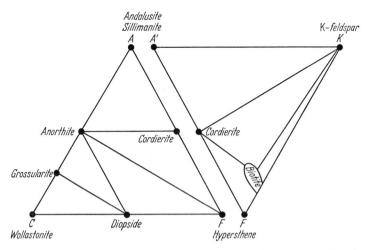

Fig. 369. ACF and $A'KF$ diagram for the pyroxene-hornfels facies. (From WINKLER, 1965)

At higher temperature, muscovite + quartz reacts to form K-feldspar + andalusite + H_2O. Andalusite first forms in the albite-epidote-hornfels facies. Sillimanite takes its place at higher temperatures.

In the *hornblende-hornfels facies* we find hornblende and anthophyllite in place of chlorite, and plagioclase instead of albite. Epidote is missing. Garnets with the composition grossularite-andradite occur, as well as diopside and the combinations muscovite + andalusite and muscovite + cordierite.

In the *pyroxene-hornfels facies*, whose mineral combinations are illustrated in Fig. 369, enstatite or hypersthene replace hornblende. It is characteristic that muscovite is replaced now by orthoclase + sillimanite, accompanied still by andalusite. Cordierite + orthoclase is likewise a diagnostic combination.

Even before the introduction of the facies concept, V. M. GOLDSCHMIDT (1911) had established 10 classes of hornfels from the Oslo region. Classes 1—10, which represent increasing CaO content, show especially well the accompanying parallel changes in mineral association. The progressive changes in mineralogy are indicated in Table 65, omitting quartz and orthoclase, which are common to all 10 classes. In naming these classes the minerals indicated in italics are used, ignoring the persistent biotite. For example, class 7 represents plagioclase-diopside hornfels. The italicized minerals of Table 65, with the exception of vesuvianite, are represented in the ACF diagram in Fig. 369 as follows.

Class 1, andalusite + cordierite; class 2, andalusite + plagioclase + cordierite, etc. If we neglect in class 1 the albite, which was obtained by calculating the norm and would be better represented as a constituent of plagioclase, we see that all of the Goldschmidt classes are included within the pyroxene-hornfels facies, since hornblende does not occur in these rocks. The Goldschmidt classification can be considered as an example of sub-division of a facies depending upon the parent rocks.

The *sanidinite facies* is rare. It occurs as inclusions in lavas and dikes near to the surface and directly in contact with magma. The diagnostic mineral is sanidine. In addition tridymite, mullite, monticellite, melilite, and larnite (β-Ca$_2$SiO$_4$) and often glass are found in association.

Regional Metamorphic Facies. We include here all of the transformations which take place isochemically over a wide area. Some workers suggest separating from regional metamorphism the load or subsidence metamorphism, during which the temperature increase is less and more gradual. However, it is disputed whether a definite separation is feasible at the present time. On the other hand, there are also gradations between contact metamorphic processes, involving more rapid temperature rise, and granite formation, which will be treated later (see p. 321).

Diagenesis certainly is a part of load or subsidence metamorphism. Mineral neoformation, for example, formation of alkali feldspar and chlorite, is observed in conjunction with diagenesis. Poorly crystallized micas, illites, can be upgraded to muscovite. A mineral assemblage specifically characteristic of diagenesis has not been recognized yet.

The *zeolite facies*, the lowest grade of the regional metamorphic facies, is so named after the occurrence of the zeolite, laumontite. Zeolites are found as newly formed minerals in rocks of certain diagenetic grade. The zeolite phillipsite is found in deep sea sediments with formation temperatures only a little above 0°C. Heulandite occurs in the Oberkreide (Cretaceous) of Hannover. The initiation of metamorphism is arbi-

Table 65. *Hornfels classes.* (After V. M. GOLDSCHMIDT)

Original rock	Class	Mineral composition							
clay	1	andalusite	albite	cordierite	biotite				
	2	andalusite	plagioclase	cordierite	biotite				
	3		plagioclase	cordierite	biotite				
	4		plagioclase	cordierite	biotite	hypersthene			
	5		plagioclase		biotite	hypersthene			
	6		plagioclase		biotite	hypersthene	diopside		
	7		plagioclase		(biotite)		diopside		
marl	8		(albite)				diopside	grossularite	
	9						diopside	grossularite	
	10						diopside	grossularite	wollastonite

(grossularite entries for classes 8, 9, 10 bracketed as *vesuvianite*)

trarily placed at the appearance of laumontite, $Ca[AlSi_2O_6]_2 \cdot 4H_2O$. Prehnite, $Ca_2[Al(OH)_2 AlSi_3O_{10}]$ occurs with laumontite. In a subfacies at somewhat higher temperature and pressure pumpellyite,

$$Ca_4(Mg, Fe^{++}, Mn) (Al, Fe^{3+}, Ti)_5 [O(OH)_3(SiO_4)_2(Si_2O_7)_2] \cdot H_2O,$$

takes the place of laumontite. Analcite belongs as a part of diagenesis. In Fig. 367, curve A represents its transformation to albite by the reaction, analcite + quartz $\rightleftharpoons$ albite + H_2O.

According to occurrences reported to date, it seems as if the zeolite facies is connected with the presence of loose volcanic material, especially glass, in sediments. This explains why this facies is so uncommon. In most instances, in which only diagenetic changes are established, sediments transform directly to the next highest grade of regional metamorphism, into the greenschist or glaucophaneschist facies.

The *glaucophane-lawsonite facies* represents an extended development of the zeolite facies at high pressure and temperature. WINKLER (1965) distinguishes two subfacies, the lawsonite-glaucophane- and the lawsonite-albite-facies.

According to WINKLER, the Na-amphibole, glaucophane, is not characterisitc. It occurs also in a high pressure greenschist facies. As Fig. 366 has indicated, transition is expected between the glaucophane and greenschist facies. The mineral lawsonite, $CaAl_2[(OH)_2Si_2O_7] \cdot H_2O$, is diagnostic. It is noteworthy, in addition, that in this facies in some places aragonite, and in others calcite, is found. From this the conclusion is drawn that in these instances aragonite has formed within its stability field, with T and P oscillating around the phase boundary calcite-aragonite, running from $100°C$ and $7,000$ km/cm² to $500°C$ and $12,000$ kg/cm², as indicated by curve C of Fig. 367. Aragonite, to be sure, also forms outside of its stability field, as in recent sediments, and persists metastably over geologic time spans.

At somewhat higher temperatures and at the same or lower pressures the next or greenschist facies follows. In contrast to the preceding facies, it is exceptionally widely distributed. Three subfacies can be distinguished:

a) quartz-albite-muscovite-chlorite,
b) quartz-albite-epidote-biotite,
c) quartz-albite-epidote-almandine.

Additional characteristic minerals are stilpnomelane or chloritoid. In the lowest temperature subfacies *a*, the Mn-garnet spessartite can form in manganese rich sediments. The subfacies *c* corresponds to the highest temperature portion of ESKOLA's epidote-amphibolite facies.

At still higher temperature the *almandine-amphibolite facies* follows, which can be divided into the following sub-facies:

a) staurolite-almandine,
b) kyanite-almandine-muscovite,
c) sillimanite-almandine-muscovite,
d) sillimanite-almandine-orthoclase.

In 1966, FYFE and TURNER introduced again ESKOLA's *albite-epidote-amphibolite* and *amphibolite facies*. With modern methods of investigation, actinolite, belonging to the greenschist facies, can be readily distinguished from hornblende, which occurs only in the albite-epidote-amphibolite facies. Since amphibolites without almandine are widely distributed, they have omitted almandine from the facies name.

Two subfacies can be distinguished in the *granulite facies*, hornblende-granulite and pyroxene-granulite. By granulite we mean a rock which carries pyrope-almandine garnet, as well as quartz and feldspar. The pyroxene is usually hypersthene.

The *eclogite facies* is defined by the mineral association omphacite (a green, iron-bearing pyroxene) and garnet (pyrope-almandine-grossularite solid solutions), which almost exclusively make up the eclogites. Some kyanite and enstatite, as well as rutile, are often present. Although the origin of eclogites is controversial, most certainly they are formed at high pressures. In contrast to the other facies, the eclogite facies consists of essentially one mineral association. All eclogitic rocks which we observe at the surface are probably not always of the same origin. Since eclogites have approximately the same composition as gabbros, it is frequently assumed that the earth's mantle consists of eclogite. Upon release of pressure in the mantle, basaltic melts could form from eclogite. The occurrence of eclogite inclusions in kimberlites speaks for the presence of eclogite in the earth's mantle. Since kimberlites contain diamonds, it is assummed that they also stem from great depth. Eclogite inclusions are exceedingly rare in normal basalts, in contrast to the wide distribution of olivine inclusions in them.

Retrograde Metamorphism

If a rock adjusts itself to the prevailing $P-T$ conditions, according to the principal supposition behind the facies classification, then the question arises as to how we have any knowledge of rocks which formed at high temperatures and pressures. Why have these rocks not adjusted to the $P-T$ conditions at the earth's surface where we observe them ? The reason is that quite generally reactions proceed much more rapidly with rising temperature and thus are inhibited as the temperature is lowered. In addition, metamorphic reactions take place with the assistance of volatile constituents, especially water. Usually these are expelled from a rock at high temperature. Where they are reintroduced, we observe the transformation of rocks back to lower facies. We call this retrogression *retrograde metamorphism* (HARKER) or *diaphthoresis* (BECKE). Such rocks are called *diaphthorites*. Mechanical stress promotes recrystallization not only with rising, but also decreasing temperature. Therefore, mica schists can become phyllitic as a result of mylonitization *(phyllonites)*.

From these considerations it follows that when a rock, during the course of its history, is subjected to several facies grades, that grade corresponding to the highest temperature persists if there has been no introduction of volatile constituents, especially water or CO_2. Whether this has been the case is not always easy to recognize. Moreover, it must always be realized that retrograde metamorphism is not confined to isochemical processes.

b) Allochemical Recrystallization. Metasomatism

General. Up to now we have considered only those processes for which the gross chemical composition of a rock remains constant. We have not considered the whole story when we noted that volatile constituents, H_2O and CO_2, in many cases are expelled from a rock complex. These hot gases and solutions can carry ions in solution and affect mineral neoformation along their paths. If they enter fissures they may form vein deposits. We must realize also that the entire country rock may be altered. This possibility in the case of silicate rocks is at the present time perhaps too often overlooked. The importance of metasomatism in the origin of mineral deposits has been recognized for a very long time. We distinguish between *impregnation deposits*, in which new material was precipitated in the rock pores, and *metasomatic* or *replacement deposits*, in which the original rock was replaced.

The more permeable a rock, the more readily can a solution penetrate it. Therefore, we very often find metasomatic phenomena associated with diagenesis. Especially common in this respect is dolomitization and silicification.

Dolomitization. We have seen earlier (p. 271) that primary dolomitization cannot take place in normal sea water. Investigations of the solution equilibria of Ca and Mg carbonates, sulfates, and chlorides (USDOWSKI, 1966) show that Ca-carbonate is not in equilibrium with sea water, but must transform to Ca-Mg carbonate in its presence. Because of the reaction kinetics, however, conversion takes place only when the sea water is concentrated by evaporation. In addition, because of the low reaction rate, this solution must remain for a long time in contact with the Ca-carbonate. This process can be represented schematically by means of the following experimentally established reaction in aqueous solution:

$$4\,CaCO_3 + MgCl_2 + MgSO_4 \rightleftharpoons 2\,CaMg(CO_3)_2 + CaCl_2 + CaSO_4.$$

By means of this reaction, as well as the experimentally established reaction:

$$2\,CaMg(CO_3)_2 + MgCl_2 + MgSO_4 \rightleftharpoons 4\,MgCO_3 + CaCl_2 + CaSO_4,$$

it is possible to interpret genetically the mineral assemblages of recent dolomitic sediments. In these equations we would substitute the minerals aragonite, Mg-calcite, calcite, protodolomite (strongly disordered dolomite), dolomite, hydromagnesite, magnesite, gypsum, and anhydrite. Of these aragonite, Mg-calcite, protodolomite, and hydromagnesite are unstable. They transform in the course of time into the stable minerals calcite, dolomite, and magnesite. Therefore, we have here a sort of metasomatic activity even at sea water temperatures and are justified in assuming that such processes were effective also in the geologic past. In addition to these early diagenetically formed dolomites, dolomitization of solid limestone rocks has occurred after deposition by the action of groundwater circulating in the crust. Analyses of such solutions show that they are so constituted that they can be in equilibrium with dolomite. If these solutions encounter limestone, a reaction must occur analogous to the first reaction above, leading to the formation of dolomite. Dolomite occurs also with magnesite, the latter forming by reaction with pore solutions according to the second reaction. This process occurs less frequently than the dolomitization of limestone, since the latter is much more common than magnesites.

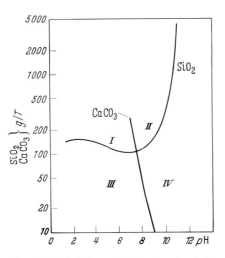

Fig. 370. Solubility of SiO$_2$-gel and calcite in water

Silicification. Another common phenomenon, silicification, begins with certainty during very early diagenesis. Even on the present day sea floor of the Pacific Ocean, silicification has been described.

Fig. 370 shows the solubility relations of silica gel and CaCO$_3$ as related to pH. These data can serve as a model to describe the processes of silicification and replacement of calcium carbonate by SiO$_2$. As an example, let us consider a solution with very low SiO$_2$ and CaCO$_3$ content at a pH of about 6.5 (Field III).

We shall imagine it permeating a limestone containing SiO_2 in the form of siliceous organic remains. At first SiO_2 and $CaCO_3$ are dissolved from the rock, but when field I is reached, SiO_2 precipitates, although $CaCO_3$ continues to dissolve. Another solution with a pH of about 8.5 cuts the solubility curve of $CaCO_3$ before that of SiO_2. In this case SiO_2 continues to dissolve, as $CaCO_3$ precipitates. One can easily follow what happens, when solutions which are already saturated with SiO_2 or $CaCO_3$ are active. The results of both processes have been observed.

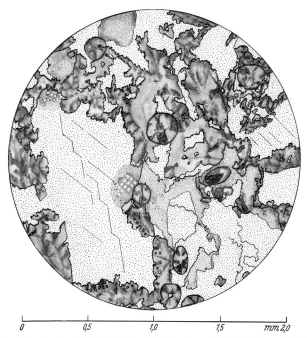

Fig. 371. Silicification in the Kohlenkalk of Velbert, north of Wuppertal. Crossed nicols. Calcite, stipples; chalcedony, gray, fibrous; Echinoderm test at center

Silicification, the replacement of calcium carbonate by silica, is especially widespread. An example is illustrated in Fig. 371. This can result also from solutions introduced from outside the rock. One can represent such a process schematically by the following equations:

1. $Na_2SiO_3 + [CaCO_3] + 2H_2CO_3 + H_2O \leftarrow 2\,NaOH + Ca(HCO_3)_2 + [SiO_2]$: $[SiO_2]$ is dissolved, $CaCO_3$ precipitated.

2. $Na_2SiO_3 + [CaCO_3] + 4H_2CO_3 \rightarrow 2\,NaHCO_3 + Ca(HCO_3)_2 + [SiO_2] + H_2O + H_2CO_3$: $[CaCO_3]$ is dissolved, SiO_2 precipitated.

In addition we must assume that colloidal SiO_2 solutions circulate within rocks and can precipitate out at alkaline reaction sites. Pure SiO_2-sols have their maximum resistance to flocculation by cations in the weakly alkaline region. Such flocculation probably explains the siliceous rings, first described by L. v. Buch in 1831.

Kaolinization. Weathering processes and hydrothermal metasomatism lead to kaolinization, which we can describe by the following equation:

$$2\,KAlSi_3O_8 + 2H_2O = Al_2(OH)_4[Si_2O_5] + K_2O + 4\,SiO_2.$$
$$\text{K-feldspar} \qquad\qquad \text{kaolinite}$$

It is always likely that acids, at least carbonic acid, are involved in this transformation. While in the case of very dilute solutions, such as those formed by weathering, the ions are transported and react only externally to the feldspar, at higher concentrations and in more or less closed systems, the reaction takes place within the feldspar crystal. This leads to the formation of pseudomorphs of the kind described later (p. 309).

Sericitization. Sericitization probably takes place at higher temperatures and in an acid environment in the following manner:

$$3\,KAlSi_3O_8 + 2\,H^+ \rightarrow KAl_2(OH)_2[Si_3AlO_{10}] + 2\,K^+ + 6\,SiO_2.$$
K-feldspar   muscovite

Sericite is the name given to finely divided muscovite.

That sericitization frequently involves more complex processes of introduction of potassium is shown by the observation that sericitized plagioclase does not contain the sodium mica, paragonite, but rather the potassium mica. In fact, it forms in amounts much in excess of that which could be formed from the potassium present in the original plagioclase (PILLER, 1951). Sericitization also yields free SiO_2 which can appear as newly formed quartz within the altered rock or in its vicinity.

Serpentinization. Serpentinization may be akin also to water metasomatism. The magnesium silicate serpentine forms from other magnesium bearing silicates by removal of iron and probably some magnesium, as indicated by reactions such as:

$$5\,Mg_2[SiO_4] + 4\,H_2O \rightarrow 2\,Mg_3(OH)_4[Si_2O_5] + 4\,MgO + SiO_2$$
700 g forsterite   552 g serpentine   removed
218 cm³   220 cm³

Serpentinization probably can result from the reaction of aqueous residual solutions produced by cooling of olivine rich peridotitic magmas, that is by *autometamorphism*. The above reaction scheme was selected because SiO_2 inclusions are observed frequently in serpentine rocks. Essentially no volume change accompanies this process.

Serpentine can react further with carbonic acid to give talc and magnesite according to the scheme:

$$Mg_6(OH)_8[Si_4O_{10}] + 3\,CO_2 \rightarrow Mg_3(OH)_2[Si_4O_{10}] + 3\,MgCO_3 + 3\,H_2O$$
serpentine   talc   magnesite
220 cm³   140 cm³   84 cm³.

By processes which are still unknown, talc can be formed diagenetically in gypsum rocks. In addition, it is formed by metamorphism from quartz, dolomite, and water.

Skarn. An important metasomatic synthesis at high temperatures is the deposition of ore minerals in limestones. These were observed especially in Sweden and Finland and have been called skarns, following the expression of Swedish miners. The most important minerals are andradite, hedenbergite-diopside, and iron-rich hornblende, as well as the iron poor silicates tremolite-actinolite and vesuvianite. Magnetite or hematite along with quartz and sulfide ores, such as galena, sphalerite, and chalcopyrite, are mineable. Their origin is disputed. MAGNUSSON (1966) assumes the parent material to have been sedimentary iron ores along with limestones and dolomites that were altered by metamorphism. The common occurrence of fluorite could indicate gaseous transport. Fluorine contents up to 12,100 ppm and chlorine to 500 ppm have been reported.

Hydrothermal Ore Metasomatism is described frequently. We wish here only to consider one example which serves to indicate the extent of material transfer during metasomatism. GILLULY (1932) estimates that at Ophir Hill, Utah, the following material was introduced into a limestone bed of $2.8 \cdot 10^5$ m^2 lateral extent and 18.3 m thickness: $270 \cdot 10^6$ kg Al_2O_3, $160 \cdot 10^6$ kg K_2O, $10 \cdot 10^6$ kg Na_2O, $900 \cdot 10^6$ kg SiO_2, $9 \cdot 10^6$ kg P_2O_5, $3 \cdot 10^6$ kg F, and $797 \cdot 10^6$ kg CuS, FeS_2, PbS, and ZnS.

Greisen. Alteration and impregnation of the country rock occurs also in the formation of cassiterite. The altered rock is called greisen. Topaz and tourmaline are usually formed also. The reaction usually assumed is:

$$SnF_4 + 2 H_2O = SnO_2 + 4 HF.$$

Alkali Metasomatism. Frequently during metamorphism alkali migration is observed. Examples are the replacement of microcline by albite, neoformation of albite and potassium feldspars in schists, alteration of hornblende to biotite, etc. A pertinent question concerns over how great a distance is such alkali migration effective. In many cases it is indicated that an exchange is confined within a restricted rock complex. In other cases the introduction takes place from without, as with contact metamorphism by granitic or syenitic plutonic rocks. At the contact of basaltic rocks have been observed albitized shales which have been described as *adinoles*. Spotted contact rocks are called *spilosites*, banded ones, *desmosites*.

Alkali metasomatism plays an important role in the theory of granite formation (see p. 322).

c) Fabric of Recrystallized Rocks

Pseudomorphs. How do we go about establishing that rock transformations take place ? We must proceed like a detective, evaluating all the clues. Especially important in this respect are pseudomorphs. These are structures which retain the outer morphology of some original crystal, but which has been altered to a new mineral. As an example one finds in greisens, topaz crystals with the morphology of feldspar. The process of pseudomorph formation can best be made clear, if we place a cleavage fragment of halite in a silver nitrate solution. If the concentration of $AgNO_3$ is sufficient (>3 molar), a thin layer of tiny crystals of AgCl forms immediately. The silver ions diffuse through this layer into the cube, the sodium ions diffusing outward. The crystallization of AgCl continues at the inner boundary of the AgCl layer and finally we obtain an exact replica of the cleavage fragment replaced by fine grained silver chloride. If the concentration is not high enough, pillow-shaped deposits occur on the crystal surface. A less than 0.5 M solution forms many tiny AgCl crystals on the bottom of the container.

An example of pseudomorphism in a rock is illustrated in Fig. 372. In this case the pseudomorphs subsequently were mechanically deformed.

Relics. Mineral remnants, or relics, give us the most important information about mineral replacement. This can involve individual minerals which may escape complete dissolution, perhaps because the metamorphic process was interrupted, as we can see frequently in silicification (Fig. 371). Sometimes the mineral is not attacked by the solution as is the case with the quartz in Fig. 372. Also a reaction rim may form around the mineral protecting the relic from further reaction. In addition, the original fabric may remain recognizable. This brings us to an especially important chapter on metamorphic rocks, metamorphic fabric. When an ancient laminated clay recrystallizes, frequently one can recognize still the original lamination (Fig. 373), in spite of complete transformation, even if very severe recrystallization has taken place. We might conclude from the laminations that the original clay sediment had characteristically formed in a glacial lake (see p. 263).

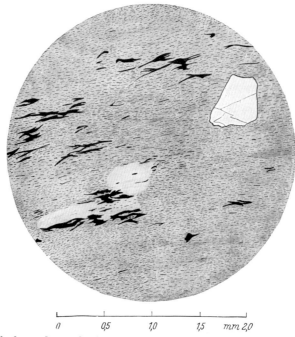

$$0 \quad\quad\quad 0{,}5 \quad\quad\quad 1{,}0 \quad\quad\quad 1{,}5 \quad\quad mm \; 2{,}0$$

Fig. 372. Stretched pseudomorph of sericite after feldspar (light gray) and relic of a quartz inclusion (white) in sericitized and schistose quartz porphyr. groundmass sericite (dark gray) and ore (black) Guinda, Minas Geraes

Blastic Structure. The new formed structure, in contrast to the original texture, is basically different in origin from that of a crystallized rock in which the individual components crystallized out of their melt successively or together. Metamorphism involves transformation of a previously solid rock. If the structural character of the original rock is preserved, the new structure is described, using the original structural nomenclature with the addition of the prefix, *blasto*. A recrystallized conglomeratic texture is called *blastopsephitic*, an ancient sandstone, *blastopsammitic*, and an old porphyry, *blastoporphyritic*.

The Idioblastic Series. If the old structure is no longer recognizable, an equigranular structure is called *granoblastic*. In this case, as was true of igneous rocks, some minerals exhibit characteristic morphologies, some do not. BECKE established the following idioblastic series in which the first-mentioned frequently show their diagnostic crystal morphology, while the last-mentioned very often do not. The series follows:

Sphene, rutile, magnetite, hematite, ilmenite, garnet, tourmaline, staurolite, kyanite;

Epidote, zoisite;

Augite, hornblende;

Breunnerite [$(Mg, Fe)CO_3$], dolomite, albite;

Mica, chlorite;

Calcite;

Quartz, plagioclase;

Orthoclase, microcline.

This does not represent, as is in the case of igneous rocks, an age or crystallization sequence. It represents the ability of a mineral to develop in opposition to its neighbor. Therefore, we speak frequently of a "power of crystallization" or even better of the "form energy" of a mineral. A satisfactory explanation for this phenomenon has never been given. One can only affirm that the oxides crystallize best and then the inosilicates. These are especially dense minerals.

Then follow the chain and ribbon structures, then those with lamellar cleavage, and finally the framework silicates with their relatively open structures. It should be added that albite would appear before mica in the series only in special cases. It is likely that surface energy forces play an essential role in determining this form energy.

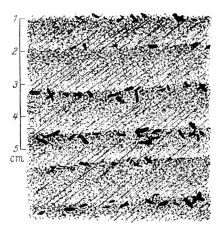

Fig. 373. Relic banding in staurolitic-mica schist. Suistamo, East Finland. The staurolite porphyroblasts occur especially in the argillaceous, darker portion of the original clay banding. The schistosity running diagonally from the upper right to lower left has not disturbed the original banding. (From BARTH-CORRENS-ESKOLA)

Porphyroblasts. Not infrequently one observes the neoformation of large individual crystals, called porphyroblasts, in recrystallized rocks. These crystals have usually developed at the expense of the fine grained groundmass, as illustrated in Fig. 374. Even during diagenesis such forms develop. Pyrite crystals in clays and shales attain diameters of one centimeter. Quartz crystals several centimeters long occur in gypsum. Sphalerite and galena are also common diagenetic porphyroblasts. "Crystallized" sandstones, in which rather large single calcite crystals grow through and incorporate sand, belong in this category. There are similar occurrences of barite, gypsum, and anhydrite. In plastic clays sulfuric acid, produced by the weathering of iron pyrite, reacts with calcium carbonate to form gypsum. These porphyroblasts are usually devoid of inclusions. Whether a crystal grows by engulfing its surroundings or by shoving it aside depends on the one hand on the boundary surface tensions between solution, crystal, and the foreign body, and on the other hand on the pressure it can impose during growth; these factors depend in turn on the supersaturation. In true metamorphic rocks the growth pressure is probably never sufficient to shove aside the surrounding matrix.

Concretions. Individual crystals owe their growth to a concentration gradient in a rock. In a supersaturated pore solution the ions diffuse to a nucleus permitting growth. Sometimes a lighter colored aureole can be observed around such crystals. During diagenesis several nuclei form at one place associated with a concentration gradient, forming concretions. It is not necessary that the entire solution be supersaturated. If, for example, at one place in the sediment included organic matter gradually decomposed forming CO_2, calcium carbonate could go into solution. At another place NH_3 may be produced by the anaerobic decomposition of protein, precipitating calcium carbonate. If the limestone also contains SiO_2 as opal (diatoms, sponge spicules), this may be dissolved at the alkaline site and precipitated where acid conditions prevail (see Figs. 331 and 370). As a result of such fluctuations in concentration of the pore solutions, silicification can result. The formation of spottiness or mottling in diagenetic and in truly metamorphized rocks is akin to these phenomena. In the case of rocks associated with contact aureoles, we speak of *nodular-* and *spotted-slates.*

3. Rock Deformation

Fabric of Deformed Rocks. Until now we have considered only those fabrics developed by recrystallization, and have avoided mention of mechanical deformation. We shall begin the discussion of deformation by considering the structural properties it produces. Especially striking in metamorphic rocks is their schistosity, which stems from the earlier frequently used expression, crystalline schist. There are also metamorphosed clastic sediments, for example, in the glaucophane-lawsonite facies, which show no foliation or schistosity. In schists we ob-

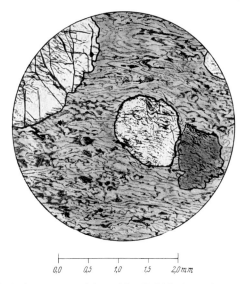

0,0   0,5   1,0   1,5   2,0 mm

Fig. 374. Porphyroblasts in garnet-sericite schist. Pebble from the Mareiter Bach at Bozen. Two large garnets (bright) and mica crystal (dark) in a groundmass of quartz, sericite and carbonaceous matter. Schistosity of groundmass preserved within large crystals

serve that mica flakes and columnar crystals, such as hornblende, lie in parallel planes, promoting separation or cleavage along these planes. While the orientation of these crystals can be observed with the naked eye and has been known for a long time, it has been realized only in the last decade that rocks devoid of obvious foliation indeed have their constituents in preferred orientation. It has been established that an apparently randomly crystallized granite exhibits up to 15% variation in compressive strength, when measurements are made using prisms oriented in different directions. A marble may show up to 27% variation. The transparency of the surface layer of marble, which gives it its warm lively tone, can depend clearly on orientation.

Description of Preferred Orientation (Foliation). How can we establish how the constituents of a rock are oriented ? For this purpose microscope investigation is especially important. This enables us to determine the orientation of the indicatrix of a mineral. Alternatively, X-ray study indicates lattice reference directions. The orientation of such directions as, for example, the optic axis of calcite or quartz, is plotted, using an equal area azimuthal projection. This is

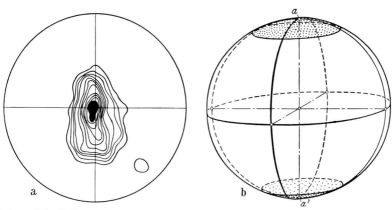

Fig. 375a and b. Fabric with axial symmetry (from BLISS-KNOPF). (a) Diagram. 138 quartz axes; Melibokus granite, after SANDER. The contour lines correspond, starting at the center, to percentages: $> 18-16-14-12-10-8-6-4-2-1-0.5-0$. (b) Schematic representation of the poles of the quartz axes on the projection sphere. a is the projection of the axes around a on the equatorial plane

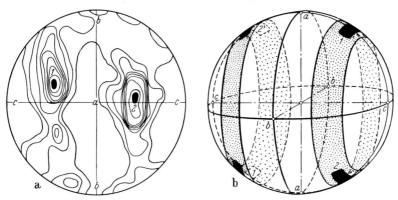

Fig. 376a and b. Fabric with orthorhombic symmetry (from BLISS-KNOPF). (a) Diagram. 380 quartz axes; Granulite, Rochsburg by Penig, after SANDER. Contour interval in percent: $> 10-8-6-5-4-3-2-1-0.5-0$. (b) Schematic representation of a on projection sphere

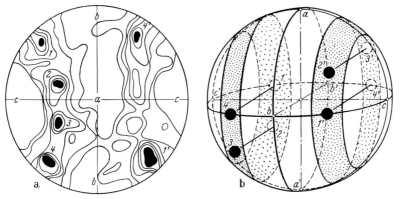

Fig. 377a and b. Fabric with monoclinic symmetry (from BLISS-KNOPF). (a) Diagram. 248 quartz axes; Granulite, Hartmannsdorf i. Sa., after SANDER. Interval in percent: $> 5-4-3-2-1-0.5-0$. (b) Schematic representation of a on projection sphere

used in a manner similar to the stereographic projection, but differs from it in that it gives true areal rather than true angular measurements. Therefore, it is not satisfactory for angular measurements. We are more interested in this case in establishing the statistical frequency of axial poles, and thus must be able to compare equal areas. If we then express the data points in terms of projection coordinates, and relate them to the other fabric properties, schistosity, weal structure, etc., we can unravel a picture of the deformation process. Fig. 375, shows a projection sphere with the poles of quartz axes plotted. Along side of it is the corresponding projection. The projection can be interpreted somewhat like a topographic map with its contour lines. The maximum concentration of poles lies at the center of the projection and decreases outward. Such a fabric has axial symmetry. The positions of the quartz axes cluster around the vertical axis of the sphere. Fig. 376 shows in the same manner the representation of an

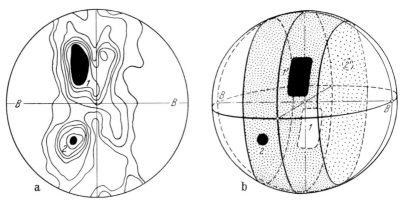

Fig. 378 a and b. Fabric with triclinic symmetry (from BLISS-KNOPF). (a) Diagram > 500 quartz axes; Griffelgneiss, Niederlautstein i. Sa., after SANDER. Interval in percent: Maximum 1 (12—6); Max. 2 (8—6)—5—4—3—2—1—0.5—0. (b) Schematic representation of a on projection sphere

orthorhombic fabric, that is, a fabric with three symmetry planes. As we can see, the precision of fit to orthorhombic symmetry is not great. The maximum at 1 should lie properly on line $c—a$. A diagram representing monoclinic symmetry is shown in Fig. 377. While the symmetry is maintained relatively well on the left side of the diagram, maxima 1' and 4' do not correspond quantitatively. A triclinic diagram is illustrated in Fig. 378.

Laminar Movement. The study of such fabrics has become very important in tectonic considerations. From such studies has come the knowledge of the importance of fabric study generally. Fabric studies are not only confined to all types of rocks, but more generally extend into all areas of science. BR. SANDER and WALTER SCHMIDT can be singled out as pioneers in this area of investigation. Here we shall confine ourselves to deformation fabrics of rocks and shall query how such regular arrangements come into existence. We can demonstrate to ourselves that the rock was made to flow. As a result of the very great viscosity characteristic of such rock flowage, laminar flow must almost always be involved. The higher the temperature, the more plastic the rock will become, until finally so much melt forms that the material flows like a fluid. In the case of actual metamorphism we are concerned with movement in the solid state. Planes of discontinuity occur frequently in rocks, and these function as glide planes. They may be bedding planes or planes of schistosity produced by metamorphism. The flowage is made possible since the rock consists of lamellae which move over one another by "lamellar" gliding. The thickness of these lamellae can be very variable, ranging from microscopic dimensions up to meter thick bands. We have here a deformation process which corresponds to the mode of translation in crystal structures. This is deformation along previously formed planes.

Homogeneous and Heterogeneous Deformation. We define a deformation as homogeneous, when the stress so changes the rock, that a rock sphere is changed to an ellipsoid. Thus, circular cross-sections become ellipses. Straight lines within

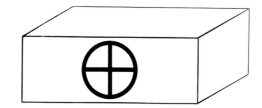

Fig. 379. Stack of cards before deformation

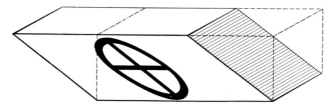

Fig. 380. Stack of cards after homogeneous deformation

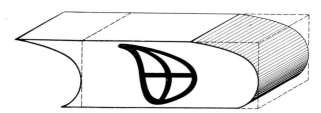

Fig. 381. Stack of cards after inhomogeneous deformation

the rock remain as such. Only their position changes. This is illustrated by comparing Figs. 379 and 380, which represent a deforming rock as a stack of cards within which homogeneous gliding takes place. An original vertical line approaches the horizontal, the more severe the deformation. Thus, preferred crystal orientation relative to the glide planes is produced.

Fig. 381 illustrates inhomogeneous deformation, during which originally straight lines acquire curvature and in which a spherical surface is irregularly deformed. As a result of such inhomogeneous deformation, fold structures can result, as structures inclined to laminations are distorted into bent configurations. Such fold structures are known as drag folds in contrast to the real folds produced by bending.

Simple Shear Translation. A special case of homogeneous deformation is simple shearing (pure shear, HELMHOLTZ), which is identical to the pressure twinning in crystals (see p. 102). Let us consider the deformation of a cube which encloses a sphere, resulting from the vertical application of differential compressional pressure in the direction of the c-(or a_3-)axis. As a result the b-(or a_2-)axis is unaffected, the c-axis reduced in dimension, and the a (or a_1) axis extended without a change in the volume of the body. A parallelepiped is produced from the cube, and the sphere becomes a triaxial ellipsoid (Fig. 382). As we have already mentioned previously, such an ellipsoid has two circular cross sections.

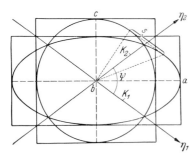

Fig. 382. Deformation ellipsoid. K_1 trace of glide plane of the 1st circular section; η_1 glide direction; K_2 trace of 2nd circular section; η_2 direction of greatest angular change; s magnitude of the gliding

In Fig. 382, these circular sections are shown in projection as the lines connecting the center of the sphere with its points of intersection with the ellipsoid. The difference between a crystal and a mechanically isotropic rock, as we can consider many rocks to be, is that in the former the loci of the glide planes are determined by the crystal structure, whereas in the latter case its locus depends upon the applied pressure. The more intense the plastic deformation of the rock, the smaller the angle between the deformation plane and the horizontal. In the case of plastic deformation these planes play only a geometric role.

If the strength of the rock is exceeded, fractures are formed along these planes. These are called *shear* or *diagonal fractures*. If the plastic deformation is extensive enough the circular sectional planes are made to coincide with the horizontal.

Formation of Preferred Orientation (Foliation). We want now to consider deformation of the constituent grains of a rock. In the case of both forms of deformation there are two kinds of possibilities that can occur. The crystal grains can be deformed themselves by translation gliding, or they can, if they are not spherical but columnar or tabular, be grasped in concordance with the rock flow and reoriented. If the grains themselves are deformed, we speak of *intragranular deformation*, while rotation or relative movement of the whole grain is called *intergranular* deformation. The two forms together produce characteristic metamorphic fabric.

When rock flowage takes place between two solid or competent boundary layers, the resulting particle orientation develops a monoclinic orientation relative to the direction of rock flowage. If the boundaries are irregular, the resulting fabric is triclinic. In the case of the simple compressional deformation of the sphere mentioned above, the deformation produces an orthorhombic fabric.

The manner in which the individual grains are deformed depends upon their crystal structure. In the case of *calcite*, preferred orientation produced is the result of simple shear translation along (10$\bar{1}$1) and (01$\bar{1}$2). The *micas* are deformed by translation on the base (001). The reader can refer to Tables 15 and 16, p. 103 and 105, concerning the properties of additional minerals.

In the case of *quartz* several forms of deformation fabric occur. In mylonites and slickensides (see p. 318), the c-axes lie parallel to the direction of movement. Other preferred orientations are observed also. For example, orientations result in quartz as if a rhombohedral plane has acted as a glide plane. In spite of considerable experimental effort, it is still not understood how the preferred orientation occurs in quartz.

Inhomogeneous deformation, corresponding to the bending of a stack of cards (Fig. 381) likewise occurs frequently in nature. If the deformation due to vertical application of pressure, as shown in Fig. 382, is inhomogeneous, the *b*-axis, which is unchanged under homogeneous deformation, can be extended also. In the extreme case, the dilation can become sufficiently great along both *a*- and *b*-axes that the rock flows plastically forming a disk-shaped body. This deformation gives rise to an axial petro-fabric diagram.

Petrofabric descriptions usually are based on a coordinate system with *a*-, *b*-, and *c*-axes corresponding to those used in crystallography. Deformation planes and directions can thus be indexed in a manner analogous to crystal faces and planes. In Fig. 382, the axes are rotated 90° relative to the standard orientation, with the *a*-axis running left to right. This was so drawn in this case, since the *b*-axis remains constant during homogeneous deformation.

Deformation with Fracture. If its strength is exceeded during deformation, a rock breaks. Such behavior is illustrated by means of a pressure-compression

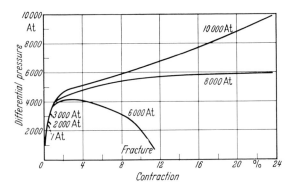

Fig. 383. Deformation of Solnhofen lithographic limestone under different pressures at 25° C.
(After GRIGGS, 1936)

diagram, which is similar to the tensile test data previously illustrated (Fig. 206). In Fig. 383, the experiments by GRIGGS on the Solnhofen lithographic limestone are illustrated. This is a uniformly very fine-grained rock. At high confining pressures (values indicated for each curve) there is initially only a slight shortening of the test specimen with increasing differential pressure, until plastic flow takes over. Then only slight increases in differential pressure result in significant deformation. The lower the confining pressure, the sooner the specimen failure occurs. Fig. 383 indicates that a confining pressure of 8,000 atmospheres is necessary to initiate plastic deformation of this limestone. This pressure corresponds to a depth of about 30 km. More recent investigations by HEARD (1960) show that at room temperature, deformation is initiated already at 7,500 atmospheres pressure, corresponding to about 28 km depth. Under constant stress conditions an increase in temperature lowers the strength of a rock. At higher temperatures deformation is initiated at lower pressures. On the other hand, the pressure of pore solutions enhances strength, decreasing the deformability of a rock.

Upon breaking, cracks or fractures form which are usually called joints. We differentiate between *shear fractures* (or diagonal fractures) and *tension fractures*, which form perpendicular to the direction of tension. H. CLOOS especially pointed out the importance of joints, interpreting them in terms of geologic-tectonic problems.

If the mechanical stress becomes sufficiently great, the rock is broken up into many small fragments, producing what we call *cataclasts* or cataclastic structures. This breakdown can proceed so far that a rock is completely pulverized, forming so-called *mylonites*. The grain size of the cataclastic products may range from several centimeters to colloidal dimensions. In Fig. 384, we can observe the initiation of the cataclastic breakdown of quartz grains. Along shear fractures very thin mylonitic layers, called *harnische*, are found frequently. Mylonites, with very coarse grain size are called *abrasion breccias*. During crushing sufficient heat can be produced due to friction to cause the rock to melt. Such rocks are called *pseudotachylites*, because of their similarity to glassy-melted rocks containing basalt glass (tachylite). It would be better to call these *melt mylonites*.

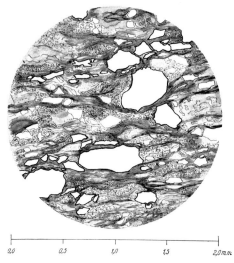

2,0	0,5	1,0	1,5	2,0 mm

Fig. 384. Initiation of mylonitization in an argillaceous sandstone of the Macahubas Series, Minas Geraes. Broken large quartz grains in a groundmass of clay and calcite (stippled)

Combined Effects of Deformation and Recrystallization. We must now consider the cooperative interaction of deformation and recrystallization. The so-called crystalline schists serve to exemplify their mutual roles. A preferred orientation can result when a mineral grain is dissolved under differential pressure according to the *Riecke principal* discussed earlier (p. 294). It was believed earlier that this was the single explanation for schistosity of rocks. Whether one and the same crystal can indeed grow further in the direction perpendicular to the applied pressure has not been demonstrated. Probably, however, we can expect that those mineral grains not under stress can grow at the expense of the compressed grains, giving a fabric perpendicular to the applied pressure. This process can act in conjunction with rock deformation. Usually, however, the foliation can be traced back to mechanical deformation alone.

The glide planes along which deformation of a rock takes place may serve as good pathways for circulating solutions and thus promote solution processes and mineral neoformation in the rock. SANDER especially has emphasized the importance of the penetrability of a rock. Foliation begins to develop even during diagenesis. For example, pressure structures or *stylolites* are formed during diagenesis as a result of differential resistance to solution along bedding and joint planes.

During deformation, recrystallization and neoformation take place as a result of the RIECKE and penetrability principles respectively. If the deformation is followed by recrystallization, we speak of a *precrystalline-deformation*. If deformation and recrystallization occur simultaneously, one speaks of *para-or syncrystalline deformation*. When deformation follows recrystallization, this is a case of *postcrystalline deformation*. Related to the processes of crystallization alone, one distinguishes pre-, para- (or syn-), and post-tectonic crystallization. The expression "kinematic" is used also in place of "tectonic".

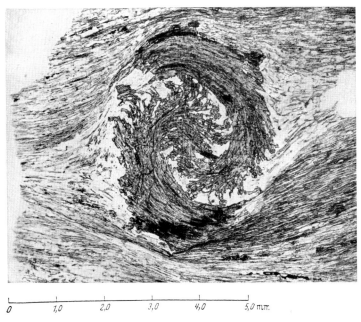

Fig. 385. Rotated garnet (almandine) with onion-like inclusion, Val Piora, Tessin

In metallurgy, the cold-working of metals is an example of postcrystalline deformation. Cold-working induces hardening of metals and requires generally a higher input of energy than hot-working. Hot-working corresponds to simultaneous deformation and recrystallization, to paracrystalline deformation.

Lattice defects which cause the hardening form during the deformation which accompanies cold-working of metals. If cold-working is followed by tempering, a sequence analogous to pre-crystalline deformation, these lattice defects serve as nuclei for recrystallization. It can be suggested that porphyroblasts in metamorphic rocks form under such conditions. If they grow while the compressional movement still persists, the crystals are rotated during growth and incorporate portions of the groundmass, which has different orientation as growth proceeds. An example of such a rotated garnet porphyroblast is illustrated in Fig. 385. In a case like this it is possible to estimate the magnitude of the shear, l/d, which caused the "flowage"; where l is the magnitude of the lateral displacement in a section of thickness d. According to MÜGGE, in the rock represented in Fig. 385, some garnets which are rotated about $90°$ give s values of 1.57 or 3.14. Thus, the top and bottom surfaces of a rock layer 100 m thick would be displaced 157 or 314 meters laterally with respect to each other.

Stress and Antistress Minerals. Different minerals react to deformation in different ways. Some minerals never occur in mechanically deformed rocks. These have been called *anti-stress minerals* (HARKER) and include leucite, nepheline, sodalite, cancrinite, scapolite, andalusite, and cordierite. On the other hand, certain other minerals are found most commonly in deformed rocks. These so-

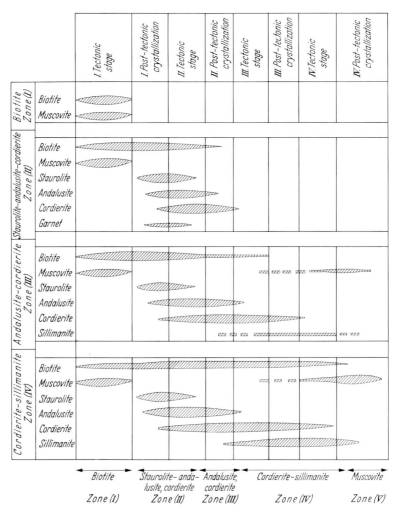

Fig. 386. Relations between several stages of tectonism and crystallization in the Bosost region (simplified after ZWART, 1962). (Shaded figures indicate growth range of indicated minerals)

called *stress-minerals* include kyanite, chloritoid, staurolite, mica, talc, chlorite, some amphiboles, epidote, and zoisite. While the antistress minerals never occur in mechanically deformed rocks, stress minerals, such as mica, kyanite, and staurolite do occur in non-deformed associations.

The factors which account for the differences in stress and anti-stress minerals are not known. Structural considerations show that the layer and chain silicates do not occur as anti-stress minerals. Inosilicates are included in both groups. Although the most important anti-stress minerals are framework silicates, others such as albite and microcline frequently occur under stress conditions.

Differential pressure or stress, such as develops during rock deformation, increases mineral reaction rates. It does not alter, however, the $P-T$ stability fields established under hydrostatic pressure. Thus aragonite can be converted to calcite, which is stable at room temperature, by grinding in a mortar. Since many metastable minerals (for example, diamond and aragonite) are not transformed during the course of geologic time into stable forms, it has been suggested that stress may be effective as a catalyst for certain transformations.

Distinctions have been made also between so-called *plus* and *minus minerals*, according to whether the sums of the molecular volumes of the oxides are greater, or less than the molecular volume of the mineral. These considerations, however have no fundamental significance today, since we now know that minerals are not just simple mixtures of oxides.

Polymetamorphic Rocks. We have been considering the processes of metamorphism as if a rock were subjected in any instance to a single crystallization and tectonic event. However, during the course of earth history frequently several metamorphic events may be superimposed. Studies of the growth and movement of porphyroblasts, may be of assistance in unravelling complex metamorphic history. Thus, ZWART could propose for the Bosost region of the central Pyrenees the sequence of metamorphic events illustrated in Fig. 386. First, there occurred progressive metamorphism under relatively low hydrostatic pressure and a presumed geothermal gradient of 15°C per 100 m. This represents an intermediate stage between regional and contact metamorphism. Finally, retrograde metamorphism occured, converting staurolite into pseudomorphs of muscovite.

4. The Problem of Anatexis and the Origin of Granite

In the vicinity of a magma chamber or by subsidence to great depths, temperatures and pressures can be reached whereby rocks undergo melting. This brings us into the region of ultrametamorphism. The most important and most widely discussed topic in this area concerns the origin of granite. In Fig. 367 (p. 300) the minimum melting temperatures for granite (K) and basalt (M) are plotted as a function of water vapor pressure, assuming that this is equivalent to the total pressure. These curves indicate in a general way the melting behavior of granite and basalt and give an indication of what to expect at high temperature. A discussion of the relation between water content and pressure has been given earlier (p. 230). We still know too little about the water budget of metamorphic rocks, to be able to assess its influence here. It appears certain, however, that even low water contents can be effective in mineral reactions. In general the water content decreases with increasing depth. WEDEPOHL estimates the water content in argillaceous sediments at $>5\%$, in sillimanite gneisses $1-2\%$, in granites about 1%, and at $0.2-0.6\%$ in granulites. It is certain that at a sufficiently high temperature a sediment can be melted. This is not to say, however, that sediments are simply changed into magmas. If a granite is melted, it produces a granite melt which again crystallizes to form a granite. Only in exceptional cases, however, do sediments have the composition of a granite. An example would be a graywacke for which chemical weathering has played a subordinate role. Generally K, and especially Na, are carried away during weathering and removed from the sediment. The average analysis of clays shown in Table 49

(p. 259) gives a Na_2O and K_2O content of 1.6% and 3.6% respectively (1.7% and 3.7% on a CO_2 and H_2O free basis). In contrast the granite analysis given in Table 37 (p. 218) indicates 3.05% Na_2O and 5.42% K_2O. The difference in alkali contents cannot be attributed to neglect of the salt content of interstitial water in sediment. These salts are included in the analysis and are too little in amount to make up the difference. There are, however, two other possibilities by which to derive high alkali products as a result of ultrametamorphism. One possibility is through partial melting (selective mobilization). When a rock is heated it does not necessarily melt completely at a given temperature. Let us consider as a model the simple two-component system illustrated in Fig. 291 (p. 189). If we heat up a mixture of diopside and anorthite, a melt first forms at the eutectic temperature, with the eutectic composition. Floating in the melt will be diopside or anorthite crystals, depending on whether the original composition falls to the right or left of the eutectic. These crystals also melt as the temperature is increased further. In the case of solid solution series, such as plagioclase, melting is initiated by heating to a temperature at which the solidus is intersected. Under equilibrium conditions, an albite-enriched melt forms along with anorthite-enriched crystals. With increasing temperature, melting continues and is finally complete when the melt phase attains the composition of the original plagioclase. If a sediment contains water, we would expect the melting curve of the system to be lowered (see Figs. 307 and 308, p. 202 and 203). Thus, partial melts, sometimes called *interstitial melts* almost always form first when a solid rock melts. These melts can form stringers or veins in the rock. These are called *venites* because, like veins in the human body, they have taken up material from the rock. As a result of tectonic movements these partial melts can be squeezed out, accumulate as a sort of magma in a different place, and crystallize again. Eskola in particular has discussed the implications of this form of magma genesis. Such partial melts, also called *mobilisates*, would be alkali rich, because the alkalis lower the melting temperature of a rock. At the eutectic temperature the melt is enriched in the low melting components. These considerations apply chiefly only to alkali rich starting materials. A ternary eutectic occurs in the case of a great many granites, as Tuttle and Bowen (1958) have shown. This can be interpreted to indicate that these granites formed as partial melts, since this eutectic is not necessarily produced as a result of differentiation of a basic magma.

If we consider an extensive sequence of normal sediments, ultra-metamorphism leading to partial melting must produce an alkali deficient residue as well as the alkali rich melt. Rocks of the pyroxene-granulite facies are plausible examples, especially those which carry hypersthene, garnet, and spinel as well as plagioclase, K-feldspar, and quartz. From rocks of the amphibolite facies, granitic rocks on the one hand and granulitic rocks on the other could result from partial melting. While crystallization of the ferromagnesium minerals from a magma follows the scheme illustrated on page 205, through metamorphism in the granulite facies the sequence is reversed, biotite $\rightarrow$ hornblende $\rightarrow$ pyroxene.

In addition to partial melting, it has been suggested frequently that alkali-rich rocks can be formed by metasomatic processes, during which alkalis in particular are introduced. The formation of zones of large K-feldspar crystals over relatively short distances (to about 100 m), round about granite contacts is a well-known phenomenon. Plagioclase formation does not appear to be connected with metasomatism in deep basement rocks, although this may be a factor in younger rocks. For example, Misch (1949) reported that in the northwest Yunnan province (China), Mesozoic sediments were transformed by neoformation of plagioclase, K-feldspar, quartz, biotite, and hornblende into granodioritic rocks under low $P-T$ conditions. The question of the origin of the granitizing substances is quite controversial. Sometimes the injection of melts is held responsible. Coarsely admixed rocks which form from both mobile and immobile components are called *migmatites*. The mobilized component can have been introduced into the host either by magmatic injection or produced in situ by partial melting. In other instances hydrothermal solutions have been evoked to cause granitization, in other cases, injection of gases. It appears quite likely that all gradations from relatively anhydrous melts to aqueous solutions to gaseous emanations indeed occur and promote the formation of alkali rich rocks.

At the present state of knowledge we may assume that there are at least three types of granite and granite-like rocks. The first are granites which form by differentiation of basic magmas.

Secondly, one can assume granites have formed from granite-like rocks either by complete or partial melting. Sediments can give rise to partial melting. We can formulate the following over-simplified model of this mode of origin. At the greatest depths we should find rocks of the pyroxene-granulite facies, the residues of the granitizing medium. The amphibolite facies above would be granitized and at the highest levels we would find granitic intrusions.

The third mode of origin involves transformation of sediments into granite or granite-like rocks by metasomatism.

Finally, it is to be noted that the interpretation of the origin of a granite is further complicated, in that granites frequently exhibit metasomatic-like replacement phenomena such as myrmekitization, chloritization, and sericitization, which are postmagmatic in origin. They belong to a pegmatitic hydrothermal after-stage, sometimes called *autometamorphism*.

A thorough discussion of the granite problem was presented by MEHNERT (1959) and constituted the source of the discussion here. We cannot examine in detail the question of how these theoretical modes of origin are represented in nature. One cannot ignore the geological side of the problem, especially the field relations. On the other hand, any interpretation, based on work in the field, which is in conflict with physical-chemical principles, must be considered unsatisfactory. When we encounter such contradictory evidence, either the observational interpretation is incorrect, or we have not considered all possible physical-chemical factors. We have encountered such a conflict of data previously when we considered evaporite deposits (see p. 289). We could not explain satisfactorily the evaporite composition on the basis of VAN'T HOFF investigations alone. Only by considering different influences, especially salt metamorphism, could we arrive at better understanding. We should not forget, however, that this understanding was only possible after VAN'T HOFF, through his classic experiments, had established the physical-chemical principles.

5. Nomenclature of Metamorphism and Metamorphic Rocks

a) Definitions of Metamorphic Processes

During the course of more than a hundred years of research in the field of metamorphism an extensive nomenclature has developed. Discussions of the origin of metamorphic rocks are often impeded by lack of consistency in usage of terms. At the 1960 meeting of the International Geological Congress "Proposals for the Nomenclature of Migmatites and Related Rocks" were published by DIETRICH and MEHNERT, with which we largely agree. A suggestion made by WEGMANN at the beginning of the discussion on nomenclature seems particularly noteworthy to me. He suggested that, in addition to distinguishing between descriptive and genetic terminology, we should in the case of the latter use functional expressions, that is to say, expressions which describe those possible processes which have been considered by the various schools of thought on metamorphism. We have in the preceding, as well as this edition of this book, attempted to supply the basic background to theory, and therefore, have used only a few of the many technical terms. Since familiarity with terminology is important for proper understanding of the technical literature, the most important terms are listed alphabetically below.

Anatexis: Rock melting (modifiers: intergranular, partial, differential, selective, complete melting.
Contamination: Change in composition of a magma by assimilation of inclusions or country rock.
Diatexis: High-grade anatexis.
Ectexis: Anatexis by in situ formation of a fluid fraction.
Entexis: Formation of migmatites by introducing a mobile fraction.
Hybridization: 1. Mixing of magmas. 2. Synonymous with contamination.
Metablastesis: 1. Recrystallization of rocks with preferential growth of certain minerals (esp. feldspar). 2. Essentially isochemical recrystallization (without separation of a mobile phase).
Metasom: Portion of a rock newly formed by metasomatism.
Metatect: Fluid portion of a migmatite during the main stage of formation.
Metatexis: Low-grade (differential or partial) anetexis.
Palingenesis: 1. New formation of a magma by melting older rocks (which have demonstratively already participated in a significant portion of the petrogenetic cycle). 2. New formation of rocks with mineral content and fabric of magmatic rocks without implications as to mechanism.
Permeation: Penetration of solid rock by geochemically mobile substances (melts, solutions, gases).
Petroblastesis: Rock genesis by crystallization from diffusing flowing ions.
Replacement: Material exchange on an atomic scale or practically simultaneous solution of older minerals and crystallization of introduced substances.
Stereogen: When the major formation process exists in the solid or predominately solid (crystallized) state.

b) Metamorphic Rock Nomenclature

As we have indicated previously, metamorphic rocks are usually mechanically deformed. For this reason the names gneiss and schist have been used for a long time, in conjunction with the characteristic mineral content; for example, hornblende gneiss, chlorite schist, etc.

In the proceedings of a symposium published in 1962 by Austrian workers, only rocks with parallel texture, and which contain over 20% feldspar and 10% mica were designated as gneiss. In 1963 WENK was in favor of using only fabric and not mineral content to characterize gneisses and schists. Schists cleave into thin plates from a millimeter to 1 cm thick or into columnar fragments of these dimensions. Gneisses cleave into plates and pieces from a centimeter to a decimeter in thickness or into thick prisms (stengle gneisses).

As clays undergo diagenesis and are subjected to increasing regional metamorphism, they transform from plastic clay with increasing consolidation and recrystallization as follows:

$$Clay \rightarrow shale \rightarrow phyllite \rightarrow mica\ schist.$$

Limestones are metamorphosed to *marble* and, like gneisses and schists, are named after characteristic minerals, for example, tremolite marble. The same is true of *quartzites*. A metamorphic rock without parallel fabric is called a *hornfel*.

Not only sediments are transformed by metamorphism, but also igneous rocks. One distinguishes between *para-gneisses*, which formed from sedimentary parents, and *orthogneisses*, which formed from originally igneous rocks. Another way to designate a metamorphic rock after its parent material, is to add the prefix *meta-* to the original rock name. For example, metagraywacke, metadiorite, etc.

Two rock names which we have used frequently without precise definition are:

Amphibolite: a rock consisting predominantly of common hornblende and plagioclase.

Granulite: a fine-grained (0.1—1 m) rock with platy structure, of granitic composition, which always contains pyrope-almandine-spessartite garnet instead of biotite, as well as K-feldspar and platy quartz.

Finally, we shall conclude with some additional definitions from the 1960 proposed nomenclature, which were designated as particularly important:

Agmatite: Migmatite with brecciated texture.
Anatexite: Product of anatexis.
Chorismite: Coarsely mixed rock consisting of petrographically distinguishable fractions of undetermined origin.
Dictyonite: Migmatite with reticular flexure zonal texture.
Ectexite: Product of ectexis.
Ectinite: Product of regional kinetometamorphism (without significant metamorphism).
Embrechite: Migmatite with banded, schlieren-, and augen-texture, in which the fabric of the original rock is still partially preserved.
Metasomatite: Product of metasomatism.
Metatexite: Product of metatexis.
Nebulite: Migmatite with schlieren- and wolken texture.
Neosom: Younger portion of a chorismite.
Ophthalmite: Chorismite with augen- or lenticular texture.
Palaeosomite: Older, original portion of a chorismite.
Phlebite: Metamorphite or migmatite with vein texture.
Stromatite: Chorismite with banded texture.

X. Geochemical Considerations

1. History of the Concept of Geochemistry

The Concept. With consideration of the origin of granite, we have concluded our review of the processes involved in the origin and transformation of rocks in the earth's crust. Thus, we have observed a cycle of processes starting with magmatic crystallization, leading to weathering, sedimentation, and finally metamorphism, which can lead in turn to the generation of new magmas. In dealing with this so-called rock cycle (or geochemical cycle) we have, in fact, considered the geochemical relations of the most important rockforming elements.

In conclusion we must examine this concept of geochemistry in somewhat greater detail. Sometimes the concept of geochemistry is restricted to determination of the terrestrial, crustal, and cosmic abundances of the elements. However, this purely analytical activity is only a prerequisite data-collecting phase of the real scientific objective of geochemistry. This objective was defined by V. M. GOLD-SCHMIDT as the discovery of laws which determine the geochemical distribution of the elements. We can subdivide geochemistry into the chemistry of the crust, of the total earth, or of the cosmos (cosmochemistry). Cosmic elemental abundances are related to the origin of the elements, and thus the empirically determined cosmic abundance values constitute a basis for considerations of theories of nucleogenesis. Space does not permit us to consider this subject here. When dealing earlier with petrogenesis, we have considered the very important processes affecting migration of the major elements, and thus have discussed already an important part of geochemistry. We shall discuss, therefore, only three additional geochemical problems. The first is the quantitative calculation of material losses and gains (geochemical balance) in the earth's crust. The second concerns the probable distribution of elements in the earth as well as the cosmos and is thus related in its strictest application to the question of the origin of the earth. Thirdly, we must consider that most elements consist of mixtures of isotopes. The investigation of the isotope distribution laws is currently one of the most vigorously developing areas of geochemistry. Before we discuss these three aspects of geochemistry, it is useful to consider some of the facts concerning the development of geochemistry, especially since the erroneous impression often prevails that geochemistry is a science which has only recently developed.

The History of Geochemistry. The word geochemistry stems from SCHOEN-BEIN who used it first in 1838, although as early as 1821 BERZELIUS had referred to mineralogy as "the chemistry of the earth's crust". Between 1848 and 1854 CARL GUSTAV BISCHOF'S "Lehrbuch der physikalischen und chemischen Geologie" appeared. BISCHOF probably can be considered as one of the real founders of the geochemistry of the earth's crust. By 1846 ELIE DE BEAUMONT in France had published the first summary of the crustal abundance of the elements. JUSTUS ROTH wrote his "Allgemeine und chemische Geologie" between 1879 and 1893. In 1904 the "Treatise on Metamorphism", by the American geologist VAN HISE appeared. This considered quite general geochemical questions as well as metamorphism, especially the geochemical material balance in the crust. Four years later the standard work by FRANK W. CLARKE, "Data on Geochemistry", was published. The fifth and last edition appeared in 1924; the sixth edition is being published in parts, some of which have appeared already.

Also, the interest in rare elements began early. W. H. HARTLEY and H. RAMAGE showed in 1897 that Ga and In are widely distributed in minerals and rocks. G. EBERHARD began in 1908 his spectrographic investigations of the rare earth elements. In similar fashion W. VERNADSKY in 1910 proved the wide distribution of In, Tl, Ga, Rb, and Cs. In 1917 HARKINS studied the relationship between abundance of elements in the crust and in meteorites and their position in the periodic table, and disclosed the rule that bears his name. HARKINS' rule states that elements with even atomic numbers are more common than those with odd numbers. In 1924 VERNADSKY's book "Géochimie" appeared in French. In 1930 the German translation of a revised Russian edition appeared. From 1922 on V. M. GOLDSCHMIDT and his colleagues showed the importance of crystal chemistry in solving geochemical questions. In addition, they determined the abundance of many rare elements in different rocks, especially by means of spectroscopic studies.

The history of isotope geochemistry began in 1902 with the explanation of radioactivity by RUTHERFORD and SODDY. The investigations of radioactive, unstable isotopes paved the way at the beginning of the twentieth century to a new understanding of the heat budget of the earth and led to the development of absolute age dating of minerals.

The abundance of stable isotopes has been investigated since the discovery of heavy hydrogen or deuterium by H. UREY in 1932. The utilization of oxygen isotope ratios for temperature determination was likewise initiated by H. UREY in 1947.

2. Determining Geochemical Balances

GOLDSCHMIDT's Calculation. We are indebted also to GOLDSCHMIDT for his determination of material balance in the earth's crust. The earlier rough estimates of chemical losses and gains during the rock cycle were further refined subsequently by other investigators, such as CLARKE. The basic assumption of all such calculations is that various elements are incorporated into sediments and into sea water as a result of weathering. Thus, the amount of an element contained in weathered primary igneous rocks must be equal to the amount contained in the derived sediments and sea water. For such considerations it is immaterial whether igneous rocks are really magmatic or whether they have been formed by metamorphic processes. In his calculations GOLDSCHMIDT followed the procedure of SCHLOESING and related material abundances to 1 cm² of the earth's surface. This has the advantage of producing more manageable smaller numbers. The amount of weathered primary crystalline rock is designated by E, sedimentary rocks by S, and seawater by M (always expressed in kg/cm²). In addition the percentage of an element or its oxide, x, in primary rocks is designated as e_x, in sediments as s_x, and in sea water as m_x. Thus, the balancing equation for any element can be expressed as follows:

$$E \cdot e_x = M \cdot m_x + S \cdot s_x. \tag{1}$$

In this expression only M and m_x are known with any great certainty. The values for e_x (Table 42, p. 221) are still somewhat uncertain. Some values for s_x, likewise still uncertain, are tabulated in Tables 67 and 68. If we take two pairs of values for e_x and s_x for two different elements, we can solve simultaneously two Eq. (1) for the unknown values of E and S. Based on the elements Na and K, we obtain values for E and S which agree rather well with those of GOLDSCHMIDT and CLARKE. For Ca and Mg, however, quite unlikely values are obtained. Probably for this reason, GOLDSCHMIDT used a somewhat different approach. He

Table 66. *Abundance of sedimentary rocks, calc. after* V. M. GOLDSCHMIDT *and* V. ENGELHARDT

	kg/cm²	%	Rounded values	
			kg/cm²	%
Shales	134.85	79.5	135	80
Sandstones	20.15	11.9	20	12
Limestones	10.17	6.0 ⎫	15	8
Dolomites	4.37	2.6 ⎭		
	169.54	100.0	170	100

inserted in Eq. (1) the Na content of argillaceous-sandy sediments, that is, carbonate-free sediments, assumed at 1%. As the second equation he used the expression:

$$S = 0.97\,E\,. \tag{2}$$

He estimated that the alteration of igneous rock to sediments was accompanied by an 8% loss in CaO, MgO, and Na_2O, compensated for by a 5% gain in H_2O. Thus, Eq. (2) indicates the net loss of 3% by weight. In this way GOLDSCHMIDT arrived at the values, $E = 160$ kg/cm² and $S = 155$ kg/cm². Taking the values of 0.6 and 2.6% as the CaO and MgO content of carbonate-free sediments, he calculated how much CaO and MgO was left over, from the 160 kg of weathered igneous rocks, for carbonate formation. He obtained the values 12.553 kg $CaCO_3$, and 1.999 kg $MgCO_3$ equivalent to 10.170 kg $CaCO_3$ and 4.372 kg $CaMg(CO_3)_2$. Including these along with the carbonate-free sediments, we arive at a total of 170 kg sediment produced from 160 kg of igneous rock. GOLDSCHMIDT included shales and sandstones together. However, following the suggestions of VON ENGELHARDT we have separated them in Table 66.

Table 67. *Calculated distribution of some readily soluble cations in sea water and sediments, released by weathering of igneous rocks; compared with observed values*

Element	kg/cm²		Calc. amounts in sediments			% in sediments	
	in ign. rocks	in sea water	kg/cm²	oxide	%	after CLARKE	after RONOV
Na	3.92	3.0	0.92	Na_2O	0.73	1.34	0.6
K	4.51	0.11	4.40	K_2O	3.12	3.06	2.54
Ca	4.59	0.11	4.48	CaO	3.69	5.83	7.28
Mg	2.22	0.36	1.86	MgO	1.82	2.85	2.55

Because of the uncertainty of values for e_x and s_x, these calculations can give only rough approximations. Nevertheless, trial calculations (CORRENS, 1949) show that the values of 160 kg/cm² for E and 170 kg/cm² for S do not significantly change when the e_x values for K and Na are varied.

Material Balance for Some Important Elements. Once we can assume correct values for E, S, and e_x, we can attempt to calculate material balances for a number of elements from Eq. (1). In doing so we can distinguish three essentially different groups of elements. Table 67 gives the pertinent information for the readily soluble common cations. A comparison of the calculated and observed amounts of these elements in sediments shows at least order of magnitude agreement in the case of Na and K. The agreement is less satisfactory in the case of magnesium and least satisfactory with calcium. This is a consequence of the Ca and Mg ions removed from sea water in the formation of carbonates incorporated into the sediments. One can characterize this same behavior by means of elemental residence times in the ocean (BARTH, 1952). These can be computed for each element as the

Table 68. *Calculated content of some relatively insoluble elements in sediments, compared with observed values*

	Calc.	CLARKE	RONOV
SiO_2	61.43	56.98	56.52
Al_2O_3	13.8	14.0	13.9
Fe_2O_3	4.86	5.41	5.11
TiO_2	0.73	0.66	0.76

Table 69. *Calculated distribution of some readily soluble anions in sea water and sediments, released from igneous rocks, compared with observed values*

Ele-ment	kg/cm²				Sediments (%)		
	ign. rocks	sea water	sedi-ments	sediments observed	calc.	observed	
F	0.1152	0.00036	0.1148	0.11	0.0675	0.065	KORITNIG
I	$8 \cdot 10^{-5}$	$8 \cdot 10^{-6}$	$7.2 \cdot 10^{-5}$	$1.35 \cdot 10^{-4}$	$4.2 \cdot 10^{-5}$	$8 \cdot 10^{-5}$	V. M. GOLD-SCHMIDT
Br	$5 \cdot 10^{-4}$	$1.8 \cdot 10^{-2}$	—	$6.6 \cdot 10^{-4}$	—	$4 \cdot 10^{-4}$ }	BEHNE[a]
Cl	0.0512	5.4	—	0.026	—	0.0154 }	
S	0.05	2.5	—	0.34	—	0.2	RICKE
B	$1.6 \cdot 10^{-3}$	$1.3 \cdot 10^{-3}$	$3 \cdot 10^{-4}$	$1.4 \cdot 10^{-2}$	$1.7 \cdot 10^{-4}$	$8.5 \cdot 10^{-3}$	HARDER

[a] The data from BEHNE came from outcrop samples. Consideration of pore water content would give values up to 100 times higher.

ratio of the total amount of an element in the sea to its annual influx, expressed in years. In 1961 BARTH estimated the following residence times (in millions of years): Na 120, K 10, Mg 23, and Ca 1.2. For these calculations, and in Table 67, the observed values after CLARKE and after RONOV were calculated as follows. From CLARKE's analyses of average clays, sands, and limestone, and the data in Table 67, the "observed" values after CLARK are calculated. The "observed" RONOV values are derived in a like manner except that data for marine clays are used instead of CLARKE's clay values.

Table 68 gives analogous values for the relatively insoluble elements. These data are derived from Eq. (1) modified to exclude the term $M \cdot m_x$ since these elements are virtually absent from sea water. The agreement between calculated and observed values for Al_2O_3 is very good. Values for Fe_2O_3 and TiO_2 agree within the limit of error. Whether the discrepancy for SiO_2 is due to too high a e_x or too low a s_x value, or to incorrect clay : sand : limestone ratios, is as yet undetermined.

The anions listed in Table 69 show in part a relationship quite different from that of the cations. Br, Cl, and S are so strongly enriched in sea water that their origin by release by weathering from igneous rocks alone is impossible. They occur in sea water alone in excess of amounts which could have been produced by weathering. In the case of boron, the observed content in sediments alone is almost 50 times higher than calculated. These four elements are derived from the interior of the earth by degassing of igneous rocks (see p. 224). It would appear that fluorine and iodine are subordinate fractions of the evolved gases. Fluorine may be tied up in rocks by autometamorphism. Iodine appears to be concentrated in sediments, perhaps due to a short residence time resulting from abstraction from sea water by algae.

3. Isotope Geochemistry

In the last decade isotope geochemistry has developed into such a comprehensive science, that here we can give only a few hints of its importance to geology and petrology. We distinguish between stable and unstable isotopes. Among the unstable isotopes we can again differentiate two groups based on origin, those which are still forming today from interaction with cosmic radiation and those in the earth's crust and in meteorites which have occurred from the beginning, or are the fission products of Th and U.

The Unstable Isotopes. The unstable isotopes newly formed by cosmic radiation have relatively short half-lives. An example is the unstable carbon-14 (C_6^{14} "radiocarbon") formed from the stable isotope N_7^{14} by neutron bombardment. Carbon-14 has a half-life of 5,700 years and is used to date carbonaceous materials from historical and pre-historical times. Tritium, H_1^3, has a much shorter half-life of 12.4 years. It thus serves as an important tracer in studying the circulation of water in the atmosphere. By means of certain isotopes the cosmic ray ages of meteorites can be determined. These ages represent the time the meteorites have resided in space.

Those unstable isotopes with half-lives $> 10^8$ years, "radioactive" isotopes in the narrow sense, are used also in absolute age determination. The U-Th "clock" has been used for some time. In the last decade use has been made more and more of two other decay series. One is the decay of Rb^{87} to Sr^{87} by β (electron) emission, with a half-life of $5 \cdot 10^{10}$ years. The other is the transmutation of K^{40} to the stable isotopes $Ar^{40} + Ca^{40}$ by K-electron and β radiation capture, with a half-life of $1.2 \cdot 10^{10}$ years.

Isotopic age determinations are not important only for establishing an absolute geologic time scale. They can give information on the relative ages of individual minerals in a rock assemblage, for example, micas and feldspars.

The unstable isotopes are important to us in another respect. When they decay radioactively, they produce heat. The three most abundant radioactive isotopes are U, Th, and K. One gram of U produces, in equilibrium with its daughter products, 0.71 cal/year; 1 g Th produces 0.20 cal/year; 1 g K $27 \cdot 10^{-6}$ cal/year. The average abundance of these elements in a number of common rocks is indicated in Table 70, along with the corresponding heat output, calculated for a column of rock 3 km long and with 1 cm^2 cross section (corresponding to approximately 1 metric ton of rock). These data show that the heat production is greatest in those SiO_2-rich rocks common in the earth's crust, and decreases with decreasing SiO_2 content. Heat production is very low in peridotites, which are assumed to comprise the upper mantle. If one wishes to calculate the temperature rise in the earth, one must make certain assumptions about the internal composition of the earth. For the temperature distribution depicted in Fig. 363, a U content of $3.3 \cdot 10^{-2}$ g/t was assumed.

The Stable Isotopes. The stable isotopes have become important in other ways for understanding geochemical processes. As the name isotope indicates, all isotopes of an element have the same atomic number. For example the isotopes C^{12}, C^{13}, C^{14} all have the atomic number of 6 for carbon. They differ in their mass numbers, 12, 13, and 14. This difference in mass, along with the vibrational energies of molecules containing different isotopes, can lead to isotope fractionation by diffusion, electrolysis or chemical reaction. Of course, these differences are very slight. Only the relatively recent development of mass spectrometry has made it possible to investigate the fractionation effects. Here we shall consider only two examples. A much-investigated problem is the distribution of oxygen isotopes in minerals. Oxygen has three stable isotopes, of which O^{16} is the most abundant, constituting 99.76% on the average. O^{17} makes up 0.04% and O^{18}

Table 70. *Average content of U, Th, and K in different rocks and their heat production in a column 3 km $\times$ 1 cm^2 (1 t of rock).* (After WEDEPOHL)

	g/t		%	cal/cm^2
	U	Th	K	year
Granite	4.0	16	4.4	7.2
Shale	3.7	12	3.0	5.7
Granodiorite	2.0	8.5	2.5	3.8
Basalt	0.6	1.6	0.75	0.95
Peridotite	0.01	0.0_x	0.004	0.0095

0.2% in the earth's crust. We can disregard the small fraction of O^{17} and consider alone the fractionation of O^{18}. This fractionation is temperature dependent. In 1947 H. UREY suggested the use of O^{18} fractionation for temperature measurements. Since this time a great number of temperature determinations have been made, especially on calcium carbonate hard parts of fossil organisms. In explanation we can consider a simple example, the equilibrium:

$$CO_2^{16} + H_2O^{18} \rightleftharpoons CO^{16}\,O^{18} + H_2O^{16}.$$

As a result of distinctly different absolute energies, the rate constants are different for each indicated reaction direction, the reaction to the right being favored somewhat. This results in a very slight enrichment of O^{18} in CO_2, or of O^{16} in H_2O. At 0°C the fractionation factor amounts to 1.045. The exchange rate increases greatly in both directions with increasing temperature. At the same time the influence of absolute energy on establishment of equilibrium is lessened, so that the fractionation factor at high temperature approaches unity (1.039 at 25°C).

Since the amount of oxygen combined in H_2O in the world's oceans is for all practical purposes infinite compared to the amount of dissolved CO_2, the exchange reaction influences effectively only the O^{18} content of CO_2. The CO_2 dissolved in water can be considered as an important ingredient in the precipitation of calcium carbonate. We cannot consider the details of the mechanism of incorporation of O^{18} into the carbonate structure, but it is clear that one can determine the temperature of crystallization from the O^{18}/O^{16} ratio. A number of precautions must be considered, however. Equilibrium must have prevailed and the O^{18} content of sea water should be known. No isotopic exchange can have taken place after deposition, that is, as a result of diagenesis. The O^{18}/O^{16} ratio, expressed in $^0/_{00}$, is usually related to a standard as follows:

$$\delta\,O^{18} = \frac{O^{18}/O^{16}\ \text{sample} - O^{18}/O^{16}\ \text{standard}}{O^{18}/O^{16}\ \text{standard}}.$$

Over a period of time different standards have been used, as can be discerned by a study of the literature.

A second important example of the application of stable isotope geochemistry involves the *isotopes* of *sulfur*. There are four stable isotopes of sulfur. S^{32}, constituting 95%, and S^{34}, 4.22% are the most abundant. S^{33}, 0.76%, and S^{38}, 0.014% can be ignored. Sulfur occurs in nature either in elemental form, or more frequently as sulfide or sulfate. Inorganic separation processes are, as with oxygen, strongly temperature dependent. The fractionation factor decreases rapidly with temperature. Bacterial reduction of sulfate to hydrogen sulfide is an important separation process at low temperatures. The light isotope S^{32} is always enriched in sulfides, the heavier S^{34} in sulfates. As previously indicated (p. 277 and 278), this bacterial reduction plays an important role in the sedimentary cycle. We can attempt, from the isotope ratios, to determine the conditions of formation of sulfide mineral deposits. We can attempt to distinguish between deposits of hydrothermal or sedimentary origin. Fig. 387 summarizes $\delta\ S^{34}$ values, calculated in a manner analogous to those for oxygen as described earlier. It indicates that the range of values for sedimentary sulfides is especially large. This is because the incorporation of the isotopes into sulfides and sulfates is dependent also on the proportions of the latter. The more sulfate used up by reduction, the remainder remaining enriched in S^{34}, the more S^{34} must be incorporated into sulfide. Thus, sedimentary sulfides can be formed which are likewise enriched in S^{34}. Only those sulfides which give $\delta\ S^{34}$ values less than $-15^0/_{00}$, can be considered of certain sedimentary origin.

An additional interesting result has come out of investigations of sulfur isotope distributions in fossil sulfates deposited in saline environments since the Pre-Cambrian. These have shown that the isotope ratios have changed during the course of time (NIELSEN, 1965).

4. Abundance of Elements in the Earth and Cosmos

Layered Structure of the Earth. In our considerations thus far the assumption was made that the abundances of individual elements in the earth's outer crust are known. If we now attempt to determine their proportions for the total earth, we are confronted with some fundamental difficulties. We have direct information about only the outer few kilometers of the earth's crust, by direct observation through borings and mine workings. At the present time these observations have been made only to a depth of about 5 km. As a result of up-folding and subsequent denudation, we get a view of still deeper layers to about 5—10 km.

From the travel time curves for earthquake waves we can draw some conclusions concerning the composition of still deeper layers. Propagation velocities change with the nature of the rock through which earthquake waves pass. They depend in addition on the depth parameters of the rock, that is, on temperature and pressure, as Fig. 388 shows. In constructing the velocity curves, it is assumed that temperature and pressure are related as shown. Through the interpretation of travel time curves from earthquakes and explosions it has been concluded that the earth can be differentiated into different zones. In Fig. 389 the velocities of longitudinal L waves, analogous to sound waves, and transverse T waves are plotted as a function of depth. Two major discontinuities are immediately apparent. One, occurring at a very shallow depth, is called the Mohorovičić discontinuity. This is considered as the lower boundary of the earth's crust. A second major discontinuity occurs at a depth of about 2,900 km. This represents the lower boundary of the earth's mantle. The innermost portion of the earth is called the core. Data relative to the dimensions, density, and mass of these three zones is given in Table 71.

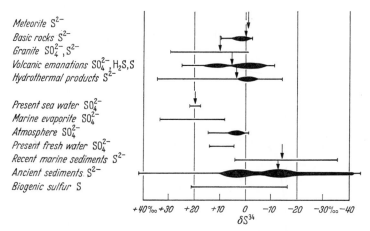

Fig. 387. Sulfur isotope abundances (arrow indicates mean values). (After HOLSER and KAPLAN, 1966)

Table 71. *Data for the structural layers of the earth*

	Radius		Volume		Aver. density	Mass	
	km	%	10^{27} cm³	%		10^{27} g	%
Crust	6 35 } 17	0,5	0.008	0.75	2.8	0.024	0.4
Mantle	2,883	45	0.899	83.4	4.5	4.075	68.1
Core	3,471	54.5	0.175	15.85	10.7	1.876	31.5
Earth	6,371	100	1.083	100	5.52	5.975	100.0

We note first that the earth's crust comprises those layers in which the propagation velocities of longitudinal waves are less than 8 km/sec. In Fig. 388 we see that granite exhibits lower and gabbro somewhat higher velocities. The outermost crust consists of sediments and granitic or metamorphic rocks; the deeper crust consists of rocks of gabbroic composition. Beneath the oceans the crust is quite thin, about 6 km; beneath the continents it reaches a thickness of about 35 km. These relations are illustrated for the north Atlantic Ocean in Fig. 390. Beneath the Mid-Atlantic Rise ascending mantle material is presumed.

While the mineralogic composition of the crust can be deduced at least in part by direct observation, data for the mantle and core, such as those summarized in Table 70, are deduced by indirect considerations. It is generally accepted today that the core consists of a nickel-iron mixture. There are a number of hypotheses concerning the constitution of the upper mantle. It is postulated by some that eclogite, a garnet-augite rock, is the main constituent of the upper mantle. Another widely held view postulates a peridotite upper mantle. Dunite would be the predominant constituent of this mantle. In addition to other arguments, the frequent occurrence of olivine inclusions in basic igneous rocks is taken as support of this hypothesis. Eclogites have a chemical composition similar to basalt. RINGWOOD has proposed an upper mantle consisting of *pyrolite*, with a chemical composition corresponding to that of a 1:3 ratio of basalt and peridotite. Olivine inclusions would then correspond to material separated from the mantle.

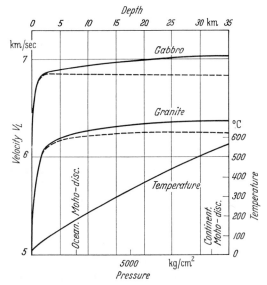

Fig. 388. Relation of propagation velocity of longitudinal waves, V_L, to pressure alone (———)
and to pressure and temperature (-----) in gabbro and granite. (From Handbook of Physical
Constants, 1966)

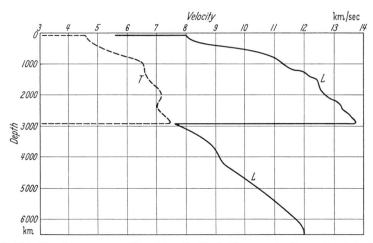

Fig. 389. Velocity of transverse (T) and longitudinal (L) waves in the earth's interior. (After
GUTENBERG and RICHTER)

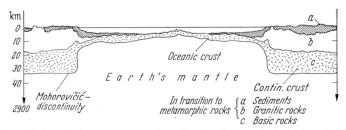

Fig. 390. Simplified vertically exaggerated profile, North America—Africa. [After HEEZEN,
THARP, and EWING (1959) from WEDEPOHL (1963)]

Table 72. *Classification of meteorites. No. of falls, 1492—1961 in ( ); no of finds in [ ].*
(After B. MASON, 1962; K. KEIL, 1961; and F. HEIDE, 1957)

Kind	Group	Class	Most common minerals
Stony meteorites (silicates predominate)	Chondrites (592) (with spherulites)	enstatite-Ch. [11]	enstatite, nickel-iron
		olivine-bronzite-Ch.	olivine, bronzite, nickel-iron
		olivine-hypersthene-Ch. } [900]	olivine, hypersthene, nickel-iron
		olivine-pigeonite-Ch. [12]	olivine, pigeonite
		carbonaceous-Ch. [17]	serpentine
	Achondrites (55) (without spherulites)	aubrites [9]	enstatite
		diogenites [8]	hypersthene
		chassignites [1]	olivine
		ureilites [3]	olivine, pigeonite, nickel-iron
		angrites [1]	augite
		nachlites [2]	diopside, olivine
		eucrites [39]	pigeonite, plagioclase
		howardites [39]	hypersthene, plagioclase
Stony-iron meteorites (transitional to iron meteorites)	Siderolites (9) (silicates predominate)	lodranites [1]	bronzite, olivine, nickel-iron
		mesosiderites [22]	pyroxenite, plagioclase, nickel-iron
	Lithosiderites (3) (iron predominates)	pallasites [40]	olivine, nickel-iron
		siderophyres [1]	bronzite, nickel-iron
Iron meteorites (39)		hexahedrites [55]	kamacite $= \alpha$ Fe with ~5.5% Ni
		octahedrites [487]	kamacite, taenite
		ataxites [36]	taenite $= \gamma$ Fe with ~8—55% Ni

This differentiation into a nickel-iron core and silicate layers has led to the hypothesis, held for some time, that the earth consists of material analogous in composition to meteoritic material. For this reason it is important that we examine this idea briefly.

Meteorites. Since it was suggested by CHLADNI in 1794, the idea has prevailed that meteorites are fragments of a celestial body which have reached the earth from somewhere in space. They probably originate from the belt of small planetoids that revolve about the sun in a strongly elliptical orbit between Mars and Jupiter. Whether they originated from one or more disintegrated planets or from smaller asteroids is not known. They exhibit great variability in composition, as Table 72 shows. By way of explanation it is to be noted that we distinguish as "falls" those meteorites which were observed to fall (in parentheses) and as "finds", those whose fall was not observed (in square brackets). The most common stony meteorites are the chondrites, so-named because they consist of chondrules, or spherolitic aggregates of silicates. Their diameters vary between

0.1 to a few millimeters. These structures are absent in the achondrites. A portion of the achondrites have chemical compositions similar to gabbroic rocks. Others are chemically similar to the chondrites which have compositions like peridotites.

To what extent we can conclude that meteoritic material is analogous to the earth's mantle, and to what extent this material has been changed during the course of earth history cannot be considered here. We shall attempt, however, to outline a very simple model for the origin of the earth, which consists of four major stages. We owe this summary to BIRCH (1965).

Table 73. *Proposed composition of the core (A), mantle (B), and the crust (C). (A and B after B. MASON, 1966, C from Table 42)*

	A	B	C
O		43.7	47.25
Si		22.5	30.54
Al		1.6	7.83
Fe	86.3	9.88	3.54
Ca		1.67	2.87
K		0.11	2.82
Na		0.84	2.45
Mg		18.8	1.39
Ti		0.08	0.47
P		0.14	0.08
Mn		0.33	0.07
Ni	7.36		0.0044
Co	0.40		0.0012
S	5.94		0.031
	100.00	99.65	99.3466

1. Matter, which had a composition similar to iron and stony meteorites, coalesced about 5,000 million years ago to form a heterogeneous agglomerate.

2. This mass was heated up by the evolution of heat from radioactive elements and from tidal friction. The melting point of iron was reached at depth after about 500 million years.

3. The fluid iron sank to the interior forming the earth's core. As a result about 600 cal/g of heat was liberated. A low melting portion of the silicates melted and ascended forming the earth's mantle. It now contained essentially all of the radioactive elements. This happened 3,500—4,500 million years ago.

4. The earth's crust began to differentiate in some regions about 3,500 million years ago. Radioactive elements were enriched in the crust relative to the mantle. Then the cycle erosion-sedimentation-mountain building began.

If we attempt to estimate the chemical composition of the core and mantle, the results are influenced greatly by a number of more or less uncertain assumptions. Values, calculated by B. MASON (1966), are compiled in Table 73 and compared with corresponding values for the crust, taken from Table 42. We can probably conclude without reservation that among the most common elements, Si, Al, Ca, K, Na, and Ti are enriched in the crust, Fe, Mg, P, and Mn in the mantle. Since, as Table 71 shows, the crust makes up only 0.4% of the mass of the earth, the approximate composition of the total earth can be calculated from data for the mantle + core.

Cosmic Abundance of the Elements. We have a much better idea of the cosmic abundance of elements as a result of spectrographic investigations of stellar light. These data, supplemented by analyses of meteorites and crustal data, are comled in the first two columns of Table 74 (SUESS-UREY, 1956 and CAMERON, 1959). The third column gives the spectral analytically determined values for the sun. The sun contains 333,400 times the mass of the earth and 99.8% of the total mass of the solar system. The data in these tables are based on Si abundance of 10^6. They are especially significant with respect to theories of the origin of the elements, with which we cannot deal here.

Table 74. *Abundance of elements in cosmos* (after H. E. SUESS and H. C. UREY, 1956, and A. G. W. CAMERON, 1959) *and of the sun* (after L. H. ALLER, 1961) (*based on Si = 10⁶*). (From ROESLER-LANGE, 1965)

Element		Cosmos		Sun ALLER
		SUESS-UREY	CAMERON	
1	H	$4.00 \cdot 10^{10}$	$2.50 \cdot 10^{10}$	$3.16 \cdot 10^{10}$
2	He	$3.08 \cdot 10^9$	$3.80 \cdot 10^9$	—
3	Li	100	100	$2.8819 \cdot 10^{-1}$
4	Be	20	20	$7.239 \cdot 10^0$
5	B	24	24	$1.58 \cdot 10^3$
6	C	$3.5 \cdot 10^6$	$9.3 \cdot 10^6$	$1.658 \cdot 10^7$
7	N	$6.6 \cdot 10^6$	$2.4 \cdot 10^6$	$3.017 \cdot 10^6$
8	O	$2.15 \cdot 10^7$	$2.5 \cdot 10^7$	$2.881 \cdot 10^7$
9	F	1600	1600	—
10	Ne	$8.6 \cdot 10^6$	$8.0 \cdot 10^5$	—
11	Na	$4.38 \cdot 10^4$	$4.38 \cdot 10^4$	$3.512 \cdot 10^4$
12	Mg	$9.12 \cdot 10^5$	$9.12 \cdot 10^5$	$7.937 \cdot 10^5$
13	Al	$9.48 \cdot 10^4$	$9.48 \cdot 10^4$	$5.008 \cdot 10^4$
14	Si	$1.00 \cdot 10^6$	$1.00 \cdot 10^6$	1.10^6
15	P	$1.00 \cdot 10^4$	$1.00 \cdot 10^4$	$6.914 \cdot 10^3$
16	S	$3.75 \cdot 10^5$	$3.75 \cdot 10^5$	$6.304 \cdot 10^5$
17	Cl	8850	2610	—
18	Ar	$1.5 \cdot 10^5$	$1.5 \cdot 10^5$	—
19	K	3160	3160	$1.583 \cdot 10^3$
20	Ca	$4.90 \cdot 10^4$	$4.90 \cdot 10^4$	$4.465 \cdot 10^3$
21	Sc	28	28	$2.087 \cdot 10^1$
22	Ti	2440	1680	$1.512 \cdot 10^3$
23	V	220	220	$1.583 \cdot 10^2$
24	Cr	7800	7800	$7.239 \cdot 10^3$
25	Mn	6850	6850	$2.509 \cdot 10^3$
26	Fe	$6.00 \cdot 10^5$	$8.50 \cdot 10^4$	$1.173 \cdot 10^5$
27	Co	1800	1800	$1.379 \cdot 10^3$
28	Ni	$2.74 \cdot 10^4$	$2.74 \cdot 10^4$	$4.465 \cdot 10^4$
29	Cu	212	212	$3.463 \cdot 10^3$
30	Zn	486	202	$7.937 \cdot 10^2$
31	Ga	11.4	9.05	$7.239 \cdot 10^0$
32	Ge	50.5	25.3	$6.162 \cdot 10^1$
33	As	4.0	1.70	—
34	Se	67.6	18.8	—
35	Br	13.4	3.95	—
36	Kr	51.3	42.0	—
37	Rb	6.5	6.50	$9.543 \cdot 10^0$
38	Sr	18.9	61.0	$1.257 \cdot 10^1$
39	Y	8.9	8.9	$5.618 \cdot 10^0$
40	Zr	54.5	14.2	$5.365 \cdot 10^0$
41	Nb	1.00	0.81	$2.816 \cdot 10^0$
42	Mo	2.42	2.42	$2.509 \cdot 10^0$
43	Tc	—	—	—
44	Ru	1.49	0.87	$8.506 \cdot 10^{-1}$
45	Rh	0.214	0.15	$1.904 \cdot 10^{-1}$
46	Pd	0.675	0.675	$5.125 \cdot 10^{-1}$
47	Ag	0.26	0.26	$4.360 \cdot 10^{-2}$
48	Cd	0.89	0.89	$9.113 \cdot 10^{-1}$
49	In	0.11	0.11	$4.566 \cdot 10^{-1}$
50	Sn	1.33	1.33	$1.095 \cdot 10^0$
51	Sb	0.246	0.227	$2.752 \cdot 10^0$
52	Te	4.67	2.91	—
53	I	0.80	0.60	—
54	Xe	4.0	3.35	—
55	Cs	0.456	0.456	—
56	Ba	3.66	3.66	$3.978 \cdot 10^0$

Table 74. (Continuation)

Element		Cosmos		Sun ALLER
		SUESS-UREY	CAMERON	
57	La	2.00	0.50	—
58	Ce	2.26	0.575	—
59	Pr	0.40	0.23	—
60	Nd	1.44	0.874	—
61	Pm	—	—	—
62	Sm	0.664	0.238	—
63	Eu	0.187	0.115	—
64	Gd	0.684	0.516	—
65	Tb	0.0956	0.090	—
66	Dy	0.556	0.665	—
67	Ho	0.118	0.18	—
68	Er	0.316	0.583	—
69	Tm	0.0318	0.090	—
70	Yb	0.220	0.393	$1.070 \cdot 10^{0}$
71	Lu	0.050	0.0358	—
72	Hf	0.438	0.113	—
73	Ta	0.065	0.015	—
74	W	0.49	0.105	—
75	Re	0.135	0.054	—
76	Os	1.00	0.64	—
77	Ir	0.821	0.494	—
78	Pt	1.625	1.28	—
79	Au	0.145	0.145	—
80	Hg	0.284	0.408	—
81	Tl	0.108	0.31	—
82	Pb	0.47	21.7	$6.756 \cdot 10^{-1}$
83	Bi	0.144	0.3	—
90	Th	—	0.027	—
92	U	—	0.0078	—

PART THREE

Appendix

A. Crystallo-

1. Summary of

System	Class	Symbol after HERMANN-MAUGUIN	Symmetry axis ⊥ to			planes in			Center
			(001)	(010)	(100)	(001)	(010)	(100)	
Triclinic	triclinic pedial	1	—	—	—	—	—	—	—
	triclinic pinacoidal	I̅	—	—	—	—	—	—	C
Monoclinic	monoclinic domatic	m	—	—	—	—	m	—	—
	monoclinic sphenoidal	2	—	$2p$	—	—	—	—	—
	monoclinic prismatic	$2/m$	—	2	—	—	m	—	C
Ortho-rhombic	rhombic pyramidal	$mm2$	$2p$	—	—	—	m	m	—
	rhombic disphenoidal	222	2	2	2	—	—	—	—
	rhombic dipyramidal	$2/m\ 2/m\ 2/m$ (mmm)	2	2	2	m	m	m	C

Note for Table 1. In the columns denoted Symmetry Axes and Planes the numbers indicate the type of symmetry axis. The letter p to the right of the number indicates a polar axis; a dash above the number indicates an inversion axis. The latter m corresponds to the Hermann-Mauguin symbol for a symmetry plane. If there is more than one equivalent symmetry axis for a class, their number is indicated to the left, separated by a dot. Thus $3 \cdot 2p$ indicates three polar 2-fold axes.

graphic Tables

the 32 Crystal Classes

Forms

{001}	{010}	{100}	{h k 0}	{h 0 l}	{0 k l}	{h k l}
1 o Pedion asym- metric	1 o Pedion asym- metric	1 o Pedion asym- metric	1 o Pedion asym- metric	1 o Pedion asym- metric	1 o Pedion asym- metric	1 o Pedion asym- metric
2 o Pinacoid asym- metric	2 o Pinacoid asym- metric	2 o Pinacoid asym- metric	2 o Pinacoid asym- metric	2 o Pinacoid asym- metric	2 o Pinacoid asym- metric	2 o Pinacoid asym- metric
1 o Pedion mono- sym- metric	2 o Pinacoid asym- metric	1 o Pedion mono- sym- metric	2 o Dome asym- metric	1 o Pedion mono- sym- metric	2 o Dome asym- metric	2 o Dome asym- metric
2 o Pinacoid asym- metric	1 o Pedion dimetric	2 o Pinacoid asym- metric	2 o Sphenoid asym- metric	2 o Pinacoid asym- metric	2 o Sphenoid asym- metric	2 o Sphenoid asym- metric
2 o Pinacoid mono- sym- metric	2 o Pinacoid dimetric	2 o Pinacoid mono- sym- metric	4 o Prism asym- metric	2 o Pinacoid mono- sym- metric	4 o Prism asym- metric	4 o Prism asym- metric
1 o Pedion disym- metric	2 o Pinacoid mono- sym- metric	2 o Pinacoid mono- sym- metric	4 o Prism asym- metric	2 o Dome mono- sym- metric	2 o Dome mono- sym- metric	4 o rhombic Pyramid asym- metric
2 o Pinacoid dimetric	2 o Pinacoid dimetric	2 o Pinacoid dimetric	4 o Prism asym- metric	4 o Prism asym- metric	4 o Prism asym- metric	4 g rhombic Di- sphenoid asym- metric
2 o Pinacoid disym- metric	2 o Pinacoid disym- metric	2 o Pinacoid disym- metric	4 o Prism mono- sym- metric	4 o Prism mono- sym- metric	4 o Prism mono- sym- metric	8 g rhombic Di- pyramid asym- metric

Above and to the left of the name for each form the number of equivalent faces is given; the symbols o or g to the right indicate either an open or a closed form. The planar symmetry for each special class is indicated beneath each form.

In the case of cubic crystals the small diagram shown for the {hhl} forms indicates the distribution of edges about the zone [111] when the crystal is viewed along [110].

System	Class	Symbol after HERMANN-MAUGUIN	Symmetry axis ⊥ to (0001)	(10Ī0)	(11Ī0)	planes in (0001)	(10Ī0)	(11Ī0)	Center
Trigonal	trigonal pyramidal	3	$3p$	—	—	—	—	—	—
	trigonal rhombohedral	$\bar{3}$	$\bar{3}$	—	—	—	—	—	C
	ditrigonal pyramidal	$3\,m$	$3p$	—	—	—	—	$3 \cdot m$	—
	trigonal trapezohedral	32	3	—	$3 \cdot 2p$	—	—	—	—
	ditrigonal scalenohedral	$\bar{3}\,2/m$ ($\bar{3}\,m$)	$\bar{3}$	—	$3 \cdot 2$	—	—	$3 \cdot m$	C
	trigonal dipyramidal	$\bar{6}$	$\bar{6}$	—	—	m	—	—	—
	ditrigonal dipyramidal	$\bar{6}\,m\,2$	$\bar{6}$	$3 \cdot 2p$	—	m	—	$3 \cdot m$	—

Forms

{0001}	{10Ī0}	{11$\bar{2}$0}	{$hki0$}	{$h0\bar{h}l$}	{$hh\bar{2}\bar{h}l$}	{$hkil$}
1 o Pedion trimetric	3 o trigonal Prism 1. Position asymmetric	3 o trigonal Prism 2. Position asymmetric	3 o trigonal Prism 3. Position asymmetric	3 o trigonal Pyramid 1. Position asymmetric	3 o trigonal Pyramid 2. Position asymmetric	3 o trigonal Pyramid 3. Position asymmetric
2 o Pinacoid trimetric	6 o hexagonal Prism 1. Position asymmetric	6 o hexagonal Prism 2. Position asymmetric	6 o hexagonal Prism 3. Position asymmetric	6 g Rhombohedron 1. Position asymmetric	6 g Rhombohedron 2. Position asymmetric	6 g Rhombohedron 3. Position asymmetric
1 o Pedion trisymmetric	3 o trigonal Prism 1. Position monosymmetric	6 o hexagonal Prism 2. Position asymmetric	6 o ditrigonal Prism asymmetric	3 o trigonal Pyramid 1. Position monosymmetric	6 o hexagonal Pyramid 2. Position asymmetric	6 o ditrigonal Pyramid asymmetric
2 o Pinacoid trimetric	6 o hexagonal Prism 1. Position asymmetric	3 o trigonal Prism 2. Position dimetric	6 o ditrigonal Prism asymmetric	6 g Rhombohedron 1. Position asymmetric	6 g trigonal Dipyramid 2. Position asymmetric	6 g trigonal Trapezohedron asymmetric
2 o Pinacoid trisymmetric	6 o hexagonal Prism 1. Position monosymmetric	6 o hexagonal Prism 2. Position dimetric	12 o dihexagonal Prism asymmetric	6 g Rhombohedron 1. Position monosymmetric	12 g hexagonal Dipyramid 2. Position asymmetric	12 g ditrigonal Scalenohedron asymmetric
2 o Pinacoid trimetric	3 o trigonal Prism 1. Position monosymmetric	3 o trigonal Prism 2. Position monosymmetric	3 o trigonal Prism 3. Position monosymmetric	6 g trigonal Dipyramid 1. Position asymmetric	6 g trigonal Dipyramid 2. Position asymmetric	6 g trigonal Dipyramid 3. Position asymmetric
2 o Pinacoid trisymmetric	3 o trigonal Prism 1. Position disymmetric	6 o hexagonal Prism 2. Position monosymmetric	6 o ditrigonal Prism monosymmetric	6 g trigonal Dipyramid 1. Position monosymmetric	12 g hexagonal Dipyramid 2. Position asymmetric	12 g ditrigonal Dipyramid asymmetric

System	Class	Symbol after Herrmann-Mauguin	Symmetry						
			axis ⊥ to			planes in			Cen-ter
			(0001)	(10$\bar{1}$0)	(11$\bar{2}$0)	(0001)	(10$\bar{1}$0)	(11$\bar{2}$0)	
Hexagonal	hexagonal pyramidal	6	6 p	—	—	—	—	—	—
	hexagonal dipyramidal	6/m	6	—	—	m	—	—	C
	dihexagonal pyramidal	6 $m m$	6 p	—	—	—	3 · m	3 · m	—
	hexagonal trapezohedral	622	6	3 · 2	3 · 2	—	—	—	—
	dihexagonal dipyramidal	6/m 2/m 2/m (6/$m m m$)	6	3 · 2	3 · 2	m	3 · m	3 · m	C

Forms

{0001}	{10$\bar{1}$0}	{11$\bar{2}$0}	{$hk\bar{i}0$}	{$h0\bar{h}l$}	{$hh\overline{2h}l$}	{$hkil$}
1 o Pedion hexa- metric	6 o hexa- gonal Prism 1. Position asym- metric	6 o hexa- gonal Prism 2. Position asym- metric	6 o hexa- gonal Prism 3. Position asym- metric	6 o hexa- gonal Pyramid 1. Position asym- metric	6 o hexa- gonal Pyramid 2. Positon asym- metric	6 o hexa- gonal Pyramid 3. Position asym- metric
2 o Pinacoid hexa- metric	6 o hexa- gonal Prism 1. Position mono- sym- metric	6 o hexa- gonal Prism 2. Position mono- sym- metric	6 o hexa- gonal Prism 3. Position mono- sym- metric	12 g hexa- gonal Dipyramid 1. Position asym- metric	12 g hexa- gonal Dipyramid 2. Position asym- metric	12 g hexa- gonal Di- pyramid 3. Position asym- metric
1 o Pedion hexa- sym- metric	6 o hexa- gonal Prism 1. Position mono- sym- metric	6 o hexa- gonal Prism 2. Position mono- sym- metric	12 o dihexa- gonal Prism asym- metric	6 o hexa- gonal Pyramid 1. Position mono- sym- metric	6 o hexa- gonal Pyramid 2. Position mono- sym- metric	12 o dihexa- gonal Pyramid asym- metric
2 o Pinacoid hexa- metric	6 o hexa- gonal Prism 1. Position dimetric	6 o hexa- gonal Prism 2. Position dimetric	12 o dihexa- gonal Prism asym- metric	12 g hexa- gonal Dipyramid 1. Position asym- metric	12 g hexa- gonal Dipyramid 2. Position asym- metric	12 g hexa- gonal Trapezo- hedron asym- metric
2 o Pinacoid hexa- symmetric	6 o hexa- gonal Prism 1. Position disym- metric	6 o hexa- gonal Prism 2. Position disym- metric	12 o dihexa- gonal Prism mono- sym- metric	12 g hexa- gonal Dipyramid 1. Position mono- sym- metric	12 g hexa- gonal Dipyramid 2. Position mono- sym- metric	24 g dihexa- gonal Di- pyramid asym- metric

System	Class	Symbol after Hermann-Mauguin	Symmetry						
			axis ⊥ to			planes in			Center
			(001)	(100)	(110)	(001)	(100)	(110)	
Tetragonal	tetragonal pyramidal	4	$4p$	—	—	—	—	—	—
	tetragonal dipyramidal	$4/m$	4	—	—	m	—	—	C
	ditetragonal pyramidal	$4mm$	$4p$	—	—	—	$2 \cdot m$	$2 \cdot m$	—
	tetragonal trapezohedral	422	4	$2 \cdot 2$	$2 \cdot 2$	—	—	—	—
	ditetragonal dipyramidal	$4/m\,2/m\,2/m$ $(4/mmm)$	4	$2 \cdot 2$	$2 \cdot 2$	m	$2 \cdot m$	$2 \cdot m$	C
	tetragonal disphenoidal	$\bar{4}$	$\bar{4}$	—	—	—	—	—	—
	tetragonal scalenohedral	$\bar{4}2m$	$\bar{4}$	$2 \cdot 2$	—	—	—	$2 \cdot m$	—

Forms

{001}	{100}	{110}	{hk0}	{h0l}	{hhl}	{hkl}
1 o Pedion tetrametric	4 o tetragonal Prism 2. Position asymmetric	4 o tetragonal Prism 1. Position asymmetric	4 o tetragonal Prism 3. Position asymmetric	4 o tetragonal Pyramid 2. Position asymmetric	4 o tetragonal Pyramid 1. Position asymmetric	4 o tetragonal Pyramid 3. Position asymmetric
2 o Pinacoid tetrametric	4 o tetragonal Prism 2. Position monosymmetric	4 o tetragonal Prism 1. Position monosymmetric	4 o tetragonal Prism 3. Position monosymmetric	8 g tetragonal Dipyramid 2. Position asymmetric	8 g tetragonal Dipyramid 1. Position asymmetric	8 g tetragonal Dipyramid 3. Position asymmetric
1 o Pedion tetrasymmetric	4 o tetragonal Prism 2. Position monosymmetric	4 o tetragonal Prism 1. Position symmetric	8 o ditetragonal Prism asymmetric	4 o tetragonal Pyramid 2. Position monosymmetric	4 o tetragonal Pyramid 1. Position monosymmetric	8 o ditetragonal Pyramid asymmetric
2 o Pinacoid tetrametric	4 o tetragonal Prism 2. Position dimetric	4 o tetragonal Prism 1. Position dimetric	8 o ditetragonal Prism asymmetric	8 g tetragonal Dipyramid 2. Position asymmetric	8 g tetragonal Dipyramid 1. Position asymmetric	8 g tetragonal Trapezohedron asymmetric
2 o Pinacoid tetrasymmetric	4 o tetragonal Prism 2. Position disymmetric	4 o tetragonal Prism 1. Position disymmetric	8 o ditetragonal Prism monosymmetric	8 g tetragonal Dipyramid 2. Position monosymmetric	8 g tetragonal Dipyramid 1. Position monosymmetric	16 g ditetragonal Dipyramid asymmetric
2 o Pinacoid dimetric	4 o tetragonal Prism 2. Position asymmetric	4 o tetragonal Prism 1. Position asymmetric	4 o tetragonal Prism 3. Position asymmetric	4 g tetragonal Disphenoid 2. Position asymmetric	4 g tetragonal Disphenoid 1. Position asymmetric	4 g tetragonal Disphenoid 3. Position asymmetric
2 o Pinacoid disymmetric	4 o tetragonal Prism 2. Position dimetric	4 o tetragonal Prism 1. Position monosymmetric	8 o ditetragonal Prism asymmetric	8 g tetragonal Dipyramid 2. Position asymmetric	4 g tetragonal Disphenoid 1. Position monosymmetric	8 g tetragonal Scalenohedron asymmetric

System	Class	Symbol after HERMANN-MAUGUIN	Symmetry					Center
			axis ⊥ to			planes in		
			(100)	(111)	(110)	(100)	(110)	
Cubic	cubic tetartoidal	23	3 · 2	4 · 3p	—	—	—	—
	cubic diploidal	2/m 3 (m3)	3 · 2	4 · 3̄	—	3 · m	—	C
	cubic hex-tetrahedral	4̄3m	3 · 4̄	4 · 3p	—	—	6 · m	—
	cubic gyroidal	432	3 · 4	4 · 3	6 · 2	—	—	—
	cubic hex-octahedral	4/m 3 2/m (m3m)	3 · 4	4 · 3̄	6 · 2	3 · m	6 · m	C

Forms

{100}	{110}	{111}	{hk0}	△ {hhl}, h < l	△ {hhl}, h > l	{hkl}
6 g Cube dimetric	12 g Rhombic dodecahedron asymmetric	4 g Tetrahedron trimetric	12 g Pentagonal dodecahedron asymmetric	12 g Tristetrahedron asymmetric	12 g Deltoiddodecahedron asymmetric	12 g Tetartoid asymmetric
6 g Cube disymmetric	12 g Rhombic dodecahedron monosymmetric	8 g Octahedron trimetric	12 g Pentagonal dodecahedron monosymmetric	24 g Deltoidicositetrahedron asymmetric	24 g Trisoctahedron asymmetric	24 g Diploid asymmetric
6 g Cube disymmetric	12 g Rhombic dodecahedron monosymmetric	4 g Tetrahedron trisymmetric	24 g Tetrahexahedron asymmetric	12 g Tristetrahedron monosymmetric	12 g Deltoiddodecahedron monosymmetric	24 g Hextetrahedron asymmetric
6 g Cube tetrametric	12 g Rhombic dodecahedron dimetric	8 g Octahedron trimetric	24 g Tetrahexahedron asymmetric	24 g Deltoidicositetrahedron asymmetric	24 g Trisoctahedron asymmetric	24 g Gyroid asymmetric
6 g Cube tetrasymmetric	12 g Rhombic dodecahedron disymmetric	8 g Octahedron trisymmetric	24 g Tetrahexahedron monosymmetric	24 g Deltoidicositetrahedron monosymmetric	24 g Trisoctahedron monosymmetric	48 g Hexoctahedron asymmetric

2. Alternative Nomenclature for the 32 Crystal Classes

Based on the general form [a]	Based on reduction of the general form as compared to that of the highest symmetry class of the same system [b]	HERMANN-MAUGUIN [c]	SCHOEN-FLIES
triclinic pedial	triclinic hemihedral	1	C_1
triclinic pinacoidal	triclinic holohedral	$\bar{1}$	C_i
monoclinic sphenoidal	monoclinic hemimorphic	2	C_2
monoclinic domatic	monoclinic hemihedral	m	C_s
monoclinic prismatic	monoclinic holohedral	$2/m$	C_{2h}
rhombic disphenoidal	orthorhombic enantiomorphic	222	$D_2(V)$
rhombic pyramidal	orthorhombic hemimorphic	$mm2$	C_{2v}
rhombic dipyramidal	orthorhombic holohedral	mmm	$D_{2h}(V_h)$
tetragonal pyramidal	tetragonal tetartohedral, 1. sort	4	C_4
tetragonal dipyramidal	tetragonal paramorphic	$4/m$	C_{4h}
tetragonal trapezohedral	tetragonal enantiomorphic	422	D_4
ditetragonal pyramidal	tetragonal hemimorphic	$4mm$	C_{4v}
ditetragonal dipyramidal	tetragonal holohedral	$4/mmm$	D_{4h}
tetragonal disphenoidal	tetragonal tetartohedral, 2. sort	$\bar{4}$	S_4
tetragonal scalenohedral	tetragonal hemihedral, 2. sort	$\bar{4}2m$	$D_{2d}(V_d)$
trigonal pyramidal	trig.-rhombohedral tetartohedral	3	C_3
trigonal rhombohedral	trig.-rhombohedral paramorphic	$\bar{3}$	C_{3i}
trigonal trapezohedral	trig.-rhombohedral enantiomorphic	32	D_3
ditrigonal pyramidal	trig.-rhombohedral hemimorphic	$3m$	C_{3v}
ditrigonal scalenohedral	trig.-rhombohedral holohedral	$\bar{3}m$	D_{3d}
trigonal dipyramidal [d]	hexagonal tetartohedral, 2. sort	$\bar{6}$	C_{3h}
ditrigonal dipyramidal [d]	hexagonal hemihedral, 2. sort	$\bar{6}m2$	D_{3h}
hexagonal pyramidal	hexagonal tetartohedral, 1. sort	6	C_6
hexagonal dipyramidal	hexagonal paramorphic	$6/m$	C_{6h}
hexagonal trapezohedral	hexagonal enantiomorphic	622	D_6
dihexagonal pyramidal	hexagonal hemimorphic	$6mm$	C_{6v}
dihexagonal dipyramidal	hexagonal holohedral	$6/mmm$	D_{6h}
cubic tetartoidal	cubic tetartohedral	23	T
cubic diploidal	cubic paramorphic	$m3$	T_h
cubic gyroidal	cubic enantiomorphic	432	O
cubic hextetrahedral	cubic hemimorphic	$\bar{4}3m$	T_d
cubic hexoctahedral	cubic holohedral	$m3m$	O_h

[a] Nomenclature used in this book, from GROTH.

[b] There are several variations of this nomenclature; usage here from Niggli, Lehrbuch der Mineralogie und Kristallographie I.

[c] Shortened form.

[d] Regarding assignment of these classes to the trigonal or hexagonal systems see p. 37.

3. Rhombohedral Axes

It is possible and sometimes useful in the case of trigonal crystals to relate them to rhombohedral as well as hexagonal axes. The relationship between these two axial systems is illustrated in Fig. 391. It is customary in X-ray crystallography to express rhombohedral cells in terms of hexagonal axes.

The relationship between the axial ratio c/a (hex.) and the rhombohedral angle ϱ can be expressed as follows:

$$\sin\frac{\varrho}{2} = \frac{3}{2\sqrt{3 + \left(\frac{c}{a}\right)^2}} \; ; \quad \frac{c}{a} = \sqrt{\frac{9}{4\sin^2\frac{\varrho}{2}} - 3}$$

Hexagonal indices $(hk \cdot l)$ can be transformed to rhombohedral indices (pqr) by the expressions:

$$p = \tfrac{1}{3}(2h + k + l),$$
$$q = \tfrac{1}{3}(k - h + l),$$
$$r = \tfrac{1}{3}(-2k - h + l).$$

Conversely:

$$h = p - q$$
$$k = q - r$$
$$l = p + q + r.$$

Thus we obtain:

$(00.1)_{\text{hex.}} = (\tfrac{1}{3}\tfrac{1}{3}\tfrac{1}{3})_{\text{rh.}}$ or $(111)_{\text{rh.}}$;
$(10.0)_{\text{hex.}} = (\tfrac{2}{3}\tfrac{\bar{1}}{3}\tfrac{\bar{1}}{3})_{\text{rh.}}$ or $(2\bar{1}\bar{1})_{\text{rh.}}$;
$(100)_{\text{rh}} = (10.1)_{\text{hex.}}$ etc.

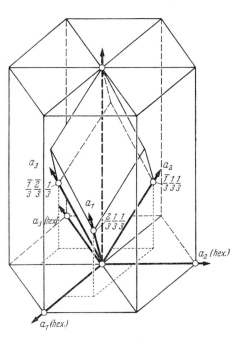

Fig. 391. Relation between hexagonal and rhombohedral coordinate axes. The origin of the rhombohedral axes has, as related to the transformation formulae of the text, the indicated coordinates (based on the a_1, a_2 and c axes of the hexagonal coordinate system).

4. Comparison of Naumann Symbols and Miller-Bravais Indices (to Assist in Interpreting the Older Crystallographic Literature)

Triclinic		Monoclinic			Orthorhombic		
$0P$	$\{001\}$	$0P$	$\{001\}$		$0P$	$\{001\}$	
P'	$\{111\}$	$+P$	$\{\bar{1}11\}$		P	$\{111\}$	
$'P$	$\{1\bar{1}1\}$	$-P$	$\{111\}$		mP	$\{hhl\}$	
$P,$	$\{\bar{1}\bar{1}1\}$	$+mP$	$\{\bar{h}hl\}$		$m\bar{P}n$	$\{hkl\}$	$(h>k)$
$,P$	$\{\bar{1}11\}$	$-mP$	$\{hhl\}$		$m\breve{P}n$	$\{hkl\}$	$(h<k)$
mP'	$\{hhl\}$	$+mPn$	$\{\bar{h}kl\}$ $(h>k)$		∞P	$\{110\}$	
$\infty P,$	$\{110\}$	$-mPn$	$\{hkl\}$ $(h>k)$		$\infty \bar{P}n$	$\{hk0\}$	$(h>k)$
∞',P	$\{1\bar{1}0\}$	$+mPn$	$\{\bar{h}kl\}$ $(h<k)$		$\infty \breve{P}n$	$\{hk0\}$	$(h<k)$
$m\bar{P}'n$	$\{hkl\}$ $(h>k)$	$-mPn$	$\{hkl\}$ $(h<k)$		$m\bar{P}\infty$	$\{0kl\}$	$(k/l=m)$
$m\breve{P}'n$	$\{hkl\}$ $(h<k)$	∞P	$\{110\}$		$m\breve{P}\infty$	$\{h0l\}$	$(h/l=m)$
$m'\bar{P}'\infty$	$\{h0l\}$	∞Pn	$\{hk0\}$ $(h<k)$		$\infty\bar{P}\infty$	$\{010\}$	
$m,\breve{P}'\infty$	$\{0kl\}$	∞Pn	$\{hk0\}$ $(h>k)$		$\infty\breve{P}\infty$	$\{100\}$	
$\infty\bar{P}'n$	$\{hk0\}$ $(h>k)$	$+mP\infty$	$\{\bar{h}0l\}$				
$\infty\breve{P}'n$	$\{hk0\}$ $(h<k)$	$-mP\infty$	$\{h0l\}$				
$\infty\bar{P}\infty$	$\{100\}$	$mP\infty$	$\{0kl\}$				
$\infty\breve{P}\infty$	$\{010\}$	$\infty P\infty$	$\{100\}$				
		$\infty P\infty$	$\{010\}$				

Hexagonal	Indices after		Rhombohedral	Tetragonal		Cubic	
	Bravais	Miller					
$0P$	$\{0001\}$	$\{111\}$	$0R$	$0P$	$\{001\}$	O	$\{111\}$
	$\{10\bar{1}1\}$	$\{100\}$	R	P	$\{111\}$	mO	$\{hhl\}$ $(h>l)$
	$\{01\bar{1}2\}$	$\{110\}$	$\frac{1}{2}R$	mP	$\{hhl\}$	mOm	$\{hkk\}$ $(h>k)$
mP	$\{h0\bar{h}l\}$	$\{prr\}$ $(p>r)$	mR	mPn	$\{hkl\}$	mOn	$\{hkl\}$
$mP2$	$\{hh\bar{2}\bar{h}l\}$			$P\infty$	$\{101\}$	∞O	$\{110\}$
mPn	$\{hkil\}$	$\{pqr\}$	mRn	$mP\infty$	$\{h0l\}$	$\infty O\infty$	$\{100\}$
∞P	$\{10\bar{1}0\}$	$\{2\bar{1}1\}$	∞R	∞P	$\{110\}$		
$\infty P2$	$\{11\bar{2}0\}$	$\{10\bar{1}\}$	$\infty P2$	∞Pn	$\{hk0\}$		
∞Pn	$\{hki0\}$	$\{p\bar{q}r\}$	∞Pn	$\infty P\infty$	$\{100\}$		
$\dfrac{mPn}{2}$	$\{hkil\}$	Hemihedral					
$\dfrac{mPn}{4}$	$\{hkil\}$	Tetartohedral					

Hemihedral and tetartohedral forms in the cubic, tetragonal, and hexagonal systems designated by $\dfrac{mPn}{2}$ and $\dfrac{mPn}{4}$ or $\dfrac{mOn}{2}$ and $\dfrac{mOn}{4}$.

5. The Symbols for the 230 Space Groups

Two types of symbols are used to designate the different space groups. According to the older Schoenflies system, the space groups associated with a particular crystal class are numbered, the number appearing as a superscript above and to the right of the class symbol. The Hermann-Mauguin system, used most widely today, is based on the crystal class notations (see p. 29 and 43). The symbol for the translation group (space lattice) is placed in first position (see p. 50). The following symbols are used:

P primitive,

A face-centered on (100),

B face-centered on (010),

C face-centered on (001),

F face-centered on (100), (010) and (001),

I body-centered,

R rhombohedral.

Following the translation group symbol comes the crystal class (point group) symbol. This symbolism includes, however, notations characteristic of the entire three-dimensional pattern (see p. 19). For example, $P4_32_12$ is a space group designation corresponding to the tetragonal trapezohedral 422 class. A second example is the space group for pyrargyrite, $R3c$, corresponding to the crystal class $3m$. If symmetry axes are perpendicular to planes, the same convention is used as with point groups, for, example, $P2_1/c$.

We have reproduced in Table 5 the organization and nomenclature of the "International Tables for X-ray Crystallography", a reference work that definitely must be consulted for intensive work with space groups and crystal structures.

Remarks on Hermann-Mauguin Symbols

1. The symbols do not include always all of the symmetry elements of the space group. As they appear in the tables they are abbreviated. For, example, only the symmetry planes, not the two-fold axes (2 or 2_1) are indicated for orthorhombic pyramidal classes. In addition it is to be borne in mind that a particular space group can contain different symmetry elements running parallel to each other. The Hermann-Mauguin symbols do not indicate all of these. If we consider the space group symbols for the two enantiomorphic forms of low quartz, $P3_121$ and $P3_221$, the 2-fold secondary axes are noted. The notation is incomplete, however, for 2_1 axes also run in the same direction.

2. The Hermann-Mauguin symbol for a particular space group varies with different arrangement possibilities, giving rise to numerous combinations. The symbol for the frequently occurring space group No. 15 (C_{2h}^5) will be $P2_1/c$, $P2_1/a$ or $P2_1/n$, depending on the direction of translation in the glide plane.

3. In the case of space groups of the tetr. scalenohedral, trig. trapezohedral, ditrig. pyramidal, trig. scalenohedral, and ditrig. dipyramidal classes, the arrangement changes within the crystal class. Characteristic examples are No. 114 (D_{2d}^4): $P\bar{4}2_1c$ and No. 115 (D_{2d}^5): $P\bar{4}m2$. In the first case (in conformity with p. 42) the horizontal symmetry axes are secondary axes, in the second case intermediate axes. The two space groups are arrayed at 45° to each other. One selects an orientation which will produce the smallest unit cell. If we described space group No. 115 with the standard orientation, we should obtain a double, C-centered cell, with the symbol $C\bar{4}2m$.

4. In the classes 3, $\bar{3}$, 32, $3m$, and $\bar{3}2/m$ the hexagonal cell is sometimes the smallest, sometimes the rhombohedral cell, producing corresponding P or R translation groups. Two members of the trigonal scalenohedral class serve as examples. Brucite, $Mg(OH)_2$ crystallizes with space group No. 164 (D_{3d}^3): $P\bar{3}m1$. Its primitive unit cell is hexagonal, however, with $a = b \neq c$ and $\gamma = 120°$. Calcite, $CaCO_3$, crystallizes in space group No. 167 (D_{3d}^6): $R\bar{3}mc$; its primitive cell is rhombohedral.

No.	Hermann-Mauguin	Schoenflies	No.	Hermann-Mauguin	Schoenflies	No.	Hermann-Mauguin	Schoenflies
1	$P1$	C_1^1	31	$Pmn2_1$	C_{2v}^7	66	$Cccm$	D_{2h}^{20}
2	$P\bar{1}$	C_i^1	32	$Pba2$	C_{2v}^8	67	$Cmma$	D_{2h}^{21}
3	$P2$	C_2^1	33	$Pna2_1$	C_{2v}^9	68	$Ccca$	D_{2h}^{22}
4	$P2_1$	C_2^2	34	$Pnn2$	C_{2v}^{10}	69	$Fmmm$	D_{2h}^{23}
5	$C2$	C_2^3	35	$Cmm2$	C_{2v}^{11}	70	$Fddd$	D_{2h}^{24}
6	Pm	C_s^1	36	$Cmc2_1$	C_{2v}^{12}	71	$Immm$	D_{2h}^{25}
7	Pc	C_s^2	37	$Ccc2$	C_{2v}^{13}	72	$Ibam$	D_{2h}^{26}
8	Cm	C_s^3	38	$Amm2$	C_{2v}^{14}	73	$Ibca$	D_{2h}^{27}
9	Cc	C_s^4	39	$Abm2$	C_{2v}^{15}	74	$Imma$	D_{2h}^{28}
10	$P\dfrac{2}{m}$	C_{2h}^1	40	$Ama2$	C_{2v}^{16}	75	$P4$	C_4^1
11	$P\dfrac{2_1}{m}$	C_{2h}^2	41	$Aba2$	C_{2v}^{17}	76	$P4_1$	C_4^2
12	$C\dfrac{2}{m}$	C_{2h}^3	42	$Fmm2$	C_{2v}^{18}	77	$P4_2$	C_4^3
13	$P\dfrac{2}{c}$	C_{2h}^4	43	$Fdd2$	C_{2v}^{19}	78	$P4_3$	C_4^4
14	$P\dfrac{2_1}{c}$	C_{2h}^5	44	$Imm2$	C_{2v}^{20}	79	$I4$	C_4^5
15	$C\dfrac{2}{c}$	C_{2h}^6	45	$Iba2$	C_{2v}^{21}	80	$I4_1$	C_4^6
16	$P222$	D_2^1	46	$Ima2$	C_{2v}^{22}	81	$P\bar{4}$	S_4^1
17	$P222_1$	D_2^2	47	$Pmmm$	D_{2h}^1	82	$I\bar{4}$	S_4^2
18	$P2_12_12$	D_2^3	48	$Pnnn$	D_{2h}^2	83	$P\dfrac{4}{m}$	C_{4h}^1
19	$P2_12_12_1$	D_2^4	49	$Pccm$	D_{2h}^3	84	$P\dfrac{4_2}{m}$	C_{4h}^2
20	$C222_1$	D_2^5	50	$Pban$	D_{2h}^4	85	$P\dfrac{4}{n}$	C_{4h}^3
21	$C222$	D_2^6	51	$Pmma$	D_{2h}^5	86	$P\dfrac{4_2}{n}$	C_{4h}^4
22	$F222$	D_2^7	52	$Pnna$	D_{2h}^6	87	$I\dfrac{4}{m}$	C_{4h}^5
23	$I222$	D_2^8	53	$Pmna$	D_{2h}^7	88	$I\dfrac{4_1}{a}$	C_{4h}^6
24	$I2_12_12_1$	D_2^9	54	$Pcca$	D_{2h}^8	89	$P422$	D_4^1
25	$Pmm2$	C_{2v}^1	55	$Pbam$	D_{2h}^9	90	$P42_12$	D_4^2
26	$Pmc2_1$	C_{2v}^2	56	$Pccn$	D_{2h}^{10}	91	$P4_122$	D_4^3
27	$Pcc2$	C_{2v}^3	57	$Pbcm$	D_{2h}^{11}	92	$P4_12_12$	D_4^4
28	$Pma2$	C_{2v}^4	58	$Pnnm$	D_{2h}^{12}	93	$P4_222$	D_4^5
29	$Pca2_1$	C_{2v}^5	59	$Pmmn$	D_{2h}^{13}	94	$P4_22_12$	D_4^6
30	$Pnc2$	C_{2v}^6	60	$Pbcn$	D_{2h}^{14}	95	$P4_322$	D_4^7
			61	$Pbca$	D_{2h}^{15}			
			61	$Pnma$	D_{2h}^{16}			
			63	$Cmcm$	D_{2h}^{17}			
			64	$Cmca$	D_{2h}^{18}			
			65	$Cmmm$	D_{2h}^{19}			

No.	Hermann-Mauguin	Schoenflies	No.	Hermann-Mauguin	Schoenflies	No.	Hermann-Mauguin	Schoenflies
96	$P4_3 2_1 2$	D_4^8	127	$P\dfrac{4}{m}bm$	D_{4h}^5	152	$P3_1 21$	D_3^4
97	$I422$	D_4^9				153	$P3_2 12$	D_3^5
98	$I4_1 22$	D_4^{10}	128	$P\dfrac{4}{m}nc$	D_{4h}^6	154	$P3_2 21$	D_3^6
99	$P4mm$	C_{4v}^1	129	$P\dfrac{4}{n}mm$	D_{4h}^7	155	$R32$	D_3^7
100	$P4bm$	C_{4v}^2				156	$P3m1$	C_{3v}^1
101	$P4_2 cm$	C_{4v}^3	130	$P\dfrac{4}{n}cc$	D_{4h}^8	157	$P31m$	C_{3v}^2
102	$P4_2 nm$	C_{4v}^4	131	$P\dfrac{4_2}{m}mc$	D_{4h}^9	158	$P3c1$	C_{3v}^3
103	$P4cc$	C_{4v}^5	132	$P\dfrac{4_2}{m}cm$	D_{4h}^{10}	159	$P31c$	C_{3v}^4
104	$P4nc$	C_{4v}^6				160	$R3m$	C_{3v}^5
105	$P4_2 mc$	C_{4v}^7	133	$P\dfrac{4_2}{n}bc$	D_{4h}^{11}	161	$R3c$	C_{3v}^6
106	$P4_2 bc$	C_{4v}^8	134	$P\dfrac{4_2}{n}nm$	D_{4h}^{12}	162	$P\bar{3}1m$	D_{3d}^1
107	$I4mm$	C_{4v}^9	135	$P\dfrac{4_2}{m}bc$	D_{4h}^{13}	163	$P\bar{3}1m$	D_{3d}^2
108	$I4cm$	C_{4v}^{10}	136	$P\dfrac{4_2}{m}nm$	D_{4h}^{14}	164	$P\bar{3}m1$	D_{3d}^3
109	$I4_1 md$	C_{4v}^{11}				165	$P\bar{3}c1$	D_{3d}^4
110	$I4_1 cd$	C_{4v}^{12}	137	$P\dfrac{4_2}{n}mc$	D_{4h}^{15}	166	$R\bar{3}m$	D_{3d}^5
111	$P\bar{4}2m$	D_{2d}^1	138	$P\dfrac{4_2}{n}cm$	D_{4h}^{16}	167	$R\bar{3}c$	D_{3d}^6
112	$P\bar{4}2c$	D_{2d}^2	139	$I\dfrac{4}{m}mm$	D_{4h}^{17}	168	$P6$	C_6^1
113	$P\bar{4}2_1 m$	D_{2d}^3	140	$I\dfrac{4}{m}cm$	D_{4h}^{18}	169	$P6_1$	C_6^2
114	$P\bar{4}2_1 c$	D_{2d}^4	141	$I\dfrac{4_1}{a}md$	D_{4h}^{19}	170	$P6_5$	C_6^3
115	$P\bar{4}m2$	D_{2d}^5				171	$P6_2$	C_6^4
116	$P\bar{4}c2$	D_{2d}^6	142	$I\dfrac{4_1}{a}cd$	D_{4h}^{20}	172	$P6_4$	C_6^5
117	$P\bar{4}b2$	D_{2d}^7	143	$P3$	C_3^1	173	$P6_3$	C_6^6
118	$P\bar{4}n2$	D_{2d}^8	144	$P3_1$	C_3^2	174	$P\bar{6}$	C_{3h}^1
119	$I\bar{4}m2$	D_{2d}^9	145	$P3_2$	C_3^3	175	$P\dfrac{6}{m}$	C_{6h}^1
120	$I\bar{4}c2$	D_{2d}^{10}	146	$R3$	C_3^4			
121	$I\bar{4}2m$	D_{2d}^{11}	147	$P\bar{3}$	C_{3i}^1	176	$P\dfrac{6_3}{m}$	C_{6h}^2
122	$I\bar{4}2d$	D_{2d}^{12}	148	$R\bar{3}$	C_{3i}^2	177	$P622$	D_6^1
123	$P\dfrac{4}{m}mm$	D_{4h}^1	149	$P312$	D_3^1	178	$P6_1 22$	D_6^2
124	$P\dfrac{4}{m}cc$	D_{4h}^2	150	$P321$	D_3^2	179	$P6_5 22$	D_6^3
125	$P\dfrac{4}{n}bm$	D_{4h}^3	151	$P3_1 12$	D_3^3	180	$P6_2 22$	D_6^4
126	$P\dfrac{4}{n}nc$	D_{4h}^4				181	$P6_4 22$	D_6^5
						182	$P6_3 22$	D_6^6

No.	HERMANN-MAUGUIN	SCHOEN-FLIES	No.	HERMANN-MAUGUIN	SCHOEN-FLIES	No.	HERMANN-MAUGUIN	SCHOEN-FLIES
183	$P6mm$	C_{6v}^1	197	$I23$	T^3	215	$P\bar{4}3m$	T_d^1
184	$P6cc$	C_{6v}^2	198	$P2_13$	T^4	216	$F\bar{4}3m$	T_d^2
185	$P6_3cm$	C_{6v}^3	199	$I2_13$	T^5	217	$I\bar{4}3m$	T_d^3
186	$P6_3mc$	C_{6v}^4	200	$Pm3$	T_h^1	218	$P\bar{4}3n$	T_d^4
187	$P\bar{6}m2$	D_{3h}^1	201	$Pn3$	T_h^2	219	$F\bar{4}3c$	T_d^5
188	$P\bar{6}c2$	D_{3h}^2	202	$Fm3$	T_h^3	220	$I\bar{4}3d$	T_d^6
189	$P\bar{6}2m$	D_{3h}^3	203	$Fd3$	T_h^4	221	$Pm3m$	O_h^1
190	$P\bar{6}2c$	D_{3h}^4	204	$Im3$	T_h^5	222	$Pn3n$	O_h^2
191	$P\dfrac{6}{m}mm$	D_{6h}^1	205	$Pa3$	T_h^6	223	$Pm3n$	O_h^3
192	$P\dfrac{6}{m}cc$	D_{6h}^2	206	$Ia3$	T_h^7	224	$Pn3m$	O_h^4
193	$P\dfrac{6_3}{m}cm$	D_{6h}^3	207	$P432$	O^1	225	$Fm3m$	O_h^5
194	$P\dfrac{6_3}{m}mc$	D_{6h}^4	208	$P4_232$	O^2	226	$Fm3c$	O_h^6
195	$P23$	T^1	209	$F432$	O^3	227	$Fd3m$	O_h^7
196	$F23$	T^2	210	$F4_132$	O^4	228	$Fd3c$	O_h^8
			211	$I432$	O^5	229	$Im3m$	O_h^9
			212	$P4_332$	O^6	230	$Ia3d$	O_h^{10}
			213	$P4_132$	O^7			
			214	$I4_132$	O^8			

6. Relation between Crystal Symmetry and Physical Properties

(Optical activity after LANGE)

Crystal class	Symmetry center	X-ray (LAUE) symmetry	Optical symmetry, thermal expansion, heat and electrical conductivity	Optical activity	Enantiomorphism, (right and left crystals)	Piezoelectricity	Pyroelectricity
1	−	a	a	a	+	+	+
$\bar{1}$	+	a	a	−	−	−	−
2	−	b	b	b	+	+	+
m	−	b	b	c	−	+	+
2/m	+	b	b	−	−	−	−
$mm2$	−	c	c	d	−	+	+
222	−	c	c	e	+	+	−
mmm	+	c	c	−	−	−	−
4	−	d	d	f	+	+	+
$\bar{4}$	−	d	d	g	−	+	−
4/m	+	d	d	−	−	−	−
4mm	−	e	d	−	−	+	+
$\bar{4}2m$	−	e	d	d	−	+	−
422	−	e	d	e	+	+	−
4/mmm	+	e	d	−	−	−	−
3	−	f	d	e	+	+	+
$\bar{3}$	+	f	d	−	−	−	−
3m	−	g	d	−	−	+	+
32	−	g	d	e	+	+	−
$\bar{3}m$	+	g	d	−	−	−	−
6	−	h	d	e	+	+	+
$\bar{6}$	−	h	d	−	−	+	−
6/m	+	h	d	−	−	−	−
6mm	−	i	d	−	−	+	+
$\bar{6}m2$	−	i	d	−	−	+	−
622	−	i	d	e	+	+	−
6/mmm	+	i	d	−	−	−	−
23	−	k	e	h	+	+	−
$m3$	+	k	e	−	−	−	−
$\bar{4}3m$	−	l	e	−	−	+	−
432	−	l	e	h	+	−	−
$m3m$	+	l	e	−	−	−	−
Number of classes	11	32	32	15	11	20	10
Number of groups	11	11	5	8			

The same letters indicate like properties.

7. Atomic and Ionic Radii Arranged

Groups / Periods	I	II	IIIa	IVa	Va	VIa	VIIa	
1	*1* H^{1-}　1.26 to 1.54 H　0.78							
2	*3* *Li*　1.57 Li^{1+}　0.78	*4* *Be*　1.13 Be　(1.07) Be^{2+}　0.34						
3	*11* Na　1.92 Na^{1+}　0.98	*12* Mg　1.60 Mg　(1.40) Mg^{2+}　0.78						
4	*19* K　2.36 K^{1+}　1.33	*20* Ca　1.97 Ca^{2+}　1.06	*21* Sc　1.65 Sc^{3+}　0.83	*22* Ti　1.45 Ti^{2+}　0.80 Ti^{3+}　0.69 Ti^{4+}　0.64	*23* V　1.36 V^{2+}　0.72 V^{3+}　0.65 V^{4+}　0.61 V^{5+} ~0.4	*24* Cr　1.28 Cr^{2+} ~0.83 Cr^{3+}　0.64 Cr^{6+} ~0.35	*25* Mn　1.31 Mn^{2+}　0.91 Mn^{3+}　0.70 Mn^{4+}　0.52	*26* Fe　1.27 Fe^{2+}　0.83 Fe^{3+}　0.67
5	*37* Rb　2.53 Rb^{1+}　1.49	*38* Sr　2.16 Sr^{2+}　1.27	*39* Y　1.81 Y^{3+}　1.06	*40* Zr　1.60 Zr^{4+}　0.87	*41* Nb　1.47 Nb^{4+}　0.69 Nb^{5+}　0.69	*42* Mo　1.40 Mo^{4+}　0.68	*43* Tc　1.36	*44* Ru　1.32 Ru^{4+}　0.65
6	*55* Cs　2.74 Cs^{1+}　1.65	*56* Ba　2.25 Ba^{2+}　1.43	*57* La　1.86 La^{3+}　1.22	*58* Ce　1.82 Ce^{3+}　1.18 Ce^{4+}　1.02	*59* Pr　1.82 Pr^{3+}　1.16 Pr^{4+}　1.00	*60* Nd　1.82 Nd^{3+}　1.15	*61* Pm	
	62 Sm　1.8 or 2.0 Sm^{3+}　1.13	*63* Eu　2.04 Eu^{2+}　1.24 Eu^{3+}　1.13	*64* Gd　1.79 Gd^{3+}　1.11	*65* Tb　1.77 Tb^{3+}　1.09 Tb^{4+}　0.89	*66* Dy　1.77 Dy^{3+}　1.07	*67* Ho　1.75 or 1.95 Ho^{3+}　1.05	*68* Er　1.75 Er^{3+}　1.04	
	69 Tu　1.74 Tu^{3+}　1.04	*70* Yb　1.93 Yb^{3+}　1.00	*71* Cp　1.74 Cp^{3+}　0.99	*72* Hf　1.59 Hf^{4+}　0.84	*73* Ta　1.46 Ta^{5+}　0.68	*74* W　1.41 W^{4+}　0.68	*75* Re　1.37	*76* Os　1.34 Os^{4+}　0.67
7	*87* Fr	*88* Ra^{2+}　1.52	*89* Ac　1.88 Ac^{3+}　1.11	*90* Th　1.80 Th^{4+}　1.10	*91* Pa　1.61 Pa^{4+}　1.06	*92* U　1.57 U^{4+}　1.05		

Ionic radii (mostly after V. M. GOLDSCHMIDT, some after PAULING = P) and element radii in metals
(van der Walls

According to the Periodic Table

VIIIa	Ia	IIa	III	IV	V	VI	VII	VIII
								2 He [1,22]
			5 B 0.95 B (0.89)	6 C 0.86 C (0.77) C^{4+} <0.2	7 N 0.8 N (0.70) N^{5+} ~0.15	8 O^{2-} 1.32 O 0.66)	9 F^{1-} 1.33 F (0.64)	10 Ne [1,60]
			13 Al 1.43 Al (1.26) Al^{3+} 0.57	14 Si 1.34 Si (1.17) Si^{4+} 0.39	15 P 1.3 P (1.10) P^{5+} ~0.35	16 S^{2-} 1.74 S (1.04) S^{6+} 0.34	17 Cl^{1-} 1.81 Cl (0.99)	18 Ar [1.92]
27 28 Co 1.26 Ni 1.24 Co^{2+} 0.82 Ni^{2+} 0.78	29 Cu 1.28 Cu (1.35) Cu^{1+} 0.96 P	30 Zn 1.37 Zn (1.31) Zn^{2+} 0.83	31 Ga 1.39 Ga (1.26) Ga^{3+} 0.62	32 Ge 1.39 Ge (1.22) Ge^{4+} 0.44	33 As 1.40 As (1.18) As^{5+} 0.47 P	34 Se^{2-} 1.91 Se 1.6 Se (1.14) Se^{6+} ~0.35	35 Br^{1-} 1.96 Br (1.11)	36 Kr [1.98]
45 46 Rh 1.34 Pd 1.37 Rh^{3+} 0.68	47 Ag 1.44 Ag (1.53) Ag^{1+} 1.13	48 Cd 1.52 Cd (1.48) Cd^{2+} 1.03	49 In 1.57 In (1.44) In^{3+} 0.92	50 Sn 1.58 Sn (1.40) Sn^{4+} 0.74	51 Sb 1.61 Sb (1.36) Sb^{5+} 0.62 P	52 Te^{2-} 2.11 Te 1.7 Te (1.32) Te^{6+} 0.63	53 I^{1-} 2.20 I (1.28) I^{5+} 0.94	54 X [2.18]
77 78 Ir 1.35 Pt 1.83 Ir^{4+} 0.66	79 Au 1.44 Au (1.50) Au^{1+} 1.37 P	80 Hg 1.55 Hg (1.48) Hg^{2+} 1.12	81 Tl 1.71 Tl (1.47) Tl^{1+} 1.49 Tl^{3+} 1.05	82 Pb 1.75 Pb (1.46) Pb^{2+} 1.32 Pb^{4+} 0.84	83 Bi 1.82 Bi (1.46)	84 Po	85 At	86 Rn

after LAVES. Covalent radii (tetrahedral radii) after PAULING and HUGGINS in ( ). Inert gas radii bonding) in [ ].

B. Summary of the Common Minerals and Their Properties

Compiled by S. KORITNIG

Preliminary Remarks

The following tables summarize the properties of the 300 most common minerals. About 520 mineral names are noted. The minerals are arranged according to the tables of STRUNZ.

A natural classification based on genetic considerations cannot be formulated. That chapter of the book which deals with the occurrence of minerals indicates that a given mineral may have formed under a variety of conditions. These various modes of origin are compiled for each mineral under the heading "occurrence". As has been pointed out in the section on Crystal Chemistry, a special difficulty in mineral classification stems from frequently varying composition of minerals. In part this is related to simple solid solution. The extent of solid solution is in most cases clearly indicated in the tables. In some cases substitution of ions takes place in a manner which is not simply described. In cases where the substitution takes place to a significant extent, the substituting ions are indicated. It is important to stress to the beginner that for these reasons the chemical formulae indicated are subject to considerable variation.

It was attempted to note in the tables all of those properties which are characteristic or diagnostic of the minerals included. Nevertheless these tables cannot be considered a substitute for the special textbooks in systematic mineralogy, such as DANA's *System of Mineralogy*.

Abbreviations

a	cryst. a-axis	h. per.	highly perfect
a_0	ident. period along a-axis	isom.	isometric
abs.	absorption	imp.	imperfect
acic.	acicular	$\varkappa$	absorption indices
An.-Eff.	anisotropic effect (obs. with crossed polarizers on opaque crystals)	met. lust.	metallic luster
		OP	optic plane
		orhomb.	orthorhombic
b	cryst. b-axis	pen. tw.	penetration twin
b_0	ident. period along b-axis	per.	perfect
Biref.	birefringence	ps.	pseudo
Birefl.	bireflection (obs. with one polarizer on opaque crystals)	poor	poor
		R	reflectivity
c	cryst. c-axis	$\bar{R}$	mean reflectivity
c_0	ident. period along c-axis	$R_{g,o,r}$	reflectivity in green, orange, red light
col.	columnar		
cub.	cubic	R_α	reflectivity parallel to n_α vibration direction
cyc.	cyclic		
diff.	different	rad.	radiating
dist.	distinct	tab.	tabular
elong.	elongate	tetr.	tetragonal
et al.	and others	trip.	triplet (twin)
fib.	fibrous	tw.	twinned after
hex.	hexagonal	tw. lam.	twin lamella

Symbols

│ a)	indicates complete solid solution between two or more minerals	For example:
		$n_\alpha/\perp$ (010) extinction of n_α against normal to (010)
│ b)	indicates gradation (contin.) between values, for example, of indices of refraction	n_γ/c 15° extinction of n_γ with respect to $c = 15°$
↓		
$\perp$	perpendicular	$n_\alpha \sim \perp$ (001) n_α approx. perpend. to (001)
‖	parallel	$r > v$ Dispersion of optic angle;
—	to; means minus when indicated with extinction angle	2 V for red greater than blue
$\sim$	approximately	$a = b_0$ Morphologic orient. different than lattice. Here a corresp. to b_0
(−)	optically negative	
(+)	optically positive	$a = 2\,a_0$ Axial intercepts of morph. orientation and lattice different. Here a corresponds to double the value of a_0

No.	Name and Formula	Crystal Class Lattice Constants	Habit, Form	Cleavage	Hardness	Sp. Gr.	Color

I. Cl. Elements

No.	Name and Formula	Crystal Class Lattice Constants	Habit, Form	Cleavage	Hardness	Sp. Gr.	Color
1	*Platinum* Pt	$m3m$ a_0 3.9237	(100) (111) (110)	—	4—$4^1/_2$	14—19 pure: 21.5	steel-grey
2	*Copper* Cu	$m3m$ a_0 3.6153	(111) (100) (110) (210) (311), tw. (111)	—	$2^1/_2$—3	8.5—9	copper-red mostly darkly tarnished
3	*Silver* Ag	$m3m$ a_0 4.0856	(100) (111) (110) (210), tw. (111)	—	$2^1/_2$—3	9.6—12 pure: 10.5	silvery-white, dull, tarnished yellow to black
4	*Gold* Au	$m3m$ a_0 4.0783	(111) (100) (110) et al., tw. (111)	—	$2^1/_2$—3	15.5 to 19.3 pure: 19.23	gold to brass-colored
5	*Arsenic* As	$\bar{3}m$ a_0 3.768 c_0 10.574	isom., ($10\bar{1}1$) ($01\bar{1}2$) (0001) tw. ($01\bar{1}2$)	(0001) per. ($01\bar{1}2$) imp.	3—4	5.4—5.9	light-grey, tarnished black
6	*Bismuth* Bi	$\bar{3}m$ a_0 4.55 c_0 11.85	isom., ($10\bar{1}1$) (0001) ($02\bar{2}1$), tw. ($01\bar{1}2$)	(0001) per. ($02\bar{2}1$) dist.	2—$2^1/_2$	9.7—9.8	reddish silvery, often multi-colored, tarnished
7	*Sulfur* α-S	mmm a_0 10.44 b_0 12.84$_5$ c_0 24.37	(111) (113) (011) (001), tw. (101) et al.	(001) (110) (111) poor	$1^1/_2$—2	2.0—2.1	yellow, waxy-yellow to brown
8	*β-Sulfur* β-S > 95.6° C	$2/m$ a_0 10.92 b_0 10.98 c_0 11.04 $β$ 96°44′	col.—tab., (001) (110) (011)	(001) (110)	~2	1.98	like α-sulfur
9	*Graphite* (−2H) α-C	$6/mmm$ a_0 2.46 c_0 6.708	tab. (0001), ($11\bar{2}0$)	(0001) per.	1	2.1—2.3 pure: 2.255	steel-grey
10	*Diamond* β-C $\gtrsim$ 1,200° C	$m3m$ a_0 3.5668	(111) tw. (111)	(111) per.	10	3.52	colorless, in all colors

Streak	Indices of refraction and Luster	Optic angle 2 V and Biref.	Optic orient.	Pleochroism Bireflection	Occurrence	No.
steel-grey	n 2.06 Na $\varkappa$ 4.28 Na R_{Na} 70.1%	—	—	—	Magm. in bas. rocks (peridotes, serpentine), placers. Imp. Pt ore	1
copper	n 0.641 Na $\varkappa$ 4.09 Na R_g 61% R_r 89% met. lust.	—	—	—	By reduction of sulfides in zone of cementation	2
silvery-white	n 0.181 Na $\varkappa$ 20.3 Na R_g 95.5% met. lust.	—	—	—	As with copper	3
gold	n 0.368 Na $\varkappa$ 7.71 R_{Na} 85.1% met. lust.	—	—	—	Hydroth., in assoc. with most acid intrus. rocks, extrus. rocks; placers; most imp. gold ore	4
black	$\overline{R}_g$ 61.5% met. lust. dull tarnish	An.-Eff. very distinct	—	Birefl. weak ω white ε grey-white	Hydroth. ore veins	5
lead-grey	n 1.78 $\varkappa$ 1.57 $\overline{R}_g$ 67.5%	An.-Eff. distinct		Birefl. very weak	Pegmat.—pneumat. with cassiterite and in Co-Ni-Ag veins	6
white	n_α 1.960 n_β 2.040 n_γ 2.248 diamond- to greasy-lust.	69° 5' 0.288	(+) OP (010) $n_\gamma \parallel c$ $r < v$	—	Vulcan. exhal., reduced from sulfates by org. substances. Imp. raw material	7
white	n 1.96	58° small	(−) OP (010)	—	Rare, as volcan. exhal. and from burning coal dumps	8
grey	n 1.93—2.07 met. lust.	An.-Eff. very strong	(−)	Birefl. very strong	Usually metam. from carbonaceous subst., contact metam. Imp. raw material	9
	n 2.4478 λ 441 n 2.4370 λ 480 n 2.4172 λ 589 n 2.4109 λ 643	—	—	—	Volcan. (Kimberlite), placers. Precious stone and imp. indust. mineral *Carbonado* = grayish-black coke-like diamond	10

No.	Name and Formula	Crystal Class Lattice Constants	Habit, Form	Cleavage	Hardness	Sp. Gr.	Color

II. Cl. Sulfides, Arsenides, Antimonides

No.	Name and Formula	Crystal Class Lattice Constants	Habit, Form	Cleavage	Hardness	Sp. Gr.	Color
11	Dyscrasite Ag_3Sb	$2mm$ a_0 2.99 b_0 5.23 c_0 4.82	col.—tab. (110) (010) (001) (111) (112) (021) tw. (110)	(011) per. (001) imp.	$3^1/_2$	9.4—10	silvery, often grey or brown tarnish
12	Chalcocite $Cu_2S < 103°$ C	$2mm$ a_0 11.92 b_0 27.33 c_0 13.44	tab. (001), (110) (010) (113) (023) tw. (110) (112), ps. hex.	(110) poor	$2^1/_2$—3	5.7—5.8	dark lead-grey
13	Chalcocite(-H) γ-$Cu_2S > 103°$ C	$6/mmm$ a_0 3.90 c_0 6.69			$2^1/_2$—3	5.7—5.8	dark lead-grey
14	Digenite Cu_9S_5	cub. a_0 27.85	(111)	(111) dist.	$2^1/_2$—3	5.7—5.8	dark lead-grey, bluish
15	Bornite Cu_5FeS_4	$\bar{4}2m$ ps. cub. a_0 10.94 c_0 21.88	(100) (111), tw. (111) (cub. indic.)	(100) imp.	3	4.9—5.3	iridescent tarnish
16	Acanthite $Ag_2S < 179°$ C	$2/m$ a_0 4.23 b_0 6.91 c_0 7.87 β 99°35′	isom., (100) (111) (110) (211) (cub. indic.)		2	7.3	dark lead-grey, black tarnish
17	Argentite Ag_2S (179° C—586° C)	$m3m$ a_0 4.89	(100)				as above
18	Pentlandite $(Ni, Fe)_9 S_8$ usually Ni:Fe~1:0.9	$m3m$ a_0 10.04 to 10.07		(111) dist.	$3^1/_2$—4	4.6—5	light-brown
19	Sphalerite α-ZnS (to 20% Fe)	$\bar{4}3m$ a_0 5.43	(110) (311) (3$\bar{1}$1) (100) (111) (1$\bar{1}$1) et al., tw. (111) (211)	(110) per.	$3^1/_2$—4	3.9—4.2 pure: 4.06	brown, yellow, red, green, black
20	Chalcopyrite $CuFeS_2$	$\bar{4}2m$ a_0 5.25 c_0 10.32	(111) (1$\bar{1}$1) (201) (101) (001), tw. (100) (111) rare (101)	(111) poor (201) poor	$3^1/_2$—4	4.1—4.3	brass-yellow to greenish often iridescent tarnish
21	Stannite Cu_2FeSnS_4	$\bar{4}2m$ a_0 5.47 c_0 10.74	cryst. rare (1$\bar{1}$1)	(110) poor	4	4.3—4.5	steel-grey (greenish)

Streak	Indices of refraction and Luster	Optic angle 2 V and Biref.	Optic orient.	Pleochroism Bireflection	Occurrence	No.
silvery	$\bar{R}_g$ 66% met. lust.	An.-Eff. weak		Birefl. very weak	Hydroth. in Ag-Sb-As bearing veins	11
grey luster.	$\bar{R}_g$ 22.5% met. lust.			—	Hydroth. and zone of cementation. Imp. Cu ore	12
grey luster.				—	As with chalcocite	13
	R_g 24.5%	—	—	—	As with chalcocite	14
grey to black	$\bar{R}_g$ 18.5% met. lust.	—	—	—	Hydroth.—pegm. and from chalcopyrite in cementation zone. Imp. Cu ore	15
grey luster.	$\bar{R}_g$ 37% fresh met. lust.	An.-Eff. distinct		Birefl. very weak	Hydroth., often in galena, cementation zone. Imp. Ag ore	16
		—	—	—	Hydroth., often in galena. Imp. Ag ore	17
black	R_g 51% met. lust.	—	—	—	Magmat. with pyrrhotite. Most imp. Ni ore	18
brown to yellowish-white	n 2.369 R_g 18.5% semimet. lust to diamond lust.	—	—	—	Hydroth. metasom., magmat., pegmat., sedimentary. Most imp. Zn ore	19
greenish-black	$\bar{R}_g$ 42% met. lust.	An.-Eff. very weak		Birefl. very weak	Hydroth., magmat., pegmat., in veins, intrus. rocks, rarely sediment. Imp. Cu ore	20
black	$\bar{R}_g$ 23% met. lust.	An.-Eff. distinct		Birefl. very weak	Pegmat.—hydroth. common in Bolivia	21

No.	Name and Formula	Crystal Class Lattice Constants	Habit, Form	Cleavage	Hardness	Sp. Gr.	Color
22	*Tennantite* $Cu_3AsS_{3,25}$ (Cu part. replaced by Ag, Fe, Zn, Hg)	$\bar{4}3m$ a_0 10.21	like Tetrahedrite	—	3—4	4.4—5.4	dark steel-grey
23	*Tetrahedrite* $Cu_3SbS_{3,25}$	$\bar{4}3m$ a_0 10.34	(111) (211) (110) (1$\bar{1}$1) et al., tw. [111]	—	3—4	4.4—5.4	light steel-grey
24	*Germanite* $Cu_3(Ge, Fe)S_4$	$\bar{4}3m$ a_0 10.58	massive	—	3	4.29	violet-pink to violet
25	*Wurtzite* β-ZnS	$6mm$ a_0 3.85 c_0 6.29	col. c to tab. (0001), (10$\bar{1}$1) (50$\bar{5}$2)	(10$\bar{1}$0) per. (0001) poor	3^1/$_2$—4	4.0	light to dark-brown
26	*Grennockite* β-CdS	$6mm$ a_0 4.15 c_0 6.73	isom., (10$\bar{1}$0) ($h0\bar{h}l$) (000$\bar{1}$)	(10$\bar{1}$0)	3	4.82	yellow to brown-yellow
27	*Enargite* Cu_3AsS_4	$2mm$ a_0 6.47 b_0 7.44 c_0 6.19	col. c, (110) (001 (100) (010), trip. twins (3$\bar{2}$0)	(110) per. (100) (010) dist.	3^1/$_2$	4.4	steel-grey to iron-black, violet-brownish
28	*Cubanite* (Chalmersite) $CuFe_2S_3$	mmm a_0 6.46 b_0 11.12 c_0 6.23	elong. c, tw. (110)	(001) and (110) various dist.	3^1/$_2$—4	4.10	bronze-yellow
29	*Galena* PbS	$m3m$ a_0 5.94	(100) (111) (110) (221) (211) (331) et al., tw. (111)	(100) per. (111) poor	2^1/$_2$	7.2—7.6	lead-grey
30	*Cinnabar* HgS	32 a_0 4.146 c_0 9.497	$a:c$ 1.1453 isom.—tab., (0001) (10$\bar{1}$1) (20$\bar{2}$1) et al., tw. (0001)	(10$\bar{1}$0) per.	2—2^1/$_2$	8.1 synth.: 8.176	red
31	*Pyrrhotite* FeS	$6/mmm$ a_0 3.45 c_0 5.65 existing also in mono-clinic modifications (Fe_7S_8)	tab. (0001), tw. (10$\bar{1}$2)	(0001) dist.	4	4.6	bronze brown

Streak	Indices of refraction and Luster	Optic angle 2 V and Biref.	Optic orient.	Pleochroism Bireflection	Occurrence	No.
black to reddish brown	R_g 29.5% met. lust.	—	—	—	As with tetrahedrite	22
reddish grey to dark red	n > 2.72 Li R_g 27% met. lust.	—	—	—	Hydroth., pegmat., sediment. In veins as impregn. Imp. Cu and Ag ore	23
dark grey to black	R_g 22% met. lust.	—	—	—	Hydroth. from Tsumeb, southwest Africa. Most imp. Ge ore	24
light brown	n_ω 2.356 Na n_ε 2.378 Na	0.022	(+)	—	Usually with sphalerite. Imp. Zn ore	25
yellow	n_ω 2.506 Na n_ε 2.529 Na	0.023	(+) for λ 523 mμ isotropic, for shorter wave light (−)	weak	Hydroth. Oxidation zone on Zn deposits, usually on sphalerite	26
greyish-black	for green: R_α 24.28% R_β 26.16% R_γ 28.50% met. lust.	An.-Eff. strong	—	Birefl. weak	Hydroth., metasom. Imp. Cu ore	27
	$\bar{R}_g$ 41% met. lust.	An.-Eff. very distinct to strong		Birefl. distinct, ‖a,b light brownish-grey, ‖c richer, darker	Usually intergrown in chalcopyrite	28
grey to black	n 4.3 $\varkappa$ 0.4 R_g 43.4%	—	—	—	Hydroth., metasom., rarely pneumat., sediment. In veins as impregn. Most imp. Pb ore	29
red	n_ω 2.913 n_ε 3.272	0.359	(+)	—	Hydroth. in veins, as impregn. Most imp. Hg ore	30
greyish-black	$\bar{R}_g$ 37% met. lust. dull tarnish	An.-Eff. strong		Birefl. distinct	Magmat., pegmat., hydroth., sediment.	31

No.	Name and Formula	Crystal Class Lattice Constants	Habit, Form	Cleavage	Hardness	Sp. Gr.	Color
32	*Niccolite* NiAs	$6/mmm$ a_0 3.58 c_0 5.11	flat pyramids, crystals rare	$(10\bar{1}0)$ (0001) imp.	$5^1/_2$	7.3—7.7	light copper
33	*Millerite* β-NiS	$3m$ a_0 9.62 c_0 3.16	acic.-fib. c, oft. twist. helix	$(10\bar{1}1)$ $(01\bar{1}2)$ per.	$3^1/_2$	5.3	brass yellow
34	*Covellite* CuS	$6/mmm$ a_0 3.80 c_0 16.36	tab. (0001), $(10\bar{1}0)$	(0001) per.	$1^1/_2$—2	4.68	bluish-black
35	*Stibnite* Sb_2S_3	mmm a_0 11.22 b_0 11.30 c_0 3.84	col. c, tw. (130) rare	(010) per. (100) (110) imp.	2	4.6—4.7	lead grey
36	*Bismuthinite* Bi_2S_3	mmm a_0 11.15 b_0 11.29 c_0 3.98	radial c	(001) per.	2	6.8—7.2	lead grey to tin white
37	*Pyrite* FeS_2	$2/m\bar{3}$ a_0 5.41 to 5.42	alone and in comb. (100) (210) (111) et al., tw. (110)	(100) dist. to imp.	6—$6^1/_2$	5—5.2	light brass
38	*Sperrylite* $PtAs_2$	$2/m\bar{3}$ a_0 5.94	(100) (111) (210)		6—7	10.6	tin white
39	*Cobaltite* CoAsS	$2/m\bar{3}$ a_0 5.61	(210) (111) (100)	(100) imp.	$5^1/_2$	6.0—6.4	silvery, reddish to grey
40	*Marcasite* FeS_2	mmm a_0 3.39 b_0 4.45 c_0 5.42	tab. (001), tw. (110)	(110) imp.	6—$6^1/_2$	4.8—4.9	light brass yellow to greenish

Streak	Indices of refraction and Luster	Optic angle 2 V and Biref.	Optic orient.	Pleochroism Bireflection	Occurrence	No.
brownish black	for green: R_ω 48.9% R_ε 42.8% met. lust. dull tarnish	An.-Eff. very strong		Birefl. strong, ω whitish-yellow to pink ε light brownish-pink	Hydroth. in veins with Co-Ni ores	32
greenish black	$\bar{R}_g$ 53% silkly met. lust.	An.-Eff. very distinct		Birefl. very weak	Hydroth., cementation zone	33
black	n_ω 1.00 λ 635 n_ω 1.97 λ 505 $\varepsilon > \omega$ for green: R_ω 18.5% R_ε 27%	An.-Eff. very distinct	(+)	Birefl. very strong ω deepblue ε bluish white	Hydroth., also from decomp. of Cu_2S-CuS mixed crystals, weathering product, also sublimation prod. at Vesuvius	34
dark lead grey	n_α 3.41 n_β 4.37 n_γ 5.12 for $\varkappa_\alpha$ 0.21 $\sim$Na $\varkappa_\beta$ 0.19 $\varkappa_\gamma$ 0.12 $\bar{R}_g$ $\|c$ 44% $\|b$ 30.5%	65—70° 1.71 An.-Eff. very distinct	(—) OP (001) $n_\gamma\|b$	Birefl. strong $\|a$ dim greyish white $\|b$ dim grey $\|c$ pure white	Hydroth. in veins metasom. Most imp. Sb ore	35
grey met. lust.	for green: R_α 41.46% R_β 48.45% R_γ 54.51% met. lust.	An.-Eff. strong		Birefl. weak $\|a$ white to light grey $\|b$ greyish-white $\|c$ light yellowish-white	Hydroth. in veins and in granite pegmat. Exhal. at Mt. Volcano	36
greenish black	R_g 54% met. lust.	—	—	—	Ubiquitous; freq. contains chalcophyrite and gold. Imp. S-raw material	37
black	R_g 56.5% met. lust.	—	—	—	Magmat. in basaltic intrus. rocks (dunites from Transvaal), also pegmat., Pt ore in Ni-pyrrhotite deposits, e.g. Sudbury	38
grey to black	R_g 52% str. met. lust.	—	—	—	Contact pneumat., hydroth. Imp. Co ore.	39
greenish to black, fresh: grey	$\bar{R}_g$ 52% met. lust.	An.-Eff. very strong		Birefl. distinct $\|a$ white to pinkish-brown $\|b$ white to cream $\|c$ pale yellow	Sediment., hydroth.	40

No.	Name and Formula	Crystal Class Lattice Constants	Habit, Form	Cleavage	Hardness	Sp. Gr.	Color
41	*Safflorite* $CoAs_2$	mmm a_0 6.35 b_0 4.86 c_0 5.80	radial c tw. (101), trip. (011)	(100) imp.	$4^1/_2$ to $5^1/_2$	6.9—7.3	tin white, often dark grey tarnish
42	*Rammelsbergite* $NiAs_2$	mmm a_0 3.54 b_0 4.79 c_0 5.79	tw. (101)	(100) imp.	$4^1/_2$ to $5^1/_2$	7.0—7.3	tin white, often dark grey tarnish
43	*Löllingite* $FeAs_2$	mmm a_0 2.86 b_0 5.26 c_0 5.93	acic. a, (011) (110)	(001) imp.	5	7.1—7.4	silvery, grey tarnish
44	*Arsenopyrite* $FeAsS$	$2/m$ ps. orthomb. a_0 6.43 b_0 9.53 c_0 5.66 β 90° 0′	col. a or c and isom., (210) tw. (010) and (100)	(110) imp.	$5^1/_2$—6	5.9—6.2	tin white to light steel grey, often dark tarnish
45	*Molybdenite* MoS_2	$6/mmm$ a_0 3.16 c_0 12.32	tab. (0001)	(0001) per.	1—$1^1/_2$	4.7—4.8	lead grey, bluish
46	*Skutterudite* $CoAs_3$	$2/m\bar{3}$ a_0 8.21 to 8.29	usu. (100) comb. w. (111) (110)	—	5.5	6.4—6.6	tin white to light steel grey, dark tarnish
47	*Chloanthite* (Ni-Skutterudite) $NiAs_3$	$2/m\bar{3}$ a_0 8.28	like Skutterudite	—	5.5	6.4—6.6	tin white to light steel grey, dark tarnish
48	*Proustite* Ag_3AsS_3	$3m$ a_0 10.76 c_0 8.66	like Pyrargyrite, not so faceted	(10$\bar{1}$1) dist.	$2^1/_2$	5.57	scarlet to vermilion, translucent
49	*Pyrargyrite* Ag_3SbS_3	$3m$ a_0 11.06 c_0 8.73	usu. col. c (11$\bar{2}$0) (21$\bar{3}$1) (01$\bar{1}$2) (11$\bar{2}$4) (32$\bar{5}$1) (10$\bar{1}$1) et al. Very faceted, tw. (11$\bar{2}$0) (10$\bar{1}$4) et al.	(10$\bar{1}$1) dist. (10$\bar{1}$2) imp.	$2^1/_2$—3	5.85	dark red, dark greyish-red, translucent

Streak	Indices of refraction and Luster	Optic angle 2V and Biref.	Optic orient.	Pleochroism Bireflection	Occurrence	No.
greyish black	$\bar{R}_g$ 58% str. met. lust.	An.-Eff. very strong		Birefl. very weak	Hydroth., occurs in Co-Ni-Ag veins. Earlier confused with skutterudite or chloanthite	41
greyish-black	$\bar{R}_{yellow} \sim 60\%$ str. met. lust.	An.-Eff. very strong		like Safflorite	As with safflorite	42
greyish-black	$\bar{R}_g$ 57% met. lust.	An.-Eff. very strong		Birefl. very weak $\|a$ pure white $\|b$ yellowish-white $\|c$ yellowish-white	Pneumat., hydroth., in veins; in serpen-tine, also contact metam. and in pegmatites	43
black	$\bar{R}_g$ 49.0% met. lust.	An.-Eff. very strong		Birefl. weak	Pneumat.—hydroth. Often Au bearing. (Au ore from Boliden)	44
dark grey	n $\sim$4.7 for green: R_ω 36% R_ε 15.5% str. met. lust.	An.-Eff. very strong		Birefl. very strong ω pure white ε greyish-white	Pegmat.—pneumat., contact metasom. Occurs in granite assn. Most imp. Mo ore	45
greyish-black	R_g 60% met. lust.	—	—	—	Hydroth., in Co-Ni-Ag deposits; Imp. Cu-Ni ore	46
greyish-black	met. lust.	—	—	—	As with skutterudite	47
scarlet to vermilion	n_ω 3.0877 Na n_ε 2.7924 Na $\bar{R}_g$ 28% adamant-diamond lust.	0.295 An.-Eff. strong	(—)	ω crimson ε vermilion Birefl. very distinct ω white ε grey	Hydroth. veins; imp. Ag ore	48
cherry red	n_ω 3.084 Li n_ε 2.881 Li $\bar{R}_g$ 32.5%	0.203 An.-Eff. strong	(—)	Birefl. distinct ω lighter than ε	As with proustite	49

24*

No.	Name and Formula	Crystal Class Lattice Constants	Habit, Form	Cleavage	Hardness	Sp. Gr.	Color
50	*Stephanite* $5\,Ag_2S \cdot Sb_2S_3$	$2mm$ a_0 7.72 b_0 12.34 c_0 8.50	col.—tab. c (001) (010) (111) (021) tw. (110), ps. hex.	(010) imp.	$2^1/_2$	6.2—6.4	lead grey to iron black
51	*Bournonite* $2\,PbS \cdot Cu_2S \cdot Sb_2S_3$	$2mm$ a_0 8.16 b_0 8.75 c_0 7.81	tab. (001) ps. tetr. (110) (010) (011) (100) (101) (102) (112) Cycl. tw. (110)	(010) dist.	3	5.8	steel to lead grey and iron black
52	*Jamesonite* $4\,PbS \cdot FeS \cdot 3\,Sb_2S_3$	$2/m$ a_0 15.57 b_0 18.98 c_0 4.03 β 91° 48′	acic.—fib. b, (001) (104) (1̄04) tw. (100)	(001) per. (010) imp.	2—$2^1/_2$	5.7	lead grey
53	*Realgar* As_4S_4	$2/m$ a_0 9.29 b_0 13.53 c_0 6.57 β 106° 33′	col. c, (110) (210) (001) (011)	(010) per.	$1^1/_2$—2	3.5—3.6	red
54	*Orpiment* As_2S_3	$2/m$ a_0 11.49 b_0 9.59 c_0 4.25 β 90° 27′	tab. (010)	(010) per.	$1^1/_2$—2	3.49	lemon yellow

III. Cl. Halides

No.	Name and Formula	Crystal Class Lattice Constants	Habit, Form	Cleavage	Hardness	Sp. Gr.	Color
55	*Halite* NaCl	$m3m$ a_0 5.6404	(100)	(100) per. (110) imp.	2	2.1—2.2	colorless and red, yellow, grey, blue
56	*Sylvite* KCl	$m3m$ a_0 6.29	(100)	(100) per.	2	1.9—2	colorless and colored
57	*Cerargyrite* AgCl	$m3m$ a_0 5.55	(100), usu. massive in pseudo-morphs	—	$1^1/_2$	5.5—5.6	fresh colorless, brown to black tarnish
58	Sal ammoniac α-NH_4Cl	$\bar{4}3m$ a_0 3.87 below 184° C CsCl-, above NaCl-lattice	(110) (211)	(111) imp.	1—2	1.53	colorless also yellow and brown

Streak	Indices of refraction and Luster	Optic angle 2V and Biref.	Optic orient.	Pleochroism Bireflection	Occurrence	No.
black lustrous	$\bar{R}_g$ 29% met. lust.	An.-Eff. strong		Birefl. weak ‖a white ‖b brownish-pinkish-white ‖c pink	Hydroth. in Ag veins	50
grey	$\bar{R}_g$ 33.5% fresh: resinous met. lust. usu. dull	An.-Eff. weak		Birefl. very weak	Hydroth. veins. Imp. Pb and Cu ore	51
grey	$\bar{R}_g$ 39% met. lust.	An.-Eff. strong		Birefl. distinct in greenish, yellowish, whitish tones	Hydroth. veins. *plumosite* = fine, needle like matted jamesonite (also partly stibnite!)	52
orange yellow	n_α 2.46 n_β 2.59 n_γ 2.61 } Li	~40° $r \gg v$ 0.15	(−) $n_\beta \| b$ n_α/c 11°	n_α orange red to colorless $n_\beta = n_\gamma$ vermilion to light gold	Hydroth., also weathering product of As ores	53
yellow	n_α 2.4 n_β 2.81 n_γ 3.02 } Li	76° $r \gg v$ 0.6	(−) $n_\alpha \| b$ n_β/c 1.5°—3°	yellow Abs. $n_\alpha > n_\beta, n_\gamma$	As with realgar	54
	n 1.5612 λ 431 n 1.5441 λ 589 n 1.5391 λ 686	—	—	—	Sediment. and sublimation product. Imp. raw material	55
	n 1.5046 λ 436 n 1.4930 λ 546 n 1.4886 λ 615	—	—	—	Sediment. and re-crystallized from carnallite. Imp. as fertilizer	56
white to grey, lustrous	n 2.096 λ 486 n 2.062 λ 589 n 2.047 λ 656	—	—	—	Alteration product sulfide silver ores. Sometimes imp. Ag ore in oxidation zone	57
	n 1.6613 λ 431 n 1.6422 λ 589 n 1.6326 λ 686	—	—	—	Sublimation product	58

No.	Name and Formula	Crystal Class Lattice Constants	Habit, Form	Cleav-age	Hard-ness	Sp. Gr.	Color
59	*Fluorite* CaF_2	$m3m$ a_0 5.46	(100) (111) (110) (310) (421)	(111) per.	4	3.1—3.2	colorless and colored
60	*Cryolite* α-$Na_3AlF_6 < 550°$ C	$2/m$ a_0 5.47 b_0 5.62 c_0 7.82 β 90° 11′	(110 (001), tw. (110), (112), (001)	part-ing after (001) (110) ($\bar{1}01$)	$2^1/_2$—3	2.95	white and colored
61	*Carnallite* $KMgCl_3 \cdot 6\ H_2O$	mmm a_0 9.56 b_0 16.05 c_0 22.56	ps. hex. cryst. rare (111) (011) (110) (010)	—	1—2	1.60	colorless and red (by Fe_2O_3)
62	*Atacamite* $Cu_2(OH)_3Cl$	mmm a_0 6.02 b_0 9.15 c_0 6.85	col. c, (110) (010) (011) tw. (110)	(010) per.	3—$3^1/_2$	3.76	light to dark green

IV. Cl. Oxides, Hydroxides

No.	Name and Formula	Crystal Class Lattice Constants	Habit, Form	Cleav-age	Hard-ness	Sp. Gr.	Color
63	*Ice* (I) H_2O	$6mm$ a_0 4.47 c_0 7.33	tab. (0001)— col. c, (0001) ($10\bar{1}0$)	—	$1^1/_2$	0.9175	colorless white to light blue
64	*Cuprite* Cu_2O	$m3m$ (morph. O) a_0 4.27	(111) (110) (100)	(111) dist.	$3^1/_2$—4	5.8—6.2	reddish brown to grey
65	*Zincite* ZnO	$6mm$ a_0 3.25 c_0 5.19	($40\bar{4}5$) ($10\bar{1}1$) cryst. rare	(0001) per. ($10\bar{1}0$) dist.	$4^1/_2$—5	5.4—5.7	crimson
66	*Periclase* MgO	$m3m$ a_0 4.21	(111) (100)	(100) per.	$5^1/_2$—6	3.64 to 3.67	colorless
67	*Tenorite* CuO	$2/m$ a_0 4.66 b_0 3.42 c_0 5.12 β 99° 29′	tab. (100), ps. hex., tw. (100) (011)	(111) (001) dist.	3—4	6.45	black
68	*Spinel* $MgAl_2O_4$ with Fe-content	$m3m$ a_0 8.10	(111), rare (110) (311) (100), tw. (111)	—	8	3.5—4.1	colorless and colored
69	*Magnetite* Fe_3O_4	$m3m$ a_0 8.391	(111) (110), rarer (100) (211) (221), tw. (111)	some-times parts along (111)	$5^1/_2$	5.2	black
70	*Chromite* $FeCr_2O_4$	$m3m$ a_0 8.361	(111)	—	$5^1/_2$	4.5—4.8	black

Streak	Indices of refraction and Luster	Optic angle 2 V and Biref.	Optic orient.	Pleochroism Bireflection	Occurrence	No.
white	n 1.43385 (20° C)	—	—	—	Ubiquitous. Esp. common hydroth. also pneumat.-hydric.	59
	n_α 1.3385 n_β 1.3389 n_γ 1.3396	43° $r > v$ 0.001	(+) $n_\alpha \| b$ $n_{\gamma/c} - 44°$		Pegmat. Almost restricted to Ivigtut, Greenland	60
white	n_α 1.466 n_β 1.475 n_γ 1.494	70° $r < v$ 0.028	(+) OP (010) $n_\alpha \| c$		Sediment. Most imp. potassium salt	61
apple-green	n_α 1.831 n_β 1.861 } Tl n_γ 1.880	75° $r \ll v$ 0.049	(−) OP (100) $n_\alpha \| b$	n_α pale green n_β yellow-ish-green n_γ grass-green	Oxidation zone of Cu-deposits, rarely sublimation product	62
	n_ω 1.30907 Na n_ε 1.31052 Na	0.0014	(+)	—		63
brownish red	n 2.849 Li R_g 30% R_r 21.5%	—	—	—	Oxidation zone of Cu-deposits	64
orange-yellow	n_ω 2.013 n_ε 2.029 R_g 11%	0.016	(+)		Metam. in limestones. Almost only at Franklin Furnace, N. J. Contains up to 9% Mn. Freq. as smelter product	65
	n 1.736	—	—	—	Metam. in dolomite	66
grey	n_β 2.63 Li n_β 3.18 blue	large, strong	(?)	Birefl. weak	Exhalation product (Vesuvius), rarely weathering product	67
white to brownish to greenish grey	n 1.72—2.0	—	—	—	Contact metam. Blue, red and green, also as gemstone. *Pleonaste* = Fe··· rich spinel, *Hercynite* = iron spinel FeAl₂O₄	68
black	n 2.42 R_g 21% met. lust. dull	—	—	—	Magmat., metam. hydroth., rarely sedimentary. Imp. Fe ore. *Titano-magnetite* = Ti-bear. magnetite, usually intergrown. *Maghemite* = magnetic cub. Fe₂O₃	69
brown	n 2.1 Li met. lust.	—	—	—	Magmat. in peridotites. Only Cr-ore	70

No.	Name and Formula	Crystal Class Lattice Constants	Habit, Form	Cleavage	Hardness	Sp. Gr.	Color
71	*Hausmannite* $MnMn_2O_4$	$4/mmm$ a_0 5.76 c_0 9.44	(111), tw. (101), oft. cycl.	(001) per.	$5^1/_2$	4.7—4.8	black
72	*Chrysoberyl* Al_2BeO_4	mmm a_0 5.48 b_0 4.43 c_0 9.41	tab. (100), (010) (011) (120) (111), tw. (031) usu. trip. ps. hex.	(010) dist.	$8^1/_2$	∼3.7	greenish yellow to green
73	*Valentinite* Sb_2O_3	mmm a_0 4.93 b_0 12.48 c_0 5.43	Fib. rad. c or a, tab. (010), (010) (110) (054) (101) (0.27.4) et al.	(010) (110) per.	2—3	5.6—5.8	colorless
74	*Senarmontite* Sb_2O_3	$m3m$ a_0 11.14	(111)	(111) dist.	2	5.2—5.3	colorless
75	*Corundum* Al_2O_3	$\bar{3}m$ a_0 4.77 c_0 13.04	col. c, $(11\bar{2}0)$ $(22\bar{4}1)$ (0001)	part. $(10\bar{1}1)$ (0001)	9	3.9—4.1	colorless and colored
76	*Hematite* Fe_2O_3	$\bar{3}m$ a_0 5.04 c_0 13.77	tab. (0001), isom., $(22\bar{4}3)$ $(10\bar{1}1)$, also fib. kidney ore	somet. part. (0001) $(10\bar{1}1)$	$6^1/_2$	5.2—5.3	steel grey to iron black, iridescent lustre or red
77	*Ilmenite* $FeTiO_3$	$\bar{3}$ a_0 5.09 c_0 14.07	tab. (0001), $(10\bar{1}1)$	part. along $(000\bar{1})$ $(10\bar{1}1)$	5—6	4.5—5.0	iron black, brownish black
78	*Perovskite* $CaTiO_3$	mmm[a] a_0 5.37 b_0 7.64 c_0 5.44 ps. cub. a_0 15.26	ps. cub. (100) with monocl. deform. tw. lam.	(100) dist.	$5^1/_2$	4.0	black to reddish brown
79	*Quartz* $SiO_2 < 573°$ C	32 a_0 4.9130 c_0 5.4045	col. c, $(10\bar{1}0)$ $(10\bar{1}1)$ $(01\bar{1}1)$ $(30\bar{3}1)$ $(51\bar{6}1)$ $(11\bar{2}1)$ et al. tw. [0001] $(11\bar{2}0)$ $(11\bar{2}2)$	$(10\bar{1}1)$ poor	7	2.65	colorless, white and different colors

[a] synthet. $CaTiO_3$.

Streak	Indices of refraction and Luster	Optic angle 2 V and Biref.	Optic orient.	Pleochroism Bireflection	Occurrence	No.
brown	n_ω 2.46 ⎫ Li n_ε 2.15 ⎭ greasy met. lust.	0.31	(−)	Birefl. weak ω lighter than ε	Metam. in carbonate rocks, infreq. hydroth.	71
white	n_α 1.747 n_β 1.748 n_γ 1.756	45°—71° $r > v$ 0.009	(+) OP (010) $n_\gamma \| c$	n_α red n_β orange n_γ green	In pegmat. and mica schists. Yellow gemstone; when green (red in art. light) is called *alexandrite*	72
	n_α 2.18 n_β 2.35 n_γ 2.35 diamond lust.	very small $r > v$ 0.17	(−) OP for red—yellow (001), for green—blue (010), $n_\alpha \| a$	—	Weathering product of antimony ores	73
	n 2.087	—	—	—	As with valentinite	74
white	n_ω 1.769 n_ε 1.761	sometimes anomal 0°—32° 0.008	(−)	Abs. $\omega > \varepsilon$	Magmat.—pegmat., metam., placers. As gemstone: blue, *sapphire*; red, *ruby*. Tech. known as *emery* when fine-grained. Also synth.	75
red to brownish red	n_ω 3.042 Li n_ε 2.7975 Li R_g 26% met. lust.	0.245 An.-Eff. distinct	(−)	ω brownish-red ε yellowish-red Birefl. very weak	Hydroth.—pneumat. and exhal., metam., sediment. Rarely magmat. Imp. Fe ore. *Martite* = pseudomorphs after magnetite	76
blackish brown	n ≫ 2.72 $\bar{R}_g$ 18%	An.-Eff. distinct		Birefl. very weak	Magmat.—pegmat., metam., hydroth., in placers. Exsolution in titanomagnetite	77
grey white	n 2.38	∼90° $r > v$ 0.017	(+) OP (010) n_γ/c 45°		Most imp. Ti-ore. In metam. rocks, alk. basalts	78
—	n_ω 1.54425 Na n_ε 1.55336 Na glassy lust.	0.009	(+) circular-polarising	—	In magmat., metam., and sediment. rocks widely distrib. Large cryst. mostly pegmat.—hydroth. Semi-precious stone and imp. raw material. *Bergcrystal*, water-clear; *amethyst*, violet; *citrine*, yellow; *Smoky quartz*, smoky gray; *morion*, dark brownish-black	79

No.	Name and Formula	Crystal Class Lattice Constants	Habit, Form	Cleavage	Hardness	Sp. Gr.	Color
80	*Chalcedony* SiO_2	as Quartz	fib. $\perp c$ (fib. $c =$ Quartzine)	—	6	2.59 to 2.61	colorless, different colors
81	*Tridymite* (low —) SiO_2	$2/m$ or m ps. hex. a_0 18.54 b_0 5.01 c_0 25.79 β 117°40′	ps. hex. tab. (0001), tw. (10$\bar{1}$6) and (30$\bar{3}$4)	(010) (110) poor	7	2.27	colorless, white
82	*Cristobalite* (low —) SiO_2	422 a_0 4.972 c_0 6.921	ps. cub. (111), tw. (111)	—	$6\frac{1}{2}$	2.32	colorless
83	*Opal* $SiO_2 +$ aq.	amorph.	—	—	$5\frac{1}{2}$ to $6\frac{1}{2}$	2.1—2.2	colorless white, colored
84	*Rutile* TiO_2	$4/mmm$ a_0 4.59 c_0 2.96	col. c, (110) (100) (111), tw. (101) (301)	(110) per. (100) dist.	6—$6\frac{1}{2}$	4.2—4.3	brownish red to iron black
85	*Cassiterite* SnO_2	$4/mmm$ a_0 4.73 c_0 3.18	isom. (110) (111) (100) rarer acic. c (110) (321) tw. (101)	(100) imp.	6—7	6.8—7.1	brown to black
86	*Pyrolusite* β-$MnO_{2.00-1.89}$	$4/mmm$ a_0 4.39 c_0 2.87	col. c—isom. (110) (111) (120) (321) (101) usu. fine-grained. oft. pseudo-morphic after manganite	(110) per.	6 some-times decr. to 2	pure: 5.06 usu. 4.9—5.0	iron grey to black
87	*Cryptomelane* $K\leqq_2Mn_8O_{16}$("α-MnO"$_2$)	$4/m$ and $2/m$ a_0 9.84 c_0 2.86	dense globular	conch-oidal	6—$6\frac{1}{2}$ fine grained decr. to 1	4.1—4.9	black to bluish-black

Streak	Indices of refraction and Luster	Optic angle 2 V and Biref.	Optic orient.	Pleochroism Bireflection	Occurrence	No.
	n ∥ fiber ~1.532 n ⊥ fiber ~1.538	0.006 approx.		—	Hydroth.—hydric. *carneol*, red; *chryoprase*, green; *agate*, banded, *jasper*, cloudy and opaque from impurities	80
	n_α 1.469 n_β 1.469+ n_γ 1.473 glassy lust.	~35° 0.004	(+) OP (100) $n_\gamma \| c$	—	Pneumat. exhal., in pores of acid extrus. rocks; contact metam. in sandstone inclus. in basalts. In meteorites	81
	n_ω 1.487 n_ε 1.484	0.003	(−)	—	Similar to tridymite, also forms at lower temperatures	82
	n 1.3—1.45	—	—	—	Hydroth.—hydric, sediment., biogen. alteration product of silicate rocks. Also gemstone (*precious opal*). *hyalite* = colorless, clear opal	83
yellow-ish-brown	n_ω 2.616 Na n_ε 2.903 Na $\bar R_g$ 20.5% metallic-diamond lust.	0.287	(+)	ω yellow to brown-ish-yellow ε brownish-yellow to yellowish-green, dark crimson	Pegmat., hydroth., metam., and in placers. Imp. Ti ore. *Sagenite* = rutile with crossed twinning accord. to both twin laws	84
yellowish to white	n_ω 1.997 n_ε 2.093 $\bar R_g$ 11% diamond lust.	0.096	(+)		Pneumat.—pegmat. in assn. with acid magm. rocks, usually granite. Also hydroth. in joints. Most imp. Sn ore	85
black	met. lust.	—	—	—	Hydric, sediment. oxidation zone. Constituent of *psilomelane* to *wad* partl. Most common Mn oxide mineral. Imp. Mn ore. Idiomorph. crystals called *polianite*	86
dark brownish-black		—			Oxidation zone, weathering product. Constituent of *psilomelane* and *wad*. Most imp. Mn oxide mineral after pyrolusite	87

No.	Name and Formula	Crystal Class Lattice Constants	Habit, Form	Cleavage	Hardness	Sp. Gr.	Color
88	*Psilomelane* $(Ba, H_2O)_2Mn_5O_{10}$	$2/m$ a_0 9.56 b_0 2.88 c_0 13.85 β 92° 30′	dense globular	conch.	6, fine grain. decr. to 2	4.4—4.7	black to bluish-black
89	*Anatase* TiO_2	$4/mmm$ a_0 3.74 c_0 9.39	(101) (001) (107) (103) et al.	(101) (001) per.	$5^1/_2$—6	3.8—3.9	yellow to brown and to bluish-black
90	*Brookite* TiO_2	mmm a_0 9.18 b_0 5.45 c_0 5.15	tab. (010), elong. c	(120) (001) imp.	$5^1/_2$—6	3.9—4.2	yellow to reddish brown
91	*Columbite* (Niobite) $(Fe, Mn)Nb_2O_6$	mmm a_0 14.27 b_0 5.74 c_0 5.60	tab. (010) or col. a	(010) dist.	6	5.3	brownish-black
92	*Tantalite* $(Fe, Mn)Ta_2O_6$ Ta→Nb	mmm $a:b:c$ 0.401:1: 0.351	usu. col. c	(010) imp.	6	8.2	black
93	*Euxenite* (Y, Er, Ce, U, Pb, Ca) $(Nb, Ta, Ti)_2(O, OH)_6$	mmm a_0 14.57 b_0 5.52 c_0 5.166	tab. (100) to col. c	—	~6	4.6—5.4	jet black to olive brown
94	*Samarskite* (Yttroniobite, Yttro-columbite) $(Y, Er)_4$ $[(Nb, Ta)_2O_7]_3$	mmm $a:b:c$ 0.5457:1: 0.5178	tab. (010)	conch.	~6	5.5—6.2	deep black
95	*Uraninite* UO_2 (Pitchblende)	$m3m$ a_0 5.449	(100), (111)	(111)	4—6	10.3 to 10.9	black, brownish
96	*Hydrargillite* (Gibbsite) γ-$Al(OH)_3$	$2/m$ ps. hex. a_0 8.64 b_0 5.07 c_0 9.72 β 94° 34′	tab. (001) ps. hex.	(001) per.	$2^1/_2$—3	2.3—2.4	colorless, white, greenish
97	*Brucite* $Mg(OH)_2$	$3m$ a_0 3.13 c_0 4.74	tab. (0001)	(0001) per.	$2^1/_2$	2.4	colorless, white, greenish
98	*Diaspore* α-$AlOOH$	mmm a_0 4.41 b_0 9.40 c_0 2.84	tab. (010)	(010) per. (110) dist.	$6^1/_2$—7	3.3—3.5	colorless and different colors

Streak	Indices of refraction and Luster	Optic angle 2 V and Biref.	Optic orient.	Pleochroism Bireflection	Occurrence	No.
black to blackish-brown					Oxidation zone, weathering product. With pyrolusite and crypomelane. Also constituent of "psilomelane" and *wad*	88
whitish	n_ω 2.5618 n_ε 2.4986 diamond lust.	0.063	$(-)$	n_α yellow to light brown n_γ orange brown or dark blue	Hydroth. in fissures. Placers	89
brownish yellow	n_α 2.583 ⎫ n_β 2.586 ⎬ Na n_γ 2.741 ⎭ met. diamond lust.	2 V λ 20.0° 660 16.5° 589 0° 555 12.5° 535 25.4° 480 0.158	$(+)$ red to yellow: OP (001) $r > v$ green—blue: OP (100) $r < v$	little, yellow to brown $n_\gamma > n_\beta > n_\alpha$ or $n_\beta > n_\gamma > n_\alpha$	Hydrotherm. in fissures crystalline schists. In placers *Arkansite* is brookite with isom. habit.	90
brown to black	n_β 2.45 Li	strong An.-Eff. very weak	$(-)$ (?)	Birefl. weak	Pegmat. Most imp. Nb ore	91
brown to black	n_α 2.26 n_β 2.32 n_γ 2.43 pitchy to met. lust.	~74° $r < v$ 0.17	$(+)$ OP (010) $n_\gamma \| c$	n_α pale red n_β crimson n_γ dark crimson	Pegmat. Most imp. Ta ore	92
reddish brown	n ~2.1 semi-met. lust.				In granite pegmatites	93
dark reddish brown	n_β ~2.25 semi-met. lust.				In granite pegmatites	94
dark green to brownish black	dull pitchy lust.	—	—	—	Pegmat. and hydroth. Imp. U and radium ore	95
	$n_\alpha \sim n_\beta$ 1.567 n_γ 1.589	~0° $r > v$ or $r < v$ 0.02	$(+)$ OP (010) $n_\gamma /c \sim 25°$ also $n_\alpha \| b$	—	In bauxites, talc schists, serpentine. Also alteration product of corundum	96
	n_ω 1.566 n_ε 1.581	0.015	$(+)$		Metam., hydroth. in fissures in serpentines, contact metam. in limestones, as at Predazzo	97
	n_α 1.702 n_β 1.722 n_γ 1.750	84° $r < v$ 0.048	$(+)$ OP (010) $n_\gamma \| a$	colored weak	Metam. in cryst. schists, contact metam. in limestones and dolomites. Transform. product of corundum. Also in bauxites	98

No.	Name and Formula	Crystal Class Lattice Constants	Habit, Form	Cleavage	Hardness	Sp. Gr.	Color
99	*Goethite* α-FeOOH	mmm a_0 4.65 b_0 10.02 c_0 3.04	acic. *c*	(010) per.	5—5$^1/_2$	4.3	blackish-brown to light yellow
100	*Manganite* γ-MnOOH	$2/m$ a_0 8.88 b_0 5.25 c_0 5.71 β 90°	col. *c*, ps. orhomb. (110) (001) tw. (011)	(010) per. (110) per.	4	4.3—4.4	brownish-black
101	*Boehmite* γ-AlOOH	mmm a_0 3.69 b_0 12.2 c_0 2.86	tab. (001), (110)	(010) per.		3.01	colorless
102	*Lepidocrocite* γ-FeOOH	mmm a_0 3.88 b_0 12.54 c_0 3.07	tab. (010)	(010) per. (001) per. (100) dist.	5	4.09	crimson to yellowish red
103	*Sassolite* B(OH)$_3$	$\bar{1}$ a_0 7.04 b_0 7.05 c_0 6.58 α 92° 35′ β 101° 10′ γ 119° 50′	tab. (001), ps. hex.	(001) per.	1	1.45	white, pale grey

V. Cl. Nitrates and Carbonates

No.	Name and Formula	Crystal Class Lattice Constants	Habit, Form	Cleavage	Hardness	Sp. Gr.	Color
104	*Soda Niter* NaNO$_3$	$\bar{3}m$ a_0 5.07 c_0 16.81	morph. ind.[a] isom. (10$\bar{1}$1), tw. (01$\bar{1}$2)	(10$\bar{1}$1) per. 73° 37′	1$^1/_2$—2	2.27	colorless or light color
105	*Niter* KNO$_3$	mmm a_0 5.43 b_0 9.19 c_0 6.46	fib. *c*	(011) per. (010) (110) imp.	2	1.9—2.1	colorless, white, grey
106	*Magnesite* MgCO$_3$	$\bar{3}m$ a_0 4.633 c_0 15.016	morph. ind.[a] isom. (10$\bar{1}$1)	(10$\bar{1}$1) per. 72° 36′	4—4$^1/_2$	~3.0	colorless, white to brown, grey
107	*Siderite* FeCO$_3$	$\bar{3}m$ a_0 4.689 c_0 15.373	morph. ind.[a] (10$\bar{1}$1), tw. (01$\bar{1}$2)	(10$\bar{1}$1) per. 73°	4—4$^1/_2$	3.89	light yellowish brown

[a] In the case of rhomb. carbonates (No. 104, 106—111), the morphological indices are based on the cleavage rhomb. as (10$\bar{1}$1). Based in lattice constants this plane is indexed as (10$\bar{1}$4).

Streak	Indices of refraction and Luster	Optic angle 2 V and Biref.	Optic orient.	Pleochroism Bireflection	Occurrence	No.
brown to brownish yellow	n_α 2.260 n_β 2.394 n_γ 2.400	0°—42° $r>v$ 0.140	(−) for red: OP (100), for yellow to blue OP (001)	n_α light yellow n_β brownish-yellow n_γ orange to olive green	Weathering product. Imp. constit. of sediment. Fe ores. Most common constit. of *limonite*	99
dark brown	n_α 2.25 n_β 2.25 n_γ 2.53 imp. met. lust.	small $r>v$ 0.28	(+) OP (010) n_γ/c 0°—4°	Abs. n_α, $n_\beta < n_\gamma$ Biref. weak	Leaching product in veins in extrus. rocks	100
	n_β ∼1.72— 1.64	∼0.02	(−) (?) OP (001) $n_\gamma\|b$	—	In bauxites	101
orange dull	n_α 1.94 n_β 2.20 Na n_γ 2.51 diamond lust.	83° 0.57	(−) OP (100) $n_\gamma\|c$	n_α yellow n_β orange yellow n_γ brownish-yellow to orange red	Weathering product., much rarer than goethite. In *limonite*	102
	n_α 1.340 n_β 1.456 n_γ 1.459 glassy to pearly lust.	5°—7° 0.119	(−) OP∼(010) $n_\alpha\sim\|c$	—	Hot spring deposits, volcan. sublim. product. Imp. B-raw material	103
	n_ω 1.585 n_ε 1.337 $n_{\varepsilon'(10\bar{1}1)}$ 1.467 glassy	0.248	(−)	—	With gypsum in the arid zones of Chile. Imp. source of fertilizer. (*Chile salt peter*)	104
	n_α 1.335 n_β 1.505 n_γ 1.506 glassy	7° $r\ll v$ 0.171	(−) OP (100) $n_\alpha\|c$	—	Efflorescence in soils in caves and in deserts	105
	n_ω 1.700 n_ε 1.509 $n_{\varepsilon'(10\bar{1}1)}$ 1.599 glassy	0.191	(−)	—	Metam. in chlorite and talc schists, metasom. in limestones and dolomites. In salt clays. Imp. raw material. *Breunnerite* = slightly Fe bearing magnesite	106
	n_ω 1.873 n_ε 1.633 $n_{\varepsilon'(10\bar{1}1)}$ 1.747 glassy	0.240	(−)	Abs. $\varepsilon < \omega$	Metasom., pegmat.— hydroth. (usually Mn bearing), sediment. Imp. Fe ore	107

No.	Name and Formula	Crystal Class Lattice Constants	Habit, Form	Cleavage	Hardness	Sp. Gr.	Color
108	*Smithsonite* $ZnCO_3$	$\bar{3}m$ a_0 4.653 c_0 15.025	morph. ind.[a] $(10\bar{1}1)$, usu. massive	$(10\bar{1}1)$ per. 72° 20′	5	4.3—4.5	colorless, mostly colored
109	*Rhodochrosite* $MnCO_3$	$\bar{3}m$ a_0 4.777 c_0 15.664	morph. ind.[a] $(10\bar{1}1)$, botryoid.	$(10\bar{1}1)$ per. $\sim$73°	4	3.3—3.6	pale to dark red
110	*Calcite* $CaCO_3$	$\bar{3}m$ a_0 4.990 c_0 17.061	morph. ind.[a] isom. $(10\bar{1}1)$, tab. (0001) and elong c, very form-rich. tw. (0001) $(01\bar{1}2)$	$(10\bar{1}1)$ per. 74° 55′	3	2.72	colorless, white and colored
111	*Dolomite* $CaMg[CO_3]_2$	$\bar{3}$ a_0 4.808 c_0 16.010	morph. ind.[a] isom. $(10\bar{1}1)$ tw. (0001) $(10\bar{1}1)$	$(10\bar{1}1)$ per. 73° 45′	$3\frac{1}{2}$—4	2.85 to 2.95	colorless, white and yellowish-grey
112	*Aragonite* $CaCO_3$	mmm a_0 4.95 b_0 7.96 c_0 5.73	col.—fib. c, (110) (010) (011), tw. (110) ps. hex.	(010) imp.	$3\frac{1}{2}$—4	2.95	colorless, white and different colored
113	*Strontianite* $SrCO_3$	mmm a_0 5.13 b_0 8.42 c_0 6.09	col.—acic. c (110) (011) (021), tw. (110) ps. hex.	(110) dist.	$3\frac{1}{2}$	3.7	colorless, white and yellowish
114	*Witherite* $BaCO_3$	mmm a_0 5.26 b_0 8.85 c_0 6.55	isom.—fib. c, (110) (021) (010), tw. (110) ps. hex. (Bipyr.)	(010) dist.	$3\frac{1}{2}$	$\sim$4.28	colorless, white, grey, yellowish
115	*Cerussite* $PbCO_3$	mmm a_0 5.15 b_0 8.47 c_0 6.11	isom.—col. a or tab. (010), tw. (110) ps. hex.	(110) (021) poor	3—$3\frac{1}{2}$	6.4—6.6	colorless, white, yellowish, black
116	*Azurite* $Cu_3[OH|CO_3]_2$	$2/m$ a_0 4.97 b_0 5.84 c_0 10.29 β 92° 24′	col. b—tab. (001), (110)	(100) dist. (110) imp.	$3\frac{1}{2}$—4	3.7—3.9	azur blue
117	*Malachite* $Cu_2[(OH)_2|CO_3]$	$2/m$ a_0 9.48 b_0 12.03 c_0 3.21 β 98° $\pm\frac{1}{2}$°	col.—fib. c, (110) (100) (010) (001), tw. (100)	(001) per.	4	4.0	green

[a] See footnote p. 382.

Streak	Indices of refraction and Luster		Optic angle 2V and Biref.	Optic orient.	Pleochroism Bireflection	Occurrence	No.
	n_ω	1.849	0.228	(−)	—	Weathering product Zn bearing deposits. Imp. Zn ore	108
	n_ε	1.621					
	$n_{\varepsilon'(10\bar{1}1)}$	1.733					
		glassy					
	n_ω	1.814	0.218	(−)	—	Hydroth. and alteration product in oxidation zone	109
	n_ε	1.596					
	$n_{\varepsilon'(10\bar{1}1)}$	1.70					
		glassy					
	n_ω	1.6584 Na	0.172	(−)	—	Sediment., metam., hydroth.—hydric, biogen. Imp. raw material. *Iceland spar* = colorless, compl. transparent calcite	110
	n_ε	1.4864 Na					
	$n_{\varepsilon'(10\bar{1}1)}$	1.566					
		glassy					
	n_ω	1.6799 Na	0.179	(−)	—	Metasom. from limestone, hydroth. rarely sediment. Imp. raw material. *Ankerite* = Mg→Fe (Fe > Mg)	111
	n_ε	1.5013 Na					
	$n_{\varepsilon'(10\bar{1}1)}$	1.588					
		glassy					
	n_α	1.530	18°11′ $r<v$ 0.156	(−) OP (100) $n_\alpha\|c$	—	Hydroth.—hydric, sediment. and biogen.	112
	n_β	1.682					
	n_γ	1.686					
		glassy					
	n_α	1.516	7°—10° $r<v$ 0.150	(−) OP (010) $n_\alpha\|c$	—	Hydroth.—hydric in veins and in limestone	113
	n_β	1.664					
	n_γ	1.666					
		glassy					
	n_α	1.529	16° $r>v$ 0.148	(−) OP (010) $n_\alpha\|c$	—	Hydroth. in veins and metasom.	114
	n_β	1.676					
	n_γ	1.677					
		glassy					
	n_α	1.804	8° 34′ 0.274	(−) OP (010) $n_\alpha\|c$	—	Oxidation zone of galena deposits	115
	n_β	2.076					
	n_γ	2.078					
		greasy diamond lust.					
bright blue	n_α	1.730	68° $r>v$ 0.108	(+) OP ⊥ (010) n_γ/c—$12^1/_2{}°$	n_α } pure n_β } blue n_γ dark blue	Oxidation zone of Cu bearing deposits	116
	n_β	1.758					
	n_γ	1.838					
		glassy					
light green	n_α	1.655	43° $r<v$ 0.254	(−) OP (010) n_α/c 23° $n_\alpha \sim \perp (001)$	n_α almost colorless n_β yellow-ish-green n_γ dark green	Like azurite. Locally an imp. Cu ore	117
	n_β	1.875					
	n_γ	1.909					
		glassy					

No.	Name and Formula	Crystal Class Lattice Constants	Habit, Form	Cleavage	Hardness	Sp. Gr.	Color
118	*Hydrozincite* $Zn_5[(OH)_3 \mid CO_3]_2$	$2/m$ a_0 13.48 b_0 6.32 c_0 5.37 β 95° 30′	tab. (100) and elong. after c, usu. massive	(100) per.	$2—2^1/_2$	3.2—3.8	snow-white to pale yellow
119	*Soda* $Na_2CO_3 \cdot 10\,H_2O$	$2/m$ a_0 12.76 b_0 9.01 c_0 13.47 β 122° 48′	tab. (010), (110) (011), tw. (001)	(100) per. (010) imp.	$1—1^1/_2$	1.42 to 1.47	colorless, pale grey, yellowish to white
120	*Hydromagnesite* $Mg_5[(OH) \mid (CO_3)_2]_2 \cdot$ $4\,H_2O$	monocl.- ps. orhomb. (222) a_0 18.58 b_0 9.06 c_0 8.42 β 90°	fib. c—tab. (100), elong. c, tw. (100)	(010) per. (100) dist.	$3^1/_2$	$\sim$2.2	white

VI. Cl. Borates

No.	Name and Formula	Crystal Class Lattice Constants	Habit, Form	Cleavage	Hardness	Sp. Gr.	Color
121	*Borax* $Na_2[B_4O_5(OH)_4] \cdot 8\,H_2O$	$2/m$ a_0 11.84 b_0 10.63 c_0 12.32 β 106° 35′	short col. tw. (100) rare	(100) per. (110) dist.	$2—2^1/_2$	1.7—1.8	colorless, grey, yellowish
122	*Kernite* $Na_2[B_4O_6(OH)_2] \cdot 3\,H_2O$	$2/m$ a_0 15.68 b_0 9.09 c_0 7.02 β 108° 52′	isom.—col. c, (100) ($\bar{1}$01) (011) (001)	(001) (100) per. ($\bar{1}$01) dist.	$2^1/_2$	1.92	colorless, white
123	*Boracite* $Mg_3[Cl \mid B_7O_{13}] < 265°\,C$	$2\,mm$ a_0 8.54 b_0 8.54 c_0 12.07	fib. a. pseu-domorph. after β-B., cycl. tw. (100) of 12 indi-vid.	—	7	2.9—3	colorless, bluish, greenish
124	*Boracite* β-$Mg_3[Cl \mid B_7O_{13}]$ $> 265°\,C$	$\bar{4}3\,m$ a_0 12.10	(100) (110) (111)	—	7	2.9—3.0	colorless, bluish, greenish

VII. Cl. Sulfates, Chromates, Molybdates, Wolframates

No.	Name and Formula	Crystal Class Lattice Constants	Habit, Form	Cleavage	Hardness	Sp. Gr.	Color
125	*Glauberite* $CaNa_2[SO_4]_2$	$2/m$ a_0 10.01 b_0 8.21 c_0 8.43 β 112° 11′	tab. (001) or col. c, (100) (111)	(001) per.	$2^1/_2$—3	2.7—2.8	colorless, white and light colors
126	*Anhydrite* $Ca[SO_4]$	mmm a_0 6.22 b_0 6.97 c_0 6.96	isom. (100) (010) (001) or col. b (101) (010) (011)	(001) per. (010) dist. (100) imp.	3—4	2.9—3	colorless, white and light colors

Streak	Indices of refraction and Luster	Optic angle 2 V and Biref.	Optic orient.	Pleochroism Bireflection	Occurrence	No.
	n_α 1.65 n_β 1.736 n_γ 1.74 variable	40° $r < v$ 0.09	(−) OP ⊥ (010) n_γ/c low	—	Oxidation zone of Zn deposits	118
	n_α 1.405 n_β 1.425 n_γ 1.440 glassy	71° $r < v$ 0.035	(−) OP ⊥ (010) $n_\alpha \| b$ n_β/c 41°	—	Soda lakes, soil efflorescence	119
	n_α 1.523 n_β 1.527 n_γ 1.545 pearly lust.	∼52° 0.022	(+)	—	Weathering product of serpentine. Also in cavities of lime-stone blocks in the Campagna tuffs	120
	n_α 1.447 n_β 1.469 n_γ 1.472 glassy to greasy lust.	39° 36′ $r > v$ 0.025	(−) OP ⊥ (010) $n_\alpha \| b$	—	Precipitated in con-tinental playa lakes	121
	n_α 1.454 n_β 1.472 n_γ 1.488	80° $r > v$ 0.034	(−) OP ⊥ (010) $n_\gamma \| b$ n_α/c 70$^1/_2$°	—	Contact metam. from borax (?), Kern Co. Most imp. source of B	122
	n_α 1.6622 n_β 1.6670 n_γ 1.6730 glassy to diamond lust.	83° 0.011	(+) $n_\gamma \|$fibers	—	Evaporate deposits, esp. in gypsum caps	123
	n 1.6714	—	—	—	Evaporate deposits	124
	n_α 1.515 n_β 1.532 n_γ 1.536 glassy to greasy lust.	71° 10′ $r \gg v$ 0.021	(−) OP ⊥ (010) n_α/c 30° 46′	—	Evaporite deposits	125
	n_α 1.569 n_β 1.575 n_γ 1.613 glassy lust.	42° $r < v$ 0.044	(+) OP(010) $n_\gamma \| a$	—	Sediment., hydroth. and exhalation product	126

No.	Name and Formula	Crystal Class Lattice Constants	Habit, Form	Cleavage	Hardness	Sp. Gr.	Color
127	*Celestite* $Sr[SO_4]$	mmm a_0 8.38 b_0 5.37 c_0 6.85	col. a, tab. (001), (110) (011) (102)	(001) per. (210) dist. (010) poor	3—3$^1/_2$	3.9—4	colorless, white, blue et al. colors
128	*Barite* $Ba[SO_4]$	mmm a_0 8.87 b_0 5.45 c_0 7.14	tab. (001), (110) (102), col. a (011) (110) (010) et al.	(001) per. (210) dist.	3—3$^1/_2$	4.48	colorless, white, colors
129	*Anglesite* $Pb[SO_4]$	mmm a_0 8.47 b_0 5.39 c_0 6.94	isom. (011) (110), tab. (001)	(001) (210) dist. 76° 16′	3	6.3	colorless white and colors
130	*Brochantite* $Cu_4[(OH)_6|SO_4]$	$2/m$ a_0 13.08 b_0 9.85 c_0 6.02 β 103° 22′	col.—fib. c,	(010) per.	3$^1/_2$—4	3.9	emerald green
131	*Alunite* $KAl_3[(OH)_6|(SO_4)_2]$	$3m$ a_0 6.97 c_0 17.38	(10$\bar{1}$1) ps. cub.	(0001) per.	3$^1/_2$—4	2.6—2.8	colorless, white, reddish, yellowish
132	*Kieserite* $Mg[SO_4]\cdot H_2O$	$2/m$ a_0 6.89 b_0 7.61 c_0 7.63 β 116° 05′	bipyramid. crystals rare	(11$\bar{1}$) (11$\bar{3}$) per. (111) (102) (012) dist.	3$^1/_2$	2.57	colorless, white, yellowish
133	*Chalcanthite* $Cu[SO_4]\cdot 5H_2O$	$\bar{1}$ a_0 6.12 b_0 10.69 c_0 5.96 α 97° 35′ β 107° 10′ γ 77° 33′	broad tab. (1$\bar{1}$0) (110) ($\bar{1}$11) (100)	(1$\bar{1}$0) (110) imp.	2$^1/_2$	2.2—2.3	blue
134	*Melanterite* $Fe[SO_4]\cdot 7H_2O$	$2/m$ a_0 14.11 b_0 6.51 c_0 11.02 β 105° 15′	short col. to isom. (110) (001), crystals rare	(001) per. (110) dist.	2	1.9	green
135	*Epsomite* $Mg[SO_4]\cdot 7H_2O$	222 a_0 11.96 b_0 12.05 c_0 6.88	fib.—col. c, (110 (111)	(010) per. (011) imp.	2—2$^1/_2$	1.68	colorless, white

Streak	Indices of refraction and Luster	Optic angle 2V and Biref.	Optic orient.	Pleochroism Bireflection	Occurrence	No.
	n_α 1.622 n_β 1.624 n_γ 1.631 glassy	51° $r < v$ 0.009	(+) OP (010) $n_\gamma \| a$	—	Hydroth.—hydric. In fissures and cavities in limestone and gypsum	127
	n_α 1.636 n_β 1.637 n_γ 1.648 glassy	36° $r < v$ 0.012	(+) OP (010) $n_\gamma \| a$	—	Hydroth., sediment. Imp. raw material	128
	n_α 1.877 n_β 1.882 n_γ 1.894 greasy diamond lust.	60°—75° $r \ll v$ 0.017	(+) OP (010) $n_\gamma \| a$	—	Oxidation zone of Pb deposits	129
light green	n_α 1.730 n_β 1.778 n_γ 1.803 glassy	72° $r < v$ 0.073	(−) OP (100) $n_\alpha \| b$	weak in bluishgreen Abs.$\| n_\gamma$ strongest	Oxidation zone of Cu deposits	130
	n_ω 1.572 n_ε 1.592	0.020	(+)	—	Alteration product of K bearing rocks	131
	n_α 1.523 n_β 1.535 n_γ 1.586 glassy	56° 44' $r > v$ 0.063	(+) OP (010) n_α / c—14°	—	Evaporite deposits	132
white	n_α 1.514 n_β 1.5368 n_γ 1.543 glassy	56° 2' $r < v$ 0.029	(−) on (1$\bar{1}$0) emerg. 1 axis, on (110) 1 axis and n_γ	—	Weathering product	133
white	n_α 1.471 n_β 1.478 n_γ 1.486 glassy	86° $r > v$ 0.015	(+) OP (010) n_α / c 29°	—	Weathering product	134
	n_α 1.433 n_β 1.455 n_γ 1.461	51° 25' $r < v$ 0.028	(−) OP (001) $n_\alpha \| b$	—	Soil efflorescence, weathering product from sulfides. Alteration product of kieserite	135

No.	Name and Formula	Crystal Class Lattice Constants	Habit, Form	Cleavage	Hardness	Sp. Gr.	Color
136	*Alunogen* $Al_2[SO_4]_3 \cdot 18\,H_2O$	$\bar{1}$ $a:b:c$ 0.8355:1 0.6752 α 89° 58′ β 97° 26′ γ 91° 52′	tab. (010) or fib. c	(010) per.	$1^{1}/_{2}$—2	1.65	white
137	*Potasium alum* $KAl[SO_4]_2 \cdot 12\,H_2O$	$2/m\bar{3}$ a_0 12.15	(111) (100), tw. (111)	—	2—$2^{1}/_{2}$	1.76	colorless
138	*Astrakanite* (Blödite) $Na_2Mg[SO_4]_2 \cdot 4\,H_2O$	$2/m$ a_0 11.06 b_0 8.17 c_0 5.50	col. c or tab. (001)	—	3	2.23	colorless, greenish, yellowish
139	*Polyhalite* $K_2Ca_2Mg[SO_4]_4 \cdot 2\,H_2O$	$\bar{1}$ ps. orhomb. a_0 6.96 b_0 6.97 c_0 8.97$_9$ α 104° 30′ β 101° 30′ γ 113° 54	elong. c or tab. (010), tw. lam. (010) (100)	(10$\bar{1}$) per. diag. part. $\sim\|$ (010)	3—$3^{1}/_{2}$	2.77	red, white, yellow, grey
140	*Mirabilite* (Glaubersalt) $Na_2[SO_4] \cdot 10\,H_2O$	$2/m$ a_0 11.48 b_0 10.35 c_0 12.82 β 107° 40′	fib.—col. b, (001) (100)	(100) per.	$1^{1}/_{2}$	1.49	colorless
141	*Gypsum* $Ca[SO_4] \cdot 2\,H_2O$	$2/m$ a_0 5.68 b_0 15.18 c_0 6.29 β 113° 50′	tab. (010) or col. c, (010) (110) (111); tw. (100) (101)	(010) per. ($\bar{1}$11) (100) dist.	$1^{1}/_{2}$—2	2.3—2.4	colorless, white, yellowish
142	*Copiapite* (Fe¨, Mg) $Fe_4^{\cdot\cdot}[(OH)|(SO_4)_3]_2 \cdot$ $\cdot 20\,H_2O$	$\bar{1}$ a_0 7.34 b_0 18.19 c_0 7.28 α 93° 50′ β 101° 30′ γ 99° 23′	tab. (001) ps. orhomb.	(001) per.	$2^{1}/_{2}$	2.1	yellow
143	*Kainite* $KMg[Cl|SO_4] \cdot 3\,H_2O$	$2/m$ a_0 19.76 b_0 16.26 c_0 9.57 β 94° 56′	tab. (001) with (111) ($\bar{1}$11) (010)	(100) per. (110) dist.	3	2.1	white, yellowish, red
144	*Crocoite* $Pb[CrO_4]$	$2/m$ a_0 7.11 b_0 7.41 c_0 6.81 β 102° 33′	acic.—col. c, (110) (111) ($\bar{4}$01) ($\bar{3}$01) (120)	(110) dist.	$2^{1}/_{2}$—3	5.9—6.0	orange red

Streak	Indices of refraction and Luster	Optic angle 2V and Biref.	Optic orient.	Pleochroism Bireflection	Occurrence	No.
	n_α 1.475 n_β 1.478 n_γ 1.485 variable	small to 69° 0.010	(+) OP ⊥ (010) n_γ/c 42°	—	Weathering product of sulfide bearing argill. rocks. Solfataros	136
	n 1.4562 Na	—	—	—	Efflorescence from lavas, sulfide bearing schists	137
	n_α 1.4826 n_β 1.4855 n_γ 1.4869 glassy lust.	69° 24′ $r \ll v$ 0.004	(−) OP (010) n_α/c 41°	—	In evaporite deposits, as precip. from alkali lakes and in salt peter deserts	138
white	n_α 1.547 n_β 1.562 n_γ 1.567 glassy to greasy lust.	62° ± $r < v$ 0.020	(−) on (010) $n'_\alpha/(010)$ 6°, on (010) $n'_\alpha/(100)$ 13°, on (001) $n'_\alpha/(010)$ 8°	—	Evaporite deposits	139
	n_α 1.394 n_β 1.396 n_γ 1.398	80° 26′ $r > v$ 0.004	(−) OP ⊥ (010) n_γ/c 31° Li	—	Salt deposits, salt lakes, soil efflorescence	140
	n_α 1.5205 n_β 1.5526 n_γ 1.5296 glassy lust.	58° 5′ $r > v$ 0.009	(+) OP (010) n_γ/c 52° 30′	—	Sediment., also crystalizes in clays and marls by weathering of sulfides. Alteration product of anhydrite. *Alabaster* = fine-grained, pure white gypsum	141
yellow-ish-white	n_α 1.531 n_β 1.546 n_γ 1.597	60°—90° 0.066	(+)	n_α yellow-ish-green n_β pale yellow n_γ sulfur yellow	Weathering product of sulfide bearing clays and marls	142
	n_α 1.495 n_β 1.506 n_γ 1.520	85° $r > v$ 0.025	(−) OP (010) n_α/c —8°	—	Evaporites, secondary from carnallite. Imp. potassium salt	143
orange	n_α 2.29 n_β 2.36 } Li n_γ 2.66 diamond lust.	57° ± $r > v$ 0.37	(+) OP (010) n_γ/c —5½°	weak in orange	Oxidation zone	144

No.	Name and Formula	Crystal Class Lattice Constants	Habit, Form	Cleavage	Hardness	Sp. Gr.	Color
145	*Wolframite* (Mn, Fe)[WO$_4$]	$2/m$ a_0 4.79 b_0 5.74 c_0 4.99 β 90° 26′	tab. (100) or col. to acic. c, (100) (110) (210) (001) (102) (011) (111), tw. (100) rare (023)	(010) per.	5—5$^1/_2$	7.14 to 7.54	dark brown to black
146	*Scheelite* Ca[WO$_4$]	$4/m$ a_0 5.25 c_0 11.40	isom. (112) (101) (213) (211), tw. (110), (100)	(101) dist. (112) poor	4$^1/_2$—5	5.9—6.1	greyishwhite to yellowish
147	*Wulfenite* Pb[MoO$_4$]	4 a_0 5.42 c_0 12.10	tab. (001) to isom. (101) or (112)	(101) dist.	3	6.7—6.9	honey to orange yellow

VIII. Cl. Phosphates, Arsenates, Vanadates

No.	Name and Formula	Crystal Class Lattice Constants	Habit, Form	Cleavage	Hardness	Sp. Gr.	Color
148	*Triphyline* Li(Fe˙˙, Mn˙˙)[PO$_4$]	mmm a_0 6.01 b_0 10.36 c_0 4.68	col. [100]	(001) per. (010) imp.	4—5	3.58 (Fe-end-memb.)	greenish, bluish, grey, blue flecks
149	*Xenotime* Y[PO$_4$]	$4/mmm$ a_0 6.89 c_0 6.04	col. c to isom., (110) (100) (111) (201)	(110) per.	4—5	4.5—5.1	light brown to reddish brown
150	*Monazite* Ce[PO$_4$] Th-bearing	$2/m$ a_0 6.79 b_0 7.04 c_0 6.47 β 104° 24′	tab. (100) to col. c, (100) (110) (101) (010), tw. (100)	(001) per. (100) dist.	5—5$^1/_2$	4.8—5.5	light yellow to dark reddish-brown
151	*Amblygonite* LiAl[(F, OH)|PO$_4$]	$\bar{1}$ a_0 5.19 b_0 7.12 c_0 5.04 α 112° 02′ β 97° 49′ γ 68° 07′	usu. massive	(001) per. (100) dist. (02$\bar{1}$) poor	6	2.9—3.1	greenish, violet, white
152	*Lazulite* (Mg, Fe˙˙)Al$_2$[OH|PO$_4$]$_2$	$2/m$ a_0 7.16 b_0 7.26 c_0 7.24 β 118° 55′	(111), usu. massive	(110) poor	5—6	3.1	sky blue to dark blue
153	*Descloizite* Pb(Zn, Cu)[OH|VO$_4$]	222 a_0 6.06 b_0 9.41 c_0 7.58	col. c or b, also tab. (100), (110) (111) (100) (021)	—	3$^1/_2$	5.5—6.2	brownish-red to black

Streak	Indices of refraction and Luster	Optic angle 2 V and Biref.	Optic orient.	Pleochroism Bireflection	Occurrence	No.
yellow-ish-brown to dark brown	n_α 2.26 n_β 2.32 n_γ 2.42 resinous met. lust.	~76° increase with Mn-content 0.16 An.-Eff. distinct	(+) OP ⊥ (010) n_γ/c 17° to 21° (increasing with Mn-content)	Abs. $n_\alpha < n_\beta < n_\gamma$ Birefl. very weak	Pegm.—pneum. in granite assn. Most imp. W ore	145
	n_ω 1.9185 n_ε 1.9345 greasy diamond lust.	0.016	(+)	—	Pegmat.—pneum. and hydroth. Accomp. cassiterite. Imp. W ore	146
white to light grey	n_ω 2.405 n_ε 2.283 diamond lust.	0.122	(−)	Abs. $\varepsilon < \omega$	Oxidation zone of lead deposits	147
—	n_α 1.694 n_β 1.695 n_γ 1.700 (for Fe:Mn =7:3) greasy	55° 0.006	(+) OP (001) $n_\alpha \| a$	—	In granite pegmatites	148
light reddish-brown	n_ω 1.721 n_ε 1.816 greasy glassy	0.095	(+)	—	Magmat. in granites and syenites, in pegmatites and hydroth.; in placers	149
light yellow to light reddish-brown	n_α 1.796 n_β 1.797 n_γ 1.841 greasy glassy to diamond lust.	6°—19° $r \lessgtr v$ 0.045	(+) OP ⊥ (010) n_γ/c 2°—6°	yellow to colorless Abs. $n_\beta > n_\alpha = n_\gamma$	Pegmat., hydroth. in fissures; in placers. Most imp. Th ore (up to 19% Th)	150
	n_α 1.578—1.607 n_β 1.593—1.614 n_γ 1.598—1.630 glassy, on (001) pearly	50°—100° (1—85% [OH]) $r \gtrless v$ 0.02	(−) from ~60% (OH) (+)	—	Pegmatitic. Imp. Li raw material	151
colorless	n_α 1.612 n_β 1.634 n_γ 1.643 glassy	69° ± $r < v$ 0.031	(−) OP (010) n_α/c—9° to —10°	n_α colorless n_β, n_γ blue	Hydroth. in quartz veins and quartz lenses in cryst. schists	152
yellow-ish-brown to light green	n_α 2.185 n_β 2.265 n_γ 2.35 diamond lust.	~89° $r \ll v$ 0.17	(−) ((+)) OP (010) $n_\alpha\|c$	n_α pale yellow n_β greenish-yellow n_γ gold	Oxidation zone of Pb-Zn deposits. Imp. V ore. *Mottramite =* Cu > Zn	153

No.	Name and Formula	Crystal Class Lattice Constants	Habit, Form	Cleavage	Hardness	Sp. Gr.	Color
154	*Apatite* $Ca_5[(F, Cl, OH)|(PO_4)_3]$	$6/m$ F-Apatite: a_0 9.39 c_0 6.89 Cl-Apatite: a_0 9.54 c_0 6.86	col. c to broad tab. (0001), (10$\bar{1}$0) (10$\bar{1}$1)	(0001) (10$\bar{1}$0) var. dist.	5	3.16 to 3.22	colorless and colors
155	*Pyromorphite* $Pb_5[Cl(PO_4)_3]$	$6/m$ a_0 9.97 c_0 7.32	col. c, (10$\bar{1}$0) (0001)	—	$3^1/_2$—4	6.7—7.0	green, brown, colorless and other colors
156	*Mimetesite* $Pb_5[Cl|(AsO_4)_3]$	$6/m$ a_0 10.26 c_0 7.44	col. c, (10$\bar{1}$0), (0001); rare broad tab. (0001);	(10$\bar{1}$1) imp.	$3^1/_2$—4	7.28	pale yellow to yellowish brown, orange, white, colorless
157	*Vanadinite* $Pb_5[Cl|(VO_4)_3]$	$6/m$ a_0 10.33 c_0 7.35	col. c or pyramid., (10$\bar{1}$0) (0001) (10$\bar{1}$1) (11$\bar{2}$1)	—	3	6.8—7.1	yellow, brown, orange
158	*Scorodite* $Fe^{\cdots}[AsO_4] \cdot 2H_2O$	mmm a_0 10.28 b_0 10.00 c_0 8.90	(111) (120) (010) (100) (001)	(120) imp.	$3^1/_2$—4	3.1—3.3	leek green to blackish green
159	*Vivianite* $Fe_3^{\cdot\cdot}[PO_4]_2 \cdot 8H_2O$	$2/m$ a_0 10.08 b_0 13.43 c_0 4.70 β 104° 30′	col. c, also tab. (010), (110) (100) (010) (111), earthy	(010) per.	$2^1/_2$	2.68	fresh colorless to white, in the air turning to blue
160	*Erythrite* $Co_3[AsO_4]_2 \cdot 8H_2O$	$2/m$ a_0 10.20 b_0 13.37 c_0 4.74 β 105° 01′	acic. c—rare tab. (010), (110) (104) (10$\bar{1}$) (350)	(010) per.	$2^1/_2$	2.95	pinkish red
161	*Annabergite* $Ni_3[AsO_4]_2 \cdot 8H_2O$	$2/m$ a_0 10.14 b_0 13.31 c_0 4.71 β 104° 45′	fib. c or tab. (010), (110) (104) (10$\bar{1}$) (350)	(010) per.	$2^1/_2$—3	3—3.1	apple green
162	*Struvite* $(NH_4)Mg[PO_4] \cdot 6H_2O$	$2mm$ a_0 6.98 b_0 6.10 c_0 11.20	isom., (101) (011) (00$\bar{1}$), tw. (001)	(001) per. (010) dist.	$1^1/_2$—2	1.72	yellow to light brown rarely colorless

Streak	Indices of refraction and Luster	Optic angle 2 V and Biref.	Optic orient.	Pleochroism Bireflection	Occurrence	No.
white	F-Apatite: n_ω 1.6335 n_ε 1.6316 greasy glassy Cl-Apatite: n_ω 1.6684 n_ε 1.6675	0.001	(−)	Abs. $\varepsilon > \omega$	Magmat., hydroth., sediment., biogen. Imp. source P and fertilizer. *Phosphorite* = finely-crystalline, nodular, sediment. apatite	154
white to grey	n_ω 2.0596 Na n_ε 2.0488 Na greasy diamond lust.	0.011	(−)	weak Abs. $\varepsilon < \omega$	Oxidation zone of Pb deposits	155
	n_ω 2.147 n_ε 2.128	0.019	(−)		Weathering product from lead deposits	156
whitish to reddish-yellow	n_ω 2.4163 Na n_ε 2.3503 Na diamond lust.	0.066	(−)	ε lemon yellow ω brown-ish-red to orange Abs. $\varepsilon < \omega$	Oxidation zone	157
greenish to white	n_α 1.738—1.784 n_β 1.774—1.796 n_γ 1.797—1.814 glassy	54°—70° $r \gg v$ 0.03 to 0.06	(+) OP (100) $n_\alpha \| b$	n_α colorless n_γ bluish-green	Weathering product of Fe-As deposits	158
colorless, white, change to indigo blue	fresh: n_α 1.580 n_β 1.598 n_γ 1.627 blue, be-comes: n_α 1.581 n_β 1.604 n_γ 1.636 glassy	80°—90° $r < v$ 0.047	(+) OP $\perp$ (010) $n_\gamma/c\ 28^1/_2°$	n_α deep blue n_β almost colorless n_γ pale olive green	Hydroth.—hydric, in fissures. Alteration product in peg-matites, clays, and coal	159
bright pinkish-red	n_α 1.629 n_β 1.663 n_γ 1.701 diamond lust.	89° ± $r > v$ 0.072	(±) OP $\perp$ (010) $n_\gamma/c\ 32°$	n_α pale reddish-brown n_β pale violet n_γ red $n_\gamma > n_\alpha > n_\beta$	Weathering product of Co-As ores	160
pale green	n_α 1.622 n_β 1.658 n_γ 1.687	84° $r > v$ 0.065	(−) OP $\perp$ (010) $n_\gamma/c\ 35^1/_2°$	weak, in green shades	Weathering product of Ni-As ores	161
	n_α 1.495 n_β 1.496 n_γ 1.504	37° $r < v$ 0.009	(+) OP (100) $n_\gamma \| b$	—	Boggy soils. Guano	162

No.	Name and Formula	Crystal Class Lattice Constants	Habit, Form	Cleavage	Hardness	Sp. Gr.	Color
163	*Wavellite* $Al_3[(OH)_3|(PO_4)_2]$ $\cdot 5H_2O$	mmm a_0 9.62 b_0 17.34 c_0 6.99	rad. fib. c, (110) (111)	(110) (011) dist.	$3^1/_2$—4	2.3—2.4	colorless, grey, yellowish, greenish
164	*Turquoise* $CuAl_6[(OH)_2|PO_4]_4$ $\cdot 4H_2O$	$\bar{1}$ a_0 7.48 b_0 9.95 c_0 7.69 α 111° 39′ β 115° 23′ γ 69° 26′	crystals rare, col.		5—6	2.6—2.8	sky-blue to bluish-green, apple green
165	*Autunite* $Ca[UO_2|PO_4]_2$ $\cdot 12$—$10H_2O$	$4/mmm$ a_0 7.00 c_0 20.67	tab. (001), tw. (110)	(001) per. (100) dist.	2	3—3.2	greenish-yellow to sulfur-yellow
166	*Carnotite* $K_2[(UO_2)_2|V_2O_8]\cdot 3H_2O$	$2/m$ a_0 10.47 b_0 8.41 c_0 6.91 β 103° 40′	tab. (001)	(001) per.	4 ?	4.5	yellow, greenish-yellow

IX. Cl. Silicates

a) Nesosilicates (Inselsilicates)

No.	Name and Formula	Crystal Class Lattice Constants	Habit, Form	Cleavage	Hardness	Sp. Gr.	Color
167	*Phenacite* $Be_2[SiO_4]$	$\bar{3}$ a_0 12.45 c_0 8.23	$(10\bar{1}0)$ $(1\bar{3}\bar{2}2)$ and other forms or col. c, $(11\bar{2}0)$ $(10\bar{1}0)$ $(1\bar{3}\bar{2}2)$	$(11\bar{2}0)$ imp.	$7^1/_2$—8	3.0	colorless, pale colored
168	*Willemite* $Zn_2[SiO_4]$	$\bar{3}$ a_0 13.96 c_0 9.34	col. c, $(10\bar{1}0)$ $(10\bar{1}1)$ $(30\bar{3}4)$	(0001) $(11\bar{2}0)$ dist. var.	$5^1/_2$	4.0—4.2	colorless and different colored, often greenish

Olivine Group (No. 169—171)

No.	Name and Formula	Crystal Class Lattice Constants	Habit, Form	Cleavage	Hardness	Sp. Gr.	Color
169	*Forsterite* (Fo) $Mg_2[SiO_4]$ 0—10 Mol.-% Fa	mmm a_0 6.00 b_0 4.78 c_0 10.28	isom. (010) (110) (011) (001), tw. (101) rare	(100) dist. (001) imp.	$6^1/_2$—7	3.2	yellowish-green
170	*Olivine* (Peridot) $(Mg, Fe)_2[SiO_4]$ 10—30 Mol.-% Fa	mmm a_0 6.01 b_0 4.78 c_0 10.30	like Forsterite, tw. (101) rare	(100) dist. (001) imp.	$6^1/_2$—7	3.4	yellowish-green
171	*Fayalite* (Fa) $Fe_2[SiO_4]$	mmm a_0 6.17 b_0 4.81 c_0 10.61	tw. (101) rare	(100) dist. (001) imp.	$6^1/_2$—7	4.34	yellowish-green to black

Streak	Indices of refraction and Luster	Optic angle 2V and Biref.	Optic orient.	Pleochroism Bireflection	Occurrence	No.
	n_α 1.525 n_β 1.535 n_γ 1.545 var. glassy	72° $r>v$ 0.020	(+) OP (100) $n_\gamma\|c$	—	Hydroth.—hydric., in fissures in shales	163
white	n_α 1.61 n_β 1.62 n_γ 1.65	40° $r\ll v$ 0.04	(+) Extinction on (1̄10) to c 12°	colorless to pale blue	In fissures in argillaceous rocks. Ornamental stone	164
yellow	n_α 1.553 n_β 1.575 n_γ 1.577	33° $r\gg v$ 0.024	(−) OP (010) $n_\alpha\|c$	n_α colorless n_β, n_γ gold	Hydroth.—hydric., secondary in granites and pegmatites, U ore veins	165
	n_α 1.750 n_β 1.925 n_γ 1.950	46° $r<v$ 0.200	(−) OP (100) $n_\alpha\|c$	n_α greyish-yellow n_β, n_γ lemon yellow	In sandstones in Colorado. Imp. U and V ore, Ra bearing	166
	n_ω 1.654 n_ε 1.670	0.016	(+)	—	Hydroth.—pneum.	167
	n_ω 1.691 n_ε 1.719	0.028	(+)	—	Hydroth.—hydric., contact metam., Zn deposits	168
white	n_α 1.635 n_β 1.651 n_γ 1.670	86° $r<v$ 0.035	(+) OP (100) $n_\gamma\|b$	—	Contact metamorphic	169
white	n_α 1.647—1.686 n_β 1.666—1.707 n_γ 1.685—1.726	by 11 Mol.% Fa 90° 0.39	up to Fa 11% (−) OP (100) $n_\gamma\|b$	—	Magmat. (basic extrus. rocks), metam. (Eclogites), in meteorites and slag. As gemstone = *chrysolite*. *Hortonolite* = with 50—70 Mol.-% Fa	170
white	n_α 1.835 n_β 1.877 n_γ 1.886 glassy	133° (47°) $r<v$ 0.051	(−) OP (100) $n_\gamma\|b$	—	Contact metam. in iron rich sediments and slags	171

No.	Name and Formula	Crystal Class Lattice Constants	Habit, Form	Cleavage	Hardness	Sp. Gr.	Color
172	*Monticellite* $CaMg[SiO_4]$	mmm a_0 6.38 b_0 4.83 c_0 11.10	isom.	(010) poor	$5—5\frac{1}{2}$	3.2	colorless, white, yellowish
	Garnets (No. 173—178)						
173	*Pyrope* $Mg_3Al_2[SiO_4]_3$	$m3m$ a_0 11.53	alone or comb. (110) (211), rarely (321) (431) (332) (210)	(110) poor	$6\frac{1}{2}$ to $7\frac{1}{2}$	$\sim$3.5	crimson
174	*Almandine* (Common garnet) $Fe_3^{..}Al_2[SiO_4]_3$	$m3m$ a_0 11.52	like Pyrope, esp. (211)	(110) poor	$6\frac{1}{2}$ to $7\frac{1}{2}$	$\sim$4.2	red, bluish-brown
175	*Spessartite* $Mn_3Al_2[SiO_4]_3$	$m3m$ a_0 11.61	like Pyrope	(110) poor	$6\frac{1}{2}$ to $7\frac{1}{2}$	$\sim$4.2	yellow to reddish-brown
176	*Grossularite* $Ca_3Al_2[SiO_4]_3$	$m3m$ a_0 11.85	like Pyrope	(110) poor	$6\frac{1}{2}$ to $7\frac{1}{2}$	$\sim$3.5	white, light green, yellowish to orange
177	*Andradite* $Ca_3Fe_2^{..}[SiO_4]_3$	$m3m$ a_0 12.04	(110) with (211)	(110) poor	$6\frac{1}{2}$ to $7\frac{1}{2}$	$\sim$3.7	brown, green, colorless, black
178	*Melanite* $Ca_3Fe_2^{..}[SiO_4]_3$ with Na, Ti for Ca, $Fe^{...}$ and Ti for Si (to 25% TiO_2)	$m3m$ a_0 12.05 to 12.16	(110) with (211)	(110) poor	$6\frac{1}{2}$ to $7\frac{1}{2}$	$\sim$3.7	brownish black
179	*Zircon* $Zr[SiO_4]$	$4/mmm$ a_0 6.59 c_0 5.94	col. *c*, (100) (101) or (110) (101) combined with (211) tw. (112), et al.	(100) imp.	$7\frac{1}{2}$	3.9—4.8	brown to brownish-red and other colors, also colorless
180	*Euclase* $Al[BeSiO_4OH]$	$2/m$ a_0 4.63 b_0 14.27 c_0 4.76 β 100° 16′	col. *c*, very faceted	(010) per.	$7\frac{1}{2}$	3.0—3.1	colorless to light green
181	*Sillimanite* $Al^{[6]}Al^{[4]}[O\,\vert\,SiO_4]$[a]	mmm a_0 7.44 b_0 7.60 c_0 5.75	fib. *c*, (110) 88°	(010) per.	6—7	3.2	yellowish-grey, grey-ish green, brownish
182	*Andalusite* $Al^{[6]}Al^{[5]}[O\,\vert\,SiO_4]$	mmm a_0 7.78 b_0 7.92 c_0 5.57	col. *c*, (110) (001)	(110) dist. 89° 12′	$7\frac{1}{2}$	3.1—3.2	greyish to reddish-grey

[a] Contains $[AlSiO_5]$-tetrahedral chains and thus can be included also with inosilicates.

Streak	Indices of refraction and Luster	Optic angle 2 V and Biref.	Optic orient.	Pleochroism Bireflection	Occurrence	No.
	n_α 1.6505 ⎫ n_β 1.6616 ⎬ Na n_γ 1.6679 ⎭	75° 0.017	(−) OP (001) $n_\gamma \| a$	—	Contact metam. in ejecta from Somma	172
	n ∼1.70	—	—	—	In serpentines (= primary perid-otitic rocks), placers	173
	n ∼1.76—1.83	—	—	—	Metam. in gneisses, mica schists	174
	n ∼1.80	—	—	—	Magmat. (Granite), pegmat., metam.	175
	n ∼1.74	—	—	—	Contact metam. *Hessonite* = hya-cinth-red grossu-larite	176
	n ∼1.89	—	—	—	Contact metam. and in cryst. schists (serpentine, chlor-ite schists)	177
	n 1.86—2.0	—	—	—	Magmat., primary. constit. of extrus. rocks, rarely	178
	n_ω 1.960 Na n_ε 2.01 Na	0.05	(+)	—	Magmat., metam., in placers. *Hyacinth*, brownish-red. Becomes blue upon heating	179
	n_α 1.652 n_β 1.655 n_γ 1.671 glassy	∼50° $r > v$ 0.019	(+) OP (010) n_γ/c 41°	—	Pegmat.—hydroth.	180
	n_α 1.657—1.661 n_β 1.658—1.670 n_γ 1.677—1.684	25°—30° $r > v$ 0.02	(+) OP (010) $n_\gamma \| c$	—	Metam., esp. in cryst. schists	181
	n_α 1.6290—1.640 n_β 1.6328—1.644 n_γ 1.6390—1.647	83°—85° $r < v$ 0.01	(−) OP (010) $n_\alpha \| c$	n_α pale pink n_β, n_γ color-less	Metam. in cryst. schists, also pegmat. *Chiastolite* = acic. and-alusite with dark pig-mented core in shales	182

No.	Name and Formula	Crystal Class Lattice Constants	Habit, Form	Cleavage	Hardness	Sp. Gr.	Color
183	*Kyanite* $Al^{[6]}Al^{[6]}[O\|SiO_4]$	$\bar{1}$ a_0 7.10 b_0 7.74 c_0 5.57 α 90° 05$\frac{1}{2}'$ β 101° 02' γ 105° 44$\frac{1}{2}'$	col. c, (100) (010) (001), tw. (100)	(100) per. (010) dist.	$\parallel c$ 4—4$\frac{1}{2}$ $\parallel b$ 6—7	3.6—3.7	colorless, white, blue or greenish stains
184	*Mullite* $Al_4^{[6]}Al^{[4]}[O_3(O_{0.5}OH,F)\|Si_3AlO_{16}]$	orhomb. a_0 7.50 b_0 7.65 c_0 5.75	fib. c	(010) dist. to imp.	?	3.03	white, pale violet
185	*Topaz* $Al_2[F_2\|SiO_4]$	mmm a_0 4.65 b_0 8.80 c_0 8.40	col. c—isom., (110) (120) (011) (021) (112) (001)	(001) per.	8	3.5—3.6	colorless and pale colors
186	*Staurolite* $Fe_2Al_9[O_6(O,OH)_2(SiO_4)_4]$	mmm a_0 7.82 b_0 16.52 c_0 5.63	col. c, (110) (001), tw. (032) (232)	(010) per.	7—7$\frac{1}{2}$	3.7—3.8	reddish to blackish-brown
187	*Chloritoid* $(Fe, Mg)_2Al_4[(OH)\|O_2(SiO_4)_2]$	$2/m$ a_0 9.45 b_0 5.48 c_0 18.16 β 101° 30'	tab. (001) ps. hex.	(001) per. (110) imp.	6$\frac{1}{2}$	3.3—3.6	blackish-green to black
188	*Chondrodite* $Mg_5[(OH, F)_2\|(SiO_4)_2]$	$2/m$ a_0 7.89 b_0 4.74 c_0 10.29 β 109° 02'	tab. (010), polysynth. tw. (100)	(100) dist.	6—6$\frac{1}{2}$	3.1—3.2	yellowish to brownish
189	*Clinohumite* $Mg_9[(OH, F)_2\|(SiO_4)_4]$	$2/m$ a_0 13.71 b_0 4.75 c_0 10.29 β 100° 50'	tw. lam. (100)	(100) dist.	6—6$\frac{1}{2}$	~3.2	brown, yellow, white
190	*Braunite* $Mn_4^{\cdot\cdot} Mn_3^{\cdot\cdot\cdot}[O_8\|SiO_4]$	$\bar{4}2m$ a_0 9.52 c_0 18.68	isom. (111) (001) (421), tw. (101)	(111) per.	6—6$\frac{1}{2}$	4.7—4.9	black
191	*Sphene* (Titanite) $CaTi[O\|SiO_4]$	$2/m$ a_0 6.56 b_0 8.72 c_0 7.44 β 119° 43'	tab. to wedge-sh. (111) (100) (001 (102) (110)	(110) imp.	5—5$\frac{1}{2}$	3.4—3.6	yellow to greenish-brown, reddish-brown

Streak	Indices of refraction and Luster	Optic angle 2V and Biref.	Optic orient.	Pleochroism Bireflection	Occurrence	No.
	n_α 1.713 n_β 1.722 n_γ 1.729 var. glassy	82° 30′ $r > v$ 0.016	(−) OP~⊥(100) n_α~⊥(100), on (100) $n_{\gamma'}/c$ 27° to 32° on (010) $n_{\gamma'}/c$ 5°—8° on (001) $n_{\alpha'}/a$ 0° to 2½°	blue colored: n_α colorless n_β violet blue n_γ dark blue	Metam., esp. in cryst. schists	183
	n_α 1.639 n_β 1.641 n_γ 1.653	45°—50° $r > v$ 0.014	(+) OP (010) $n_\gamma‖c$	—	Contact metam. Imp. constit. of porcelain	184
	n_α 1.607—1.629 n_β 1.610—1.630 n_γ 1.617—1.638 glassy	65°—48° $r > v$ 0.008 to 0.01	(+) OP (010) $n_\gamma‖c$	—	Pneum.—pegmat. Esp. in granites (greisen) and their country rock. In placers. As gemstone, yellow, blue or red	185
colorless	n_α 1.736—1.747 n_β 1.741—1.754 n_γ 1.746—1.762 glassy	79°—88° $r > v$ 0.010 to 0.015	(+) OP (100) $n_\gamma‖c$	n_α colorless n_β pale yellow n_γ yellow	Metam. in cryst. schists. In placers	186
greenish-white	n_α 1.714—1.725 n_β 1.717—1.728 n_γ 1.730—1.737	36°—68° $r > v$ 0.007 to 0.016	(+) OP (010) $n_{\gamma'}/⊥$ (001) 3°—30°	n_α olive green n_β indigo-blue n_γ greenish-yellow to colorless	Metam. (epizone)	187
	n_α 1.601—1.635 n_β 1.606—1.645 n_γ 1.622—1.663	72°—90° $r ≷ v$ 0.02 to 0.03	(±) OP ⊥ (010) n_α/c 22° to 30°	n_α yellow n_β pale yellow n_γ colorless	Contact metam. esp. in dolomites and limestones	188
	n_α 1.625—1.652 n_β 1.638—1.663 n_γ 1.653 to ~1.67 increases with increasing (FeO + MnO) content	74°—90° $r > v$ 0.02 to 0.03	(+) OP ⊥ (010) n_α/c 7°—15°	without to n_α pale yellow to brownish n_β, n_γ very pale yellow to colorless	Contact metam. Most common kind of humite at Vesuvius. *Titanclinohumite* = Ti bearing. In talc schists and serpentines	189
black	greasy met. lust.	An.-Eff. very weak		Birefl. very weak	Regional—contact metam. Metasom. in carbonate rocks, rarely hydrothermal	190
white to light grey	n_α 1.91—1.88 n_β 1.92—1.89 n_γ 2.04—2.01	23°—34° $r ≫ v$ 0.13	(+) OP (010) n_γ/c 51° n_γ ~ ⊥ (102)	weak, Abs. $n_\gamma > n_\beta > n_\alpha$	Hydroth. in fissures, magmat. (syenites) and metam.	191

No.	Name and Formula	Crystal Class Lattice Constants	Habit, Form	Cleavage	Hardness	Sp. Gr.	Color
192	*Datolite* $CaB^{[4]}[OH|SiO_4]$	$2/m$ a_0 9.66 b_0 7.64 c_0 4.83 β 90° 09′	short col. *c* or *a* or broad tab. (100), (100) (110) (011) (102) (111)	—	5—5$^1/_2$	2.9—3.0	colorless, white, greenish, yellowish, rarely other colors
193	*Gadolinite* $Y_2FeBe_2[O|SiO_4]_2$ besides Y also other rare earths	$2/m$ a_0 9.89 b_0 7.55 c_0 4.66 β 90° 33$^1/_2$′	often col. *c*	(001)	6$^1/_2$	4—4.7	pitch-black
194	*Dumortierite* $(Al, Fe)_7[O_3|BO_3|(SiO_4)_3]$	mmm a_0 11.79 b_0 20.21 c_0 4.70	(110) 56°	(100) dist.	7	3.3—3.4	dark blue, bluish-grey to red

b) Sorosilicates (Group Silicates)

No.	Name and Formula	Crystal Class Lattice Constants	Habit, Form	Cleavage	Hardness	Sp. Gr.	Color
195	*Thortveitite* $Sc_2[Si_2O_7]$ $Sc \rightarrow Y$	$2/m$ a_0 6.57 b_0 8.60 c_0 4.75 β 103° 08′	col. *c* (110), tw. (110)	(110) per.	6$^1/_2$	∼3.6	dark greyish-green to black
196	*Melilite* $(Ca, Na)_2(Al, Mg)[(Si, Al)_2O_7]$ (solid soln. of *Gehlenite* $Ca_2Al[SiAlO_7]$ and *Åkermanite* $Ca_2Mg[Si_2O_7]$.)	$\bar{4}2m$ a_0 7.74 c_0 5.02	tab.—short col. *c*, (001) (100) (110) (102)	(001) (110) imp.	5—5$^1/_2$	2.9—3.0	colorless, yellow, brown, grey
197	*Lawsonite* $CaAl_2[(OH)_2|Si_2O_7] \cdot H_2O$	222 a_0 8.90 b_0 5.76 c_0 13.33	col. *b* or tab. (010), tw. (101)	(010) per. (100) dist.	6	3.1	colorless to bluish
198	*Ilvaite* (Lievrite) $CaFe_2^{··}Fe^{···}[OH|O|Si_2O_7]$	mmm a_0 8.84 b_0 5.87 c_0 13.10	col. *c* (110) (120) (010) (111) (101)	(010) dist.	5$^1/_2$—6	4.1	black
199	*Hemimorphite* $Zn_4[(OH)_2|Si_2O_7] \cdot H_2O$	$2mm$ a_0 10.72 b_0 8.40 c_0 5.12	tab. (010), (010) (110) (001) (301) (12$\bar{1}$), tw. (001)	(110) per. (101) dist.	5	3.3—3.5	colorless and pale colors

Streak	Indices of refraction and Luster	Optic angle 2V and Biref.	Optic orient.	Pleochroism Bireflection	Occurrence	No.
	n_α 1.626 n_β 1.654 n_γ 1.670	74° $r > v$ 0.044	(−) OP (010) $n_\gamma/c - 1°$ to $-4°$	—	Pneum.—hydroth.—contact pneumat. in granitic dikes and in fissures in basic extrus. rocks	192
greenish-grey	n_α 1.801 n_β 1.812 n_γ 1.824 isotrop.[a] n ~1.78	~85° $r \ll v$ 0.023	(+) OP (010) n_γ/c 6°—14°	n_α olive green n_β, n_γ grass green	Pegmat.—hydroth., also in alpine fissures	193
	n_α 1.659—1.678 n_β 1.684—1.691 n_γ 1.686—1.692	20°—40° $r \ll v$ $\gg$ 0.015 to 0.027	(−) OP (010) $n_\alpha \parallel c$	n_α strong cobalt blue n_β, n_γ colorless to pale blue	Pegmat.—pneumatolitic	194
	n_α 1.756 n_β 1.793 n_γ 1.809	66° 0.053	(−) OP (010) n_α/c 5°	n_α dark green n_β, n_γ yellow	In granite pegmatites	195
	n_ω 1.63—1.66 n_ε 1.64—1.67 sometimes anom. interf. colors (dark blue), glassy	0.001 to 0.013	(+) (−)		Magmat. in very basic Ca rich extrus. rocks	196
	n_α 1.665 n_β 1.674 n_γ 1.684 glassy	84° $r \gg v$ 0.019	(+) OP (100) $n_\gamma \parallel b$	in thick sections: n_α blue n_β yellowish n_γ colorless	Metam., esp. in gabbros, alt. basalts, and glaucophane schists. Also in fissures	197
greenish, blackish-grey	n_α ~1.88$_7$ n_β ~1.89 n_γ ~1.91 glassy	~32° $r < v$ 0.02	(−) OP (100) $n_\gamma \parallel c$	n_α brown to brownish-yellow n_β brown to opaque n_γ dark green to opaque	Contact pneumat.	198
	n_α 1.614 n_β 1.617 n_γ 1.636 glassy	46° $r > v$ 0.022	(+) OP (100) $n_\gamma \parallel c$	—	Metasom. in Zn deposits. Together with smithsonite. Imp. Zn ore	199

[a] Metamict.

26*

No.	Name and Formula	Crystal Class Lattice Constants	Habit, Form	Cleavage	Hardness	Sp. Gr.	Color
200	*Clinozoisite* Ca_2Al_3 $[O|OH|SiO_4|Si_2O_7]$	$2/m$ a_0 8.94 b_0 5.61 c_0 10.23 β 115°	col. b, (100) (101) (001) ($\bar{1}$11) (110) (011), tw. (100)	(001) per.	$6\frac{1}{2}$	3.35 to 3.38	greyish-green
201	*Epidote* $Ca_2(Al, Fë^{..})Al_2$ $[O|OH|SiO_4|Si_2O_7]$	$2/m$ a_0 8.98 b_0 5.64 c_0 10.22 β 115° 24′	like clinozoisite	(001) per. (100) dist.	6—7	3.3—3.5	dark green to yellowish-green, rarely red
202	*Allanite* (Orthite) $(Ca, Ce)_2(Fë,Fë^{..})Al_2$ $[O|OH|SiO_4|Si_2O_7]$	$2/m$ a_0 8.98 b_0 5.75 c_0 10.23 β 115° 00′	tab. (100) to col. b, tw. (100)	(001) (100) poor	$5\frac{1}{2}$	3—4.2	pitch-black
203	*Zoisite* Ca_2Al_3 $[O|OH|SiO_4|Si_2O_7]$	mmm a_0 16.24 b_0 5.58 c_0 10.10	col. b, (110) (010) (021)	(010) per.	$6\frac{1}{2}$	3.2 to 3.38	greenish-grey to green
204	*Pumpellyite* $Ca_2(Mg, Fe, Mn, Al)$ $(Al, Fe, Ti)_2$ $[(OH, H_2O)_2$ $SiO_4Si_2O_7](?)$	$2/m$ a_0 8.81 b_0 5.94 c_0 19.14 β 97.6°	tab. (001) or fib., tw. (001)	(001) per. (100) imp.	6	3.18 to 3.23	blue-green, green, brownish
205	*Vesuvianite* $Ca_{10}(Mg, Fe)_2Al_4[(OH)_4|$ $(SiO_4)_5|(Si_2O_7)_2]$	$4/mmm$ a_0 15.66 c_0 11.85	isom. to col. c, (100) (110) (100)	(100) poor	$6\frac{1}{2}$	3.27 to 3.45	brown to diff. shades of green, rarely blue, rose

c) Cyclosilicates (Ring Silicates)

No.	Name and Formula	Crystal Class Lattice Constants	Habit, Form	Cleavage	Hardness	Sp. Gr.	Color
206	*Benitoite* $BaTi[Si_3O_9]$	$\bar{6}m2$ a_0 6.61 c_0 9.73	(01$\bar{1}$1) (10$\bar{1}$1) (10$\bar{1}$0) (0001)	—	$6\frac{1}{2}$	3.7	pale to sapphire blue

Streak	Indices of refraction and Luster	Optic angle 2 V and Biref.	Optic orient.	Pleochroism Bireflection	Occurrence	No.
	n_α 1.724 n_β 1.729 n_γ 1.734	85° $r < v$ 0.010	(+) OP (010) $n_\alpha/c - 2°$ to $- 12°$	Abs. $n_\beta > n_\gamma > n_\alpha$	Metam., contact metam.	200
gray	n_α 1.734 n_β 1.763 n_γ 1.780	73°—68° $r \ll v$ $\gg$ 0.046	(−) OP (010) n_α/c 0°—5°	n_α colorless to pale green n_β pale green n_γ yellow-ish-green	As with clinozoisite, also hydroth. *Piedmontite* = Mn bearing epidote	201
	n_α ∼1.72 n_β ∼1.74 n_γ ∼1.76 var. sometimes iso-trop. decr. to $n = 1,52$, glassy	large $r > v$ ∼0.04	(−) OP (010) n_α/c 22°—40°	n_α greenish-brown n_β dark brown n_γ reddish-brown	Pegmat., magm. (gran-ite) also in gneisses	202
	n_α 1.702 n_β 1.703 n_γ 1.706 var. glassy	30°—60° 0.004	(+) OP (010) rarely (001) $n_\gamma \| a$	—	Metam., contact metam. Constit. of *saussurite* = altered plagioclase. Pinkish-red zoisite = *thulite*	203
	n_α 1.678—1.703 n_β 1.681—1.716 n_γ 1.688—1.721	26°—85° $r \gg v$ $\ll$ 0.01 to 0.02	(+) OP ‖ or ⊥ (010) n_α/a 4°—32°	α colorless to pale yellowish-brown β bluish-green to brown-ish-yel-low γ colorless to pale yellowish-brown	Hydroth.—low-grade metamorphism	204
	n_ω 1.705—1.736 n_ε 1.701—1.732 glassy	anom. 17°—33° strong anom. disp. 0.001 to 0.008	(−) (+) partly anom. biaxial	Abs. $\omega \lessgtr \varepsilon$	Contact metam. and in fissures. Very rarely magmatic	205
	n_ω 1.757 n_ε 1.804	0.047	(+)	ω colorless ε blue	With natrolite in glaucophane schists, San Benito, Calif.	206

No.	Name and Formula	Crystal Class Lattice Constants	Habit, Form	Cleavage	Hardness	Sp. Gr.	Color
207	*Axinite* $Ca_2(Mn, Fe)Al_2$ $[OH|BO_3|Si_4O_{12}]$	$\bar{1}$ a_0 7.15 b_0 9.16 c_0 8.96 α 88° 04′ β 81° 36′ γ 77° 42′	flat, $(1\bar{1}0)$ (010) $(1\bar{1}1)$ $(0\bar{1}1)$ $(1\bar{2}1)$ $(1\bar{2}0)$ orient. after MILLER	(100) dist.	$6^1/_2$—7	3.3	clove-brown, violet, smokey-grey, and other colors
208	*Beryl* $Al_2Be_3[Si_6O_{18}]$	$6/mmm$ a_0 9.23 c_0 9.19	col. c, $(10\bar{1}0)$ (0001) $(10\bar{1}1)$ $(11\bar{2}1)$et al., tw. $(11\bar{2}2)$ rare	(0001) imp.	$7^1/_2$—8	2.63 to 2.80	colorless and colored
209	*Cordierite* $Mg_2Al_3[AlSi_5O_{18}]$ $Mg{\to}Fe$	mmm a_0 17.13 b_0 9.80 c_0 9.35	col. c, (110) (100) (130) (001), tw. (110) (130) ps. hex.	(010) imp.	7—$7^1/_2$	2.6	gray to violet to dark blue
210	*Tourmaline* $XY_3Z_6[OH, F)_4|(BO_3)_3|$ $Si_6O_{18}]$ X $=$ Na, Ca, Y $=$ Li, Al, Mg, Fe¨, Mn Z $=$ Al, Mg	$3m$ a_0 16.03[a] c_0 7.15[a]	$a:c=1:0.448$ col.—acic. c, $(10\bar{1}0)$ $(11\bar{2}0)$ $(10\bar{1}1)$ $(02\bar{2}1)$ $(32\bar{5}1)$ et al.	—	7	3—3.25	colorless and all colors to black, often zoned or term. in diff. color
211	*Dioptase* $Cu_6[Si_6O_{18}]\cdot 6H_2O$	$\bar{3}$ a_0 14.61 c_0 7.80	col. c, $(11\bar{2}0)$ $(02\bar{2}1)$et al., for ex. $(1.15.\bar{1}\bar{6}.7)$, tw. $(10\bar{1}1)$ rare	$(10\bar{1}1)$ per.	5	3.3	emerald-green
212	*Chrysocolla* $CuSiO_3\cdot nH_2O$	amorph. ?	Encrust.	—	2—4	2—2.2	emerald-green to blue
213	*Milarite* $KCa_2AlBe_2[Si_{12}O_{30}]$ $\cdot^1/_2H_2O$	$6/mmm$ a_0 10.45 c_0 13.88	$(10\bar{1}1)$ $(10\bar{1}0)$ (0001)	—	6	2.6	colorless to light yellowish-green

[a] For Schorlite.

Streak	Indices of refraction and Luster	Optic angle 2 V and Biref.	Optic orient.	Pleochroism Bireflection	Occurrence	No.
	n_α 1.679 n_β 1.685 n_γ 1.689 var. glassy	63°—76° blue var. also 83°—90° $r < v$ 0.010	(—) OP$\sim \perp (1\bar{1}1)$ $n_\alpha \sim \perp (1\bar{1}1)$ $n_{\gamma'}$ on (111) to (110) 40° to (0$\bar{1}$1) 25°	in yellow and violet colors, Abs. $n_\beta > n_\alpha > n_\gamma$	Contact pneum. in Ca silicate hornfels, hydroth. in fissures	207
	n_ω 1.57—1.602 n_ε 1.56—1.595 glassy	0.004 to 0.008	(—)	emerald in thick layers ω bluish- green to colorless ε blue	Pegmat.—hydroth. Precious beryl as gemstone (emerald). *Smaragd*, green; *aquamarine*, pale blue	208
	n_α 1.538 n_β 1.543 n_γ 1.545 greasy glassy	40°—80° rare —90° $r < v$ 0.007	(—) OP (100) $n_\alpha \| c$	very strong, visible to the eye n_α yellow, green, brown n_β violet n_γ blue	Metam., magmat. Frequently contact product	209
	n_ω 1.639—1.692 n_ε 1.620—1.657 glassy	0.019 to 0.035	(—)	Abs. $\omega \gg \varepsilon$ Schorlite: ω dark green, brown- ish-black ε light brown violet shade	Pneum. (granites, pegmatites), metam., in placers. Also as gemstone. *Schorlite* (black) Fe-rich; *dravite* (brown) Mg-rich; *rubellite* (red) Mn bearing	210
green	n_ω $\sim$1.644 to 1.658 n_ε $\sim$1.697 to 1.709 $n_{\varepsilon'}$ 1.66—1.69 glassy	0.05	(+)	weak	Hydroth.—hydric. In fissures and veins in Cu deposits	211
greenish-white	n $\sim$1.46 to 1.635 (?)	—	—	—	Oxidation zone	212
	n_ω 1.532 n_ε 1.529	at rm. temp. biax. small (orhomb.) 0.003	(—)	—	Pegmatitic	213

No.	Name and Formula	Crystal Class Lattice Constants	Habit, Form	Cleavage	Hardness	Sp. Gr.	Color

d) Inosilicates (Chain or Ribbon Silicates)

Pyroxenes (No. 214—225)
Clinopyroxenes (No. 214—222)

No.	Name and Formula	Crystal Class Lattice Constants	Habit, Form	Cleavage	Hardness	Sp. Gr.	Color
214	*Clinoenstatite* $Mg_2[Si_2O_6]$ (pure)	$2/m$ a_0 9.62 b_0 8.83 c_0 5.19 β 108° $21^1/_2'$	col. c	(110) dist. 88°	6	3.19	colorless to yellowish
215	*Pigeonite* $(Mg, Fe, Ca)_2[Si_2O_6]$	$2/m$ a_0 9.71 b_0 8.96 c_0 5.25 β 108° 33′	col. c	(110) dist.	6	3.30 to 3.46	greenish to black
216	*Diopside* $CaMg[Si_2O_6]$ (pure)	$2/m$ a_0 9.73 b_0 8.91 c_0 5.25 β 105° 50′	col. c, (100) (010) (001) (111) et.al.	(110) dist. 87°	$5^1/_2$—6 [001] $\sim$7	3.27	green, light green, grey, colorless
217	*Hedenbergite* $CaFe[Si_2O_6]$ (pure)	$2/m$ a_0 9.85 b_0 9.02 c_0 5.26 β 104° 20′	oft. tab. (010)	(110) dist. 87°	$5^1/_2$—6	3.55	black to blackish-green
218	*Augite* approx.: $Ca_{0.81}Mg_{0.75}$ $Fe^{..}_{0.12}Na_{0.06}$ $(Al, Fe^{...}, Ti)_{0.25}$ $[Si_{1.81-1.51}Al_{0.19-0.49}O_6]$	$2/m$ $a_0 \simeq 9.8$ $b_0 \simeq 9.0$ $c_0 \simeq 5.25$ $\beta \simeq 105°$	short col. c, (110) (100) (010) (Ī11) et al., tw. (100) also (101), (001) and (122)	(110) dist. 87°	$5^1/_2$—6	3.3—3.5	leek-green to greenish-black, brown
219	*Spodumene* $LiAl[Si_2O_6]$	$2/m$ a_0 9.52 b_0 8.32 c_0 5.25 β 110° 28′	col. c, (100) (110) (130) (021) (221), tw. (100)	(110) dist. 87°	6—7	3.1—3.2	ash-grey, yellowish, greenish and other colors
220	*Jadeite* $NaAl[Si_2O_6]$ (pure)	$2/m$ a_0 9.50 b_0 8.61 c_0 5.24 β 107° 26′	fib. c	(110) 87°	$6^1/_2$	3.3—3.5	white to greenish

Streak	Indices of refraction and Luster	Optic angle 2 V and Biref.	Optic orient.	Pleochroism Bireflection	Occurrence	No.
	n_α 1.651 n_β 1.654 n_γ 1.660	$53^1/_2°$ $r < v$ 0.009	(+) OP $\perp$ (010) n_γ/c 22°	—	Magmat., seldom pure, in stony meteorites and some extrus. rocks, Fe bearing in basalts	214
	n_α 1.69—1.71 n_β 1.70—1.71 n_γ 1.71—1.74	0°—50° $r > v$ 0.023 to 0.029	(+) OP $\perp$, $\parallel$(010) n_γ/c 44°	—	Magmat. In basalts, gabbros	215
	n_α 1.664 n_β 1.6715 n_γ 1.694	~59° $r > v$ 0.030	(+) OP (010) n_γ/c 39°	—	Magmat., metam., contact metam. (horn-fels), also hydroth. in fissures. Similar but containing Al and Fe are *fassaite* (in contact zones) and *omphacite* (in eclogites)	216
light green	n_α 1.739 n_β 1.745 n_γ 1.757	60° $r > v$ 0.018	(+) OP (010) n_γ/c 48°	n_α pale green n_β yellow-ish-green n_γ dark green	Metam., in contact rocks, in magnetite deposits	217
greyish-green	n_α 1.69—1.74 n_β 1.70—1.77 n_γ 1.71—1.78	25°—85° $r > v$ 0.02 to 0.04	(+) OP (010) n_γ/c 35° to 54°	n_α pale green yellowish n_β brown-ish, yellow n_γ pale green	Magmat. (esp. in basic rocks), metam., contact metam., also in fissures. *Diallage* = augite with well developed parting along (100)	218
	n_α 1.65 —1.668 n_β 1.66 —1.674 n_γ 1.676—1.681	54°—68° $r < v$ 0.014 to 0.027	(+) OP (010) n_γ/c 23° to 27°	weak n_α, n_β colored n_γ colorless	Pegmat. Imp. source of Li; as gemstone, pinkish-red (*kunzite*), yellow or green (*hiddenite*)	219
	n_α ~1.64 n_β ~1.65 n_γ ~1.67	70°—72° $r < v$ ~0.03	(+) OP (010) n_γ/c 33° to 35°	very weak n_α light green n_β colorless n_γ light yellow	Metam., in veins. As veins in basic rocks. Semi-precious stone called *jade*	220

No.	Name and Formula	Crystal Class Lattice Constants	Habit, Form	Cleavage	Hardness	Sp. Gr.	Color
221	*Aegirine* (Acmite) $NaFe\overset{...}{}[Si_2O_6]$ (pure)	$2/m$ a_0 9.66 b_0 8.79 c_0 5.26 β 107° 20′	col.—acic. c, (110) (661) (221) (310)	(110) dist. 87°	6—6½	3.5—3.7	green to black, brown to black
222	*Aegirinaugite* Formula similar to No. 218, but Fe- and Na-richer	$2/m$	col. c	(110) dist. 87°	5½—6	3.4 to 3.55	leek green to greenish black

Orthopyroxenes (No. 223—225)

No.	Name and Formula	Crystal Class Lattice Constants	Habit, Form	Cleavage	Hardness	Sp. Gr.	Color
223	*Enstatite* $Mg_2[Si_2O_6]$ 0—12 Mol.-% Fe-Sil.	mmm a_0 18.22 b_0 8.81 c_0 5.21	short col. c, (210) (100) (101) (403)	(210)[a] imp. 88°	5—6	~3.1 ↓	grey, yellowish-green to dark green
224	*Bronzite* (Mg, Fe) [Si_2O_6] 12—30 Mol.-% Fe-Sil.	mmm a_0 18.20 b_0 8.86 c_0 5.20	tab. (100)	(210)[a] imp. 88°	5—6	~3.3 ↓	brownish-green, partly bronze-like iridescence on (100)
225	*Hypersthene* (Mg, Fe) [Si_2O_6] 30—50 Mol.-% Fe-Sil.	mmm a_0 18.24 b_0 8.88 c_0 5.21	tab. (100) or (010) elong. c, (100) (010) (210) (211) (111)	(210)[a] imp. 88°	5—6	~3.5 to 3.8 ↓	blackish-brown, blackish-green, partly copper iridescence on (100)

[a] According to morph. axial ratios (110).

Streak	Indices of refraction and Luster	Optic angle 2 V and Biref.	Optic orient.	Pleochroism Bireflection	Occurrence	No.
yellow-ish-grey to dark green	n_α 1.76—1.78 n_β 1.80—1.82 n_γ 1.81—1.83	60°—70° $r < v$ 0.04 to 0.06	(−) OP (010) $n_\alpha/c \sim 5°$	strong, n_α grass-green (brown) n_β light green (light brown) n_γ brown-ish-yellow (greenish-yellow)	Magmat., in soda rich rocks and their pegmatites. Brown colored transparent aegirine is called acmite	221
greyish-green	n_α ∼1.70—1.75 n_β ∼1.71—1.78 n_γ ∼1.73—1.80	70°—90° ∼ 0.030 to 0.050	(±) OP (010) n_α/c 0°—20°	n_α green, brown-ish-green n_β light green, yellowish-green n_γ greenish-yellow, brown-ish-green	Magmat., in soda rich rocks and their pegmatites	222
	n_α 1.650 n_β 1.653 n_γ 1.659 (pure end-member)	∼55° $r < v$ 0.009	(+) OP (100) $n_\gamma \| c$	—	Magmat., in intrus. and extrus. rocks, pegmatitic in apatite veins; also in meteorites	223
	n_α 1.671—1.689 n_β 1.676—1.699 n_γ 1.681—1.702	90°—63° 0.01 to 0.013	(−) OP (100), rarely (010) $n_\gamma \| c$	—	Magmat. in intrus. rocks (norite, gab-bros, bronzitites) and in meteorites; extrus. rocks	224
	n_α 1.689—1.711 n_β 1.699—1.725 n_γ 1.702—1.727	63°—45° 0.013 to 0.016	(−) OP (100) $n_\gamma \| c$	—	Magmat., esp. in gabbros, metam. in hornfels. *Ferrohypersthene* (50—70 Mol.-% Fe-sil.), *eulite* (70—88 Mol.-% Fe-sil.), *orthofer-rosilite* (88—100 Mol.-% Fe-sil.)	225

No.	Name and Formula	Crystal Class Lattice Constants	Habit, Form	Cleavage	Hardness	Sp. Gr.	Color
	Amphiboles (No. 226—232) Ca-Amphiboles (No. 226—228)						
226	*Tremolite* $Ca_2Mg_5[(OH,F)_2Si_8O_{22}]$ *Actinolite* $Mg \rightarrow Fe^{..}$	$2/m$ $a_0 \cong 9.85$ $b_0 \cong 18.1$ $c_0 \cong 5.3$ $\beta\ 104°\ 50'$	fib.-long col. c, (110) (100) tw. (100)	(110) per. 124° 11' (010) poor	5—6	2.9—3.4	colorless, white, grey, dark green
227	*Common Hornblende* $(Na,K)_{0.25-1}Ca_{1.5-2}$ $Mg_{1.5-4}Fe^{..}_{1-2}(Al,Fe^{...})$ $[(OH)_2Si_{7-6}Al_{1-2}O_{22}]$	$2/m'$ $a_0\ 9.96\ (?)$ $b_0\ 18.42$ $c_0\ 5.37$ $\beta\ 105°\ 45'$	short col. c, (110) (010), tw. (100)	(110) per. 124°	5—6	3.0 to 3.45	green, bluish-green to black
228	*Oxyhornblende* $Ca_2(Na,K)_{0.5-1.0}$ $(Mg,Fe^{..})_{3-4}(Fe^{...}Al)_{2-1}$ $[(O,OH,F)_2Si_6Al_2O_{22}]$	$2/m$ $a_0\ 9.96(?)$ $b_0\ 18.42$ $c_0\ 5.37$ $\beta\ 105°\ 45'$	short col. c, (110) (010) (\overline{1}01) (011) (211) tw. (100)	(110) per. 124°	5—6	3.2—3.3	brownish-black
	Alkali-Amphiboles (No. 229—231)						
229	*Glaucophane* $Na_2Mg_{1.5-3}Fe^{..}_{1-1.5}$ $Fe^{...}_{0-0.25}Al_{1.75-2}[(OH)_2$ $Si_{7.75-8}Al_{0-0.25}O_{22}]$	$2/m$ $a_0\ 9.74\ (?)$ $b_0\ 18.02$ $c_0\ 5.38$ $\beta\ 104°$ $10'\ (?)$	col.—fib. c	(110) per. 124°	5—6	3—3.15	bluish-grey to blackish-blue
230	*Riebeckite* $(Na,K)_{2-3}Ca_{0-0.5}Mg_{0-1}$ $Fe^{..}_{1.5-4}Fe^{...}_{0-3}[(OH,O)_2$ $Si_{7.5-8}Al_{0.5-0}O_{22}]$	$2/m$ $a_0\ 9.90\ (?)$ $b_0\ 18.14$ $c_0\ 5.32$ $\beta\ 103°$ $30'\ (?)$	col.—fib. c	(110) per. 124°	5—6	~ 3.4	bluish-black

Streak	Indices of refraction and Luster	Optic angle 2 V and Biref.	Optic orient.	Pleochroism Bireflection	Occurrence	No.
	n_α 1.599—1.688 n_β 1.613—1.697 n_γ 1.624—1.705 glassy	65°—88° $r < v$ 0.027 to 0.017	(−) OP (010) n_γ/c 10°—20°	α pale yellow-ish-green β pale green γ bluish-green	Metam. in marbles and hornfels, horn-blende-, chlorite-, and talc-schists. Constit. of *horn-blende asbestos*; actinolite constit. of byssolite; Dense actinolite constit. sometimes of *nephrite*	226
greyish-green, dark green	n_α 1.61—1.705 n_β 1.62—1.714 n_γ 1.63—1.730 glassy	60°—88° $r \lesseqgtr v$ ~0.022	(−) OP (010) n_γ/c 13° to 34°	n_α light greenish-yellow n_β green to brown-ish-green n_γ olive- to bluish-green	Magmat. in acid and intermed. intrus. rocks, metam. in cryst. schists and contact-min.; *ura-lite* = fibrous common hornblende pseudo-morph. after augite	227
greyish-yellow	n_α 1.667—1.690 n_β 1.672—1.730 n_γ 1.680—1.72 glassy	50°—80° $r > v$ 0.018 to 0.070	(−) OP (010) n_γ/c 0°—18°	n_α pale brown n_β brown n_γ dark brown	Magmat. in extrus. rocks, lamproph. dike rocks, alkali syenites; *barke-vikite*, sim. to basalt. hbl.	228
bluish-grey	n_α 1.606—1.661 n_β 1.622—1.667 n_γ 1.627—1.670	50°—0° $r \gg v$ ~0.008 to 0.022	(−) OP (010) n_γ/c 4°—14°	n_α colorless to bluish-green, greenish-yellow n_β violet to lavender blue n_γ azure to brown-ish-blue	Metam. in cryst. schists (mica schists, eclogites); *crossite* (with OP ⊥ (010) is more iron rich	229
dark blue to grey	n_α ~1.654 to 1.701 n_β ~1.662 to 1.711 n_γ ~1.668 to 1.717	40°—90° 0.006 to 0.016	(∓) OP (010) also ⊥ (010) n_α/c −1° to −8°, partly to −20°	n_α dark blue, greyish-green n_β brown to violet n_γ dark grey, violet, greenish-yellow	Magmat. in alkali intrus. rocks	230

No.	Name and Formula	Crystal Class Lattice Constants	Habit, Form	Cleavage	Hardness	Sp. Gr.	Color
231	*Arfvedsonite* $Na_{2.5}Ca_{0.5}$ $(Fe^{..}, Mg, Fe^{...}, Al)_5$ $[(OH,F)_2Si_{7.5}Al_{0.5}O_{22}]$	$2/m$ a_0 9.89 (?) b_0 18.35 c_0 5.34 β 104° $15^1/_2'$ (?)	crystals rare	(110) per. 124°	5—6	$\sim$3.45	bluish-black
232	*Anthophyllite* $(Mg, Fe)_7[(OH)_2Si_8O_{22}]$	mmm a_0 18.56 b_0 18.08 c_0 5.28	fib.—col. c	(210) per. 125° 37'	$5^1/_2$	2.9—3.2	clove-brown to yellowish-grey
233	*Wollastonite* $(-1\,T)$ $Ca_3[Si_3O_9] < 1126°$ C	tricl., ps.-monocline a_0 7.94 b_0 7.32 c_0 7.07 α 90° β 95° 16' γ 103° 25'	tab. (100) or (001) elong. b, (100) (001) (101) (540) (Ī11) (320), tw. (100)	(100) per. (001) per.	$4^1/_2$—5	2.8—2.9	white or pale colors
234	Pectolite $Ca_2NaH[Si_3O_9]$	Ī a_0 7.99 b_0 7.04 c_0 7.02 α 90° 31' β 95° 11' γ 102° 28'	fib. b, tw. (100)	(100) (001) per.	$4^1/_2$—5	2.74 to 2.88	white, colorless
235	*Rhodonite* $CaMn_4[Si_5O_{15}]$	Ī a_0 7.79 b_0 12.47 c_0 6.75 α 85° 10' β 94° 04' γ 111° 29'	tab. (010) or col. b	(001) (100) per.	$5^1/_2$ to $6^1/_2$	3.4 to 3.68	light red, black (weathered)

e) Phyllosilicates (Layer Silicates)

No.	Name and Formula	Crystal Class Lattice Constants	Habit, Form	Cleavage	Hardness	Sp. Gr.	Color
236	*Apophyllite* $KCa_4[F\,|\,(Si_4O_{10})_2]$ $\cdot 8\,H_2O$	$4/mmm$ a_0 9.00 c_0 15.84	isom., (100) (111)	(001) per. (110) imp.	$4^1/_2$—5	2.3—2.4	colorless, white, reddish, greenish,

Streak	Indices of refraction and Luster	Optic angle 2 V and Biref.	Optic orient.	Pleochroism Bireflection	Occurrence	No.
dark bluish-grey	n_α 1.674—1.700 n_β 1.679—1.709 n_γ 1.686—1.710	0° to 50° (?) ~0.005 to 0.015	(−) OP (010) n_α/c 0° to −28°	n_α dark bluish-green n_β brown, violet, dark blue n_γ dark blue, grey or greenish-brown	Magmat. in alkali intrus. rocks, esp. eläolite syenites	231
	n_α 1.596—1.64 n_β 1.605—1.66 n_γ 1.615—1.67	~90° $r > v$ 0.013 to 0.02	(∓) OP (010) $n_\gamma \| c$	n_α, n_β colorless to pale yellow n_γ clove-brown	Metam., in cryst. schists, esp. with serpentine	232
	n_α 1.619 n_β 1.632 n_γ 1.634 glassy	35°—40° $r > v$ 0.015	(−) OP (010) n_α/c 32°	—	Contact metam., esp. in limestones	233
	n_α 1.595—1.610 n_β 1.606—1.642 n_γ 1.633—1.643 glassy	60° $r > v$ 0.035	(+) OP ⊥ (010) n_α/a low	—	In basic extrus. rocks and their fissures	234
white	n_α 1.721—1.733 n_β 1.726—1.740 n_γ 1.730—1.744	~76° $r < v$ 0.012	(+) Extinct. on (1$\bar{1}$0) $n_{\gamma'}/c$ 14° to 20°, on (110) $n_{\gamma'}/c$ 17° to 30°, on (001) $n_{\gamma'}$/trace (1$\bar{1}$0) 39$^1/_2$° trace (1$\bar{1}$0) 54$^1/_2$°	—	Metam. in schists, contact metasom., hydroth. Mn ore	235
	n_ω 1.535—1.543 n_ε 1.537—1.543	often anomal. biaxial 0.002	(±) partly (001) divided in sections, which are biaxial (+)	—	Hydroth. in vesicles of basalt. rocks; in ore veins	236

No.	Name and Formula	Crystal Class Lattice Constants	Habit, Form	Cleavage	Hardness	Sp. Gr.	Color
237	*Pyrophyllite* $Al_2[(OH)_2 \mid Si_4O_{10}]$	$2/m$ a_0 5.15 b_0 8.92 c_0 18.59 β 99° 55′	tab. (001)	(001) per.	$1\frac{1}{2}$	2.8	silvery, yellowish, apple-green
238	*Talc* $Mg_3[(OH)_2 \mid Si_4O_{10}]$	$2/m$ a_0 5.27 b_0 9.12 c_0 18.85 β 100° 00′	tab. (001), ps. hex.	(001) per.	1	2.7—2.8	colorless, white to apple-green, grey, yellowish and other colors

Muscovite Series (dioctahedral) (No. 239—243)

No.	Name and Formula	Crystal Class Lattice Constants	Habit, Form	Cleavage	Hardness	Sp. Gr.	Color
239	*Paragonite* $NaAl_2$ $[(OH,F)_2 \mid AlSi_3O_{10}]$	$2/m$ a_0 5.15 b_0 8.88 c_0 19.28 $\beta \sim 94°$	tab. (001)	(001) per.	$2\frac{1}{2}$—3	2.8—2.9	white to apple-green
240	*Muscovite* KAl_2 $[(OH,F)_2 \mid AlSi_3O_{10}]$	$2/m$ a_0 5.19 b_0 9.04 c_0 20.08 β 95° 30′	tab. (001) ps. hex., rarely (110) (010) (1̄11) et al., tw. (010) with (001) or (001̄) as comp.-plane	(001) per.	2—$2\frac{1}{2}$	2.78 to 2.88	colorless, yellowish, greenish, brownish
241	*Glauconite* $(K, Ca, Na)_{<1}(Al, Fe^{\cdot\cdot},$ $Fe^{\cdot\cdot\cdot}, Mg)_2$ $[(OH)_2 Si_{3.65}Al_{0.35}O_{10}]$	$2/m$ (?) a_0 5.25 b_0 9.09 c_0 20.07 β 95° 00′	scaly grains	(001)	—	2.2—2.8	green
242	*Celadonite* (1 M) $K(Mg, Fe^{\cdot\cdot})(Al, Fe^{\cdot\cdot\cdot})$ $[(OH)_2Si_4O_{10}]$	$2/m$ a_0 5.21 b_0 9.02 c_0 10.27 β 100° 06′	scaly., radial-col.	(001) per.	1—2	2.8	bluish-green
243	*Margarite* $CaAl_2[(OH)_2 \mid Al_2Si_2O_{10}]$	$2/m$ a_0 5.13 b_0 8.92 c_0 19.50 β 100° 48′	tab. (001), ps. hex.	(001) per.	$3\frac{1}{2}$ to $4\frac{1}{2}$	3.0—3.1	white, reddish-white, pearl-grey

Streak	Indices of refraction and Luster	Optic angle 2 V and Biref.	Optic orient.	Pleochroism Bireflection	Occurrence	No.
	n_α 1.552 n_β 1.588 n_γ 1.600	53°—60° $r>v$ 0.048	(−) OP ⊥ (010) $n_\gamma \| b$	—	Hydroth. in quartz veins and lenses in cryst. schists. *Agalmatolite* = dense pyrophyllite mostly	237
	n_α 1.539—1.550 n_β 1.589—1.594 n_γ 1.589—1.600	0°—30° $r>v$ ~0.05	(−) OP ⊥ (010) $n_\alpha \sim \perp (001)$	—	Metam., metasom., hydroth., alteration product of olivine, enstatite and similar Mg minerals	238
	n_α 1.564—1.580 n_β ~ 1.594 to 1.609 n_γ 1.600—1.609	0°—40° $r>v$ ~ 0.028 to 0.038	(−) OP ⊥ (010) $n_\alpha \sim \perp (001)$	—	Metam. in crystalline schists	239
	n_α 1.552—1.574 n_β 1.582—1.610 n_γ 1.588—1.616	30°—45° $r>v$ 0.036 to 0.049	(−) OP ⊥ (010) $n_\gamma \| b$ $n_\alpha/c \, 1/2°—2°$	—	Magmat., pegmat., metam. Tech. imp., esp. in elect. industry. *sericite* = fine flakey muscovite; *fuchsite* = Cr bearing; *Illite* (dioctahed.) = one of the most common clay minerals. Contains less K and more Si than muscovite. Trioctah. illites also occur	240
	n_α 1.590—1.615 n_β 1.609—1.643 n_γ 1.610—1.645	0°—40° $r<v$ 0.014 to 0.030	(−) OP (010) $n_\alpha \sim \perp (001)$	n_α pale yellow to greenish-yellow n_β, n_γ green to yellowish-green	Sediment., marine	241
	n_α ~1.61 n_β ~1.634 n_γ to 1.644	10°—24° 0.030	(−) OP (010) $n_\alpha \sim \perp (001)$	n_α yellowish-green n_β, n_γ bluish-green	Hydroth.—hydric (?), weathering product.	242
	n_α 1.632 n_β 1.645 n_γ 1.647	0°—67° $r>v$ (?) 0.015	(−) OP ⊥ (010) $n_\alpha/\perp (001)$ 6°—8°	—	Metam. with corundum and in chlorite schists	243

No.	Name and Formula	Crystal Class Lattice Constants	Habit, Form	Cleavage	Hardness	Sp. Gr.	Color
244	*Prehnite* $Ca_2Al[(OH)_2AlSi_3O_{10}]$	$2mm$ a_0 4.63 b_0 5.49 c_0 18.48	$a:b:c$ 0.842:1: 1.127 tab. (001) or col. c, (110) (010) (031) (111), tw. (100)	(001) dist.	6—$6^1/_2$	2.8 to 2.95	colorless, white, yellowish-green

Biotite Series (trioctahedral) (No. 245—248)

No.	Name and Formula	Crystal Class Lattice Constants	Habit, Form	Cleavage	Hardness	Sp. Gr.	Color
245	*Phlogopite* KMg_3 $[(F, OH)_2 \mid AlSi_3O_{10}]$ $Mg \rightarrow Fe^{\cdot\cdot}$	$2/m$ a_0 5.33 b_0 9.23 c_0 20.52 β 100° 12′	like muscovite	(001) h. per.	2—$2^1/_2$	2.75 to 2.97	reddish-brown, yellowish, greenish, colorless
246	*Biotite* $K(Mg, Fe, Mn)_3$ $[(OH, F)_2AlSi_3O_{10}]$	$2/m$ a_0 5.31 b_0 9.23 c_0 20.36 β 99° 18′	like muscovite and (112) (I01) (132) (221), tw. like muscovite	(001) h. per.	$2^1/_2$—3	2.8—3.4	dark brown and dark green
247	*Lepidolite* $K(Li, Al)_{2.5-3}$ $[(OH), F)_2Si_{3-3.5}$ $Al_{1-0.5}O_{10}]$	$2/m$ a_0 5.21 b_0 8.97 c_0 20.16 β 100° 48′	like muscovite, oft. scaly	(001) h. per.	$2^1/_2$—4	2.8—2.9	rose-red, white, grey, greenish
248	*Zinnwaldite* $K(Li_{1-1.5}Fe^{\cdot\cdot}_{1-0.5}Al)$ $[(F_{1.5-1}OH_{0.5-1})Si_{3-3.5}$ $Al_{1-0.5}O_{10}]$	$2/m$ a_0 5.27 b_0 9.09 c_0 20.14 β 100° 00′	sim. to muscovite	(001) h. per.	$2^1/_2$—4	2.9—3.1	silvery-grey, pale violet, brownish to almost black
249	*Stilpnomelane* $(K, Na, Ca)_{0-0.7}$ $(Fe^{\cdot\cdot\cdot}, Fe^{\cdot\cdot}, Mg, Al,$ $Mn)_{2.95-4.1} [(OH)_2Si_4O_{10}$ $(O, OH, H_2O)_{1.8-4.25}]$	monocl. ps. hex. a_0 5.40 b_0 9.42 c_0 12.14 [a] β 97° (?)	platy to rad.	(001) per. (010) poor.	3—4	2.6—3.0	black to greenish-black, olive-green to brown transparent

Montmorillonite Series (No. 250—252)

No.	Name and Formula	Crystal Class Lattice Constants	Habit, Form	Cleavage	Hardness	Sp. Gr.	Color
250	*Beidellite* $\left\{ \begin{array}{l} Al_{2.17}[(OH)_2Al_{0.83} \\ Si_{3.17}]^{0.32-}Na_{0.32} \\ (H_2O)_4 \end{array} \right\}$	monocl. $a_0 \sim 5.23$ $b_0 \sim 9.06$ c_0 15.8 to 9.2	tab. (001)		< 2		white, reddish, green
251	*Montmorillonite* $\left\{ \begin{array}{l} (Al_{1.67}Mg_{0.33})[(OH)_2 \\ Si_4O_{10}]^{0.33-}Na_{0.33} \\ (H_2O)_4 \end{array} \right\}$	monocl. a_0 5.17 b_0 8.94 c_0 15.2 to 9.6 $\beta \sim 90°$	tab. (001)	(001) per.	1—2	$\sim$2.5 calc. 2.1	white, brownish, greenish

[a] $d_{(001)}$.

Streak	Indices of refraction and Luster	Optic angle 2V and Biref.	Optic orient.	Pleochroism Bireflection	Occurrence	No.
	n_α 1.615—1.635 n_β 1.624—1.642 n_γ 1.645—1.665 glassy	66°—69° $r \gg v$ also 0°—30° $r < v$ 0.03	(+) OP (010) rarely (100)	—	Hydroth.—hydric. In basic extrus. rocks and cryst. schists; freq. in vesicles and in fissures	244
	n_α 1.530—1.590 n_β 1.557—1.637 n_γ 1.558—1.637	0°—35° $r < v$ 0.028 to 0.049	(−) OP∥(010) n_α/c 2°—4°	Abs. $n_\gamma > n_\beta > n_\alpha$	Pneumat. in contact zones of limestones and dolomites	245
	n_α 1.565—1.625 n_β 1.605—1.696 n_γ 1.605—1.696	0°—10° also to 70° $r \gtrless v$ 0.04	(−) OP (010) rarely ⊥ (010) n_α/c 0°—9°	n_α light yellow or light green n_β, n_γ dark brown or dark green	Magmat., metam., also pegmat. Biotite with OP∥(010) called *meroxene*; OP ⊥ (010) called *anomite*	246
	n_α 1.525—1.548 n_β 1.551—1.585 n_γ 1.554—1.587	0°—58° $r > v$ 0.018 to 0.038	(−) OP∥(010) or ⊥ (010) n_α/c 0°—7°	n_α colorless n_β, n_γ clove-brown, violet	Pneumat., in granites and pegmatites; source of Li	247
	n_α 1.535—1.558 n_β 1.570—1.589 n_γ 1.572—1.590	0°—35° $r > v$ 0.35	(−) OP (010) n_α/c ∼0°—2°	n_α yellowish to reddish n_β, n_γ brownish-grey to brown	Pneumat., in cassiterite bearing granites, greisen	248
	n_α 1.543—1.634 n_β 1.576—1.745 n_γ 1.576—1.745	0° 0.300 to 0.110	(−) OP∥(010) n_α/c∼ 7°	n_α light yellow to yellow n_β, n_γ { dark green to olive brown }	Metam. in cryst. schists	249
	n_α ∼1.49 n_β } 1.52—1.56 n_γ	small to 16° ∼0.025	(−) OP (010) n_α ∼ ⊥ (001)	—	Like montmorillonite	250
	n_α ∼1.488 n_β 1.513 n_γ 1.513	7°—27° 0.025	(−) OP (010) n_α ∼ ⊥ (001)	—	In fuller's earth, bentonites, clays and soils; alteration product of volcanic glass	251

No.	Name and Formula	Crystal Class Lattice Constants	Habit, Form	Cleavage	Hardness	Sp. Gr.	Color
252	*Nontronite* $\{Fe_2^{\cdot\cdot\cdot}[(OH)_2Al_{0.33}Si_{3.67}$ $O_{10}]^{0.33-}Na_{0.33}(H_2O)_4\}$	monocl. $a_0 \sim 5.24$ $b_0 \sim 9.08$ c_0 15.8 to 9.2 $\beta \sim 90°$	tab. (001) and fib.	(001) per. (110) poor.	1—2	2.3—2.5	olive green to yellowish-green and yellowish-orange
253	*Saponite* $\{Mg_3[(OH)_2Al_{0.33}$ $Si_{3.67}O_{10}]^{0.33-}$ $Na_{0.33}(H_2O)_4\}$	m $d_{(001)}$ 14.8	fib. (also tab. ?)		$1\frac{1}{2}$	~ 2.3	white, yellowish, greenish
254	*Vermiculite* $\{Mg_{2.36}Fe_{0.48}^{\cdot\cdot\cdot}Al_{0.16}$ $[(OH)_2Al_{1.28}Si_{2.72}$ $O_{10}]^{0.64-}Mg_{0.32}(H_2O)_4\}$	m ps. hex. a_0 5.33 b_0 9.18 c_0 28.90 β 97°	tab. (001)	(001) per.	1,5	2.4	brown, bronze, yellow, green, colorless
	Chlorites (No. 255—259)						
255	*Penninite* $\{(Mg, Al)_3[(OH)_2Al_{0.5-0.9}$ $Si_{3.5-3.1}O_{10}]Mg_3(OH)_6\}$	$2/m$ [a] a_0 5.2 to 5.3 b_0 9.2 to 9.3 c_0 28.6 β 96° 50′	tab. (001), ($\bar{1}01$) (132)	(001) per.	2—$2\frac{1}{2}$	2.6 to 2.84	bluish-green
256	*Clinochlore* $\{(Mg, Al)_3$ $[(OH)_2AlSi_3O_{10}]$ $Mg_3(OH)_6\}$	$2/m$ [a], similar to penninite	tab. (001), (112) ($\bar{1}11$) (010)	(001) per.	2—$2\frac{1}{2}$	2.55 to 2.78	bluish- to blackish-green
257	*Prochlorite* $\{(Mg, Fe, Al)_3$ $[(OH)_2Al_{1.2-1.5}$ $Si_{2.8-2.5}O_{10}]$ $Mg_3(OH)_6\}$	$2/m$ [a] a_0 5.36 b_0 9.28 c_0 2.84 β 97° 09′	freq. vermic.	(001) per.	1—2	2.78 to 2.95	leek- to brownish-green, blackish-green
258	*Chamosite* $\{(Fe^{\cdot\cdot}, Fe^{\cdot\cdot\cdot})_3$ $[(OH)_2AlSi_3O_{10}]$ $(Fe^{\cdot\cdot}, Mg)_3(O, OH)_6\}$	$2/m$ (?) a_0 5.40 b_0 9.36 c_0 14.03 β 90°	massive, oolitic	?	$2\frac{1}{2}$—3	3.2	blackish-green
259	*Thuringite* $\{(Fe^{\cdot\cdot}, Fe^{\cdot\cdot\cdot}, Al)_3[(OH)_2$ $Al_{1.2-2}Si_{2.8-2}O_{10}]$ $(Mg, Fe^{\cdot\cdot}, Fe^{\cdot\cdot\cdot})_3$ $(O, OH)_6\}$	$2/m$ a_0 5.39 b_0 9.33 c_0 14.10 β 97° 20′	tab. (001)	(001) per.	1—2	3.2	olive- to dark green

[a] Also triclinic (1 T, 2 T, 3 T) modifications known.

Streak	Indices of refraction and Luster	Optic angle 2V and Biref.	Optic orient.	Pleochroism Bireflection	Occurrence	No.
	n_α 1.56—1.62 n_β 1.58—1.65 n_γ 1.58—1.66	~20° to 66° 0.02 to 0.04	(−) (+) OP (010) $n_\alpha \perp$ (001) $n_\gamma \parallel$ fibers	n_α pale yellow	Hydroth. alteration product, also in soils	252
	n_α 1.48—1.53 n_β 1.50—1.58 n_γ 1.51—1.59	medium 0.01 to 0.036	(−)		Hydroth.—hydric. in basalts	253
	n_α 1.525—1.564 n_β 1.545—1.583 n_γ 1.545—1.583	0°—8° 0.02 to 0.03	(−) OP (010) $n_\alpha \sim \perp$ (001)	n_α colorless n_β, n_γ pale brown, brownish-green	Alteration product of micas, esp. biotites	254
greenish-grey	n_α ~1.560 n_β 1.58—1.60 n_γ ~1.571 Oft. anom. interf. colors, lavend. to ultra blue	small to 0° $r<v$ 0° to small $r>v$ ~0.004	(−) (+) OP (010) $n_\gamma \perp$ (001)	n_α colorless to bluish-green n_β green n_γ pale yellowish-green to green	Hydroth. in fissures, metam. in chlorite schists	255
greenish-grey	n_α ~1.57 n_β 1.57—1.59 n_γ ~1.596	0°—90° $r<v$ 0.004 to 0.01	(+) $n_\gamma/\perp$ (001) 0°—2½°	n_α colorless to bluish-green n_β green n_γ pale yellowish-green to green	Like penninite. *Leuchtenbergite* = Fe poorer, *grochauite* = Fe rich clinochlore	256
greenish-grey	n_α ~1.59 n_β n_γ} 1.60—1.65	0°—30° $r<v$ 0.004	(+) OP (010) $n_\gamma/\perp$ (001) 0°—2°	n_α, n_β green to yellowish-green n_γ colorless to greenish-yellow	Metam. In chlorite schists. Alteration product of augite in diabases	257
light greyish-green	n_β ~1.64—1.66 anom. interf. color (lavender blue)	0° to very small 0.005	(−) OP (?) $n_\alpha \sim \perp$ (001)	n_α yellowish to colorless n_β, n_γ pale green	Like thuringite. *Delessite* similar to chamosite, Mg bearing	258
greyish-green	n_α 1.669 n_β 1.682 n_γ 1.683	small to medium 0.014	(−)	n_α almost colorless n_β, n_γ dark green	Metam. from sedimentary iron ores	259

No.	Name and Formula	Crystal Class Lattice Constants	Habit, Form	Cleavage	Hardness	Sp. Gr.	Color
260	*Kaolinite* $Al_4[(OH)_8 \mid Si_4O_{10}]$	$\overline{1}$ a_0 5.14 b_0 8.93 c_0 7.37 α 91° 48′ β 104° 30′ γ 90°	tab. (001), (110) (010) ps. hex.	(001) per.	2—2$^1/_2$	2.6	white, yellowish, greenish, bluish
261	*Antigorite* (Platy serpentine) $Mg_6[(OH)_8 \mid Si_4O_{10}]$	2/m a_0 43.3 b_0 9.23 c_0 7.27 β 91° 36′	tab. (001)	(001) per.	3—4	2.5—2.6	light to dark green, yellow to reddish-brown, greenish to black
262	*Chrysotile* (Fibrous serpentine, Serpentine asbestos) $Mg_6[(OH)_8 \mid Si_4O_{10}]$	2/m a_0 5.34 b_0 9.25 c_0 14.65 β 93° 16′	fib. a_0 (fib. $b_0 =$ *parachrysotile*)	(110) imp. $\sim$130°	2—3	2.36 to 2.50	oil green to gold
263	*Amesite* $Mg_{3.2}Al_{2.0}Fe_{0.8}^{\cdot\cdot}$ $[(OH)_8 \mid Al_2Si_2O_{10}]$	6mm a_0 5.31 c_0 14.04	tab. (001)	(001) per.	1—2	2.8	pale bluish-green
264	*Cronstedtite* $Fe_2^{\cdot\cdot}Fe_4^{\cdot\cdot}$ $[(OH)_8 \mid Si_2Fe_2^{\cdot\cdot\cdot}O_{10}]$	m a_0 5.49 b_0 9.51 c_0 7.32 β 104° 31′	elong. to fib. c, also tab. (001), (hkl) ps. hex.	(001) per.	3$^1/_2$	3.45	deep black to deep green
265	*Halloysite* (Endellite) $\{Al_4[(OH)_8Si_4O_{10}] \atop (H_2O)_4\}$	m a_0 5.15 b_0 8.9 c_0 10.1 to 9.5 β 100° 12′	tab. (001)	—	1—2	2.0—2.2 calc. 2.12	white, bluish, greenish, grey
266	*Metahalloysite* $Al_4[(OH)_8 \mid Si_4O_{10}]$	m a_0 5.15 b_0 8.9 c_0 7.9 to 7.5 β 100° 12′	tab. (001)	—	1—2	calc. 2.61	white, brownish
267	*Palygorskite* (Attapulgite) $(Mg, Al)_2[OH \mid Si_4O_{10}] \cdot$ $2 H_2O + 2 H_2O$	2/m or orhomb. a_0 5.2 b_0 2·9.0 c_0 13.4 β 90°—93°	fibrous				white, grey, yellowish

Streak	Indices of refraction and Luster	Optic angle 2V and Biref.	Optic orient.	Pleochroism Bireflection	Occurrence	No.
	n_α 1.553—1.563 n_β 1.559—1.569 n_γ 1.560—1.570	20°—50° r > v 0.007	(−) OP ⊥ (010) n_α/ ⊥ (001) 1°—3½°	—	Hydroth.—hydric., also weathering product in soils. China clay. With same chem. comp. but with 2M structure = *dickite*; with 6M struct. = *nacrite*. Disorder in direction of *b* axis = *fireclay mineral*	260
	n_α 1.560 n_β 1.570 n_γ 1.571	37°—60° r > v 0.011	(−) OP ⊥ (010) n_α ~ ⊥ (001)	almost imperceptible n_α pale greenish-yellow n_β, n_γ pale green	Hydroth.—hydric, metam. alteration product of Mg rich silicates. *Jenkinsite* = Fe bearing antigorite	261
	n_α 1.53—1.549 n_β ~1.54 n_γ 1.545—1.556	30°—35° also greater r > v 0.013	(+) OP (010) n_γ ∥ c	n_α, n_β greenish-yellow to colorless n_γ green or yellow	In veins and fissures of serpentine. Imp. tech. raw material	262
	n_α} ~1.58—1.61 n_β} n_γ ~1.612	small 0.018	(+) OP (010) n_γ ~ ⊥ (001)	—	With diaspore from Chester, Mass. *Corundophyllite* = Mg richer, Al poorer amesite	263
dark green	n_β 1.80 glassy	~0° strong	(−) OP (010) (?) n_α ⊥ (001)	n_α dark red to brown or emerald n_β, n_γ deep-darkolive-green	Hydroth. in ore veins	264
	n 1.490 theoret., usu. to ~1.55 as result of impurities	—	—	—	Hydric, like kaolinite, also mixed with it, in clays and soils	265
	n ~1.55	—	—	—	Like endellite	266
	n_α 1.511 n_β ~n_γ n_γ 1.532—1.540	small 0.02 to 0.03	(−) OP (?)		Sediment., constit. of *mountain cork* and *mtn. leather*	267

No.	Name and Formula	Crystal Class Lattice Constants	Habit, Form	Cleavage	Hardness	Sp. Gr.	Color

f) Tectosilicates (Framework Silicates)

No.	Name and Formula	Crystal Class Lattice Constants	Habit, Form	Cleavage	Hardness	Sp. Gr.	Color
268	*Nepheline* (Na, K)[AlSiO$_4$] Na:K usually ~3:1	6 a_0 10.01 c_0 8.41	short col. c, (10$\bar{1}$0) (0001) rarely (10$\bar{1}$1) (11$\bar{2}$1) (11$\bar{2}$0)	(10$\bar{1}$0) (0001) imp.	5$^1/_2$—6	2.6 to 2.65 pure 2.619	colorless, white, grey and other colors
269	*Analcime* Na[AlSi$_2$O$_6$]·H$_2$O	$m3m$ a_0 13.71	(211) (100), tw. (001)	—	5$^1/_2$	2.2—2.3	white, grey, yellowish, flesh colored
270	*Leucite*, low- K[AlSi$_2$O$_6$] < 605° C	4/m ps. cub. a_0 13.04 c_0 13.85	(211) rare (110), tw. lam. (110) (cub. indic.)	—	5$^1/_2$	2.5	white to grey

Feldspars (No. 271—280)
Alkali Feldspars (No. 271—275)

No.	Name and Formula	Crystal Class Lattice Constants	Habit, Form	Cleavage	Hardness	Sp. Gr.	Color
271	*Sanidine* (High-temp. modif.) K[AlSi$_3$O$_8$] K→Na	2/m a_0 8.564 b_0 13.030 c_0 7.175 β 115° 59.6′	tab. (010); (001) (110) ($\bar{1}$01), tw. (100)	(001) per. (010) dist. (110) poor	6	2.57 to 2.58	colorless, yellowish, grey
272	*Anorthoclase* (K, Na)[AlSi$_3$O$_8$] solid soln. of Or 70 Ab 30 to Or 20 Ab 80[a]	tricl.[b]	col. c, (110) (20$\bar{1}$), tw. lattice pattern after albite and pericline laws	(001) per. (010) dist. (110) (1$\bar{1}$0) poor	6	2.56 to 2.62	colorless, grey
273	*Orthoclase* (Intermed. state) K[AlSi$_3$O$_8$] K→Na	2/m a_0 8.5616 b_0 12.996 c_0 7.193 β 116° 0.9′	broad tab. (010) or col. a; (010) (001) (110) (130) (20$\bar{1}$) (10$\bar{1}$) et al.	(001) per. (010) dist. (110) poor	6	2.53 to 2.56	white, yellowish, reddish to red, greenish to green
274	*Microcline* (Low temp. modif.) K[AlSi$_3$O$_8$] K→Na	$\bar{1}$ a_0 8.574 b_0 12.981 c_0 7.222 α 90° 41′ β 115° 59′ γ 87° 30′	like orthoclase, tw. lattice pattern after albite and pericline laws	(001) per. (010) dist. (110) (1$\bar{1}$0) poor	6	2.54 to 2.57	like orthoclase

[a] Usually with higher An-content as orthoclase, but rarely more than 20—25 Mol-% An.
[b] Structurally undefined phase (paramorph. after high temperature mod.).

Streak	Indices of refraction and Luster	Optic angle 2 V and Biref.	Optic orient.	Pleochroism Bireflection	Occurrence	No.
	n_ω 1.536—1.549 n_ε 1.532—1.544 pure n_ω 1.537 n_ε 1.533 glassy to greasy	0.003 to 0.005	(−)	—	Magmat.—pegmat. in soda rich rocks. *Elaeolite* is the variety in intrusive rocks, exolution of *kalsilite*	268
	n 1.479—1.489 glassy	—	—	—	Hydroth.—hydric. In vesicles in extrus. rocks and also in ore veins	269
	n_α 1.508 n_β ? n_γ 1.509 glassy	very small 0.001	(+)	—	Magmat. in potassium rich extrus. rocks	270
	n_α 1.5203 n_β 1.5248 n_γ 1.5250	∼10° to 20° $r > v$ 0.005	(−) OP (010), High-S. ⊥ (010) Sanidine n_α/a 0°—9°	—	Magmat. in young volcanic rocks. *Potassium monalbite* is the monocl. high temp. modification with K > Na	271
	n_α 1.5234 n_β 1.5294 n_γ 1.5305	43° 38′ 0.007	(−) OP ∼ ⊥ (010), on (010) n_α/c 8°—10°	—	Magmat., esp. in foyaite extrus. rocks	272
	n_α 1.5168 n_β 1.5202 n_γ 1.5227	66° 58′ $r > v$ 0.006	(−) OP ⊥ (010) also ∥ (010) n_α/a 5°	—	Magmat., pegmat., hydroth., also in fissures (*adularia*), metam., diagen.	273
	n_α 1.5186 n_β 1.5223 n_γ 1.5250	80° $r > v$ 0.006	(−) OP ∼ ⊥ (010), on (010) n_α/a 5°, on (001) 15°—20°	—	Like orthoclase. Green microcline = *amazon stone*, used as gemstone. Inter-grown with albite spindles = *perthite*; with Or-spindles = *antiperthite*	274

No.	Name and Formula	Crystal Class Lattice Constants	Habit, Form	Cleav-age	Hard-ness	Sp. Gr.	Color
	Plagioclases (No. 275—280)[a]						
275	*Albite* (Ab) $Na[AlSi_3O_8]$ 0—10 Mol.-% An	$\bar{1}$ a_0 8.144 b_0 12.787 c_0 7.160 α 94.26° β 116.58° γ 87.67°	tab. (010) lath shaped c col. b, (010) (001) (110) (1$\bar{1}$0) (100) (10$\bar{1}$) (20$\bar{1}$) (0$\bar{2}$1) (021)	(001) per. (010) dist. (110) (1$\bar{1}$0) imp.	6—6$^1/_2$	2.605	colorless, white, grey, greenish
276	*Oligoclase* 10—30 Mol.-% An		like albite	like albite	6—6$^1/_2$	2.65	like albite
277	*Andesine* 30—50 Mol.-% An	An 31 a_0 8.171 b_0 12.846 c_0 7.129 α 93.75° β 116.44° γ 89.25°	like albite	like albite	6—6$^1/_2$	2.69	like albite
278	*Labradorite* 50—70 Mol.-% An	An 51 a_0 8.180 b_0 12.859 c_0 7.112 α 93.52° β 116.27° γ 89.89°	like albite	like albite	6—6$^1/_2$	2.70	like albite
279	*Bytownite* 70—90 Mol.-% An		like albite	like albite	6—6$^1/_2$	2.75	like albite
280	*Anorthite* (An) $Ca[Al_2Si_2O_8]$ 90—100 Mol.-% An	$\bar{1}$ ~An 100 a_0 8.1768 b_0 12.8768 c_0 7.0845 ×2 α 93.17° β 115.85° γ 91.22°	sim. albite	like albite	6—6$^1/_2$	2.77	like albite

[a] All values for lattice constants and opt. properties apply to low temperature modification (for high temperature modification see supplementary Table 2, p. 433).

Streak	Indices of refraction and Luster	Optic angle 2V and Biref.	Optic orient.	Pleochroism Bireflection	Occurrence	No.
	n_α 1.5286 n_β 1.5326 n_γ 1.5388	77.2° $r<v$ 0.0102	(+) $OP\sim\perp c$ ↓ (+) An 18 (−)	—	Magmat., pegmat., hydroth., metam., also in fissures. *b* axis elongated crystals occur. in fissures are called *pericline. Analbite* (tricl.) is the low temp. unstable modif. *Monalbite* is the monocl. high temp. modification	275
	An 21.6 n_α 1.5390 n_β 1.5431 n_γ 1.5467	86.5° 0.00768 ↓ $r>v$ $r<v$ ↓	↓ (−) An 38 (+)	—	Magmat., metam. Plagioclase between An_5—An_{17}, exol. in an An_2 and an An_{25}—An_{28} component, is called *peristerite*	276
	An 44.2 n_α 1.5516 n_β 1.5547 n_γ 1.5590	82° 0.0074		—	Magmat., metam.	277
	An 59.2 n_α 1.5582 n_β 1.5615 n_γ 1.5662	79.5° 0.008	(+) ↓ An 75 (−)	—	Magmat., metam. In the region between about An_{30}—An_{70} plagioclases exhibit prelim. stage of exosolution (into $An_{25-30}+An_{70-75}$) called the *labradorite state*	278
	An 80 n_α 1.5671 n_β 1.5729 n_γ 1.5778	85.0° 0.0107		—	Magmat., in basic rocks	279
	An 100 (synth.) n_α 1.5750 n_β 1.5834 n_γ 1.5883	75.2° $r>v$ 0.0133	(−) $OP\sim\parallel c$	—	Magmat., in very basic extrus. rocks, metam. in volcanic ejecta and cryst. schists	280

No.	Name and Formula	Crystal Class Lattice Constants	Habit, Form	Cleavage	Hardness	Sp. Gr.	Color
281	*Cancrinite* $(Na_2, Ca)_4$ $[CO_3 \mid (H_2O)_{0-3} \mid$ $(AlSiO_4)_6] \, CO_3 \rightarrow SO_4$	6 a_0 12.63 to 12.78 c_0 5.11 to 5.19	col.-acic. c, $(10\bar{1}0)$ (0001) $(10\bar{1}1)$, tw. lam. rare	$(10\bar{1}0)$ per.	5—6	2.4—2.5	colorless, yellowish, pink, light blue

Sodalite-Group (No. 282—285)

No.	Name and Formula	Crystal Class Lattice Constants	Habit, Form	Cleavage	Hardness	Sp. Gr.	Color
282	*Sodalite* $Na_8[Cl_2 \mid (AlSiO_4)_6]$	$\bar{4}3\,m$ a_0 8.83 to 8.91	(110), less frequent (100) (211) (210) (111), tw. (111)	(110) dist.	5—6	2.3	colorless, white, grey, blue, rarely green, red
283	*Nosean* $Na_8[SO_4 \mid (AlSiO_4)_6]$	$\bar{4}3\,m$ a_0 8.98 to 9.15	like sodalite	(110) dist.	5—6	2.3—2.4	like sodalite
284	*Hauynite* $(Na, Ca)_{8-4}$ $[(SO_4)_{2-1} \mid (AlSiO_4)_6]$	$\bar{4}3\,m$ a_0 9.12	like sodalite	(110) dist.	5—6	2.5	like sodalite
285	*Lazurite* (Lapis lazuli) $(Na, Ca)_8$ $[(SO_4, S, Cl)_2 \mid (AlSiO_4)_6]$	$\bar{4}3\,m$ a_0 9.08	crystals rare, (110)	—	5—5½	2.38 to 2.45	dark blue also greenish

Scapolites (No. 286—289)

No.	Name and Formula	Crystal Class Lattice Constants	Habit, Form	Cleavage	Hardness	Sp. Gr.	Color
286	*Marialite* (Ma) 0—20% Me $Na_8[(Cl_2, SO_4, CO_3)$ $(AlSi_3O_8)_6]$	$4/m$ a_0 12.075 c_0 7.516	$a = a_0\sqrt{2}$ c/a 0.4425, col. c, (110) (100) (111) (101), rarely (311) (210)	(100) per. (110) dist.	5—6½	2.50	colorless, white, grey greenish, also red and blue
287	*Dipyre* 20—50% Me		like Ma	(100) per. (110) dist.	5—6½		like Ma
288	*Mizzonite* 50—80% Me		like Ma	(100) per. (110) dist.	5—6½		like Ma
289	*Meionite* (Me) 80—100% Me $Ca_8[(Cl_2, SO_4, CO_3)_{2\,(?)}$ $(Al_2Si_2O_8)_6]$	$4/m$ a_0 12.13 c_0 7.69	like Ma c/a 0.4393	(100) per. (110) dist.	5—6½	2.78	like Ma

Streak	Indices of refraction and Luster	Optic angle 2V and Biref.	Optic orient.	Pleochroism Bireflection	Occurrence	No.
	n_ω 1.515—1.524 n_ε 1.491—1.502	0.025 to 0.012	(—)	—	Magmat., in nepheline syenites	281
	n ~1.483 to 1.487	—	—	—	Magmat., in soda rich rocks	282
	n ~1.495	—	—	—	Magmat., in nepheline- and leucite-bearing extrus. rocks	283
	n ~1.502	—	—	—	Like nosean	284
lighter blue	n ~1.50	—	—	—	Metam., contact mineral in limestones; gemstone	285
	n_ω 1.539 n_ε 1.537	0.002	(—)	—	Pneumat. in tuffs, hydroth. Regional metam.	286
			(—)	—	Metam. in schists and contact rocks	287
			(—)	—	Metam. in contact rocks, pegmat., in extrus. rocks. Often as alteration product of feldspars (constit. of *saussurite*). Most common scapolite. Also gemstone	288
	n_ω 1.596 n_ε 1.557 glassy	0.039	(—)	—	Contact metam. in limestone inclusions of Vesuvius	289

No.	Name and Formula	Crystal Class Lattice Constants	Habit, Form	Cleavage	Hardness	Sp. Gr.	Color
	Zeolites (No. 290—299)						
290	*Natrolite* $Na_2[Al_2Si_3O_{10}] \cdot 2\,H_2O$	$2mm$ a_0 18.35 b_0 18.70 c_0 6.61	acic. c, ps. tetr., (110) (111)	(110) per. 88° 45′	5—5$^1/_2$	2.2—2.4	colorless, white, grey, yellowish, reddish
291	*Mesolite* $Na_2Ca_2[Al_2Si_3O_{10}]_3 \cdot$ $8\,H_2O$	2 a_0 3·18.9 b_0 6.55 c_0 18.48 β 90° 00′	acic. — fib. b, ps. orhomb.	(101), (10$\bar{1}$) per.	5—5$^1/_2$	2.2—2.4	like natrolite
292	*Thomsonite* $NaCa_2[Al_2(Al, Si)$ $Si_2O_{10}]_2 \cdot 5\,H_2O$	mmm ps. tetr. a_0 13.07 b_0 13.09 c_0 13.25	col. — fib. c, (110) (011), tw. (110)	(010) per. (100) per.	5—5$^1/_2$	2.3—2.4	white, grey, yellow, red
293	*Scolecite* $Ca[Al_2Si_3O_{10}] \cdot 3\,H_2O$	m (?) a_0 18.48 b_0 18.94 c_0 6.54 β 90° 45′	ps. orhomb., tw. (100)	(110) per. 36°	5—5$^1/_2$	2.2—2.4	like natrolite
294	*Laumontite* $Ca[AlSi_2O_6]_2 \cdot 4\,H_2O$	2 or m a_0 14.90 b_0 13.17 c_0 7.55 β 111° 30′	col. c, (110) tw. (100)	(010) (110) per. 93° 46′	3—3$^1/_2$	2.25 to 2.35	white, colorless, yellowish, reddish
295	*Heulandite* $Ca[Al_2Si_7O_{18}] \cdot 6\,H_2O$	$2/m$ a_0 17.71 b_0 17.84 c_0 7.46 β 116° 20′	tab. (010), elong. c; tw. lam. (001)	(010) per.	3$^1/_2$—4	2.2	colorless, white, grey, brownish, brick red
296	*Stilbite* $Ca[Al_2Si_7O_{18}] \cdot 7\,H_2O$	$2/m$ a_0 13.63 b_0 18.17 c_0 11.31 β 129° 10′	tab. (010) elong. a; (110) (010) (001), almost always cruciform tw. (001)	(010) per.	3$^1/_2$—4	2.1—2.2	colorless, white, grey, brownish, rarely red
297	*Phillipsite* $KCa[Al_3Si_5O_{16}] \cdot 6\,H_2O$	$2/m$ a_0 10.02 b_0 14.28 c_0 8.64 β 125° 40′	tab. (010) elong. a or acic. c, (110) (010) (001) almost always tw. (001) and (021), partly ps. cub.	(010), (100) per.	4$^1/_2$	2.2	colorless, white, yellowish, grey

Streak	Indices of refraction and Luster	Optic angle 2 V and Biref.	Optic orient.	Pleochroism Bireflection	Occurrence	No.
	n_α 1.480 n_β 1.482 n_γ 1.493	60°—63° $r < v$ 0.013	(+) OP (010) $n_\gamma \| c$	—	Hydrotherm. in vesicles and fissures of phonolites, basalts; also syenites	290
	n_α ~1.504 n_β ~1.505 n_γ ~1.505	80° $r \gg v$ ~0.001	(+) OP (010) n_α / c 8° $n_\beta \| b$	—	Like natrolite	291
	n_α 1.511—1.530 n_β 1.513—1.532 n_γ 1.518—1.545 glassy	47°—75° $r > v$ 0.006 to 0.015	(+) OP (001) $n_\gamma \| b$	—	Hydroth. in vesicles of basalt and phonolitic extrus. rocks	292
	n_α 1.507—1.513 n_β 1.516—1.520 n_γ 1.517—1.521	36°—56° $r \ll v$ 0.007	(−) OP ⊥ (010) n_α / c 15°—18°	—	Like natrolite, also in alpine fissures	293
	n_α 1.505—1.513 n_β 1.515—1.524 n_γ 1.517—1.525	26°—47° $r \ll v$ 0.01	(−) OP (010) n_γ / c 8°—33°	—	Hydroth. in fissures and vesicles, esp. in bas. extrus. rocks, cryst. schists, and ore veins	294
	n_α 1.498—1.496 n_β 1.499—1.497 n_γ 1.505—1.501 glassy on (010) pearly	0°—55° $r > v$ 0.005	(+) OP ⊥ (010) n_β / c ~6°	—	Hydroth., esp. in vesicles of basalt and similar rocks., fissures in metam. rocks and in ore veins	295
	n_α 1.494—1.500 n_β 1.498—1.504 n_γ 1.500—1.508 glassy	33° $r < v$ 0.01	(−) OP (010) n_α / a 5°	—	Hydroth. in vesicles of basalts, granite druses, in fissures in cryst. schists and in ore veins	296
	n_α ~1.48—(?) n_β = 1.48—1.57 n_γ ~1.503—(?)	60°—80° $r < v$ 0.003 to 0.01	(+) OP ⊥ (010) n_γ / c 10°—30°	—	Hydroth. in vesicles in basalts. Also in deep sea clays	297

No.	Name and Formula	Crystal Class Lattice Constants	Habit, Form	Cleavage	Hardness	Sp. Gr.	Color
298	*Harmotome* $Ba[Al_2Si_6O_{16}] \cdot 6\,H_2O$	$2/m$ a_0 9.82 b_0 14.13 c_0 8.68 β 124° 50′	cruciform tw. (001) and (021)	(010) dist.	$4^1/_2$	2.44 to 2.5	white and light colors
299	*Chabasite* (Ca, Na_2) $[Al_2Si_4O_{12}] \cdot 6\,H_2O$	$3\,m$ a_0 13.78 c_0 14.97	isom. ps. cub., $(10\bar{1}1)\,(01\bar{1}2)$ $(02\bar{2}1)$, tw. (0001)	$(10\bar{1}1)$ imp.	$4^1/_2$	2.1	colorless, white, reddish brown

X. Cl. Organic Compounds

| 300 | *Whewellite* $Ca[C_2O_4] \cdot H_2O$ | $2/m$ a_0 6.29 b_0 14.59 c_0 9.97$_5$ β 107° 18′ | short col. c, tw. $(\bar{1}01)$ | $(\bar{1}01)$ per. (010) imp. | $2^1/_2$—3 | 2.23 | colorless to translucent |

Supplementary Table 1 (No. 271—275). *Alkali Feldspars*

	Chem. comp. Mol.-%	n_α	n_β	n_γ	Opt. sign	2V	$n_{\alpha'}$ for P (001)	$n_{\alpha'}$ for M (010)	$n_{\gamma'}$ for P (001)	$n_{\gamma'}$ for M (010)	Extinction $n_{\alpha'}$ on	
											P (001) to trace of (010)	M (010) to trace of (001)
Sanidine	77.8 Or 22.2 Ab	1.5202	1.5247	1.5249	(—)	24.0°	1.5202	1.5202	1.5249	1.5226	0°	5°—8°
Anorthoclase	42.1 Or 52.3 Ab 5.6 An	1.5264	1.5309	1.5317	(—)	47° 45′	1.5267	1.5264	1.5317	1.5309	1°	6.3°
Orthoclase	90.5 Or 7.1 Ab 2.4 An	1.5188	1.5230	1.5236	(—)	43.6°	1.5188	1.5188	1.5236	1.5213	0°	5.3°
Orthoclase — Microperthite	68.1 Or 30.2 Ab 1.7 An	1.5217	1.5259	1.5279	(—)	69.1°	1.5217	1.5217	1.5279	1.5256	0°	9.5°
Microcline — Microperthite	85.2 Or 13.4 Ab 1.4 An	1.5195	1.5232	1.5255	(—)	76.2°	1.5200	1.5217	1.5255	1.5247	15°—20°	7.5°
Albite	100 Ab					See supplementary Table 2						

Streak	Indices of refraction and Luster	Optic angle 2V and Biref.	Optic orient.	Pleochroism Bireflection	Occurrence	No.
	n_α 1.503 n_β 1.505 n_γ 1.508	43° 0.005	(+) OP ⊥ (010) n_β/c 28°—32°	—	Hydroth. in ore veins and in vesicles in extrus. rocks	298
	$\left.\begin{matrix}n_\omega\\n_\varepsilon\end{matrix}\right\}\sim 1.48$	anomal: 0°—32° ~0.002	(−) ((+))	—	Hydroth. in vesicles of basalts, phono-lites, granites and porphyrites	299
	n_α 1.491 n_β 1.555 n_γ 1.650 pearly, glassy	83° 55′ r < v 0.06	(+) OP ⊥ (010) n_γ/c 30°	—	Sediment. in conjunction with coal or organic matter, diagenetic; also with ores	300

Supplementary Table 2 (No. 275—280). *Plagioclases*

	Mol.-% An	n_α	n_β	n_γ	Opt. sign	2V	$n_{\alpha'}$ for P (001) M (010)	Extinction $n_{\alpha'}$ on		n_D of Plagio-clase glass
								P (001)	M (010)	
								to trace of		
								M (010)	P (001)	
Albite	0.2	*1.5273* 1.5286	*1.5344* 1.5326	*1.5357* 1.5388	*(−)* (+)	*46.9°* 77.2°	*1.5275* 1.5285	*+ 3.6°* + 3.0°	*+22.5°* +20.0°	} 1.487
Oligoclase	21.6	*1.5386* 1.5390	*1.5440* 1.5431	*1.5459* 1.5467	*(−)* (−)	*62.1°* 86.5°	*1.5390* 1.5399	*+ 2.0°* + 1.0°	*+ 3.5°* + 4.5°	} 1.506
	29.8	*1.5437* 1.5439	*1.5483* 1.5479	*1.5510* 1.5514	*(−)* (−)	*75.6°* 86.4°	*1.5445* 1.5445	*+ 1.5°* 0.0°	*0.0°* − 2.2°	} 1.512
Andesine	44.2	*1.5522* 1.5516	*—* 1.5547	*1.5595* 1.5590	*(+)* (+)	*~88°* 82°	*1.5515* 1.5515	*− 1.5°* − 3.5°	*−10.5°* −13.0°	} 1.525
Labradorite	51.8	*1.5547* 1.5547	*1.5576* 1.5575	*1.5621* 1.5621	*(+)* (+)	*76.8°* 76.4°	*1.5558* 1.5558	*− 6.0°* − 6.5°	*−18.6°* −17.5°	} 1.531
	59.2	*1.5582* 1.5582	*1.5611* 1.5617	*1.5662* 1.5662	*(+)* (+)	*73.9°* 79.5°	*1.5589* 1.5589	*−12.5°* −10.0°	*−27.2°* −23.5°	} 1.537
Bytownite	80.0	*1.5671* 1.5671	*1.5716* 1.5729	*1.5765* 1.5778	*(+)* (−)	*87.5°* 85.0°	*1.5695* 1.5695	*−27.5°* −22.5°	*−35.0°* −34.0°	} 1.556
Anorthite	100	*1.5750* 1.5756	*1.5834* 1.5835	*1.5883* 1.5885	*(−)* (−)	*75.2°* (83°)	*1.5793* 1.5793	*−37.0°* −43.0°	*−39.0°* −39.5°	} 1.5755

Italicized figures apply to high temperature modification.

Supplementary Table 3 (No. 226—231). *Amphiboles.* (*After* Rosenbusch, Adamson, Koritnig, Leinz)

	n_γ/c on (010)	$n_{\gamma'}/c$ on (110)	$n_{\alpha'}$ for (110)	Opt. sign	2V	n_α	n_β	n_γ
Tremolite	16° 39′	15.0°	1.6100	(−)	81° 31′	1.5996	1.6131	1.6224
Actinolite	14° 59′	13.2°	1.6296	(−)	81° 38′	1.6173	1.6330	1.6412
Green Hornblende	13°	12.5°	1.666	(−)	75°	1.656	1.669	1.678
Common Hornblende	18°	20.1°	1.666	(−)	63°	1.660	1.675	1.683
Karinthine[a]	21.5°	19°	1.643	(−)	85°	1.636	1.647	1.659
Basalt. Hornblende	4°	3.1°	1.697	(−)	84°	1.684	1.701	1.720
Riebeckite	7°	5°	1.685	(+)	85°	1.677	1.688	1.699
Eckermannite[b]	25°	29°	1.642	(−)	74°	1.636	1.644	1.649

[a] A hornblende from eclogites which comp. between common and basaltic hornblende.
[b] An alkali hornblende from a S. Swedish alkali rock (lakarpite).

C. Petrologic Tables

1. Igneous Rocks (after Tröger 1935)

a) Intrusive Rocks without Feldspathoids

1. *Alkaligranite*
   (Arab. Desert, Egypt.)

	Vol.-%
Quartz	38
Orthoclase	22
Microcline	±
Anorthoclase	21
Riebeckite (Alkalihornblende)	19
Aegirine (Na-Fe-Augite)	±
Zircon, Monazite, Xenotime	Tr.

2. *Aplitgranite* (Fürstenstein, nw. Görlitz)
   = light acid Granite

	Vol.-%
Orthoclase ⎰ Microperthite ⎱	42
Microcline ⎱ $Or_{62}Ab_{34}An_{04}$ ⎰	
Quartz	33
Plagioclase An_{12}	22
Biotite ⎱	
Apatite, Ore, Zircon ⎰	3
Fluorite, Muscovite ⎰	

Intrusive rocks without feldspathoids

	1. Alkali-granite	2. Aplit-granite	3. Grano-diorite	4. Quartz-diorite	5. Orthoclase-syenite	6. Natron-syenite	7. Syenite	8. Diorite	9. Gabbro
SiO_2	75.22	75.70	63.85	64.07	62.03	60.00	58.70	56.06	48.61
TiO_2	0.13	0.09	0.58	0.45	0.53	0.42	0.95	0.60	0.17
Al_2O_3	9.93	13.17	15.84	15.82	16.39	16.88	17.09	17.61	17.83
Fe_2O_3	2.31	0.43	1.91	3.40	0.72	1.83	3.17	1.65	2.08
FeO	2.19	0.74	2.75	1.44	0.86	3.02	2.29	7.59	5.23
MnO	0.17	n.d.	0.07	Tr.	n.d.	0.12	n.d.	0.16	n.d.
MgO	0.09	0.15	2.07	3.39	1.60	1.40	2.41	3.38	8.23
CaO	1.08	0.92	4.76	4.43	3.60	3.16	4.71	7.26	13.72
Na_2O	4.78	3.59	3.29	4.06	1.08	9.31	4.38	3.47	2.63
K_2O	4.06	4.77	3.08	2.27	12.38	0.94	4.35	1.67	0.32
H_2O^+	0.31	0.68	1.65	0.42	0.61	1.53	0.89	0.95	0.99
H_2O^-	.	.	0.28	0.10	0.24	0.43	0.23	.	.
P_2O_5	n.d.	Tr.	0.13	0.18	0.13	0.14	0.23	n.d.	0.08
CO_2	.	.	.	.	.	0.59	0.00	.	0.00
BaO	.	.	0.06	.	.	0.06	.	.	.
SrO	.	.	Tr.	.	.	0.02	.	.	.
Li_2O	.	.	Tr.	.	.	.	.	.	.
ZrO_2	.	.	.	.	.	0.03	.	.	.
NiO	.	.	.	0.05	.	.	.	.	.
FeS_2	.	.	0.04	.	.	.	.	.	.
S	.	.	.	.	.	Tr.	.	.	0.05
SO_3	.	.	.	.	.	.	.	.	0.00
Sum	100.27	100.24	100.36	100.08	100.17	99.88[a]	99.40	100.40	99.94
si	418	460	241	227	237	207	196	158	105
ti	0.5	0.4	1.6	1.2	1.6	1.1	2.4	1.3	0.3
p	n.d.	Tr.	0.2	0.3	0.3	0.2	0.3	n.d.	0.1
al	32	47	35	33	$36\frac{1}{2}$	34	$33\frac{1}{2}$	$29\frac{1}{2}$	$22\frac{1}{2}$
fm	$21\frac{1}{2}$	7	26	31	$14\frac{1}{2}$	21	26	36	$39\frac{1}{2}$
c	$6\frac{1}{2}$	6	$19\frac{1}{2}$	17	$14\frac{1}{2}$	12	17	22	32
alk	40	40	$19\frac{1}{2}$	19	$34\frac{1}{2}$	33	$23\frac{1}{2}$	$12\frac{1}{2}$	6
k	0.36	0.47	0.38	0.27	0.88	0.06	0.40	0.24	0.08
mg	0.04	0.19	0.45	0.58	0.65	0.35	0.46	0.40	0.68

[a] With tr. Li_2O.

3. *Granodiorite* (Hecla Gorge, ne. Sacramento, Cal.)

	Wt.-% calc.
Quartz	21
Orthoclase $Or_{85}Ab_{15}$	18
Plagioclase $Ab_{67}An_{30}Or_{03}$	40
Hornblende	17
Biotite	$\pm$
Ore, Sphene, Apatite	4

4. *Quartzdiorite* (Electric Peak, Yellowstone-Park)

	Wt.-% calc.
Plagioclase $Ab_{65}An_{29}Or_{06}$	47
Quartz	22
Biotite	17
Hornblende $+$ Augite	8
Orthoclase $Or_{67}Ab_{30}An_{03}$	5
Ore, Apatite	1

5. *Orthoclase-Syenite* (Copper-Mtn., South-Alaska)

	Wt.-% calc.
Orthoclase $Or_{88}Ab_{10}An_{02}$	84
Albite	$\pm$
Diopside	14
Sphene, Apatite	2

6. *Natronsyenite* (Coalinga, Fresno-Co., Cal.)

	Wt.-% calc.
Albite with Andesine Core ($Ab_{88}An_{05}Or_{07}$)	83
Barkevikite (Alkalihornblende)	15
Biotite, Aegirine (Na-Fe-Augite)	$\pm$
Ore, Apatite, Zircon	2
Analcime, Calcite, Zeolites	sec.

7. *Syenite* (Plauenscher Grund, Dresden)

	Wt.-% calc.
Quartz	5
Natronorthoclase	51
Orthoclaseperthite $Or_{53}Ab_{43}An_{04}$	$\pm$
Microcline	$\pm$
Plagioclase $Ab_{75}An_{25}$	20
Hornblende	19
Biotite, Diopside	$\pm$
Sphene, Ore, Apatite	5

8. *Diorite* (Lavia, West Finland)

	Wt.-% calc.
Plagioclase zoned An_{41}—An_{31}	53
Hornblende	22
Biotite	9
Quartz	7
Microcline	6
Ore, Apatite	3

9. *Gabbro* (Zobten, Silesia)

	Wt.-% calc.
Plagioclase $Ab_{35}An_{64}Or_{01}$	52
Diallage (Pyroxene)	35
Hypersthene	10
Olivine	$\pm$
Ore, Apatite	3

b) Extrusive Rocks without Feldspathoids

10. *Quartzkeratophyre* (Alsenberg, Fichtelgebirge)

	Wt.-% calc.
Quartz	19
Albite $Ab_{86}An_{00}Or_{14}$	66
Hornblende $\pm$ Biotite (chloritized)	13
Ore, Apatite	2

11. *Pantellerite* (Costa Zeneti, Pantelleria)

	Wt.-% calc.
Quartz	20
Anorthoclase $Or_{43}Ab_{57}$ (in part inclus).	63
Aegirine diopside (Na-Fe-bearing Augite)	14 / 3
Cossyrite $\pm$ Aenigmatite (Alkalihornblendes)	in part inclus.
Apatite, Zircon	$\pm$

12. *Quartzporphyre* (Thal, s. Eisenach)

			Wt.-% calc.
Quartz			34
Orthoclase $Or_{70}Ab_{28}An_{02}$	in part	⎱	47
Plagioclase $Ab_{80}An_{15}Or_{05}$	inclus.	⎰	15
Biotite (altered)		⎱	
Hematite, Ore, Apatite		⎰	4

13. *Rhyolite* (Sugarloaf-Hill, Arizona)

				Wt.-% calc.
Quartz			few inclus.	30
Natron-			Portion of	
sanidine	$Or_{47}Ab_{53}$		ground	64
Albite			mass glassy	
Plagioclase-inclus. $Ab_{80}An_{20}$				4
Biotite-inclus.				1
Apatite, Ore				1

14. *Plagiophyre* (Pap-Craig, South Scotland)

		Wt.-% calc.
Plagioclase ⎰ -inclus. An_{30} ⎱		50
⎱ -groundmass An_{20} ⎰		
Orthoclase $Or_{60}Ab_{40}$		23
Quartz		17
Chlorite (after Augite ?),		10
Ore, Apatite		

15. *Rhyodacite* (Marysville, Victoria)

	Wt.-% calc.
Plagioclase zoned An_{50}—An_{15}	34
(in part inclus.)	
Quartz (in part inclus.)	29
Orthoclase (in part inclus.)	18
Biotite (in part inclus.)	16
Apatite, Ore	3
Garnet	±

16. *Quartzporphyrite* (Grass-Valley, ne. Sacramento, Cal.)

	Wt.-% calc.
Quartz (in part inclus.)	17
Orthoclase $Or_{67}Ab_{30}An_{03}$	19
Plagioclase $Ab_{60}An_{34}Or_{06}$	45
(in part inclus.)	
Hornblende ⎱ -inclus.	16
Augite ⎰	
Ore, Apatite	3
Epidote, Chlorite, Sericite	sec.

17. *Dacite* (Kis-Sebes, Siebenbürgen)

	Vol.-% meas.
Quartz (incl. 5 inclus.)	30
Orthoclase	9
Plagioclase $Ab_{60}An_{34}Or_{06}$	46
(incl. 30 inclus. An_{35})	
Biotite ⎱ -inclus.	5
Hornblende ⎰	
Ore, Apatite	2
Chlorite pseudom. (after diopside ?)	8

18. *Keratophyre* (Rübeland, Harz)

	Wt.-% calc.
Microperthite $Or_{70}Ab_{30}$	19
Albite $Ab_{90}An_{00}Or_{10}$	63
Aegirinaugite (Na-Fe-bearing Augite) and alteration product	15
Ore, Apatite	3

19. *Natrontrachyte* (Angorony, NW-Madagascar)

		Wt.-% calc.
Anorthoclase $Or_{37}Ab_{60}An_{03}$		89
(in part inclus.)		
Aegirinaugite (Na-Fe-Augite)	⎱	
(in part inclus.)		
Laneite (Alkalihornblende)		8
Aegirine (Na-Fe-Augite)	⎰	
Quartz		±
Ore, Sphene, Apatite		3

20. *Orthophyre* (Friedland, Silesia)

	Wt.-% calc.
= anchimetamorphic Trachyte	
Orthoclase $Or_{67}Ab_{30}An_{03}$	62
Plagioclase $Ab_{77}An_{15}Or_{08}$	22
Augite (altered) ⎱	16
Quartz, Ore, Apatite ⎰	
Glass	±

21. *Trachyte* (Siebengebirge, Rheinland)

	Wt.-% calc.
Sanidine $Or_{60}Ab_{36}An_{04}$	75
(in part inclus.)	
Plagioclase $Ab_{74}An_{19}Or_{07}$	11
(in part inclus.)	
Diopside	10
Biotite	±
Sphene, Apatite, Ore	4
Glass (corr. to Quartz + Sanidine + Oligoclase)	±

22. *Porphyrite* (Ilmenau, Thüringen)

	Wt.-% calc.
Orthoclase $Or_{67}Ab_{30}An_{03}$	15
Plagioclase $Ab_{56}An_{39}Or_{05}$ (in part inclus.)	58
Enstatite inclus.	16
Augite $\pm$ Biotite	5
Ore, Quartz, Apatite	6
Glass	$\pm$

24. *Diabase* (Wenern-See, Sweden)

	Wt.-% calc.
Plagioclase $Ab_{38}An_{55}Or_{07}$	48
Augite	41
Ore, Apatite	6
Orthoclase + Quartz	5
sec.: Uralite (Hornblende forming from Augite) Chlorite	

23. *Andesite* (Hoyada, Catamarca, Argentina)

	Wt.-% estim.
Plagioclase Inclus. zoned An_{70}—An_{35} Groundm. An_{35}	46
Hornblende (in part inclus.)	31
Pyroxene, Biotite	$\pm$
Ore, Apatite	3
Glass, (corr. to Andesine + Sanidine + Quartz)	20

25. *Basalt* (Mauna Iki, Kilauea)

	Wt.-% calc.
Plagioclase $Ab_{44}An_{52}Or_{04}$	44
Augite	49
Olivine	$\pm$
Ore, Apatite	7
Glass	$\pm$

Extrusive rocks without

	10. Quartz-kerato-phyre	11. Pantel-lerite	12. Quartz-porphyre	13. Rhyolite	14. Plagio-phyre	15. Rhyo-dacite	16. Quartz-porphyrite	17. Dacite	18. Kerato-phyre
SiO_2	67.90	69.79	76.03	74.02	64.54	67.17	63.39	66.76	61.67
TiO_2	0.24	0.89	n.d.	0.02	1.09	0.87	0.44	1.02	0.34
Al_2O_3	14.36	11.91	11.76	13.20	15.83	14.86	16.58	14.41	17.47
Fe_2O_3	4.36	5.35	1.99	0.75	1.75	0.43	1.41	2.74	1.37
FeO	1.44	1.43	n.d.	0.29	2.80	3.87	3.08	2.23	3.92
MnO	0.32	0.20	n.d.	Tr.	0.26	0.07	Tr.	n.d.	Tr.
MgO	0.22	0.25	0.27	0.06	1.01	1.61	2.15	2.01	2.13
CaO	1.34	0.25	0.45	0.56	2.13	2.84	4.76	3.64	0.18
Na_2O	6.89	5.66	3.36	4.18	5.25	2.48	3.47	3.02	8.52
K_2O	1.85	4.59	5.61	4.82	2.95	3.77	2.79	2.51	3.38
H_2O^+	1.52	0.17	0.63	1.86	1.39	0.90	1.87	0.62	0.45
H_2O^-	.	0.04	.	.	0.42	0.12	0.22	0.77	.
P_2O_5	n.d.	0.13	n.d.	n.d.	0.00	0.53	0.14	0.39	0.06
CO_2	.	.	.	.	0.27	0.20	.	.	0.05
BaO	.	.	.	.	0.06	.	0.11	.	.
ZrO_2	.	.	.	.	0.00	.	.	.	.
FeS_2	Tr.	.	.	.	0.15	.	.	.	.
FeS	.	.	.	.	0.00	.	.	.	.
Cl	.	.	.	Tr.	0.00	.	.	.	.
S	.	.	.	.	.	0.02	.	.	.
SO_3	.	.	.	.	.	.	.	.	.
SO_2	.	.	.	.	.	.	.	.	.
Sum	100.44	100.66	100.10	99.76	99.91 [a]	99.74	100.41	100.12	99.54
si	297	325	470	450	268	298	236	280	217
ti	0.8	3.1	n.d.	0.1	3.4	2.9	1.2	3.2	0.9
p	n.d.	0.3	n.d.	n.d.	0.0 (?)	1.0	0.2	0.7	0.1
al	37	$32\frac{1}{2}$	43	$47\frac{1}{2}$	39	39	36	$35\frac{1}{2}$	36
fm	22	27	$11\frac{1}{2}$	$5\frac{1}{2}$	$22\frac{1}{2}$	$26\frac{1}{2}$	$25\frac{1}{2}$	29	$26\frac{1}{2}$
c	$6\frac{1}{2}$	$1\frac{1}{2}$	3	$3\frac{1}{2}$	$9\frac{1}{2}$	$13\frac{1}{2}$	19	16	$\frac{1}{2}$
alk	$34\frac{1}{2}$	39	$42\frac{1}{2}$	$43\frac{1}{2}$	29	21	$19\frac{1}{2}$	19	37
k	0.15	0.35	0.53	0.43	0.27	0.50	0.35	0.35	0.21
mg	0.07	0.06	0.22	0.10	0.28	0.40	0.47	0.44	0.43

[a] With 0.01 Cr_2O_3, 0.00 Li_2O.

26. *Sideromelane*. (After HOPPE, 1941.) (Portella di Palagonia, Sicily)

almost pure glass
5 % Plagioclase and Olivin inclus.
Index of ref. $n = 1.586 \pm 0.01$

27. *Palagonite*. (After HOPPE, 1941.) (Portella di Palagonia, Sicily)

almost pure glass
almost free of zeolites
Index of ref. $n = 1.49 \pm 0.02$

c) Intrusive Rocks with Feldspathoids or almost only Dark Minerals

28. *Foyaite* (Monchique, Portugal)

	Wt.-% calc.
Orthoclase microperthite $Or_{36}Ab_{56}An_{08}$	67
Nepheline $\pm$ Hauyine	24
Aegirinaugite (Na-Fe-bearing Augite)	7
Sphene, Zircon,	2
Ore, Sulfides, Apatite	
Lepidomelane (iron-rich Biotite)	$\pm$

29. *Leucite syenite* (ejecta from Somma, Vesuv)

	Vol.-% calc.
Sanidine	44
Leucite (inclusion-like)	37
Sodalite	12
Hornblende	3
Augite, Biotite	$\pm$
Melanite (Ti-bear. Ca-Fe-Garnet), } Ore, Apatite, Sphene }	4

feldspathoids

19. Natron-trachyte	20. Ortho-phyre	21. Trachyte	22. Por-phyrite	23. Andesite	24. Diabase	25. Basalt	26. Sidero-melane	27. Palagonite	
62.91	63.24	61.25	54.94	57.35	50.20	50.32	51.90	33.00	SiO_2
0.94	Tr.	0.05	1.11	0.64	1.21	3.10	1.60	2.30	TiO_2
18.25	16.83	17.70	18.38	17.54	16.08	12.83	14.70	8.30	Al_2O_3
2.08	4.86	2.95	3.15	3.33	9.30	1.74	1.60	15.20	Fe_2O_3
1.47	0.07	1.40	3.02	3.87	3.87	9.93	8.60	.	FeO
n.d.	Tr.	n.d.	n.d.	Tr.	0.54	0.10	Tr.	0.10	MnO
0.20	0.57	0.07	3.59	4.29	6.82	7.39	8.70	5.00	MgO
0.87	0.72	3.10	6.29	6.91	7.85	11.06	10.40	7.00	CaO
6.87	4.02	3.40	3.97	4.01	2.34	2.38	2.60	0.70	Na_2O
5.85	7.37	8.08	2.31	2.54	1.24	0.41	0.40	0.30	K_2O
0.47	1.13	1.35	2.39	0.79	0.67	0.33	0.20	9.30	H_2O+
.	.	.	.	.	.	0.05	0.16	18.30	H_2O-
0.19	0.16	1.10	0.27	0.08	n.d.	0.30	.	.	P_2O_5
.	0.00	.	0.69	.	.	.	.	.	CO_2
.	.	.	.	.	.	.	.	.	BaO
.	.	.	.	.	.	.	.	.	ZrO_2
.	.	.	.	.	.	.	.	.	FeS_2
.	.	.	.	.	.	.	.	.	FeS
.	.	.	.	.	.	0.04	.	.	Cl
.	.	.	.	0.03	.	.	.	.	S
.	0.43	.	.	.	.	.	.	.	SO_3
.	.	.	0.12	.	.	.	.	.	SO_2
100.10	99.40	100.45	100.23	101.38	100.12	99.98	100.86	99.50	Sum
250	265	239	166	162	120	118	118	101.8	*si*
2.8	n.d.	0.2	2.5	1.3	2.2	5.4	2.7	5.3	*ti*
0.3	0.3	1.8 (?)	0.3	0.1	n.d.	0.3	—	—	*p*
$42\frac{1}{2}$	$41\frac{1}{2}$	$40\frac{1}{2}$	$32\frac{1}{2}$	$29\frac{1}{2}$	$22\frac{1}{2}$	$17\frac{1}{2}$	19.7	15	*al*
$12\frac{1}{2}$	19	$13\frac{1}{2}$	31	$34\frac{1}{2}$	50	$48\frac{1}{2}$	48.6	59	*fm*
$3\frac{1}{2}$	$3\frac{1}{2}$	13	$20\frac{1}{2}$	21	20	28	25.4	23.3	*c*
$41\frac{1}{2}$	36	33	16	$15\frac{1}{2}$	$7\frac{1}{2}$	6	6.3	2.7	*alk*
0.36	0.55	0.61	0.27	0.30	0.26	0.10	0.09	0.22	*k*
0.10	0.18	0.04	0.52	0.53	0.49	0.53	0.60	0.39	*mg*

30. *Essexite* (Essex-Co., Massachusetts)

	Wt.-% calc.
Hornblende ⎫	
Biotite ⎬	39
Diopside + Aegirine augite ⎭	
(Na-Fe-bearing Augite)	
Plagioclase $Ab_{50}An_{50}$	30
Microperthite + Natron-	12
microcline $Or_{40}Ab_{60}$	
Nepheline ± Analcime	10
Sphene, Apatite, Ore	9

31. *Sommaite* (Somma, Vesuv)

	Vol.-% calc.
Sanidine	31
Augite	28
Plagioclase zoned An_{70}—An_{60}	25
Leucite	9
Olivine ± Biotite	4
Apatite, Ore	3

32. *Ijolite* (Iivaara, N-Finland)

	Wt.-% calc.
Nepheline	52
Aegirine augite (Na-Fe-bearing Augite)	39
Apatite	5
Sphene, Calcite, Iivaarite (like melanite a Ti-bearing Ca-Fe-garnet)	4

33. *Missourite* (Shonkin-Creek, Montana)

	Wt.-% calc.
Diopside (aegirine- and Ti-bearing)	50
Leucite	16
Olivine	15
Analcime + Zeolites	8
Biotite	6
Ore, Apatite	5

Intrusive rocks with feldspathoids or almost only dark minerals

	28. Foyaite	29. Leucite-syenite	30. Essexite	31. Sommaite	32. Ijolite	33. Missourite	34. Jacupi-rangite	35. Horn-blendite	36. Dunite
SiO_2	55.22	54.62	46.99	51.65	43.70	46.06	38.38	44.78	38.82
TiO_2	0.59	Tr.	2.92	1.58	0.89	0.73	4.32	0.74	0.00
Al_2O_3	22.59	22.85	17.94	17.50	19.77	10.01	6.15	9.38	2.24
Fe_2O_3	1.14	1.51	2.56	0.93	3.35	3.17	11.70	4.51	3.04
FeO	1.17	1.08	7.56	6.23	3.47	5.61	8.14	7.70	4.90
MnO	0.13	n.d.	Tr.	n.d.	Tr.	Tr.	0.16	1.90	0.28
MgO	0.28	0.36	3.22	4.24	3.94	14.74	11.47	16.85	44.28
CaO	2.12	3.00	7.85	9.72	10.30	10.55	18.60	10.85	0.00
Na_2O	8.76	5.25	6.35	2.38	9.78	1.31	0.78	2.24	0.20
K_2O	5.59	11.19	2.62	4.90	2.87	5.14	0.13	0.20	n.d.
H_2O^+	1.77	0.36	0.65	1.38	0.89	1.44	0.54	0.25	5.68
H_2O^-	0.39	.	.	.	.	.	0.18	0.08	.
P_2O_5	0.00	0.10	0.94	0.41	1.34	0.21	0.17	0.00	n.d.
CO_2	.	.	.	.	.	.	0.00	0.00	0.60
BaO	.	.	0.00	.	.	0.32	.	0.00	.
SrO	.	.	.	.	.	0.20	.	.	.
Cr_2O_3	.	.	.	.	.	.	.	0.24	0.28
ZrO_2	.	.	.	.	.	.	.	0.00	.
Cl	0.43	.	.	.	.	0.03	.	.	.
S	.	.	.	.	.	.	.	0.29	.
SO_3	0.09	.	.	.	.	0.05	.	.	.
Sum	100.27	100.32	99.60	100.92	100.30	99.57	100.72	100.17[a]	100.32
si	185	173	118	134	96	90	67	80	52
ti	1.5	Tr.	5.5	3.1	1.5	1.1	5.7	1.0	0.0
p	0.0	0.1	1.0	0.5	1.2	0.2	0.1	0.0	n.d.
al	$44\frac{1}{2}$	43	$26\frac{1}{2}$	27	$25\frac{1}{2}$	$11\frac{1}{2}$	6	10	$1\frac{1}{2}$
fm	8	8	33	32	25	57	$57\frac{1}{2}$	$65\frac{1}{2}$	98
c	$7\frac{1}{2}$	10	21	27	$24\frac{1}{2}$	$22\frac{1}{2}$	35	$20\frac{1}{2}$	0
alk	40	39	$19\frac{1}{2}$	14	25	9	$1\frac{1}{2}$	4	$\frac{1}{2}$
k	0.30	0.58	0.22	0.58	0.16	0.72	0.10	0.05	0.0(?)
mg	0.18	0.21	0.37	0.51	0.52	0.76	0.52	0.71	0.91

[a] Includes 0.16 CuO, 0.00 NiO, 0.00 Li_2O.

34. *Jacupirangite* (Jacupiranga, S. Paulo), Brazil.)

	Wt.-% calc.
Titanaugite + green Augite	80
Titanomagnetite	19
Nepheline, Apatite	1
Perowskite	±

36. *Dunite* (Bowen-Mtn., New Zealand)

	Wt.-% calc.
Olivine $Fo_{90}Fa_{10}$	97
Magnetite, Chromite	3
Picotite (Cr-bear., spinel), Sulfides	
sec.: Carbonate, Antigorite	

35. *Hornblendite* (Maracas, Bahia, Brazil.)

	Wt.-% meas.
Hornblende	91
Olivine	4
Magnetite	5

Extrusive rocks with feldspathoids or almost only dark minerals

	37. Phonolite	38. Leucite-phonolite	39. Nepheline-tephrite	40. Leucite-tephrite	41. Nephelinite	42. Olivine-Leucitite	43. Picrite
SiO_2	56.56	55.87	46.26	48.74	40.99	42.20	40.02
TiO_2	0.23	0.79	1.69	1.04	2.41	2.44	0.59
Al_2O_3	21.31	20.85	18.98	16.38	16.50	12.13	8.32
Fe_2O_3	1.03	2.34	7.39	1.64	10.62	7.27	1.51
FeO	1.79	1.10	3.27	5.30	n.d.	4.62	11.14
MnO	0.11	n.d.	n.d.	0.14	0.35	n.d.	0.85
MgO	0.15	0.48	3.09	7.07	3.29	9.24	27.63
CaO	1.24	3.07	10.59	12.19	12.63	14.32	4.04
Na_2O	9.47	4.81	5.51	2.01	5.95	2.75	0.65
K_2O	5.25	10.49	1.99	4.95	2.36	3.69	0.32
H_2O^+	0.25	0.34	0.96	0.55	2.63	0.66	4.30
H_2O^-	1.70	.	.	0.16	.	.	0.70
P_2O_5	0.06	0.11	0.49	0.18	0.89	0.80	n.d.
CO_2	0.24	0.00	.	.	.	.	.
BaO	.	0.09	.	.	.	.	.
ZrO_2	.	0.07	.	.	.	.	.
Cr_2O_3	.	.	.	.	.	.	Tr.
Cl	0.35	.	.	0.07	0.36	.	.
S	0.26	.	.	.	.	0.04	.
SO_3	.	0.14	.	.	0.64	.	.
FeS_2	.	.	.	.	.	.	0.51
Sum	100.00	100.55	100.22	100.42	99.62	100.16	100.58
si	195	184	110	110	94	83	64
ti	0.6	2.0	3.0	1.8	4.1	3.6	0.7
p	0.1	0.2	0.6	0.2	0.9	0.7	n.d.
al	43½	40½	26½	22	22	14	7½
fm	9	11	30½	37	30½	46	84
c	4½	11	27	29½	31	30	7
alk	43	37½	16	11½	16½	10	1½
k	0.27	0.59	0.19	0.62	0.21	0.47	0.23
mg	0.09	0.21	0.36	0.65	0.37	0.60	0.79

d) Extrusive Rocks with Feldspathoids or almost only Dark Minerals

37. *Phonolite* (Bilin, Czechoslovakia)

	Wt.-% calc.
Natronsanidine Or$_{47}$Ab$_{53}$ (in part inclus.)	66
Nepheline	18
Aegirine diopside (Na-Fe-bear. Diopside)	8
Sodalite + Hauyine	7
Sphene, Apatite	1

38. *Leucite phonolite* (Braccianer Lake, nw. Rome)

	Vol.-% meas.
Natronsanidine Or$_{60}$Ab$_{40}$	71
Leucite (incl. 10 inclus.)	14
Nepheline + Hauyine	6
Aegirine augite (Na-Fe-bear. Augite) (incl. 2 inclus.)	6
Ore, Apatite	3

39. *Nepheline tephrite* (Frenzelberg, Lausitz)

	Wt.-% calc.
Plagioclase An$_{60}$—An$_{45}$ zoned (Ab$_{45}$An$_{50}$Or$_{05}$)	42
Titanaugite (in part inclus.)	30
basalt. Hornblende-inclus. (resorbed)	±
Nepheline ± Hauyine	15
Ore	6
Natronsanidine	4
Apatite	3

40. *Leucite tephrite* (Vesuv, Italy)

	Vol.-% meas.
Plagioclase An$_{70}$	35
Leucite	27
Pyroxene (in part inclus.)	27
Olivine inclus.	5
Nepheline, Sodalite	3
Ore, Apatite	3

41. *Nephelinite* (Hochstradener Kogel, Steiermark)

	Wt.-% calc.
Titanaugite (rare inclus.)	44
Nepheline	23
Hauyine	14
Ore ± Olivine	7
Apatite	2
Glass (corr. to Plagioclase + Sanidine + Nepheline)	10

42. *Olivine leucitite* (Killerlopf, Südeifel)

	Wt.-% meas.
Titanaugite (incl. 16 inclus.)	53
Leucite	24
Nepheline + Sodalite	8
Olivine (from 6 inclus.)	7
Ore, Biotite, Apatite	8

43. *Picrite* (Wommelshausen, Hessen)

	Wt.-% calc.
Olivine (serpentinized)	51
Augite (chloritized)	37
Hornblende, Biotite	±
Plagioclase Ab$_{12}$An$_{88}$	8
Ore, Apatite, Sulf., Picotite (Cr-bear. Spinel)	4

e) Lamprophyres

44. *Minette* (Weißenburg, Alsace)

	Vol.-% meas.
Orthoclase	36
Plagioclase few Inclus. An$_{60}$ prepond. Groundm. An$_{30}$	25
Biotite	12
Diopside (incl. 15 inclus.)	20
Olivine inclus. (serpentined) Ore, Apatite, Sphene	7

45. *Kersantite* (Brest, Brittany)

	Vol.-% meas.
Plagioclase Ab$_{70}$An$_{25}$Or$_{05}$	53
Biotite (incip. chloritization)	24
Pyroxene (compl. chloritized)	8
Quartz (primar, as wedges and in sheaves)	9
Calcite (primar. as wedges and in sheaves)	4
Ore, Apatite	2

46. *Camptospessartite* (Golenz, Lausitz)

	Vol.-% meas.
Plagioclase zoned An_{45}—An_{27} ($Ab_{58}An_{42}$)	40
Titanaugite	24
basalt. Hornblende	19
Olivine inclus.	9
Ore, Apatite	8

47. *Tinguaite* (Serra do Tinguá, Brazil.)

		Wt.-% calc.
Sanidine, Microcline Perthite, Anorthoclase	} $Or_{65}Ab_{35}$	46
Nepheline		32
Aegirine (Na-Fe-Augite)		21
± Biotite		
Apatite		1

Lamprophyres

	44. Minette	45. Ker- santite	46. Campto- spessartite	47. Tinguaite	48. Leucite- tinguaite	49. Teschenite with Analcime	50. Leucite- mon- chiquite	51. Kim- berlite without feldspar
	without Feldspathoids				with Feldspathoids			
SiO_2	52.70	51.34	42.58	53.10	52.91	41.42	45.53	30.66
TiO_2	1.71	1.40	3.49	n.d.	0.00	3.14	1.50	1.63
Al_2O_3	15.07	14.03	14.68	19.07	19.49	15.07	18.37	2.86
Fe_2O_3	8.41	0.92	5.96	5.57	4.78	6.40	4.85	3.08
FeO	n.d.	5.60	11.29	0.00	2.05	7.93	3.43	5.98
MnO	n.d.	n.d.	0.13	n.d.	0.44	0.20	0.72	0.16
MgO	7.23	10.02	6.32	0.17	0.29	4.82	4.11	31.24
CaO	5.33	6.40	10.10	1.33	2.47	10.16	8.15	10.92
Na_2O	3.12	2.41	3.39	9.41	7.13	4.00	3.93	0.17
K_2O	4.81	2.60	0.64	6.84	7.88	1.98	4.16	1.23
H_2O^+	2.38	2.75	1.55	3.98	1.19	2.73	2.62	3.01
H_2O^-	.	0.65	.	.	.	0.27	1.68	0.93
P_2O_5	Tr.	0.47	0.22	n.d.	Tr.	1.57	0.86	1.64
CO_2	n.d.	1.70	.	0.10	.	.	1.54	6.00
BaO	.	.	.	.	.	.	.	0.14
SrO	.	.	.	.	0.09	.	.	0.08
Rare Earths	.	.	.	.	0.48	.	.	.
NiO	.	.	.	.	.	.	.	0.13
V_2O_3	.	.	.	.	.	.	.	0.02
Cr_2O_3	.	.	.	.	.	.	.	0.10
F	.	.	.	.	.	0.10	.	0.04
Cl	.	.	.	.	0.53	0.05	.	0.04
S	.	.	.	.	0.52	0.37	.	0.04
Sum	100.76	100.29	100.35	99.57	100.25[a]	100.21	101.45	100.10[a]
si	139	130	91	174	165	95	116	45
ti	3.4	2.7	5.6	n.d.	0.0	5.4	2.9	1.8
p	n.d.	0.5	0.2	n.d.	Tr.	1.5	0.9	1.0
al	$23\frac{1}{2}$	21	$18\frac{1}{2}$	37	$35\frac{1}{2}$	$20\frac{1}{2}$	27	$2\frac{1}{2}$
fm	$45\frac{1}{2}$	$51\frac{1}{2}$	$50\frac{1}{2}$	$14\frac{1}{2}$	19	43	34	79
c	15	$17\frac{1}{2}$	23	$4\frac{1}{2}$	$8\frac{1}{2}$	25	22	17
alk	16	10	8	44	37	$11\frac{1}{2}$	17	$1\frac{1}{2}$
k	0.51	0.41	0.11	0.32	0.42	0.25	0.42	0.83
mg	0.63	0.74	0.40	0.06	0.07	0.38	0.47	0.86

[a] With Tr. Li_2O.

48. *Leucite tinguaite* (Magnet-Cove, Arkansas)

	Wt.-% calc.
Natronsanidine	30
Pseudoleucite	25
Nepheline	17
Aegirine diopside (Na-Fe-bear. Diopside)	15
Sodalite	10
Ore, Apatite	3
Biotite, Melanite (Ti-bear. Ca-Fe-Garnet)	±

49. *Teschenite with Analcime* (Paskau, west Teschen, Czechoslov.)

	Wt.-% calc.
Titanaugite with aegirine bearing border	
Barkevikite (Alkalihornblende)	43
± Biotite	
Plagioclase zoned An_{60}—An_{45}	27
Analcime	16
Ore	10
Apatite, Sulfides	4

50. *Leucite monchiquite* (Neschwitz, Czechoslov.)

	Vol.-% meas.
Titanaugite (-inclus.)	31
Leucite (-inclus.)	7
Ore (-inclus.)	5
Plagioclase An_{50} (-inclus.)	2
Glass with Microlites of Titanaugite, basalt. Hornblende, Plagioclase, Ore, Apatite	55

51. *Kimberlite* (Kimberley, South Africa)

	Wt.-% calc.
Olivine $Fo_{89}Fa_{11}$ (in part inclus.)	60
Calcite (from Melilite)	14
Phlogopite (in part inclus.)	13
Pyrope (-inclus.)	
Diopside (-inclus.)	6
Apatite, Ore, Perowskite	7

2. Sedimentary Rocks

a) Sandstones and Graywackes

1. Mineral composition

1. *Fine-grained Lower Dev. sandstone*, Schalker Layer, Rammelsberg, underground. (After GÖRZ, 1962)

	Vol.-% obs.
Quartz	80.7
Mica	16.7
Carbonate	2.5
Ore	0.1
	100.0

2.—4. *Kulm graywacke*, Harz. (After MATTIAT, 1960)

	Vol.-% obs.		
	coarse grain 2	med. grain 3	fine-grain 4
Quartz	25.7	31.6	26.2
Feldspar	10.4	23.1	20.4
Chlorite	7.5	9.6	26.1
Mica	1.0	2.6	2.1
Calcite	4.4	0.0	0.0
Rock frag.	50.0	31	23
Residue	1.0	2.1	2.2
	100.0	100.0	100.0

5. *Middle Buntsandstein*, Hauptgervillienlager, Salzdetfurth. (After OKRAJEK, 1965)

	Wt.-% obs.
Quartz	71.3
Oligoclase	9.7
Alkalifeldspar	13.8
Muscovite	2.5
Chlorite	2.3
Residue	0.4
	100.0

6. *Tert. sandstone*, boring Neusiedl. (After BOLTER, 1960 unpubl.)

	Wt.-% obs.
Quartz	82.9
Na-Feldspar	1.4
K-Feldspar	2.0
Ca-Feldspar	0.2
Biotite	0.7
Muscovite	0.8
Illite	3.8
Vermiculite	4.9
Chamosite	2.3
Siderite	0.2
Apatite	0.1
Pyrite	0.1
TiO_2-Zircon	0.6
	100.0

2. Chemical analyses

	1. Lower Devon.	2. Coarse	3. Med.	4. Fine	5. Bund- sandstein	6. Tertiary sandstone
			Kulm graywacke			
SiO_2	87.01	77.2	69.7	65.2	87.6	90.32
TiO_2	0.48	0.4	0.9	0.9	0.1	0.50
Al_2O_3	6.80	9.6	14.4	16.6	6.3	3.27
Fe_2O_3	0.55	0.9	2.6	3.3	0.4	1.28
FeO	0.44	1.5	1.0	1.6	0.06	1.08
MnO	0.14	0.1	0.1	0.1	0.02	—
MgO	0.47	1.5	1.5	1.6	0.5	1.41
CaO	0.30	1.9	1.4	0.6	0.7	0.12
Na_2O	0.05	2.7	3.5	3.3	1.6	0.17
K_2O	1.77	1.1	1.8	2.5	2.0	0.80
H_2O^+	0.90	2.3	2.8	3.2	0.6	1.10
H_2O^-	0.30	0.1	0.3	0.7	—	—
P_2O_5	0.09	0.2	0.2	0.3	0.1	0.04
CO_2	0.70	1.3	0.2	—	C: 0.03	0.1
	100.00	100.8	100.4	99.9	100.01	100.19

All analyses from: Beiträge zur Mineralogie etc.

b) Clays and Shales

1. Mineral composition

1., 2. *Fireclay, Upper Miocene, Freshwater molass* (after KÖSTER and NORDMEIER, 1961), Rohrhof, Oberpfalz

	Wt.-% calc.	
	1.	2.
Quartz	17.3	4.6
Kaolinite	60.6	88.5
Muscovite	18.3	4.5
Hematite	2.4	1.7
Rutile	1.4	0.7
	100.0	100.0

3. *Hagenowi-clay*, Lias α Göttingen. (After KHARKWAL, 1959)

	Vol.-% obs.
Quartz	17.0
Muscovite-Illite	30.5
Feldspar	0.3
Mix-layed Illite-Montmor.	17.1
Chlorite	7.6
Kaolinite	6.4
Aggregate (Quartz + Illite)	18.6
Hematite?	1.7
Carbonate	0.7
	99.9

4a and b. *Buntsandstein-clay*, Main Gervillien zone, well boring Hämelwald Z 1. (After OKRAJEK, 1965)

	Wt.-%	
	obs. 4.a	calc. 4.b
Quartz	23.7	30.1
Oligoclase	11.6	9.2
Alkalifeldspar	7.8	6.2
Muscovite	36.2	36.7
Chlorite	17.3	14.9
Hematite	0.7	0.7
Dolomite	1.0	1.0
Anhydrite	0.5	0.5
Anatase, Rutile	0.7	0.2
Apatite	0.4	0.4
C	0.1	0.1
	100.0	100.0

5. *Calcareous shale*, Mid-devonian (Eifel), Königsee by Goslar. (After KNOKE, 1966)

	Wt.-% obs.
Quartz	28.0
Plagioclase An_{10-15}	5.3
K-Feldspar	1.8
Chlorite	27.2
Muscovite-Illite	25.4
Calcite	12.3
	100.0

2. Chemical analyses

	1.	2.	3. Hagenowi-clay	4. Bunt-sandstein-clay	5. Calcareous shale, Mid-Dev.	6. Calcareous shale, Upper-Dev.
	Fireclay, Upper Miocene, freshwater molass					
SiO_2	51.89	45.75	53.63	58.2	51.79	43.15
TiO_2	1.31	0.64	1.92	0.81	0.70	0.58
Al_2O_3	30.76	35.08	20.11	20.3	15.55	14.58
Fe_2O_3	2.13	1.67	3.16	5.5	0.80	2.11
FeO	—	—	1.46	0.18	4.70	7.49
MnO	—	—	0.0	0.04	0.13	0.71
CaO	—	0.14	2.72	1.2	6.53	9.29
MgO	0.47	0.21	4.82	3.8	4.46	4.10
Na_2O	0.12	0.06	0.25	1.7	0.83	0.14
K_2O	1.97	0.51	3.57	4.9	3.34	3.84
P_2O_5			0.24	0.2	0.17	0.16
H_2O^+			7.10	3.3	3.80	4.09
CO_2			0.21	0.5	5.40	9.3
SO_3			0.75 FeS_2	0.3		
C				0.1	1.50	0.24
Loss on ign.	11.40	16.76				
	100.05	100.82	99.94	101.03	99.70	99.75

Analyses 1 and 2 from: Berichte der Dtsch. Keram. Ges., remain. from: Beiträge zur Mineralogie etc.

6. *Calcareous shale*, Upper-dev. (Wocklum-Dasberg) Junkernberg by Goslar. (After KNOKE, 1966)

	Wt.-% obs.
Quartz	22.1
Plagioclase An_{10-15}	0.8
K-Feldspar	—
Chlorite	21.3
Muscovite-Illite	34.6
Calcite	21.2
	100.0

c) Limestones, Marls, Siliceous Limestones, Dolomite

1. Mineral composition

1. *Limestone lense in Mid-devonian* (Eifel), Königsee by Goslar. (After KNOKE, 1966)

	Wt.-% obs.
Calcite	89.6
Quartz	4.5
Plagioclase An_{10-15}	0.4
K-Feldspar	+
Chlorite	1.5
Muskovite-Illite	4.0
	100.0

2. *Calcareous lense in Upper devonian* (Wocklum-Dasberg), Junkernberg by Goslar. (After KNOKE, 1966)

	Wt.-% obs.
Calcite	72.4
Quartz	12.3
Plagioclase An_{10-15}	4.5
K-Feldspar	+
Chlorite	5.8
Muscovite-Illite	5.0
	100.0

3. *Lower Muschelkalk*, Plesse by Göttingen. (After FÜCHTBAUER, 1950)

	Wt.-% obs.
Calcite	92.0
Quartz	1.15
Na-Feldspar	0.4
K-Feldspar	0.45
Illite	0.6
	100.0

4. *Clay-marl from Upper Muschelkalk* (mo) Hainberg by Göttingen. (After FÜCHT-BAUER, 1950)

	Wt.-% obs.
Calcite	26.6
Quartz	6.2
Na-Feldspar	3.5
K-Feldspar	1.5
Illite	62.7
FeOOH	0.4
	100.9

5. *Siliceous limestone*, Kulm, Wallau. (After HOSS, 1957)

	Wt.-% calc.
Calcite	64.5
Quartz	28.4
$MnCO_3$	0.5
Albite	1.7
Illite	4.0
Remainder	0.9
	100.0

6. *Mottled marl* (Oberalb Wrisbergholzen). (After KNOCKE, 1967)

	Wt.-% obs.	calc.
Calcite	38	38.9
Siliceous substance	52	38.3
Muscovite-Illite	5	9.5
Montmorillonite	5	6.8
Chlorite	+	2.2
Glauconite	+	1.5
Plagioclase	+	0.7
K-Feldspar	+	0.4
Heavy minerals	+	0.5
Limonite	+	1.1
Org. substance	+	0.1
	100.0	100.0

7. *Zechsteindolomite* (Werra), Bad Lauterberg. (After SMYKATZ-KLOSS, 1966)

	Wt.-% obs.
Dolomite	89.8
Calcite	5.1
Quartz	1.0
Illite	1.0
Chlorite	0.2
Montmorillonite	0.1
Limonite	0.1
Feldspar	0.2
Fluorite	1.5
	99.0

8. *Zechstein-Main dolomite*, boring Herste. (After SMYKATZ-KLOSS, 1966)

	Wt.-% obs.
Dolomite	53.60
Calcite	6.11
Anhydrite	37.40
Gypsum	0.25
Halite	1.45
Quartz	0.3
Muscovite	0.27
Pyrite	0.17
Feldspar	0.04
Fluorite	0.03
	99.62

9. *"Steinmergel" Middle Keuper*, Elkershausen by Göttingen. (After ECHLE, 1960)

	Vol.-% obs.
Dolomite	62
Quartz	26
Plagioclase	2
K-Feldspar	+
Illite	3
Corrensite	6
Chlorite	1
	100

2. Chemical analyses

	1.	2.	3. Mussel-kalk	4. Clay marl	5.	6.	7.	8.	9. "Stein-mergel"
	Devonian lime-stone				Siliceous lime-stone		Dolomite		
SiO_2	6.90	18.19	4.41	37.64	30.9	47.27			27.7
TiO_2	0.07	0.17	0.02	0.09	0.08	0.26			0.1
Al_2O_3	1.47	3.81	1.75	15.10	1.80	5.44			2.7
Fe_2O_3	0.36	0.50	0.38	4.36	0.60	1.60			0.6
FeO	0.80	1.44	0.28	0.95	—	0.17			0.2
MnO	0.36	0.22	0.02	0.04	0.33	0.03			0.2
CaO	47.41	38.86	50.26	14.34	35.70	21.20	30.18	35.86	18.6
MgO	1.84	2.08	0.97	3.13	Tr.	1.37	19.50	12.20	18.1
Na_2O	0.07	0.58	0.09	0.4	0.2	0.18			0.2
K_2O	0.40	0.58	0.45	3.16	0.4	1.25			0.3
P_2O_5	0.03	0.07	0.15	0.04	0.14	0.06			0.05
CO_2	39.30	31.80	40.3	11.75	28.0	16.94	45.83	27.11	29.3
Cl	—	—	0.3	0.13				NaCl 1.45	—
SO_4	—	—	Tr.	Tr.				22.14	
H_2O^-			0.36	4.15	0.1	2.10			—
H_2O^+	0.41	0.91	—	—	0.5	1.30			
C	0.32	1.08	—	—	0.6	0.24	4.1[a]	0.85[a]	2.4
Loss on ign.	—	—	0.5	5.0	—	—			
	99.74	100.29	99.97	100.28	99.35	99.41	99.61	99.66	100.45

All analyses from: Beiträge zur Mineralogie etc.

[a] Acid insoluble residue.

d) Siliceous Rocks, Tuffites, Iron Ores

1. Mineral composition

1.—3. *Kulm lydite*, Harz. (After Hoss, 1957)

	Wt.-% calc.		
	1.	2.	3.
Albite	1.1	2.8	5.0
Chlorite	3.5	1.5	2.7
Illite	8.2	10.6	22.0
Quartz	84.5	82.2	66.9
Residue	2.7	2.9	3.4
	100	100	100

4. *Siliceous rock* in mottled marl (Oberalb), Hohe Schanze by Freden. (After KNOKE, 1967)

	Wt.-%	
	obs.	calc.
Calcite	+	0.1
Siliceous substance	86	81.4
Muscovite-Illite	8	8.1
Montmorillonite	3	3.3
Chlorite	1	1.4
Glauconite	2	1.4
Plagioclase	+	1.1
Heavy mineral	+	0.4
Limonite	+	2.7
Org. Substance	+	0.1
	100	100

5., 6. *Tuffites* (Adinole) in Kulm (after Hoss, 1957); 5 *Eifa* (rhein. Schiefergebirge), 6 Lerbach (Harz)

	Wt.-% calc.	
	5.	6.
Albite	58.0	48.5
Quartz	31.5	36.0
Chlorite	abs.	6.5
Biotite	2.5	abs.
Illite	4.0	3.0
Calcite	2.0	abs.
Dolomite	abs.	5.0
Residue	2.0	1.0
	100	100

7. *Chamosite iron ore*, Lias, Echte. (After HARDER, 1951)

	Wt.-% calc.
Calcite	16.12
Siderite	3.53
Pyrite	0.41
Chamosite	72.11
Apatite	3.82
Gypsum	3.16
"Humus" (C × 1.7)	0.58
	99.73

8. *Hematite iron ore*, Lias, Markoldendorf.
(after HARDER, 1951)

	Wt.-% calc.
Calcite	32.09
Siderite	1.25
Pyrite	0.60
Iron silicate	~ 4.00
Hematite	~54.00
Apatite	5.53
Gypsum	2.27
"Humus" (C × 1.7)	0.56
	100.00

2. Chemical Analyses

	1.	2.	3.	4.	5.	6.	7.	8.
	Kulm lydite			Chert, mottled marl	Tuffite		Lias, Iron ore	
SiO_2	90.60	89.6	80.8	86.38	73.7	71.8	21.78	13.36
TiO_2	0.05	0.10	0.16	0.23	0.10	0.10	0.53	0.45
Al_2O_3	4.0	4.8	9.7	4.25	13.0	11.4	10.67	7.89
Fe_2O_3	1.8	1.6	2.9	2.87	1.79	0.5	6.2	29.62
FeO	n.d.	n.d.	n.d.	0.13	n.d.	1.3	22.7	2.69
MnO	0.6	0.10	0.16	0.08	0.15	0.48	0.08	0.33
CaO	0.4	0.2	0.1	0.24	0.86	1.5	12.25	21.90
MgO	1.0	0.4	0.8	0.62	0.36	2.2	3.61	0.93
Na_2O	0.1	0.3	0.5	0.17	6.8	5.5	0.079	0.014
K_2O	0.6	0.8	1.8	1.05	0.5	0.6	0.089	0.50
P_2O_5	0.06	0.04	0.05	0.07	0.03	0.07	1.62	2.35
CO_2	n.d.	n.d.	n.d.	0.07	0.7	2.3	8.45	14.59
H_2O^+	1.3	2.3	2.8	1.11	0.7	2.0	8.36	1.48
H_2O^-	0.1	0.1	0.4	2.11	0.02	0.02	1.01	1.85
C	0.06	0.13	0.05	0.14	0.5	Tr.	0.50	0.33
SO_3							1.47	1.05
$S^=$							0.22	0.32
V_2O_3							0.23	0.28
B_2O_5							0.05	
CO							0.002	
NiO							0.06	
	100.67	100.47	100.22	99.52	99.21	99.77	99.96	99.93

All analyses from: Beiträge zur Mineralogie etc.

3. Metamorphic Rocks

a) Diagenetic and Regional Metamorphic Rocks

1. Mineral composition

1. *Diagenite*, Oberkreide (Campan), Limestone by Hannover (after SCHÖNER, 1959)

	Wt.-% obs.
Calcite	81.2
Quartz	3.1
Illite	8.5
Montmorillonite	5.0
Heulandite	1.7
Residue	0.5
	100.0

2. *Greenschist facies*, Greenschist, Furulund, Sulitelma, Norway (after ESKOLA, 1939)

	Wt.-% calc.
Quartz	1.1
Albite	39.9
Chlorite	29.4
Epidote	23.0
Actinolite Hornblende	3.5
Calcite et al.	2.6
	99.5

3. *Greenschist facies*, "Prasinite", Sp. "Ovardite" (Greenschist), Grand Paradise. (after MICHEL, 1953)

	Wt.-% obs.
Quartz	5.5
Albite (An$_0$)	35
Chlorite	25
Epidote ⎫ Clinozoisite ⎬ Zoisite ⎭	18
Actinolite	9
Residue	7.5
	100.0

4. *Glaucophane-Lawsonite facies*, Metabasalt. (after COLEMAN a. LEE, 1963), Ward Creek, north California

	Wt.-% obs.
Glaucophane	56.3
Lawsonite	34.0
Pumpellyite	1.2
Muscovite	0.3
Sphene	5.2
Chlorite	0.5
CaCO$_3$	2.5
	100.0

5. *Glaucophane-Lawsonite facies*, Metaschist. (after COLEMAN a. LEE, 1963) Ward Creek, north California

	Wt.-% obs.
Crossite-Riebeckite	48.4
Muscovite	23.9
Quartz	26.6
Sphene	1.1
	100

6. *Glaucophane-Lawsonite facies*, Metahornstone. (after COLEMAN a. LEE, 1963) Ward Creek, north California

	Wt.-% obs.
Crossite-Riebeckite	3.0
Stilpnomelane	17.6
Orthoamphibole	14.6
Garnet	5.8
Quartz	57.9
Pyrite	1.3
	100

7. *Albite-Epidote-Amphibolite facies*, Epidote amphibolite, Carlotta, Sulitelma, Norway. (after ESKOLA, 1939)

	Wt.-% obs.
Albite (An$_9$)	42.8
Hornblende	42.2
Clinozoisite	12.3
Chlorite	2.9
Rutile et al.	0.5
	100.7

8. *Amphibolite facies*, Amphibolite, Kisko, Finland. (after ESKOLA, 1939)

	Wt.-% obs.
Plagioclase	26.5
Hornblende	71.5
Quartz	2.0
	100.0

9. *Amphibolite facies*, Staurolite-Garnet-Plagioclase-Gneiss, Spessart. (after MATTHES, 1954)

	Vol.-% obs.
Quartz	30.0
Plagioclase (An$_{20-32}$)	26.4
Muscovite	13.2
Biotite	21.3
Staurolite	9.1
Almandine garnet	1.3
Accessories	2.1
	103.4

10. *Amphibolite facies*, schistose zone in feldspar schist, Dutches County, N.Y. (after BARTH, 1936)

	Wt.-% calc.
Quartz	2.5
Plagioclase (An$_{50}$)	30.7
Biotite[1]	48.2
Almandine garnet	14.6
Kyanite	3.3
Apatite	0.3
	99.6

[1] FeO/MgO = 1.26.

11. *Amphibolite facies*, Sillimanite bearing biotite schist, Iron County, Michigan. (after JAMES, 1955)

	Wt.-% obs.
Quartz	35.9
Biotite	40.7
Muscovite	7.6
Plagioclase (An$_{15}$)	9.4
Garnet	3.0
Staurolite	0.3
Sillimanite	3.1
	100.0

12. *Granulite facies*, Norite-Granulite, Här-
käselkä, Lappland. (after ESKOLA, 1939)

	Wt.-% obs.
Quartz	2.5
K-Feldspar	7.1
Plagioclase	49.5
Hypersthene	25.3
Diopside	9.6
Iron ore, et al.	4.9
	98.9

14. *Eclogite facies*, Eclogite, Glenelq, Scotland. (after YODER a. TILLEY, 1962)

	Wt.-% calc.
Pyroxene[a]	53.6
Garnet[b]	30.2
Quartz	8.1
Hornblende, Rutile et al.	8.1

[a] Diopside	49	[b] Almandine	51.2
Hedenbergite	13	Pyrope	21.9
Tschermaks Mol.	8	Spessartite	1.4
Jadeite + Acmite	30	Grossular	22.7
		Andradite	2.8

13. *Granulite facies*, Paragneiss, Colton N.Y.
(after ENGEL a. ENGEL, 1958 and 1960)

	Vol.-% obs.
Quartz	22.58
K-Feldspar	3.08
Plagioclase (An$_{64}$)	46.83
Biotite	15.66
Garnet	9.70
Chlorite	0.76
Ore (mainly Magnetite)	0.08
Zircon	Tr.
Apatite	Tr.
Sericite	0.51
Residue	0.80
	100.0

15. *Eclogite facies*, Kyanite-Eclogite, Silber-
bach, Fichtelgebirge. (after YODER a.
TILLEY, 1962)

	Wt.-% calc.
Omphacite[a]	58.5
Kyanite	18
Garnet[b]	18
Quartz	4
Pyrrhotite	0.9
Residue	0.6

[a] Diopside	70	[b] Almandine	33.9
Hedenbergite	4	Pyrope	43.9
Tschermaks Mol.	6	Spessartite	1.2
Jadeite + Acmite	20	Grossular	20.6
		Andradite	0.4

b) Metasomatically Altered Rocks

16. Sericitized Granodiorite. (after LIND-
GREN, 1928)

	Wt.-% calc.
Quartz	25.00
Sericite	61.46
CaCO$_3$	7.23
MgCO$_3$	2.70
FeCO$_3$	0.58
Rutile	0.25
Pyrite	2.87
Apatite	0.46
	100.55

17. *Fluorite-Skarn*, Huddersfield Twp.,
Quebec. (after SHAW, 1963)

	Wt.-% obs.
Calcite	45—50
Fluorite	25
Apatite	10
Pyroxene + Mica	7
Scapolite	4
Quartz, Sphene, Pyrite, Uranothorite	Tr.

2. Chemical Analyses of Rocks of Diagenesis, Regional Metamorphism, and Metasomatism

	1. Diagenite	2. Greenschist facies	3.	4. Metabasalt	5. Metaschist	6. Meta- hornstone
				Glaucophane-Lawsonite facies		
SiO_2	11.8	49.22	47.50	46.5	69.3	85.8
TiO_2	0.15	0.18	2.25	1.2	0.41	0.06
Al_2O_3	3.4	18.56	18.79	13.8	12.0	1.1
Fe_2O_3	0.9	2.22	4.65	1.3	1.1	3.3
FeO	n.d.	5.35	6.30	7.6	3.9	3.5
MnO	0.01	0.12	0.10	0.20	0.06	0.65
CaO	45.6	7.17	7.68	12.1	0.67	0.22
MgO	0.3	8.15	5.92	7.4	4.2	0.16
Na_2O	0.07	4.65	3.76	3.1	2.2	0.05
K_2O	0.6	0.10	0.30	0.18	3.3	0.05
P_2O_5	0.01	n.d.	0.46	0.16	0.14	0.22
CO_2	35.7	0.43	1.50	2.6	< 0.05	< 0.05
H_2O^+	1.3	3.15	1.12	3.6	2.1	0.82
H_2O^-	—	—	—	0.16	0.09	0.18
S^{--}	0.07	0.02	—	0.09 FeS_2	<0.05	4.2
	99.91	99.32	100.33	99.99	99.57	100.36

	7. Albite- Epidote- Amphi- bolite	8. Amphi- bolite	9. Staurolite- Garnet- Plagioclase- gneiss	10. Schistose Zone in Feldspar- schist	11. Sillimanite- bearing Biotite- schist
SiO_2	52.45	49.73	58.71	45.10	55.90
TiO_2	0.38	0.56	0.83	1.42	0.85
Al_2O_3	17.23	16.05	20.78	22.18	19.31
Fe_2O_3	4.36	2.44	4.24	0.99	0.95
FeO	4.96	7.96	3.46	10.97	7.83
MnO	0.08	0.20	0.18	0.74	0.04
CaO	8.55	10.22	1.15	4.10	1.17
MgO	6.71	7.84	2.56	5.79	4.01
Na_2O	4.94	2.99	1.65	2.15	1.73
K_2O	0.39	0.61	4.05	4.28	4.91
P_2O_5	Tr.	0.12	0.24	0.11	0.18
CO_2	—	—	0.0	—	0.0
F	—	—			
S	0.04			n.d.	
H_2O^+	0.69	1.03	1.70	1.29	2.77
H_2O^-				0.08	0.19
	100.78	99.75	99.55	99.20	99.84

	12. Norite-granulite	13. Paragneiss	14. Eclogite	15. Kyanite-eclogite	16. Sericitized Granodiorite
SiO_2	52.03	61.27	50.05	50.24	56.25
TiO_2	2.27	0.78	1.55	0.26	0.25
Al_2O_3	16.39	17.94	13.37	19.98	17.65
Fe_2O_3	0.82	0.67	3.71	1.44	0.76
FeO	9.13	6.81	10.39	3.12	2.64
MnO	0.17	0.05	0.25	0.10	0.0
CaO	8.78	3.29	11.00	12.95	4.46
MgO	7.04	3.01	6.49	9.84	1.69
Na_2O	2.14	3.51	2.38	1.93	0.30
K_2O	1.21	1.93	0.36	0.09	6.01
P_2O_5	0.06	0.56	0.12	0.02	0.21
CO_2	—	—	0.14	—	4.82
F	—	0.04	—	—	
S	0.04	—	0.08	0.35	2.87 FeS_2
H_2O^+			0.39	0.31	2.36
H_2O^-	0.35	n.d.	0.06	0.0	0.30
Cr_2O_3	0.10		0	n.d.	
BaO	0.03		0	n.d.	0.03
	100.51	99.86	100.34	100.63	99.35
			0.03 for $O = S$	0.15 for $O = S$	
			100.31	100.48	

Analyses 1: Beiträge z. Min. etc. 2, 7, 8, 12: BARTH, CORRENS, ESKOLA. 3: Science de la Terre (Nancy). 4, 5, 6, 14, 15: Journ. of Petrology. 9: Abh. Hess. Landesamt Bodenforsch. 10, 11, 13: Bull. Geol. Soc. Am. 16: LINDGREN, Mineral Deposits. 17: Canad. Mineralogist.

c) Contact Metamorphic Rocks (after V. M. Goldschmidt, 1911; see also p. 301—303)

1. Mineral composition

18. *Pyroxene-Hornfels, Class 1*

	Wt.-% calc.
K-Feldspar	34.87
Albite	10.24
Anorthite	0.40
Andalusite	6.94
Cordierite	13.81
Quartz	20.97
Biotite	1.00
K-mica	5.00
Rutile	1.32
Apatite	1.43
Pyrrhotite	1.32
Graphite	1.58
Water	0.66
	99.54

19. *Pyroxene-Hornfels, Class 3*

	Wt.-% calc.
K-Feldspar	13
Albite	9
Anorthite	7
Cordierite (with secondary water)	21
Quartz	22
Biotite	25
Iron ores (?)	1
Apatite	1
Graphite	0.5
	99.5

20. *Pyroxene-Hornfels, Class 4*

	Wt.-% calc.
K-Feldspar	5.0
Albite	11.3
Anorthite	9.4
Hypersthene	1.5
Cordierite	20.5
Quartz	21.0
Biotite	31.0
Apatite	0.2
	99.9

21. *Pyroxene-Hornfels, Class 5*

	Wt.-% calc.
K-Feldspar	10.0
Albite	11.9
Anorthite	24.9
Hypersthene	15.0
Quartz	13.7
Biotite	24.4
Apatite	0.2
	100.1

22. *Pyroxene-Hornfels, Class 7*

	Wt.-% calc.
K-Feldspar	29.9
Albite	23.2
Anorthite	4.3
Pyroxene	32.0
Biotite	4.0
Quartz	2.4
Sphene	1.2
Apatite	2.1
Calcite	0.8
Water	0.1
	100.0

23. *Hornblende-Hornfels*, Skrukkelien, Norway

	Wt.-% calc.
Plagioclase (An_{40})	51
Amphibole	13
Biotite	21
Quartz	13
Magnetite	1
	99

2. Chemical Analyses, Hornfels

	18. Class 1	19. Class 3	20. Class 4 Pyroxene-Hornfels	21. Class 5	22. Class 7	23. Hornblende- Hornfels
SiO_2	62.80	58.83	58.28	56.59	57.24	55.54
TiO_2	1.36	0.59	0.21	0.29	0.65	0.57
Al_2O_3	19.74	17.54	17.98	18.15	12.30	19.43
Fe_2O_3	0.0	0.00	2.42	4.23	1.77	2.35
FeO	1.98	8.42	6.52	5.21	2.95	5.06
MnO	0.02	0.09	0.17	0.21	0.09	0.06
MgO	1.34	3.40	4.88	5.01	4.80	5.65
CaO	0.87	2.24	2.01	5.14	10.31	6.15
Na_2O	1.22	1.35	1.39	1.41	2.78	3.06
K_2O	6.56	4.35	4.29	3.64	5.41	1.92
P_2O_5	0.60	0.46	0.07	0.10	0.90	n.d.
S	0.52	—				
H_2O^+	0.86	1.96 ⎫	2.19 ⎫	0.64	0.18 ⎫	0.5
H_2O^-	0.27	0.13 ⎭	⎭		0.06 ⎭	
C	1.58	0.50	—		—	—
CO_2		—			0.35	—
Sum	99.72	99.86	100.41	100.62	99.79	100.29
$O = S$	0.23					
	99.49					

Literature

Books on History of Mineralogy and Petrology

FISCHER, W.: Gesteins- und Lagerstättenbildung im Wandel der wissenschaftlichen An-schauung. Stuttgart 1961.

GROTH, P.: Entwicklungsgeschichte der mineralogischen Wissenschaften. Berlin 1926. (Ex-cludes petrology.)

TERTSCH, H.: Das Geheimnis der Kristallwelt. Wien 1947. (Popular.)

ZITTEL, K. A.: Geschichte der Geologie und Palaeontologie. München-Leipzig 1899. (Includes petrology.)

Handbooks and Tables

DANA'S System of mineralogy, 7. ed., C. PALACHE, H. BERMAN and C. FRONDEL, Vol. 1—3. New York-London 1944—1962. (To be continued.)

D'ANS-LAX: Taschenbuch für Chemiker und Physiker. 3. ed. (Edited by E. LAX and CL. SYNO-WIETZ.) Bd. I: Makroskopische physikalisch-chemische Eigenschaften. Berlin 1967.

DEER, W. A., R. A. HOWIE, and J. ZUSSMAN: Rock-forming minerals. Vol. 1—5. London: Longmans 1962.

DOELTER, C., u. H. LEITMEIER: Handbuch der Mineralchemie. Dresden u. Leipzig 1912—1931.

GMELINs Handbuch der anorganischen Chemie, 8. ed. Frankfurt (Main).

HINTZE, C.: Handbuch der Mineralogie. Leipzig u. Berlin 1897—1933. 1. Ergänzungsbd. (v. G. LINCK), Berlin u. Leipzig 1938; 2. Ergänzungsbd. (K. F. CHUDOBA), Berlin 1960.

LANDOLDT-BÖRNSTEIN: Zahlenwerte und Funktionen (Bd. I/4, 6. Aufl. der „Physikalisch-chemischen Tabellen"). Berlin 1955.

TRÖGER, W. E.: Optische Bestimmung der gesteinsbildenden Minerale. Edited by O. BRAITSCH. Stuttgart: Schweizerbart 1967.

Recent Texts, with Similar Treatment

BERRY, L. G., and B. MASON: Mineralogy. San Francisco 1959.

ESKOLA, P.: Kristalle und Gesteine. Wien 1946.

HURLBUT, JR. C. S.,: DANA's manual of mineralogy, 17. ed. New York 1959.

RAMDOHR, P., u. H. STRUNZ: KLOCKMANNS Lehrbuch der Mineralogie, 15. ed. Stuttgart 1967.

Part 1

General

AZAROFF, L. V.: Introduction to solids. New York-Toronto-London 1960.

FISCHER, E.: Einführung in die mathematischen Hilfsmittel der Kristallographie. (Lehr-briefe der Bergakademie Freiberg.) Leipzig 1966.

LIEBISCH, TH.: Grundriß der physikalischen Kristallographie. München u. Berlin 1921.

JAGODZINSKI, H.: Kristallographie. In: Handbuch der Physik, Bd. VII/1. Berlin-Göttingen-Heidelberg: Springer 1955. (S. 1—103.)

JONG, W. F. DE: Kompendium der Kristallkunde. Wien 1959.

KLEBER, W.: Einführung in die Kristallographie, 8. ed. Berlin 1965.

MACHATSCHKI, F.: Grundlagen der allgemeinen Mineralogie und Kristallchemie. Wien 1946

NIGGLI, P.: Lehrbuch der Mineralogie und Kristallchemie, 3. ed., Bd. 1. Berlin 1941; Bd. 2, Berlin 1942.

WINKLER, H. G. F.: Struktur und Eigenschaften der Kristalle, 2. ed. Berlin-Göttingen-Heidelberg: Springer 1955.

I. (p. 1—54)

BELOV, N. V.: A class-room method for the derivation of the 230 space groups. Translated from the Russian.) Leeds 1966.

BUERGER, M. J.: Elementary crystallography. New York-London 1956.

BURCKHARDT, J. J.: Die Bewegungsgruppen der Kristallographie, 2. ed. Basel u. Stuttgart 1966.

FRIEDEL, G.: Leçons de Cristallographie. Paris 1921.

GOLDSCHMIDT, V.: Atlas der Kristallformen. Heidelberg 1913—1926. (9 Volumes with Figures and Tables.)

GROTH, P.: Chemische Kristallographie, 5 Volumes. Leipzig 1906—1919.

— Elemente der physikalischen und chemischen Krystallographie. München u. Berlin 1921.

PHILLIPS, F. C.: An introduction to crystallography, 3. ed. London 1963.

RAAZ, F., u. H. TERTSCH: Einführung in die geometrische und physikalische Kristallographie, 3. ed. Wien 1958.

SCHOENFLIES, A.: Krystallsysteme und Krystallstruktur. Leipzig 1891.

SPEISER, A.: Die Theorie der Gruppen von endlicher Ordnung, 4. ed. Basel 1956.

TERPSTRA, P., and L. W. CODD: Crystallometry. London 1961.

TERTSCH, H.: Die stereographische Projektion in der Kristallkunde. Wiesbaden 1954.

TUTTON, A. E. H.: Crystallography and practical crystal measurement. London 1922.

II. (p. 55—100)

AMINOFF, G., u. B. BROMÉ: Strukturtheoretische Studien über Zwillinge. Z. Krist. 80, 355 (1931).

BARTH, T.: Polymorphic phenomena and crystal structure. Am. J. Sc. 27, 277 (1934).

BRAGG, W. L.: The crystalline state, vol. I, A general survey. 3. printing. London 1949.

—, and G. F. CLARINGBULL: The crystalline state, vol. IV, Crystal structures of minerals. London 1965.

BRILL, R., H. G. GRIMM, C. HERMANN u. C. PETERS: Anwendung der röntgenographischen Fourieranalyse auf Fragen der chemischen Bindung. Ann. Phys. (5) 34, 393 (1939).

BUERGER, M. J.: The lineage structure of crystals. Z. Krist. 89, 193 (1934).

— Polymorphism and phase transformations. Fortschr. Mineral. 39, 9 (1961).

DONNAY, J. D. H. (Editor): Crystal data. Amer. Cryst. Ass. Monogr. Nr. 5. 2. ed. Washington 1963.

EVANS, R. C.: An introduction to crystal chemistry, 2. ed. Cambridge 1964.

GOLDSCHMIDT, V. M.: Geochemische Verteilungsgesetze der Elemente. I.—VIII. Akad. Wiss. Oslo, Math.-naturw. Kl. 1923—1927.

HASSEL, O.: Kristallchemie. Dresden 1934.

HAUFFE, K.: Reaktionen in und an festen Stoffen, 2. ed. Berlin 1966.

HEDVALL, J. A.: Einführung in die Festkörperchemie. Braunschweig 1952.

HUME-ROTHERY, W., and G. V. RAYNOR: The structure of metals and alloys, 4. ed. London 1962.

JENSEN, H., G. MEYER-GOSSER u. H. ROHDE: Zur physikalischen Deutung der kristallographischen Ionenradien. Z. Physik. 110, 277 (1938).

LAVES, F.: Kristallographie der Legierungen. Naturwissenschaften 27, 65 (1939).

LIEBAU, F.: Die Systematik der Silikate. Naturwissenschaften 49, 481 (1962).

MACHATSCHKI, F.: Kristallchemie nichtmetallischer anorganischer Stoffe. Naturwissenschaften 26, 67, 86 (1938); 27, 670, 685 (1939).

MÜGGE, O.: Über die Lage des rhombischen Schnittes im Anorthit und die Benutzung derartiger irrationaler Zusammensetzungsflächen von Kristallzwillingen als geologisches Thermometer. Nachr. Ges. Wiss. Göttingen, Math.-physik. Kl. 1930, 219.

NEWKIRK, J. B., and J. H. WERNICK: Direct observation of imperfections in crystals. New York and London 1962.

PAULING, L.: The nature of the chemical bond, 3. ed. Ithaca 1960.

READ, W. T.: Dislocations in crystals. New York 1953.

SCHOTTKY, W., C. WAGNER, F. LAVES et al.: Übergänge zwischen Ordnung und Unordnung in festen und flüssigen Phasen. Z. Elektrochem. **45**, 1 (1939).

SEEGER, A.: Theorie der Gitterfehlstellen. In: Handbuch der Physik, Bd. VII/1. Berlin-Göttingen-Heidelberg: Springer 1955. (S. 383—665.)

SMEKAL, A.: Strukturempfindliche Eigenschaften der Kristalle. In: Handbuch der Physik, Bd. XXIV/2. Berlin 1933.

Strukturberichte, Bd. 1—7. Leipzig 1931—1943. Anschließend *Structure reports*, Bd. 8—21. Oosthoek. (Reference to all crystal structure determinations; to be continued.)

STRUNZ, H.: Mineralogische Tabellen, 4. ed. Leipzig 1966.

WASASTJERNA, I. A.: On the radii of ions. Soc. Sci. Fennica. Commentationes Phys.-Math. **38**, (1923).

WELLS, A. F.: Structural inorganic chemistry. 3. ed. Oxford 1962.

WYCKOFF, R. W. G.: Crystal structures. 5 volumes. New York and London 1948—1960. (Vol. 1—3 have appeared in a new edition; to be continued.)

ZEMANN, J.: Kristallchemie. Sammlung Göschen, Bd. 1220/1220a. Berlin 1966.

III. General

BORN, M., and K. HUANG: Dynamic theory of crystal lattices. Oxford 1954.

KITTEL, CH.: Introduction to solid state physics. New York and London 1954.

KLEBER, W.: Angewandte Gitterphysik, 3. ed. Berlin 1960.

WOOSTER, W. A.: A text-book of crystal physics. Cambridge 1938.

— Experimental crystal physics. Oxford 1957.

III$_{1-3}$. (p. 100—119)

BECKER, R.: Thermische Inhomogenitäten. Z. Physik **26**, 919 (1925).

BERGMANN, L.: Schwingende Kristalle und ihre Anwendung in der Hochfrequenz- und Ultraschalltechnik, 2. ed. Stuttgart 1953.

BHAGAVANTAM, S.: Crystal symmetry and physical properties. London and New York 1966.

COTTRELL, A. H.: Dislocations and plastic flow in crystals. Oxford 1953.

ENGELHARDT, W. V.: Schleiffestigkeit und Grenzflächenenergie fester Stoffe. Naturwissenschaften **33**, 195 (1934).

—, u. S. HAUSSÜHL: Festigkeit und Härte von Kristallen. Fortschr. Mineral. **42**, 5 (1955).

EXNER, F.: Härte an Krystallflächen. Wien 1873.

FISHER, I. C.: Dislocations and mechanical properties of crystals. New York and London 1957.

GRAILICH, J., u. F. PEKÁREK: Das Sklerometer, ein Apparat zur genaueren Messung der Härte der Kristalle. Sitzber. Akad. Wiss. Wien, Math.-naturw. Kl. **13**, 410 (1854).

LEIBFRIED, G.: Gittertheorie der mechanischen und thermischen Eigenschaften der Kristalle. In: Handbuch der Physik, Bd. VII/1, Berlin-Göttingen-Heidelberg: Springer 1955. (p. 104—324.)

NYE, J. F.: Physical properties of crystals. Oxford 1957.

OROWAN, E.: Zur Kristallplastizität. I und II. Z. Physik. **89**, 605 u. 614 (1934).

ROSIWAL, A.: Neuere Ergebnisse der Härtebestimmung von Mineralien und Gesteinen. — Ein absolutes Maß für die Härte spröder Körper. Verh. geol. Reichsanstalt Wien **1916**, 117.

SCHMID, E., u. W. BOAS: Kristallplastizität. Berlin 1935.

STRANSKI, I. N.: Über die Reißfestigkeit abgelöster Steinsalzkristalle. Ber. dtsch. chem. Ges. **75**, 1667 (1942).

TAYLOR, G. J.: A theory of the plasticity of crystals. Z. Krist. **89**, 375 (1934).

TERTSCH, H.: Die Festigkeitserscheinungen der Kristalle. Wien 1949.

VOIGT, W.: Lehrbuch der Kristallphysik (excluding crystal optics). Leipzig u. Berlin 1910.

III₄. (p. 119—145)

AMBRONN, H., u. A. FREY: Das Polarisationsmikroskop. Leipzig 1926. (For form birefringence).

BUCHWALD, E.: Einführung in die Kristalloptik. Sammlung Göschen, Bd. 619/619a. 5. ed. Berlin 1963.

BURRI, C.: Das Polarisationsmikroskop. Basel 1950.

CAMERON, E.: Ore microscopy. New York and London 1961.

CORRENS, C. W., u. G. NAGELSCHMIDT: Über Faserbau und optische Eigenschaften von Chalzedon. Z. Krist. 85, 199 (1933).

FREUND, H. (Editor): Handbuch der Mikroskopie in der Technik. Bd. I, Teil 1: Allgemeines Instrumentarium der Durchlichtmikroskopie. Frankfurt (Main) 1957. Bd. I, Teil 2: Allgemeines Instrumentarium der Auflichtmikroskopie. Frankfurt (Main) 1960.

HARTSHORNE, N. H., and A. STUART: Practical optical crystallography. London 1964.

JOHNSEN, A.: Form und Brillanz der Brillanten. Sitzber. Akad. Wiss. Berlin, Math.-physik. Kl. 23, 322 (1926).

POCKELS, F.: Lehrbuch der Kristalloptik. Leipzig 1906.

POHL, R.: Optik und Atomphysik, 12. ed. Berlin-Heidelberg-New York: Springer 1967.

PRIBRAM, K.: Verfärbung und Lumineszenz. Wien 1953.

RAAZ, F., u. H. TERTSCH: See under I.

RAMACHANDRAN, G. N., and S. RAMASESHAN: Crystal optics. In: Handbuch der Physik, Bd. XXV/1. Berlin-Göttingen-Heidelberg: Springer 1961. (p. 1—217.)

REINHARD, M.: Universal-Drehtischmethoden. Basel 1931.

RINNE, F., u. M. BEREK: Anleitung zur optischen Untersuchung mit dem Polarisationsmikroskop, 2. ed. (prepared by M. BEREK). Stuttgart 1953.

ROSENBUSCH, H., u. A. WÜLFING: Mikroskopische Physiographie der petrographisch wichtigen Mineralien, Bd. I, 1. Hälfte. Stuttgart 1921.

SCHNEIDERHÖHN, H.: Erzmikroskopisches Praktikum. Stuttgart 1952.

SCHUMANN, H.: Über den Anwendungsbereich der konoskopischen Methodik. Fortschr. Mineral. 25, 217 (1941).

III₅. (p. 145—161)

BACON, G. E.: Neutron diffraction, 2. ed. Oxford 1962.

BIJVOET, M. J., N. H. KOLKMEIJER, and C. H. MACGILLAVRY: X-ray analysis of crystals. London 1951.

BOUMAN, J.: Theoretical principles of structural research by X-rays. In: Handbuch der Physik, Bd. XXXII. Berlin 1957. (p. 97—237.)

BUERGER, M. J.: X-ray crystallography. New York and London 1942.

— Crystal-structure analysis. New York and London 1960.

GUINIER, A., et G. VON ELLER: Les méthodes expérimentales des déterminations de structures cristallines par rayons X. In: Handbuch der Physik, Bd. XXXII. Berlin 1957. (p. 1—96.)

International Tables for X-Ray Crystallography. Vol. 1—3. Birmingham 1952—1962.

JAMES, R. W.: The crystalline state, vol. II. The optical principles of the diffraction of X-rays, 2. ed. London 1963.

LAUE, M. VON: Röntgenstrahlinterferenzen, 2. ed. Leipzig 1948.

LIPSON, H., and W. COCHRAN: The crystalline state, vol. III. The determination of crystal structures, 3. ed. London 1966.

RAETHER, H.: Elektroneninterferenzen. In: Handbuch der Physik, Bd. XXXII. Berlin 1957. (p. 443—551.)

WILSON, A. J. C.: X-ray optics, 2. ed. London 1962.

WOOSTER, W. A.: Diffuse X-ray reflections from crystals. Oxford 1962.

IV. (p. 162—178)

BECKE, F.: Ätzversuche am Fluorit. Tschermak's mineral. u. petrog. Mitt. 11, 349 (1890).

BUCKLEY, H. E.: Crystal growth. New York and London 1951.

BUEREN, H. G. VAN: Imperfections in crystals. Amsterdam 1960.

Crystal growth. Discussions of the Faraday society, No. 5. London 1949.

DEKEYSER, W., et S. AMELINCKX: Les dislocations et la croissance des cristaux. Paris 1955.

DOREMUS, R. H., B. W. ROBERTS, and D. TURNBULL: Growth and perfection of crystals. London 1958.

EAKLE, A. S.: Beiträge zur kristallographischen Kenntnis der überjodsauren und jodsauren Salze. Z. Krist. **26**, 558 (1896).

GROSS, R.: Zur Theorie des Wachstum- und Lösungsvorganges kristalliner Materie. Abhandl. math.-naturw. Kl. sächs. Akad. Wiss. **35**, 137 (1918).

—, u. H. MÖLLER: Kristallauslese auf Grund der Wachstumsgeschwindigkeit. Z. Physik **19**, 375 (1923).

HAHN, O.: Die verschiedenen Arten der Abscheidung kleiner Substanzmengen in kristallisierenden Salzen und ihre photographische Sichtbarmachung. Z. Krist. **87**, 387 (1934).

HONIGMANN, B.: Gleichgewichts- und Wachstumsformen von Kristallen. Darmstadt 1958.

KALB, G.: Die Bedeutung der Vizinalerscheinungen für die Bestimmung der Symmetrie und Formenentwicklung der Kristallarten. Z. Krist. **39**, 220 (1903).

KNACKE, O., u. I. STRANSKI: Die Theorie des Kristallwachstums. Ergeb. exakt. Naturw. **26**, 383—427 (1952).

MIERS, H. A.: Untersuchung über die Variation der an Krystallen beobachteten Winkel, speziell von Kalium- und Ammoniumalaun. Z. Krist. **39**, 220 (1904).

NACKEN, R.: Über das Wachsen von Kristallpolyedern in ihrem Schmelzfluß. Neues Jahrb. Mineral. Geol. Paläont. **1915/II**, 133.

SHOCKLEY, W.: Imperfections in nearly perfect crystals. New York and London 1962.

SMAKULA, A.: Einkristalle. Berlin-Göttingen-Heidelberg: Springer 1962.

SPANGENBERG, K.: Wachstum und Auflösung der Kristalle. Handwörterbuch der Naturwiss., 2. ed. Jena 1934.

TOLANSKI, S.: Surface microtopography. New York 1960.

TYNDALL, J.: Die Wärme. Braunschweig 1894.

VOLMER, M.: Kinetik der Phasenbildung. Dresden u. Leipzig 1939.

Part 2

General

BARTH, T.: Theoretical petrology, 2. ed. New York: John Wiley & Sons 1962.

— C. W. CORRENS u. P. ESKOLA: Die Entstehung der Gesteine. Berlin 1939.

BRINKMANN, R. (Editor): Lehrbuch der Allgemeinen Geologie, Bd. I, 1964, Bd. III, 1967. Stuttgart: Ferdinand Enke.

HOWELL, J. V. (ed.): Glossary of geology and related sciences, 2. ed.: Amer. Geol. Inst. 1960.

JUNG, J.: Précis de Pétrographie, II. ed. Paris: Masson & Cie. 1963.

MASON, B.: Principles of geochemistry, III. ed. New York: John Wiley & Sons 1966.

NIGGLI, P.: Lehrbuch der Mineralogie, 1. ed. Leipzig 1920.

— Gesteine und Minerallagerstätten. Basel 1948.

ROSENBUSCH, H., u. A. OSANN: Elemente der Gesteinslehre. Stuttgart 1923.

TURNER, FR. J., and J. VERHOOGEN: Igneous and metamorphic petrology, 2. ed. New York-Toronto-London-Paris: McGRAW-Hill Book Co. 1960.

WEDEPOHL, K. H.: Geochemie. Samml. Göschen. Berlin: W. de. Gruyter & Co. 1967.

V. (p. 181—203)

BOVENKERK, H. P., F. P. BUNDY, H. T. HALL, H. M. STRONG, and R. H. WENTORF JR.: Preparation of diamond. Nature **184**, 194—198 (1959).

BOWEN, N. L., and O. F. TUTTLE: The system $NaAlSi_3O_8$—$KAlSi_3O_8$—H_2O. J. Geol. **58**, 489—511 (1950).

BOYD, F. R., and J. L. ENGLAND: The quartz-coesite transition. J. Geophys. Research **65**, 749—756 (1960).

EITEL, W.: Silicate science. New York and London: Academic Press 5 Vols., 1964—1966.

FINDLAY, A.: Die Phasenregel und ihre Anwendung. Weinheim 1953.

KERN, R., et A. WEISBROD: Thermodynamique de base pour minéralogistes, pétrographes et géologues. Paris: Masson & Cie. 1964.

ROY, R., and O. F. TUTTLE: Investigations under hydrothermal conditions. In: Physics and chemistry of the earth, V. I, p. 138—180. London-Oxford-New York-Paris: Pergamon Press 1956.

TUTTLE, O. F., and N. L. BOWEN: Origin of granite in the light of experimental studies in the system $NaAlSi_3O_8$—$KAlSi_3O_8$—SiO_2—H_2O. Geol. Soc. Am. Mem. **74** (1958).

VOGEL, R.: Die heterogenen Gleichgewichte. In: Handbuch der Metallphysik, 2. ed., Bd. II. Leipzig 1959.

WINKLER, H. G. F.: Kristallgröße und Abkühlung. Heidelberger Beitr. Mineral u. Petrogr. **1**, 86 (1947).

YODER, H. S., D. B. STEWART, and J. R. SMITH: Ternary feldspars. Ann. Rep. Geophys. Lab. Carnegie Inst. 1956/57, p. 206—214.

VI. (p. 204—242)

BACKHUIS ROOZEBOOM, H. W.: Heterogene Gleichgewichte. Braunschweig 1901—1918.

BOWEN, N. L.: The evolution of igneous rocks. Princeton 1928.

BURRI, C.: Petrochemische Berechnungsmethoden auf äquivalenter Grundlage. Basel 1959.

DALY, R. A.: Igneous rocks and the depths of the earth. New York 1933.

DRESCHER-KADEN, F. K.: Die Feldspat-Quarz-Reaktionsgefüge der Granite und Gneise und ihre genetische Bedeutung. Berlin-Göttingen-Heidelberg: Springer 1948.

GOLDSCHMIDT, V. M.: Geochemische Verteilungsgesetze. IX. Akad. Oslo, math.-nat. Kl. 1938.

GORANSON, R. W.: Silicate-water systems: Phase equilibria in the $NaAlSi_3O_8$—H_2O and $KAlSi_3O_8$—H_2O systems at high temperatures and pressures. Amer. J. Sci. A **35**, 71 (1938).

HOLMES, A.: Petrographic methods and calculations. London 1921.

JASMUND, K.: Löslichkeit von KCl in der Gasphase von überkritisch erhitztem Wasser. Heidelberger Beitr. Mineral. u. Petrog. **3**, 380—405 (1952).

JOHANNSON, A.: A descriptive petrography of the igneous rocks, vol. 1—4. Chicago: Chicago University Press 1939, 2. ed., vol. 1.

KENNEDY, G. C.: Some aspects of the role of water in rock melts. Geol. Soc. Am. Spec. Papers No. 62, 489—504 (1955).

KRAUSKOPF, K.: Übersicht über moderne Ansichten zur physikalischen Chemie erzbildender Lösungen. Naturwissenschaften **48**, 441—445 (1961).

LIESEGANG, R. E.: Geologische Diffusionen. Dresden u. Leipzig 1913.

— Die Achate. Dresden u. Leipzig 1915.

LINDGREN, W.: Mineral deposits, 4. ed. New York 1933.

MAUCHER, W.: Leitfaden für den Geologieunterricht, 2. ed. Freiberg i. Sa. 1914.

MOREY, G. W.: The solubility of solids in gases. Econ. Geol. **52**, 225—251 (1957).

NACKEN, R.: Über die hydrothermale Entstehung der Achatmandeln im Gestein. Naturwissenschaften **293** (1917).

NIGGLI, P.: Gesteins- und Mineralprovinzen, Bd. I. Berlin 1923.

— Die quantitative mineralogische Klassifikation der Eruptivgesteine. Schweiz. mineral. petrog. Mitt. **11**, 296 (1931).

— Zur mineralogischen Klassifikation der Eruptivgesteine. Schweiz. mineral. petrog. Mitt. **15**, 295 (1935).

— Das Magma und seine Produkte, Teil 1. Leipzig 1937.

RITTMANN, A.: Vulkane und ihre Tätigkeit, II. ed. Stuttgart: Ferdinand Enke 1960.

SCHNEIDERHÖHN, H.: Lehrbuch der Erzlagerstättenkunde, Bd. I, Jena 1941.

— Erzlagerstätten, III. ed. Stuttgart 1955.

TRÖGER, E.: Spezielle Petrographie der Eruptivgesteine. Berlin 1935. Nachtrag 1938.

WINKLER, H. G. F.: Viel Basalt und wenig Gabbro — wenig Rhyolith und viel Granit. Beitr. Mineral. u. Petrog. **8**, 222—231 (1962).

YODER, H. S., and C. E. TILLEY: Origin of basalt magmas. J. Petr. **3**, 342—532 (1962).

VII. (p. 243—252)

BLANCK, E. (Editor): Handbuch der Bodenlehre, Bd. I—VII. Berlin: Springer 1929—1931 u. I. Erg.-Bd. 1939.

CORRENS, C. W.: Experiments on the decomposition of silicates and discussion of chemical weathering. In: Clays and clay minerals V. X, p. 443—459. London-Oxford-New York-Paris: Pergamon Press. 1963.

CORRENS, C. W., u. W. STEINBORN: Experimente zur Messung und Erklärung der sogenannten Kristallisationskraft. Z. Krist. A 101, 117 (1939).

SCHEFFER, FR.: Lehrbuch der Bodenkunde, 6. ed. Stuttgart: Ferdinand Enke 1966.

SHERMAN, G. D.: The genesis and morphology of the alumina rich laterite clays. In: Problems of clay and laterite genesis. Am. Inst. Min. a Met. Ing. New York 1952.

VIII. (p. 253—291)

BORCHERT, H.: Ozeane Salzlagerstätten. Berlin: Gebrüder Bornträger 1959.

BRAITSCH, O.: Entstehung und Stoffbestand der Salzlagerstätten. Berlin-Göttingen-Heidelberg: Springer 1962.

BROWN, G. (ed.): The x-ray identification and crystal structures of clay minerals. Min. Soc. London 1961.

CHAVE, K. E.: Aspects of biochemistry of magnesium I. Calcareous marine organisms. J. Geol. 62, 266—283 (1954).

CHILINGAR, G. V., H. J. BISSELL, and R. W. FAIRBRIDGE (ed.): Carbonate rocks. Physical and chemical aspects. Amsterdam-London-New York: Elsevier Publ. Co. 1967.

CONWAY, E. J.: Mean geochemical data in relation to oceanic evolution. Proc. Roy. Irish Acad. B 48, 119—159 (1942).

CORRENS, C. W.: Die Sedimente des äquatorialen Atlantischen Ozeans. Wiss. Ergebn. dtsch. Atl. Exped., Bd. III/1 (1935); III/2 (1937).

— Tonminerale. Fortschr. Geol. Rheinld. u. Westf. 10, 307—318 (1963).

D'ANS, J.: Die Lösungsgleichgewichte der Systeme der Salze ozeanischer Salzablagerungen. Berlin 1933.

ENGELHARDT, W. V., H. FÜCHTBAUER u. G. MÜLLER: Sedimentpetrologie. I. G. MÜLLER: Methoden der Sedimentuntersuchung. Stuttgart 1964.

GARRELS, R. M., and C. L. CHRIST: Solutions, minerals and equilibria. New York: Harper & Row 1965.

GRIM, R. E.: Clay mineralogy. New York-Toronto-London-Paris: McGraw-Hill Book Co. 2. ed. 1968.

HEM, J. D.: Chemistry of iron in natural water. U.S. Geol. Survey Water-Supply Papers No. 1459-B (1964).

IRELAND, H. A. (ed.): Silica in sediments. Soc. Ec. Pal. Min. Spec. Publ. 7, Tulsa 1959.

LOTZE, F.: Steinsalz und Kalisalze, II. ed., Bd. I. Berlin 1957.

MILLOT, G.: Géologie des argiles. Paris: Masson & Cie. 1964.

MILNER, H. B.: Sedimentary petrography, 4. ed. London 1962.

PENCK, A.: Morphologie der Erdoberfläche. Stuttgart: Engelhorn 1894.

PETTIJOHN, F. J.: Sedimentary petrography II. ed. HARPER and BROTH. New York 1957.

POSNJAK, E.: The system $CaSO_4$—H_2O. Amer. J. Sci. 5, 35, 247 (1938).

PRAY, L. C., and R. C. MURRAY (ed.): Dolomitization and limestone diagenesis. A Symposium. Soc. Ec. Pal. Min. Spec. Publ. 12, Tulsa 1965.

PURDY, E. G.: Recent calcium carbonate facies of the Great Bahama Bank. 2. Sedimentary facies. J. Geol. 71, 472—497 (1963).

RICHARDS, FR. A.: In: J. P. RILEY and G. SKIRROW, Chemical oceanography, vol. I, chap. 13. London-New York: Academic Press 1965.

RUCHIN, L. B.: Grundzüge der Lithologie. Berlin: Akad.-Verlag 1958.

STUTZER: Lagerstätten der Nichterze. IV. Phosphat-Nitrat (W. WETZEL). Berlin 1932.

TWENHOFEL, W. H.: Principles of sedimentation, II. ed. New York-Toronto-London-Paris: MacGraw-Hill Book Co. 1950.

USDOWSKI, H.-E.: Die Genese von Dolomit in Sedimenten. Berlin-Heidelberg-New York: Springer 1967.

VAN'T HOFF, J. H.: Zur Bildung der ozeanischen Salzablagerungen. Braunschweig: Bd. I 1905, Bd. II 1909.

WATTENBERG, H.: Das chemische Beobachtungsmaterial und seine Gewinnung. Kalzium-karbonat- und Kohlensäuregehalt des Meerwassers. Wiss. Ergebn. dtsch. Atl. Exped., Bd. VIII/1 (1963).

IX. (p. 292—325)

BECKE, FR.: Mineralbestand und Struktur der kristallinischen Schiefer. Denkschr. Akad. Wiss. Wien 75 (1913).

BLISS-KNOPF, E., and E. INGERSON: Structural petrology. Geol. Soc. Am. Mem. No. 6 (1938).

CORRENS, C. W.: Über Verkieselung von Sedimentgesteinen. Neues Jahrb. Mineral., Geol. Beil.-Bd. 52, 170 (1925).

— Diagenese. In: BRINKMANN, Lehrbuch der Allgemeinen Geologie, Bd. III. Stuttgart: Ferdinand Enke 1967.

DANIELSSON, A.: Das Calcit-Wollastonitgleichgewicht. Geochim. et Cosmochim. Acta 1, 55—69 (1950).

DIETRICH, R. V., and K. R. MEHNERT: Proposal for the nomenclature of migmatite and associated rocks. Rep. Intern. Geol. Congr. Norden 26, 56—68 (1960).

ENGELHARDT, W. v.: Der Porenraum der Sedimente. Berlin-Göttingen-Heidelberg: Springer 1960.

ESKOLA, P.: Om sambandet mellan kemisk och mineralogisk sammansättning hos Orijärvi-traktens metamorfa bergarter. Bull. comm. géol. Finlande No 44 (1915).

FYFE, W. S., and FR. J. TURNER: Reappraisal of the metamorphic facies concept. Contr. Mineral. and Petrol. 12, 354—364 (1966).

GILLULY, J.: Geology and ore deposits of the Stockton and Fairfield Quadrangles, Utah. U.S. Geol. Survey Prof. Paper No. 173 (1932).

GOLDSCHMIDT, V. M.: Die Kontaktmetamorphose im Kristianiagebiet. Skr. Akad. Wiss. Oslo, math.-nat. Kl. Nr. 1 (1911).

GREENWOOD, H. J.: Metamorphic reactions involving two volatile components. Carnegie Inst. Year Book 61, 82—85 (1962).

GRIGGS, D., and J. HANDIN (ed.): Rock deformation. Geol. Soc. Am. Mem. No. 79 (1960).

GRUBENMANN, U., u. P. NIGGLI: Die Gesteinsmetamorphose, 3. ed., Bd. I. Berlin 1924.

HARKER, A.: Metamorphism, a study of the transformation of rock masses, III. ed. London 1952.

HARKER, R. T., and O. F. TUTTLE: Experimental data on the P_{CO_2}—T Curve for the reaction: Calcite + quartz $\rightleftharpoons$ wollastonite + carbon dioxide. Am J. Sci. 254, 239—256 (1956).

JAGITSCH, R.: Geologische Diffusion in kristallisierten Phasen 2. Arkiv Mineral. Geol. 1, Nr. 3 (1949).

KARL, FR.: Anwendung der Gefügekunde in der Petrotektonik. I. Clausthal-Zellerfeld: Ellen Pilger 1964.

LAFITTE, P.: Introduction à l'étude des roches métamorphiques et des gites métallofères. Paris: Masson & Cie. 1957.

MACDONALD, G. J. F.: Dependence of the surface heat flow on the radioactivity of the earth. J. Geophys. Research 69, 2933—2946 (1964).

MEHNERT, K. R.: Der gegenwärtige Stand des Granitproblems. Fortschr. Mineral. 37, 117—206 (1959).

MÜGGE, O.: Bewegungen von Porphyroblasten in Phylliten und ihre Messung. Nachr. Ges. Wiss. Göttingen, math.-phys. Kl. IV, 164 (1930).

PILLER, H.: Über die Verwitterungsbildungen des Brockengranits. Heidelberger Beitr. Mineral. u. Petrog. 2, 498—522 (1951).

RAMBERG, H.: The origin of metamorphic and metasomatic rocks. Chicago: Chicago University Press 1952.

SANDER, BR.: Einführung in die Gefügekunde der geologischen Körper, Bd. I 1948, Bd. II 1950. Wien: Springer.

WEGMANN, C. E.: Zur Deutung der Migmatite. Geol. Rundschau 26, 305 (1935).

— Remarques sur le métamorphisme régional. Geol. Rundschau 36, 40 (1948).

WENK, E.: Zur Definition von Schiefer und Gneis. Neues Jahrb. Mineral. Monatsh. 97—107 (1963).

WINKLER, H. G. F.: Die Genese der metamorphen Gesteine. Berlin-Heidelberg-New York: Springer 1965.

ZWART, H. J.: On the determination of polymetamorphic mineral associations, and its application to the Borost area (Central Pyrenees). Geol. Rundschau **52**, 38—65 (1962).

X. (p. 326—338)

BIRCH, FR.: Speculations of the earth's thermal history. Bull. Geol. Soc. Am. **76**, 133—154 (1965).

CLARK, S., JR. (ed.)- Handbook of physical constants. Geol. Soc. Am. Mem. No. 97 (1966).

CLARKE, F. W.: Data of geochemistry (V. ed.). U.S. Survey Bull. 770 (1924).

—, and H. ST. WASHINGTON: The composition of the earth's crust. U.S. Geol. Survey Prof. Papers No. 127 (1924).

CORRENS, C. W.: Die geochemische Bilanz. Naturwissenschaften **35**, 7 (1948).

ENGELHARDT, W. V.: Die Geochemie des Barium. Chem. Erde **10**, 187—246 (1936).

FLEISCHER, M. (ed.): Data of geochemistry (sixth ed.). U.S. Geol. Survey Prof. Papers 440, since 1962.

GOLDSCHMIDT, V. M.: Geochemistry. Oxford: Clarendon Press 1954.

GUTENBERG, B., and W. RICHTER: On seismic waves. Gerlands Beitr. Geophys. 45 (1935).

HEIDE, FR.: Kleine Meteoritenkunde, II. ed. Berlin-Göttingen-Heidelberg: Springer 1957.

HISE, CH. R. VAN: A Treatise on metamorphism. U.S. Geol. Survey Monogr. **47** (1904).

HOLSER, W. T., and I. R. KAPLAN: Isotope geochemistry of sedimentary sulfates. Chem. Geol. **1**, 93—135 (1966).

KEIL, K.: On the phase composition of meteorites. J. Geophys. Research **67**, 4055 (1962).

MASON, B.: Meteorites. New York: John Wiley & Sons 1962.

— Composition of the earth. Nature **211**, 616—618 (1966).

NIELSEN, H.: Schwefelisotope im marinen Kreislauf und das $\delta^{34}S$ der früheren Meere. Geol. Rundschau **55**, 160—172 (1965).

RANKAMA, K.: Isotope geology. London: Pergamon Press 1954.

— Progress of isotope geology. New York and London: Interscience Publ. 1963.

—, and TH. G. SAHAMA: Geochemistry. Chicago: Chicago University Press 1950.

RÖSLER, H. J., u. H. LANGE: Geochemische Tabellen. Leipzig 1965.

RONOV, A. B., and Z. V. KHLEBNIKOWA: Chemical composition of the main genetic clay types. Geochemistry **1957**, 527—552.

WEDEPOHL, K. H.: Beispiele von Stofftransport in und auf der Erdkruste. Naturwissenschaften **50**, 71—76 (1963).

Author Index

Subject Index

Mineral Index

Italicized numbers refer to numbers in the Mineralogical Tables, pages 361—434

Universitätsdruckerei H. Stürtz AG Würzburg

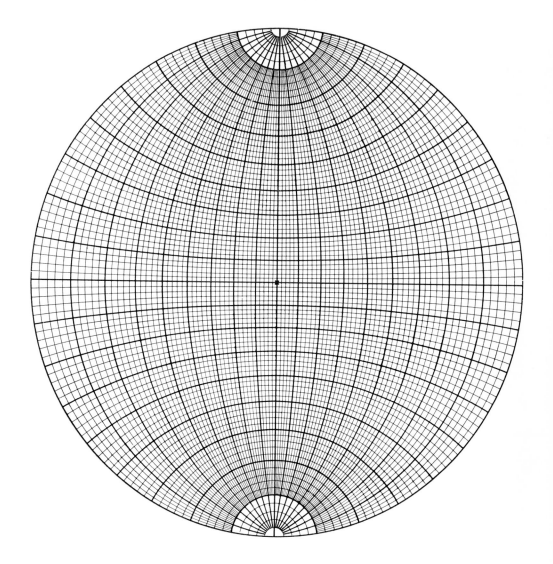

WULFF Net

Correns, Introduction to Mineralogy   Springer-Verlag Berlin · Heidelberg · New York